MECHANICS

Point Objects and Particles

MECHANICS
Point Objects and Particles

TERRY TRIFFET

Professor of Mechanics
Michigan State University

John Wiley and Sons, Inc., New York | London | Sydney

Library of Congress Catalog Card Number: 67-19785
Printed in the United States of America

To My Wife, Millicent

Preface

It is my conviction that mathematics and mechanics stand in the same relation to the sciences and engineering as language and literature to the humanities. This book is a reflection of that conviction. No one would deny that many excellent mechanics textbooks for undergraduates exist, but to my knowledge there is none with the coverage and degree of integration attempted here. From the outset, particles are recognized to possess constant mass only when their velocity is low and, as soon as possible, their wave properties are introduced. In the volume to follow this one, systems of particles are analyzed for their state properties from the point of view of statistical thermodynamics, as well as for their transfer properties and the motions of traditional continuum mechanics.

There are several important benefits to be realized from a beginning one-year sequence in mechanics of this kind. For one thing, after completing it the student should possess a solid foundation for a modern scientific education. He will at least be aware of the various kinds of mechanics and where each is applicable. Furthermore, his grasp of the basic principles of each and its related mathematical tools should enable him to understand most of the important technological problems of today, and to make routine applications of his knowledge. This is not to say that his mechanics education should be considered complete. More advanced, specialized courses will be required before he can hope to do original work.

The point is that this foundation can support whatever educational superstructure may be required. There was a time when, in the light of the applications that he was apt to encounter, a young engineer or scientist who had taken the conventional undergraduate courses in mechanics could claim to be adequately prepared for future work; this is no longer true. Many contemporary design and production problems, and even the devices in common use, cannot be properly understood without some knowledge of quantum, relativistic, and statistical mechanics. Even more, it is unlikely that a man will be able to work productively at a level commensurate with a graduate degree in most technical fields without some facility in one or more of these subjects.

For a student not specializing in mechanics the usual procedure has been to take the standard courses emphasizing classical statics and dynamics, and a few others more or less at random. All too often the result has been detailed knowledge in a few areas of limited importance, inadequate knowledge in a few more which seem almost unrelated to the first, and complete ignorance in all others. It is felt that the present approach is one practical way of correcting this situation. Moreover, it appears to be nearly the only academically sound way to achieve the large curriculum economies that are needed if our universities are to continue to award baccalaureate degrees without unrealistic increases in the total number of credits required.

The greatest danger in such an approach is that the material may not be presented in adequate depth. I have employed various means to avoid this, the foremost of which is integration. Hardly any part of the present book stands alone, but rather is carefully related to what has gone before and what is to come after. In each topic the assumptions are stressed in such a way as to make the next topic seem inevitable. Hopefully, the final result is a structure of ideas which clearly depends on all of its parts. To promote this end, continual reference is made to a relatively small number of key problems like the harmonic oscillator, the two-body problem, and plane wave motion. My basic method is to develop examples like these on successively higher levels to satisfy new and more sophisticated requirements.

This suggests the importance of a careful selection of material. Every effort has been made to restrict the presentation to essentials. Of course, it is not easy to decide what these are, and to some extent different individuals would probably make different selections. As already implied, I have been guided by the criterion that essentials will tend to reappear in all of the aspects of mechanics. In each aspect, however, some things have been presented for their own sake alone, just because they are useful. Except in the sense of repetition of key examples, drill too has been much reduced. Instead of multiple problems designed to generate proficiency in one technique, the problems and exercises in this book tend to make use of earlier methods as well as those just developed and to emphasize similarities rather than differences. The text material is often extended by them, and algebraic details are also left for exercises in some cases.

Were it not for the time limitations imposed by the extent of the coverage, more drill would be desirable, just as more intensive treatments of various topics would be. But selected references are given that can be counted on to provide both of these things at various levels of difficulty, and the desirability of consulting them for more detail is repeatedly stressed. In general, every statement such as "It can be shown. . . " is accompanied by a specific reference to the literature. A real effort has been made to use a unified notation and methods of presentation which, insofar as possible, are common to the references. Additionally, it is expected that advanced courses will provide detailed treatments and more drill in special areas.

I have also economized wherever possible by using mathematical rather than prose statements. This has the additional advantage that it encourages the student to become proficient in his proper language, as well as to appreciate the ideas involved for themselves alone. At the same time it has the disadvantage of lacking the color of some of the more literary treatments, and laying little emphasis on the interesting historical circumstances associated with the development of certain ideas. Again, it is hoped that use of the references will fill this need.

Before beginning the sequence the student should complete his basic courses in calculus and, preferably, ordinary differential equations, although the latter may be taken concurrently. He should also have completed the usual beginning sequences in chemistry and physics. A few other concepts that he will need, which may not have been included in these courses, are developed in Sections 1.1 to 1.3 and 2.1; ideally however, very little class time should have to be devoted to these sections. This volume is intended to contain enough material for two, three-credit-hour courses, of the term rather than semester type; but it may easily be expanded for use in two, four-credit courses or, possibly, compressed for one, five-credit course.

With the support of the National Science Foundation I have been teaching such a set of courses at Michigan State University for the last four years. Juniors and some sophomores from various fields, differing widely in ability since no special selection techniques were applied, have taken them; in general, their interest has been much higher and their performance better than that of students in the more conventional courses at the same level which I have taught simultaneously. Gradually, I have come to feel that this is due primarily to the fact that the students have grown up in an environment where the objects and creations of modern mechanics are made manifest.

I hope it will be clear from the foregoing that I consider myself much indebted, not only to the men who originated many of the concepts presented here, but also to those who have expounded them in more detail elsewhere, as represented by the numerous references. In addition, I would like to express my deep personal gratitude to W. B. Plum, D. H. Young, J. D. Ryder, and H. S. Green, friends whose criticism and encouragement have meant much to me, as well as to G. H. Conners, K. N. Subramanian, and R. T. Sedgwick, graduate students who have helped me in many ways.

East Lansing, Michigan   T. Triffet
September 1967

Contents

... the distinguishing characteristics which differentiate the various material systems of nature from each other are, according to our conception, simply and solely the connections of their masses.

H. Hertz, 1893

MECHANICS

Point Objects and Particles

1

Introduction

1.1 Measures of the Motion of a Point

For our purposes it is sufficient to define space as the sum of all possible locations and time as the succession of instants proceeding from the past into the future. It is clear that both must be more than this, for both are actually continuous. These definitions, however, have the advantage of making it possible to describe the motion of an arbitrary point on a moving object in such a way that we can test our results by physical observations. To begin with we shall not concern ourselves with the nature or properties of the object, except to remark that it is some real object in our world, and that this fact defines the motions that are possible for the point.

We may now imagine that, as the point moves, it will occupy certain definite locations at specific instants of time, and use the shortest distances between adjacent locations and the intervals between the corresponding instants as the basis of our description. Of course, these may be very small, but it is important to recognize that they are necessarily finite and, therefore, in principle subject to measurement with a rod or a clock.

Because the shortest distance from one location to any other in our space can be determined from the Pythagorean theorem once three mutually perpendicular lengths connecting them are known, it is convenient to establish a coordinate system at some fixed point consisting of three mutually perpendicular or orthogonal axes. Points corresponding to all real positive and negative numbers are then assumed to lie on each of these axes and the zeros of all three to coincide at the reference point O. This is called a Cartesian coordinate system, and we shall adopt the method shown in Fig. 1.1 of representing such systems. Only the positive portions of the axes will be shown, unless there is some special reason for showing the negative parts too.

Now we can compute the straight line distance OP, a pure magnitude and necessarily positive, between the location O and any other location P as shown in Fig. 1.2 and in (1.1):

$$OP = |(x^2 + y^2 + z^2)^{1/2}| \qquad (1.1)$$

The absolute value sign has been used to indicate that the positive square root is intended. Upper-case letters will consistently be used to designate

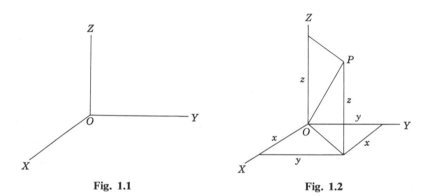

Fig. 1.1   **Fig. 1.2**

the axes and, for the present, the corresponding lower-case letters are used to indicate distances from the origin O along these axes, in this case the three projections of the line OP. Of course x, y, and z are also the coordinates of the three locations defining the lengths of these projections, and taken together (x, y, z) they constitute the coordinates of the location P. Because they can also take on negative values, they inherently convey more information than pure magnitudes. Signed magnitudes of this type are called "scalar" quantities.

If we were to proceed from O a distance x in the X-direction, from this location a distance y in the Y-direction, and from this a distance z in the Z-direction, we would certainly find ourselves at P. But we could also use the same information to go there in a more direct way. From the three scalar quantities x, y, z we could compute the three direction cosines, also scalar quantities, of the straight line OP (Fig. 1.3):

$$\cos \alpha = \frac{x}{OP}, \qquad \cos \beta = \frac{y}{OP}, \qquad \cos \gamma = \frac{z}{OP} \qquad (1.2)$$

Of course, any of these could be negative, allowing OP to fall in any of the quadrants of the coordinate system; but from them we can determine both the magnitudes of the angles α, β, γ and whether they should be measured from the positive or negative extensions of the axes. Thus, we could determine the direction from O specified by the three angles measured from the proper extensions of the axes, then proceed a distance OP in this direction. Because the three scalar quantities $\cos\alpha$, $\cos\beta$, $\cos\gamma$ are required and in addition the distance OP, it may appear that more information is required in this case than in the other; but this is not true, because the three direction

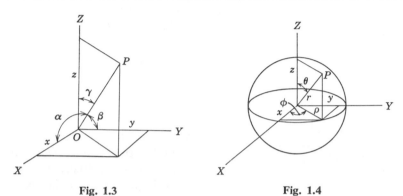

Fig. 1.3   **Fig. 1.4**

cosines are necessarily interconnected. Squaring the relations (1.2) and adding their sides separately gives:

$$\cos^2\alpha + \cos^2\beta + \cos^2\gamma = \frac{x^2 + y^2 + z^2}{(OP)^2} = 1 \qquad (1.3)$$

This introduces the concept of angular measure, but in principle presents no new difficulties, because it merely amounts to using a measuring rod in a different manner. Often, however, it provides a more convenient way of specifying relative locations than the Cartesian system. Suppose, for example, that we are only interested in locations on the surfaces of spheres of radius r centered on O. Then we can specify any of these uniquely by stating r, ϕ, and θ, where ϕ and θ are angles defined as shown in Fig. 1.4, and it is understood that ϕ can vary from 0 to 2π and θ from 0 to π. The quantities (r, ϕ, θ) are called spherical coordinates; they are, of course, related to the Cartesian coordinates (x, y, z) in the following way:

$$r = |(x^2 + y^2 + z^2)^{\frac{1}{2}}| \qquad (1.4)$$

$$\phi = \tan^{-1}\frac{y}{x} \qquad (1.5)$$

$$\theta = \cot^{-1}\frac{z}{\rho} = \cot^{-1}\frac{z}{|(x^2 + y^2)^{\frac{1}{2}}|} \qquad (1.6)$$

Evidently, ϕ and θ are equivalent to scalar quantities and r is only a magnitude, whereas at least three scalar quantities have been required to fully identify a location up to now. But we should expect some reward for restricting ourselves to spherical surfaces.

Similarly, if we are interested in locating a point when it is on the surface of a right circular cylinder of radius ρ, we need only to state the cylindrical coordinates (ρ, ϕ, z), where ϕ can vary from 0 to 2π and is an equivalent scalar, z is a scalar, and ρ is a magnitude (Fig. 1.5):

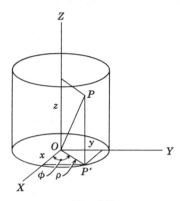

$$\rho = |(x^2 + y^2)^{\frac{1}{2}}| \qquad (1.7)$$

$$\phi = \tan^{-1}\frac{y}{x} \qquad (1.8)$$

$$z = z \qquad (1.9)$$

This also makes it clear that if we wish to identify locations on a plane circle of radius ρ, we merely need to specify (ρ, ϕ), which are called polar coordinates (Fig. 1.6). Under such a severe constraint it is hardly surprising that we would need only one scalar quantity and one pure magnitude.

Fig. 1.5

Various other types of coordinate systems can be defined, based on different geometrical figures, but because those mentioned are the ones most commonly used, no others will be described. Clearly, all serve the same purpose of identifying any arbitrary location in space relative to a fixed point by the statement of three quantities that can be obtained by

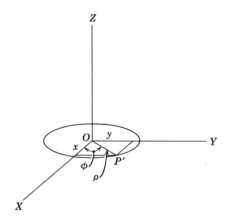

Fig. 1.6

direct measurement. By using any one of them we can easily compute straight line distances like OP.

To describe the motion of a point in such a coordinate system, however, we must also be able to compute time intervals, for we know that a point on a moving object can never occupy two different locations simultaneously. But if we assume that a clock is attached to the coordinate system, we can obtain the time interval between any two events that occur in the system simply by subtracting readings made coincident with these. For example, if we were to read t_1 when the moving point was at O and t_2 when slightly later it was at P, we could conclude that the time interval Δt between these two events was

$$\Delta t = t_2 - t_1. \tag{1.10}$$

If we wish, there is nothing to prevent us from selecting some particular time to coincide with the zero of the real number system, just as we did for some particular point in space; however, if we do, t can as well be negative as positive, in the same way that x, y, or z can, so that it must be considered a scalar quantity. Taken together, the coordinate system and clock constitute what we shall call a reference system, and, of course, any reference system must include an observer to carry out the operations described above.

As observers in our reference system, we note that a point on an object may move in different directions in space, and that in a fixed time interval it may move both different distances and in different directions. Accordingly, we must develop quantitative and unambiguous measures of each of these aspects of point motion. The first presents no real problem now, for our coordinate system enables us to describe any direction in space by means of three quantities. Provided that we can identify the origin of the coordinate system with the point at the instant of interest, we can specify its direction at that instant by describing the straight line along which it is headed and, in addition, by stating which way along the line it is moving. An arrowhead can be attached to the line for the latter purpose; and, of course, we can establish the location of the point relative to some fixed location in the usual way.

For example, if we knew that at a certain time the point was at a location P directed toward a location P'', the Cartesian coordinates of P and P'' being known relative to a fixed origin O, we could imagine an auxiliary coordinate system $X'Y'Z'$ at P parallel to the fixed system XYZ at O and describe the direction of the point by a line segment of any length directed from P through P'' (Fig. 1.7). The orientation of the line segment can be specified by the three scalar quantities x', y', and z', the direction of the arrowhead on it stated, and P located relative to O by giving the three scalars x_1, y_1, z_1. Furthermore, x', y', and z' can be calculated from

$$x' = x_2 - x_1, \qquad y' = y_2 - y_1, \qquad z' = z_2 - z_1. \tag{1.11}$$

We conclude that the direction of point motion can be represented satisfactorily by a directed line segment.

The second aspect of point motion—the fact that the point may move different distances in successive time intervals of the same duration—is more difficult to deal with; but fortunately we can make use of the concept of the derivative of a function from differential calculus.[1] Let us suppose, for the sake of simplicity, that the point is moving along the X-axis and that we know what location, defined by x, it will occupy at every instant of time t; in other words, we know x as a function of t, $x(t)$. Then, as a

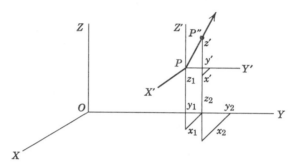

Fig. 1.7

measure of the rate at which the point is covering distance—or the distance that it would cover in a standard time interval if its motion remained the same—at any location x, we may use the derivative of $x(t)$, written $\dot{x}(t)$. This has the meaning

$$\dot{x}(t) = \lim_{\Delta t \to 0} \frac{x(t + \Delta t) - x(t)}{\Delta t} \tag{1.12}$$

and consequently depends on whether the limit exists or not. It is called the instantaneous linear speed in the X-direction.

Furthermore, we may develop a measure for the rate at which the instantaneous speed is changing at any x in the same way, and these two things together will enable us both to specify the rate at which the point is covering distance at any location and to predict this rate for an adjacent location. It follows that

$$\ddot{x}(t) = \lim_{\Delta t \to 0} \frac{\dot{x}(t + \Delta t) - \dot{x}(t)}{\Delta t}, \tag{1.13}$$

which is called the instantaneous linear acceleration in the X-direction. Of course, we could imagine that $\ddot{x}(t)$ is also changing at some rate and

[1] Apostol, T. M., *Calculus*, Vol. 1, pp. 100–119; Blaisdell, Waltham, Mass., 1961.

proceed in the same manner, but most physical problems do not require it. Also, in most physical problems it can be proved that the required limits actually do exist.

Because in the preceding discussion the X-direction could be any straight line with a zero and all positive and negative numbers, it could be made to coincide with the line through PP'' in Fig. 1.7, with the zero superimposed on P. Thus we can now describe both the straight line direction that a moving point may have and the speed with which it is

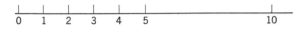

Fig. 1.8. Instantaneous linear speed in feet per second.

moving in this direction, as well as the rate at which its speed is changing, at any location in space and instant of time. Furthermore, the length of the directed line segment that we require is, so far, of arbitrary magnitude. This suggests that we identify it with the speed, allowing the arrowhead to indicate which way along the line the point is moving. The speed can then be regarded as a pure magnitude, and the direction of the directed line segment can be relied on to fully establish the direction of the motion.

For example, we could create the scale of magnitudes shown in Fig. 1.8; if we know the speed of the point to be 1.0 ft/sec when it is at P, directed toward P'' (in Fig. 1.7), we could summarize all of this information in the manner illustrated in Fig. 1.9. Or if we wished to avoid a scaled drawing, we could draw the arrow any length and simply write the length that it should have directly on it, 1.0 ft/sec. For that matter, we do not need to show its direction accurately either; instead, we can state its direction cosines relative to an auxiliary coordinate system $X'Y'Z'$ with its origin at P. Better still, we could give its projections (x', y', z') in this system, for we know from (1.1) and (1.2) that these three scalar quantities determine both the length and the direction cosines.

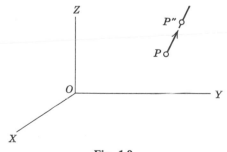

Fig. 1.9

The last statement amounts to a completely analytical description of a scaled and directed line segment by three scalar quantities, in the same way that a signed magnitude can be specified by one scalar quantity. It is customary to call quantities that can be represented by such line segments "vector" quantities, and to give all of the information that any one vector quantity represents a single name—linear velocity in this case. The directed line segments themselves are then also called vectors.

We shall indicate each such quantity by an appropriate boldface letter, for example,

$$\mathbf{v} = \text{instantaneous linear velocity.}$$

The magnitude only of the quantity is indicated by the same symbol. enclosed in an absolute value sign:

$$|\mathbf{v}| = \text{absolute instantaneous linear speed}$$

The scalar counterpart of this magnitude is designated by the same letter in lightface type:

$$v = \text{instantaneous linear speed}$$

Finally, the projections of the length representing the magnitude oriented in the proper direction are shown by the same letter with the subscripts x, y, and z,

$$(v_x, v_y, v_z) = \text{scalar components of the instantaneous linear speed,}$$

instead of simply by (x, y, z). Of course, in the case of velocity and speed the word "instantaneous," and often the words "absolute" and "linear," are usually taken for granted and omitted. Linear acceleration, $\mathbf{a}$, is also a vector quantity; thus it should now be clear that the following representations are equivalent:

$$\dot{x}(t) = v_x(t) \tag{1.14}$$

$$\ddot{x}(t) = a_x(t) \tag{1.15}$$

We have seen that angles can sometimes be used instead of length coordinates to specify locations, and this suggests that we should be able to define an angular velocity $\boldsymbol{\omega}$ and an angular acceleration $\boldsymbol{\alpha}$ corresponding to the linear velocity $\mathbf{v}$ and linear acceleration $\mathbf{a}$ defined above. If a point is moving around the circumference of a circle of fixed radius ρ and if we know $\phi(t)$, then in the same way as before we may write for the instantaneous angular speed

$$\dot{\phi}(t) = \lim_{\Delta t \to 0} \frac{\phi(t + \Delta t) - \phi(t)}{\Delta t} \tag{1.16}$$

and for the instantaneous angular acceleration

$$\ddot{\phi}(t) = \lim_{\Delta t \to 0} \frac{\dot{\phi}(t + \Delta t) - \dot{\phi}(t)}{\Delta t} . \tag{1.17}$$

Once again the magnitudes can be made to correspond to the length of a line segment for a vectorial representation, but a new convention is required regarding the direction that this line segment should have relative to that of the point. In the case of angular velocity, because in addition

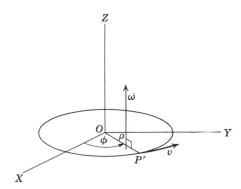

Fig. 1.10

to (1.16) the characteristic feature of the motion is the orientation of the plane in which the point moves and the sense of its rotation around the origin, it is customary to require that the vector be perpendicular to the plane of motion, with the direction of the arrowhead following the right-hand screw rule. That is, it should have the direction that the thumb of the right hand has if the fingers are curled in the sense of the rotation of the point. For example, if the point is moving in a counterclockwise direction around a circle lying in the XY-plane and centered on the origin of coordinates, its vector representation should be as shown in Fig. 1.10, where the location of $\boldsymbol{\omega}$ within the circle in the XY-plane is arbitrary. The vector need not be attached to the point, because it is the motion of the radius ρ connecting the point to the origin, rather than the instantaneous motion of the point in space, which is being represented. Such vectors are said to be free. In the present illustration

$$\dot{\phi}(t) = \omega_z(t) = \omega(t), \tag{1.18}$$

but in general the plane of motion can be inclined to the XY-plane and $\boldsymbol{\omega}$ can have three components (ω_x, ω_y, ω_z). The direction of the vector $\boldsymbol{\alpha}$ is defined in the same way as the direction of $\boldsymbol{\omega}$.

Algebraically, it is convenient to represent operations of the type described in (1.12),

$$\lim_{\Delta t \to 0} \frac{x(t + \Delta t) - x(t)}{\Delta t},$$

by symbols such as

$$\frac{d}{dt} x(t), \tag{1.19}$$

and we shall so do for the most part from now on. This notation, first introduced by Leibniz, is probably preferable to any other, as long as we keep clearly in mind the finite nature of the processes involved in arriving at a limiting value and the fact that in some cases no such value may exist. We can, for example, summarize (1.14) to (1.17) in the following way:

$$v_x(t) = \dot{x}(t) = \frac{d}{dt} x(t) \tag{1.20}$$

$$a_x(t) = \dot{v}_x(t) = \ddot{x}(t) = \frac{d}{dt} \dot{x}(t) = \frac{d^2}{dt^2} x(t) \tag{1.21}$$

$$\omega_z(t) = \dot{\phi}(t) = \frac{d}{dt} \phi(t) \tag{1.22}$$

$$\alpha_z(t) = \dot{\omega}_z(t) = \ddot{\phi}(t) = \frac{d}{dt} \dot{\phi}(t) = \frac{d^2}{dt^2} \phi(t) \tag{1.23}$$

Formulas for calculating the derivatives of common functional forms of $x(t)$ and $\phi(t)$ can, of course, be developed by the methods of differential calculus and may be found in various reference works.[2]

The final aspect of point motion—the possibility of the point changing its direction in successive time intervals—could be dealt with by specifying the instantaneous angular speed and absolute angular acceleration of a directed line segment passing through the point at any instant and location, just as we handled the possibility that it might change the amount of straight line distance it was covering in successive time intervals by specifying its instantaneous speed along a directed line segment and its absolute linear acceleration. Actually, it is not necessary to treat these aspects separately now that we can use vector representation.

Suppose that we construct a position vector **r**, locating the point at any position relative to the origin of coordinates and, furthermore, that we recognize that the length and orientation of this vector may vary with time

[2] Peirce, B. O., *A Short Table of Integrals*, pp. 97–106, Ginn, Boston, Mass., 1929.

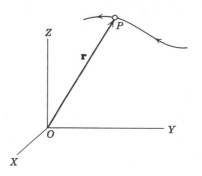

Fig. 1.11

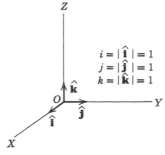

$$i = |\hat{\mathbf{i}}| = 1$$
$$j = |\hat{\mathbf{j}}| = 1$$
$$k = |\hat{\mathbf{k}}| = 1$$

Fig. 1.12

if it follows a moving point (Fig. 1.11):

$$\mathbf{r} = \mathbf{r}(x, y, z, t) \tag{1.24}$$

Of course, its projections $r_x = x$, $r_y = y$, and $r_z = z$ will then be scalar functions of time.

Also, let us define positive vectors $\hat{\mathbf{i}}$, $\hat{\mathbf{j}}$, and $\hat{\mathbf{k}}$ of unit magnitude directed along the three coordinate axes (Fig. 1.12) and agree that a vector of any magnitude originating at the origin and directed along one of these axes can be expressed as the product of its scalar length with the proper unit vector [Fig. 1.13, (1.25); Fig. 1.14, (1.26)]:

$$\mathbf{r}_x = r_x\hat{\mathbf{i}}, \qquad \mathbf{r}_y = r_y\hat{\mathbf{j}}, \qquad \mathbf{r}_z = r_z\hat{\mathbf{k}} \tag{1.25}$$

$$-\mathbf{r}_x = (-r_x)\hat{\mathbf{i}}, \qquad -\mathbf{r}_y = (-r_y)\hat{\mathbf{j}}, \qquad \mathbf{r}_z = (-r_z)\hat{\mathbf{k}} \tag{1.26}$$

The vectors $\hat{\mathbf{i}}$, $\hat{\mathbf{j}}$, $\hat{\mathbf{k}}$ are called unit vectors, and we shall always indicate such vectors by using a caret over the boldface letter symbol. These three are said to provide a "basis" for three-dimensional space because they may be

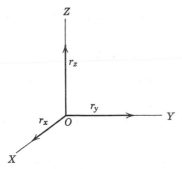

Fig. 1.13

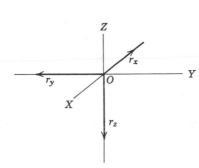

Fig. 1.14

shown[3] to "span" this space, in the sense that every vector in it can be written as a linear combination of them, and to be "linearly independent," in the sense that

$$r_x\hat{\mathbf{i}} + r_y\hat{\mathbf{j}} + r_z\hat{\mathbf{k}} = 0 \qquad (1.27)$$

means

$$r_x = r_y = r_z = 0. \qquad (1.28)$$

We shall examine other inferences to be drawn from these definitions in the next section. But now, as suggested above, it follows that at any

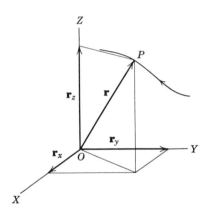

Fig. 1.15

instant of time there are three mutually orthogonal vectors intersecting at O whose sum is the position vector $\mathbf{r}$. For in general

$$|\mathbf{r}| = |(r_x^2 + r_y^2 + r_z^2)^{1/2}|, \qquad (1.29)$$

and we can construct (Fig. 1.15)

$$\mathbf{r} = \mathbf{r}_x + \mathbf{r}_y + \mathbf{r}_z = r_x\hat{\mathbf{i}} + r_y\hat{\mathbf{j}} + r_z\hat{\mathbf{k}}. \qquad (1.30)$$

We can assume that $\hat{\mathbf{i}}$, $\hat{\mathbf{j}}$, and $\hat{\mathbf{k}}$ will remain constant when $\mathbf{r}$ varies with time; therefore, we may write

$$\mathbf{r}(x, y, z, t) = r_x(t)\hat{\mathbf{i}} + r_y(t)\hat{\mathbf{j}} + r_z(t)\hat{\mathbf{k}}$$
$$= x(t)\hat{\mathbf{i}} + y(t)\hat{\mathbf{j}} + z(t)\hat{\mathbf{k}} \qquad (1.31)$$

and conclude that the time derivative of this vector function will provide a complete measure of the motion of the point, as will be demonstrated below.

[3] Dettman, J. W., *Mathematical Methods in Physics and Engineering*, pp. 18–24, McGraw-Hill New York, 1962.

First, we can see that

$$\dot{\mathbf{r}}(x, y, z, t) = \lim_{\Delta t \to 0} \frac{\mathbf{r}(x, y, z, t + \Delta t) - \mathbf{r}(x, y, z, t)}{\Delta t}$$

$$= \lim_{\Delta t \to 0} \left[\frac{r_x(t + \Delta t) - r_x(t)}{\Delta t} \hat{\mathbf{i}} + \frac{r_y(t + \Delta t) - r_y(t)}{\Delta t} \hat{\mathbf{j}} \right.$$

$$\left. + \frac{r_z(t + \Delta t) - r_z(t)}{\Delta t} \hat{\mathbf{k}} \right]$$

$$= \dot{r}_x(t)\hat{\mathbf{i}} + \dot{r}_y(t)\hat{\mathbf{j}} + \dot{r}_z(t)\hat{\mathbf{k}} = \dot{x}(t)\hat{\mathbf{i}} + \dot{y}(t)\hat{\mathbf{j}} + \dot{z}(t)\hat{\mathbf{k}}, \qquad (1.32)$$

and we know that $\dot{x}(t)$, $\dot{y}(t)$, and $\dot{z}(t)$ measure the speed of a point in the three coordinate directions at any location (x, y, z) determined by $\mathbf{r}$. These

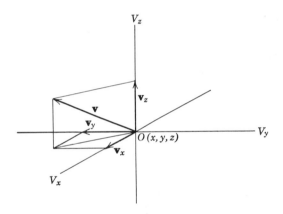

Fig. 1.16

must be the scalar components of the velocity vector at that location, because

$$|(\dot{x}^2 + \dot{y}^3 + \dot{z}^2)^{1/2}| = |(v_x^2 + v_y^2 + v_z^2)^{1/2}| = |\mathbf{v}|. \qquad (1.33)$$

In the same way it follows that these three scalar quantities establish the direction of the velocity vector at (x, y, z). We can create a three-dimensional "velocity space," cause the origin of coordinates to coincide with (x, y, z) and the coordinate axes to be parallel to their counterparts in geometric space, and use the $\hat{\mathbf{i}}$, $\hat{\mathbf{j}}$, $\hat{\mathbf{k}}$ system to define orthogonal component vectors (Fig. 1.16):

$$\mathbf{v} = \mathbf{v}_x - \mathbf{v}_y + \mathbf{v}_z = v_x\hat{\mathbf{i}} - v_y\hat{\mathbf{j}} + v_z\hat{\mathbf{k}} = \dot{x}\hat{\mathbf{i}} - \dot{y}\hat{\mathbf{j}} + \dot{z}\hat{\mathbf{k}} \qquad (1.34)$$

In other words,

$$\dot{\mathbf{r}} = \frac{d\mathbf{r}}{dt} \tag{1.35}$$

completely determines the velocity vector **v** of the moving point at every location and instant of time specified by **r**. Similarly, from

$$\ddot{\mathbf{r}}(x, y, z, t) = \lim_{\Delta t \to 0} \frac{\dot{\mathbf{r}}(x, y, z, t + \Delta t) - \dot{\mathbf{r}}(x, y, z, t)}{\Delta t}$$

$$= \ddot{x}(t)\hat{\mathbf{i}} + \ddot{y}(t)\hat{\mathbf{j}} + \ddot{z}(t)\hat{\mathbf{k}} \tag{1.36}$$

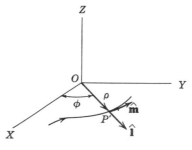

Fig. 1.17

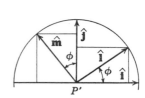

Fig. 1.18

we can infer that

$$\ddot{\mathbf{r}} = \frac{d^2\mathbf{r}}{dt^2} \tag{1.37}$$

determines the acceleration vector **a** at the same point.

It is also desirable to develop expressions for **v** and **a** in curvilinear coordinates, because points commonly move along curved paths in space. Let us begin with polar coordinates by defining orthogonal unit vectors $\hat{\mathbf{l}}$ and $\hat{\mathbf{m}}$ at the tip of the position vector $\boldsymbol{\rho}$ (Fig. 1.17). Here $\hat{\mathbf{l}}$ is in the direction of $\boldsymbol{\rho}$ and $\hat{\mathbf{m}}$ is perpendicular to $\boldsymbol{\rho}$, not necessarily tangent to the path of the point. In terms of the unit vectors $\hat{\mathbf{i}}$ and $\hat{\mathbf{j}}$ it follows that, at any time t (Fig. 1.18),

$$\hat{\mathbf{l}} = (1 \cdot \cos \phi)\hat{\mathbf{i}} + (1 \cdot \sin \phi)\hat{\mathbf{j}} \tag{1.38}$$

and

$$\hat{\mathbf{m}} = -(1 \cdot \sin \phi)\hat{\mathbf{i}} + (1 \cdot \cos \phi)\hat{\mathbf{j}}. \tag{1.39}$$

But because, according to the rule stated earlier, we can express the positive vector $\boldsymbol{\rho}(\phi, t)$ as

$$\boldsymbol{\rho}(\phi, t) = \rho(t)\hat{\mathbf{l}}, \tag{1.40}$$

the velocity vector **v** of the point at the location P' should be given by

$$\mathbf{v} = \frac{d\boldsymbol{\rho}(\phi, t)}{dt} = \rho(t)\frac{d\hat{\mathbf{l}}}{dt} + \hat{\mathbf{l}}\frac{d\rho(t)}{dt}, \tag{1.41}$$

assuming that the product of a scalar function and a vector function can be differentiated in the same way as the product of two scalar functions, which can easily be proved to be true.

Of course, we can see from (1.38) that $\hat{\mathbf{l}}$ depends on ϕ, and ϕ may itself depend on t. However, applying the chain rule of differential calculus we can write

$$\frac{d\hat{\mathbf{l}}}{dt} = \frac{d\hat{\mathbf{l}}}{d\phi}\frac{d\phi}{dt}; \tag{1.42}$$

and, according to the procedure developed above for calculating the derivative of a vector function,

$$\frac{d\hat{\mathbf{l}}}{d\phi} = \left(\frac{d\cos\phi}{d\phi}\right)\mathbf{i} + \left(\frac{d\sin\phi}{d\phi}\right)\mathbf{j} = -(\sin\phi)\mathbf{i} + (\cos\phi)\mathbf{j} = \hat{\mathbf{m}}, \tag{1.43}$$

using (1.38) and (1.39). Thus (1.41) can be written in the form

$$\mathbf{v} = \frac{d\boldsymbol{\rho}(\phi, t)}{dt} = \rho(t)\hat{\mathbf{m}}\frac{d\phi}{dt} + \hat{\mathbf{l}}\frac{d\rho(t)}{dt} \tag{1.44}$$

or simply

$$\mathbf{v} = \dot{\rho}\hat{\mathbf{l}} + \rho\dot{\phi}\hat{\mathbf{m}} = \dot{\rho}\hat{\mathbf{l}} + \rho\omega\hat{\mathbf{m}}, \tag{1.45}$$

where $\dot{\phi}$ is recognized to be the instantaneous angular speed ω and the functional dependence is suppressed. If we make use of the relation analogous to (1.43),

$$\frac{d\hat{\mathbf{m}}}{d\phi} = -\hat{\mathbf{l}}, \tag{1.46}$$

it follows that

$$\mathbf{a} = \frac{d\mathbf{v}}{dt} = (\ddot{\rho} - \rho\omega^2)\hat{\mathbf{l}} + (\rho\alpha + 2\dot{\rho}\omega)\hat{\mathbf{m}}. \tag{1.47}$$

Under these circumstances the velocity and acceleration vectors will always lie in the XY-plane, as (1.45) and (1.47) make clear, and their directions will depend entirely on the signs of their scalar components.

For example, if the point were moving in a circle of constant radius ρ with constant angular speed ω, these equations would reduce to

$$\mathbf{v} = \rho\omega\hat{\mathbf{m}} \tag{1.48}$$

and

$$\mathbf{a} = -\rho\omega^2\hat{\mathbf{l}} \tag{1.49}$$

Introduction

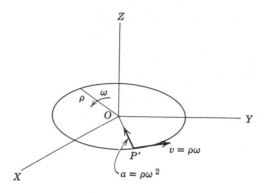

Fig. 1.19

with the vector representation as shown in Fig. 1.19. The vector $-\rho\omega^2\hat{\mathbf{l}}$ represents a special case of centripetal acceleration, acceleration in the ρ-direction arising from the motion of the point in the ϕ-direction. Similarly, the vector $2\dot{\rho}\omega\hat{\mathbf{m}}$, which does not appear in circular motion, represents a special case of Coriolis acceleration.

By defining orthogonal unit vectors $\hat{\mathbf{l}}$, $\hat{\mathbf{m}}$, and $\hat{\mathbf{k}}$ at the tip of the position vector $\mathbf{r}$ (whose projection $\boldsymbol{\rho}$ is the position vector of the path projected on the XY-plane), where $\hat{\mathbf{l}}$ is parallel to $\boldsymbol{\rho}$, $\hat{\mathbf{k}}$ is parallel to the Z-axis as defined earlier, and $\hat{\mathbf{m}}$ is perpendicular to both $\hat{\mathbf{l}}$ and $\hat{\mathbf{k}}$, a convenient representation of $\mathbf{v}$ and $\mathbf{a}$ in cylindrical coordinates can be developed[4] in much the same way (Fig. 1.20):

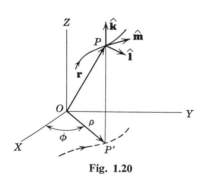

Fig. 1.20

$$\mathbf{v} = \frac{d\mathbf{r}}{dt} = \dot{\rho}\hat{\mathbf{l}} + \rho\dot{\phi}\hat{\mathbf{m}} + \dot{z}\hat{\mathbf{k}} \quad (1.50)$$

$$a = \frac{d^2\mathbf{r}}{dt^2} = (\ddot{\rho} - \rho\dot{\phi}^2)\hat{\mathbf{l}}$$

$$+ (\rho\ddot{\phi} + 2\dot{\rho}\dot{\phi})\hat{\mathbf{m}} + \ddot{z}\hat{\mathbf{k}} \quad (1.51)$$

Similarly, with the orthogonal unit vectors $\hat{\mathbf{n}}$, $\hat{\mathbf{m}}$, and $\hat{\mathbf{h}}$ defined at the tip of $\mathbf{r}$, $\hat{\mathbf{h}}$ being in the direction of $\mathbf{r}$, $\hat{\mathbf{n}}$ perpendicular to $\mathbf{r}$ and in the plane with it and the Z-axis, and $\hat{\mathbf{m}}$ perpendicular to the plane of $\mathbf{r}$ and the Z-axis as before, expressions for $\mathbf{v}$ and $\mathbf{a}$ in spherical coordinates can

---

[4] Symon, K. R., *Mechanics*, 2nd edition, pp. 87–95, Addison-Wesley, Reading, Mass., 1960.

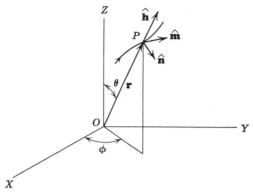

Fig. 1.21

be obtained (Fig. 1.21):

$$\mathbf{v} = \frac{d\mathbf{r}}{dt} = \dot{r}\hat{\mathbf{h}} + r\dot{\theta}\hat{\mathbf{n}} + (r\dot{\phi}\sin\theta)\hat{\mathbf{m}} \tag{1.52}$$

$$\mathbf{a} = \frac{d^2\mathbf{r}}{dt^2} = (\ddot{r} - r\dot{\theta}^2 - r\dot{\phi}^2\sin^2\theta)\hat{\mathbf{h}} + (r\ddot{\theta} + 2\dot{r}\dot{\theta} - r\dot{\phi}^2\sin\theta\cos\theta)\hat{\mathbf{n}}$$

$$+ (r\ddot{\phi}\sin\theta + 2\dot{r}\dot{\phi}\sin\theta + 2r\dot{\theta}\dot{\phi}\cos\theta)\hat{\mathbf{m}} \tag{1.53}$$

Problems 1.1

1. In Fig. P1.1 (1):
   a. Find the length of line *AF*.
   b. Determine the direction cosines of lines directed from *A* to *F* and from *F* to *B*.
   c. What happens to the direction cosines if the lines are reversed to run from *F* to *A* and *B* to *F*?

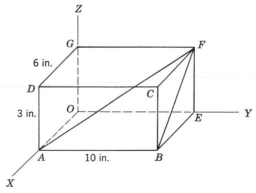

Fig. P1.1 (1)

Solution

(a) $AF = \sqrt{(0-6)^2 + (10-0)^2 + (3-0)^2} = \sqrt{145}$ in.

(b)

Line AF $\begin{cases} \cos\alpha = \dfrac{0-6}{\sqrt{145}} = \dfrac{-6}{\sqrt{145}} \\[2mm] \cos\beta = \dfrac{10-0}{\sqrt{145}} = \dfrac{10}{\sqrt{145}} \\[2mm] \cos\gamma = \dfrac{3-0}{\sqrt{145}} = \dfrac{3}{\sqrt{145}} \end{cases}$

Line FB $\begin{cases} \cos\alpha = \dfrac{6-0}{\sqrt{45}} = \dfrac{6}{\sqrt{45}} \\[2mm] \cos\beta = 0 \\[2mm] \cos\gamma = \dfrac{0-3}{\sqrt{45}} = \dfrac{-3}{\sqrt{45}} \end{cases}$

(c) The algebraic sign of each direction cosine is changed.

2. Show that for any points P_1 and P_2 in Fig. P1.1 (2) the sum of the squares of the direction cosines of the line joining the two points is equal to unity.

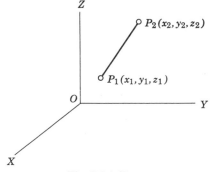

Fig. P1.1 (2)

Solution

$$l = [(x_2 - x_1)^2 + (y_2 - y_1)^2 + (z_2 - z_1)^2]^{1/2}$$

$$\cos\alpha = \frac{(x_2 - x_1)}{l}$$

$$\cos\beta = \frac{(y_2 - y_1)}{l}$$

$$\cos\gamma = \frac{(z_2 - z_1)}{l}$$

$$\cos^2\alpha + \cos^2\beta + \cos^2\gamma = \frac{(x_2 - x_1)^2}{l^2} + \frac{(y_2 - y_1)^2}{l^2} + \frac{(z_2 - z_1)^2}{l^2} = \frac{l^2}{l^2} = 1$$

3. Describe the surfaces generated in cylindrical coordinates for ρ = constant, ϕ = constant, z = constant. Determine the curves produced by the intersection of any two of these surfaces.

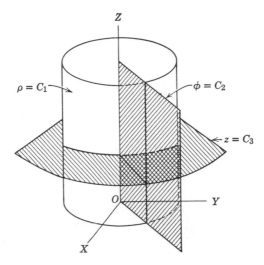

Fig. P1.1 (3)

Solution [*See Fig.* P1.1 (3)]

ρ = constant, C_1;   cylinder coaxial with Z-axis.

ϕ = constant, C_2;   vertical plane through Z-axis.

z = constant, C_3;   horizontal plane perpendicular to Z-axis.

Intersections of:

$\rho = C_1$, $\phi = C_2$ vertical line (z-curve)

$\phi = C_2$, $z = C_3$ horizontal line (ρ-curve)

$z = C_3$, $\rho = C_1$ horizontal circle (ϕ-curve)

4. Sketch the differential volume elements, giving the magnitudes of their edges, for:

a. Cylindrical coordinates
b. Spherical coordinates

Solution

(a) See Fig. P1.1 (4a).
(b) See Fig. P1.1 (4b).

Products of differentials are neglected for the edges.

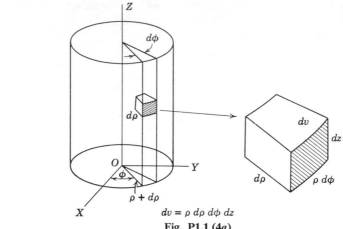

$$dv = \rho\, d\rho\, d\phi\, dz$$

Fig. P1.1 (4a)

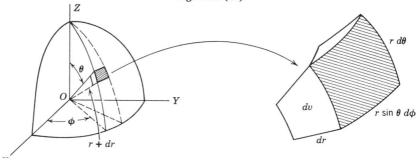

$$dv = r^2 \sin\theta\, dr\, d\theta\, d\phi$$

Fig. P1.1 (4b)

5. If $x(t) = 2t^3$, find $\dot{x}(t)$ and $\ddot{x}(t)$ using the basic definitions of the derivatives.

    Solution

$$\dot{x}(t) = \lim_{\Delta t \to 0} \frac{2(t + \Delta t)^3 - 2t^3}{\Delta t}$$

$$= \lim_{\Delta t \to 0} \frac{2(t^3 + 3t^2(\Delta t) + 3t(\Delta t)^2 + (\Delta t)^3 - t^3)}{\Delta t}$$

$$= \lim_{\Delta t \to 0} 2[3t^2 + 3t(\Delta t) + (\Delta t)^2]$$

$$= 6t^2$$

$$\ddot{x}(t) = \lim_{\Delta t \to 0} \frac{6\{[t + (\Delta t)]^2 - t^2\}}{\Delta t}$$

$$= \lim_{\Delta t \to 0} \frac{6[t^2 + 2t(\Delta t) + (\Delta t)^2 - t^2]}{\Delta t}$$

$$= \lim_{\Delta t \to 0} 6[2t + (\Delta t)]$$

$$= 12t$$

6. Find the instantaneous speed of a rectilinear motion described by the equation

$$x = 2t^2 - 6t + 10$$

at the instant when $t = 3$, if x is in feet and t is in seconds.

Solution

$$\dot{x}(t) = 4t - 6$$
$$\dot{x}(3) = 12 - 6 = 6 \text{ ft/sec}$$

Also:

$$\ddot{x}(t) = 4 \text{ ft/sec}^2, \qquad \text{constant for all } t.$$

7. The displacement of a point moving along the X-axis is given by

$$x = t^3 - 4t^2 + 10, \qquad t \geq 0$$

where x is in feet and t is in seconds. Determine:

a. The time at which the point has a speed of 6 ft/sec.
b. The acceleration of the point when the speed is 6 ft/sec.
c. The displacement of the point during the fifth second.

Solution

(a) $\dot{x} = 3t^2 - 8t$; when $\dot{x} = 6$ ft/sec,

$$3t^2 - 8t - 6 = 0, \qquad t^2 - \tfrac{8}{3}t - 2 = 0$$

$$t = \frac{\tfrac{8}{3} \pm \sqrt{\tfrac{64}{9} + 8}}{2} = \frac{4}{3} \pm \sqrt{\frac{16}{9} + 2}$$

$$= 1.33 \pm \sqrt{3.78} = 1.33 \pm 1.94$$

$$= 3.27 \text{ sec}$$

(b) $\ddot{x} = 6t - 8$; when $\dot{x} = 6$ ft/sec, $t = 3.27$ sec,
$\ddot{x} = 6(3.27) - 8 = 11.62$ ft/sec²;

(c)
$$x(5) = (5)^3 - 4(5)^2 + 10 = 35 \text{ ft}$$
$$x(4) = (4)^3 - 4(4)^2 + 10 = 10 \text{ ft}$$

Thus $x(5) - x(4) = 25$ ft.

8. A flywheel starts rotating from rest. At the times $t = 2$ sec and $t = 4$ sec the absolute angular acceleration α is found to be 2 and 4 rad/sec², respectively. Assuming that α varies linearly with time, determine the instantaneous angular velocity ω and the angular displacement ϕ at $t = 3$ sec.

Solution [(*See Fig.* P1.1 (8)]

$$d\omega = \alpha \, dt = t \, dt$$
$$\omega = \tfrac{1}{2}t^2 + C_1$$

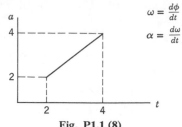

$$\omega = \frac{d\phi}{dt}$$

$$\alpha = \frac{d\omega}{dt}$$

Fig. P1.1 (8)

At $t = 0$, $\omega = 0$, so $C_1 = 0$, hence $\omega = \frac{1}{2}t^2$; and at $t = 3$, $\omega = \frac{1}{2}(3)^2 = \frac{9}{2}$ = 4.5 rad/sec.

$$d\phi = \omega \, dt = \tfrac{1}{2}t^2 \, dt;$$
$$\phi = \tfrac{1}{6}t^3 + C_2.$$

At $t = 0$, $\phi = 0$, so $C_2 = 0$; and $\phi = \frac{1}{6}t^3$. Thus, at $t = 3$, $\phi = \frac{27}{6} = 4.5$ rad.

9. For a given motion along the X-axis it is found that
$$t = kx^2, \qquad k = \text{constant};$$
show that the acceleration varies as the cube of the velocity.

Solution

Differentiating $kx^2 = t$,

$$2kx\dot{x} = 1,$$

$$x\dot{x} = \frac{1}{2k}\,;$$

and again

$$x\ddot{x} + (\dot{x})^2 = 0.$$

Substituting $x = \dfrac{1}{2k\dot{x}}$,

$$\frac{\ddot{x}}{2k\dot{x}} + (\dot{x})^2 = 0;$$

or

$$\ddot{x} = -2k(\dot{x})^3.$$

10. Find the square of the element of arc length ds in cylindrical and spherical coordinates.

Solution

Cylindrical:
$$x = \rho \cos \phi, \qquad y = \rho \sin \phi, \qquad z = z$$
$$dx = -\rho \sin \phi \, d\phi + \cos \phi \, d\rho$$
$$dy = \rho \cos \phi \, d\phi + \sin \phi \, d\rho$$
$$dz = dz$$
$$ds^2 = dx^2 + dy^2 + dz^2$$
$$= (-\rho \sin \phi \, d\phi + \cos \phi \, d\rho)^2 + (\rho \cos \phi \, d\phi + \sin \phi \, d\rho)^2 + dz^2$$
$$= \rho^2 \sin^2 \phi \, (d\phi)^2 - 2\rho \sin \phi \cos \phi \, d\rho \, d\phi + \cos^2 \phi \, (d\rho)^2$$
$$\quad + \rho^2 \cos^2 \phi \, (d\phi)^2 + 2\rho \sin \phi \cos \phi \, d\rho \, d\phi + \sin^2 \phi \, (d\rho)^2 + dz^2$$
$$= (d\rho)^2 + \rho^2 \, (d\phi)^2 + (dz)^2$$

Spherical:

$$x = r \sin \phi \cos \phi, \qquad y = r \sin \phi \sin \phi, \qquad z = r \cos \phi$$

$$dx = dr \sin \theta \cos \phi + r \cos \theta \cos \phi \, d\theta - r \sin \theta \sin \phi \, d\phi$$

$$dy = dr \sin \theta \sin \phi + r \cos \theta \sin \phi \, d\theta + r \sin \theta \cos \phi \, d\phi$$

$$dz = dr \cos \theta - r \sin \theta \, d\theta$$

$$ds^2 = dx^2 + dy^2 + dz^2$$

$$= (dr)^2 \sin^2 \theta \cos^2 \theta + r \, dr \sin \theta \cos \theta \cos^2 \phi \, d\theta$$

$$\qquad - r \, dr \sin^2 \theta \sin \theta \cos \theta \, d\theta + r \, dr \sin \theta \cos \theta \cos^2 \phi \, d\theta$$

$$\qquad + r^2 \cos^2 \theta \cos^2 \phi \, (d\theta)^2 - r^2 \sin \theta \cos \theta \sin \phi \cos \phi \, d\theta \, d\phi$$

$$\qquad - r \, dr \sin^2 \theta, \ldots, \text{etc.}$$

$$= (dr)^2 + r^2 \, (d\theta)^2 + r^2 \sin^2 \theta \, (d\phi)^2$$

11. If $\mathbf{r} = 3t^2 \hat{\mathbf{l}} - 2\hat{\mathbf{k}}$, find $\mathbf{v}$ and $\mathbf{a}$ in cylindrical coordinates.

Solution

$$\mathbf{v} = \dot{\mathbf{r}} = 6t\hat{\mathbf{l}} + 3t^2\dot{\hat{\mathbf{l}}}$$

$$\dot{\hat{\mathbf{l}}} = \omega\hat{\mathbf{m}}$$

$$\mathbf{v} = 6t\hat{\mathbf{l}} + 3t^2\omega\hat{\mathbf{m}}$$

$$\mathbf{a} = \dot{\mathbf{v}} = 6\hat{\mathbf{l}} + 6t\dot{\hat{\mathbf{l}}} + 6t\omega\hat{\mathbf{m}} + 3t^2\alpha\hat{\mathbf{m}} + 3t^2\omega\dot{\hat{\mathbf{m}}}$$

$$\dot{\hat{\mathbf{l}}} = \omega\hat{\mathbf{m}}$$

$$\dot{\hat{\mathbf{m}}} = -\omega\hat{\mathbf{l}}$$

$$\mathbf{a} = 6\hat{\mathbf{l}} + 6t\omega\hat{\mathbf{m}} + 6t\omega\hat{\mathbf{m}} + 3t^2\alpha\hat{\mathbf{m}} - 3t^2\omega^2\hat{\mathbf{l}}$$

$$= (6 - 3t^2\omega^2)\hat{\mathbf{l}} + (12t\omega + 3t^2\alpha)\hat{\mathbf{m}}$$

12. If $\mathbf{A} = \hat{\mathbf{l}} + \hat{\mathbf{m}} - \hat{\mathbf{k}}$, $\phi_A = 30°$, and $\mathbf{B} = 2\hat{\mathbf{l}} + 3\hat{\mathbf{k}}$, $\phi_B = 0$, find the following in Cartesian coordinates:

a. $\mathbf{A} + \mathbf{B} = \mathbf{C}$.
b. The unit vector in the direction of $\mathbf{C}$.
c. The direction cosines of $\mathbf{C}$.

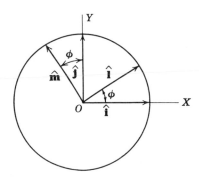

Fig. P1.1 (12)

Solution [See Fig. P1.1 (12)]

$$\hat{\mathbf{l}} = \cos\phi\,\hat{\mathbf{i}} + \sin\phi\,\hat{\mathbf{j}}$$
$$\hat{\mathbf{m}} = -\sin\phi\,\hat{\mathbf{i}} + \cos\phi\,\hat{\mathbf{j}}$$
$$\hat{\mathbf{k}} = \hat{\mathbf{k}}$$
$$\mathbf{A} = (\cos\phi\,\hat{\mathbf{i}} + \sin\phi\,\hat{\mathbf{j}}) + (-\sin\phi\,\hat{\mathbf{i}} + \cos\phi\,\hat{\mathbf{j}}) - \hat{\mathbf{k}}$$
$$= (\cos\phi - \sin\phi)\hat{\mathbf{i}} + (\sin\phi + \cos\phi)\hat{\mathbf{j}} - \hat{\mathbf{k}}$$
$$\phi_A = 30°, \quad \sin\phi_A = \tfrac{1}{2}, \quad \cos\phi_A = 0.866$$
$$\mathbf{A} = 0.366\hat{\mathbf{i}} + 1.366\hat{\mathbf{j}} - \hat{\mathbf{k}}$$
$$\mathbf{B} = 2(\cos\phi\,\hat{\mathbf{i}} + \sin\phi\,\hat{\mathbf{j}}) + 3\hat{\mathbf{k}}$$
$$\phi_B = 0, \quad \cos\phi_B = 1, \quad \sin\phi_B = 0$$
$$\mathbf{B} = 2\hat{\mathbf{i}} + 3\hat{\mathbf{k}}$$

(a)
$$\mathbf{C} = \mathbf{A} + \mathbf{B} = 2.366\hat{\mathbf{i}} + 1.366\hat{\mathbf{j}} + 2\hat{\mathbf{k}}$$

(b)
$$\hat{\mathbf{c}} = \frac{2.366\hat{\mathbf{i}} + 1.366\hat{\mathbf{j}} + 2\hat{\mathbf{k}}}{[(2.366)^2 + (1.366)^2 + 4]^{1/2}}$$
$$= \frac{2.366\hat{\mathbf{i}} + 1.366\hat{\mathbf{j}} + 2\hat{\mathbf{k}}}{(11.47)^{1/2}}$$
$$= \frac{2.366\hat{\mathbf{i}} + 1.366\hat{\mathbf{j}} + 2\hat{\mathbf{k}}}{3.38}$$
$$= 0.7\hat{\mathbf{i}} + 0.404\hat{\mathbf{j}} + 0.592\hat{\mathbf{k}}$$

(c) The direction cosines of a directed line are the coefficients of $\hat{\mathbf{i}}$, $\hat{\mathbf{j}}$, and $\hat{\mathbf{k}}$ of a unit vector in that direction.

13. A $3 \times 4 \times 5$ in. right triangle rotates in its plane about point *B*. If $\phi = (2t^2 - t)$ determine **v** and **a** for points *A* and *C* at the instant $t = 1$ sec, using polar coordinates [Fig. P1.1 (13)].

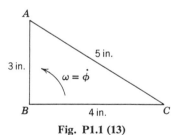

Fig. P1.1 (13)

Solution

$$\mathbf{v} = \dot{\rho}\hat{\mathbf{l}} + \rho\dot{\phi}\hat{\mathbf{m}}$$
$$\mathbf{a} = (\ddot{\rho} - \rho\dot{\phi}^2)\hat{\mathbf{l}} + (\rho\ddot{\phi} + 2\dot{\rho}\dot{\phi})\hat{\mathbf{m}}$$
$$\phi = 2t^2 - t; \quad \phi(1) = 1 \text{ rad}$$
$$\dot{\phi} = 4t - 1; \quad \dot{\phi}(1) = 3 \text{ rad/sec}$$
$$\ddot{\phi} = 4 \text{ rad/sec}^2$$
$$\dot{\rho} = 0$$
$$\mathbf{v} = \rho\dot{\phi}\hat{\mathbf{m}}$$
$$\mathbf{a} = -\rho\dot{\phi}^2\hat{\mathbf{l}} + \rho\ddot{\phi}\hat{\mathbf{m}}$$

Point A: $\rho = 3$ in.

$$\mathbf{v} = 9\hat{\mathbf{m}} \text{ in./sec}$$
$$\mathbf{a} = -27\hat{\mathbf{l}} + 12\hat{\mathbf{m}} \text{ in./sec}^2$$

Point C: $\rho = 4''$

$$\mathbf{v} = 12\hat{\mathbf{m}} \text{ in./sec}$$
$$\mathbf{a} = -36\hat{\mathbf{l}} + 16\hat{\mathbf{m}} \text{ in./sec}^2$$

14. The vector $\mathbf{F} = 10\hat{\mathbf{i}} + 9\hat{\mathbf{j}} - 5\hat{\mathbf{k}}$ acts at a point P, and the position vector of P is given as

$$\mathbf{r} = 3\hat{\mathbf{i}} + \hat{\mathbf{j}} - \hat{\mathbf{k}}$$

Express $\mathbf{F}$ in cylindrical coordinates using the unit vectors $\hat{\mathbf{l}}$, $\hat{\mathbf{m}}$, and $\hat{\mathbf{k}}$.

Solution

$$x = \rho \cos \phi$$
$$y = \rho \sin \phi$$
$$z = z$$

$$\tan \phi = \frac{y}{x}$$

$$\phi_r = \tan^{-1} \tfrac{1}{3}$$
$$\phi_F = \tan^{-1} \tfrac{9}{10}$$
$$\mathbf{F} = F_\rho \hat{\mathbf{l}} + F_\phi \hat{\mathbf{m}} + F_z \hat{\mathbf{k}}$$

where, if F_{xy} is the projection of F in the XY plane,

$$F_\rho = F_{xy} \cos (\phi_F - \phi_r) = \sqrt{181} \cos [\tan^{-1} 0.9 - \tan^{-1} 0.33]$$
$$= \sqrt{181} \cos (42° - 18.4°) = \sqrt{181} \, (0.92) = 12.39$$
$$F_\phi = F_{xy} \sin (\phi_F - \phi_r) = \sqrt{181} \sin [\tan^{-1} 0.9 - \tan^{-1} 0.33]$$
$$= \sqrt{181} \sin 23.6 = \sqrt{181} \, (0.4) = 5.38$$
$$\mathbf{F} = 12.39\hat{\mathbf{l}} + 5.38\hat{\mathbf{m}} - 5\hat{\mathbf{k}}$$

Alternate Solution

$$\hat{\mathbf{l}} = \cos \phi \, \hat{\mathbf{i}} + \sin \phi \, \hat{\mathbf{j}} = \frac{3}{\sqrt{10}} \, \hat{\mathbf{i}} + \frac{1}{\sqrt{10}} \, \hat{\mathbf{j}}$$

$$\hat{\mathbf{m}} = -\sin \phi \, \hat{\mathbf{i}} + \cos \phi \, \hat{\mathbf{j}} = \frac{-1}{\sqrt{10}} \, \hat{\mathbf{i}} + \frac{3}{\sqrt{10}} \, \hat{\mathbf{j}}$$

$$\hat{\mathbf{k}} = \hat{\mathbf{k}}$$

Solving for $\hat{\mathbf{i}}$ and $\hat{\mathbf{j}}$ in terms of $\hat{\mathbf{l}}$ and $\hat{\mathbf{m}}$:

$$\hat{\mathbf{j}} = \frac{1}{\sqrt{10}} (\hat{\mathbf{l}} + 3\hat{\mathbf{m}})$$

$$\hat{\mathbf{i}} = \frac{1}{\sqrt{10}} (3\hat{\mathbf{l}} - \hat{\mathbf{m}})$$

Therefore

$$\mathbf{F} = \frac{10}{\sqrt{10}} (3\hat{\mathbf{l}} - \hat{\mathbf{m}}) + \frac{9}{\sqrt{10}} (\hat{\mathbf{l}} + 3\hat{\mathbf{m}}) - 5\hat{\mathbf{k}}$$
$$= 12.39\hat{\mathbf{l}} + 5.38\hat{\mathbf{m}} - 5\hat{\mathbf{k}}.$$

15. If **v** is the velocity of a point in a plane with components v_ρ along the radius vector ρ and v_x parallel to the fixed X-axis, show that the corresponding components of the acceleration are

$$\frac{dv_\rho}{dt} - \frac{v_\rho v_x}{\rho} \cos \phi \quad \text{and} \quad \frac{dv_x}{dt} + \frac{v_\rho v_x}{\rho}$$

where ϕ is the angle between the fixed X-axis and the radius vector. Note that the two reference directions are not orthogonal.

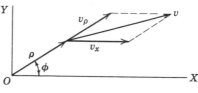

Fig. P1.1 (15)

Solution [*See Fig.* P1.1 (15)]

$$\mathbf{v} = v_\rho \hat{\mathbf{l}} + v_x \hat{\mathbf{i}}$$
$$\hat{\mathbf{l}} = \cos \phi \, \hat{\mathbf{i}} + \sin \phi \, \hat{\mathbf{j}}$$
$$\mathbf{a} = \frac{d\mathbf{v}}{dt} = \frac{dv_\rho}{dt} \hat{\mathbf{l}} + v_\rho \frac{d\hat{\mathbf{l}}}{dt} + \frac{dv_x}{dt} \hat{\mathbf{i}}$$

We now attempt to eliminate the expression $d\hat{\mathbf{l}}/dt$:

$$\frac{d\hat{\mathbf{l}}}{dt} = \frac{d\hat{\mathbf{l}}}{d\phi} \frac{d\phi}{dt}$$
$$= -\sin \phi \frac{d\phi}{dt} \hat{\mathbf{i}} + \cos \phi \frac{d\phi}{dt} \hat{\mathbf{j}}$$
$$= \frac{d\phi}{dt} (-\sin \phi \, \hat{\mathbf{i}} + \cos \phi \, \hat{\mathbf{j}})$$

But since

$$\hat{\mathbf{l}} \cos \phi = \cos^2 \phi \, \hat{\mathbf{i}} + \cos \phi \sin \phi \, \hat{\mathbf{j}}$$

and

$$\frac{-d\hat{\mathbf{l}}}{dt} \sin \phi = \frac{d\phi}{dt} (\sin^2 \phi \, \hat{\mathbf{i}} - \sin \phi \cos \phi \, \hat{\mathbf{j}}),$$

$$\frac{d\phi}{dt} \cos \phi \, \hat{\mathbf{l}} - \frac{d\hat{\mathbf{l}}}{dt} \sin \phi = \frac{d\phi}{dt} \hat{\mathbf{i}}$$

or

$$\frac{d\hat{\mathbf{l}}}{dt} = \frac{d\phi}{dt} \frac{\cos \phi}{\sin \phi} \hat{\mathbf{l}} - \frac{d\phi}{dt} \frac{1}{\sin \phi} \hat{\mathbf{i}}.$$

Also, however,

$$\mathbf{v} = \dot{\rho} \hat{\mathbf{l}} + \rho \dot{\phi} \hat{\mathbf{m}} + \dot{z} \hat{\mathbf{k}}$$

and here $\dot{z} = 0$, together with

$$\rho \dot{\phi} = \rho \frac{d\phi}{dt} = -v_x \sin \phi.$$

Therefore

$$\frac{d\phi}{dt} = \frac{-v_x \sin \phi}{\rho}$$

and

$$\frac{d\hat{\mathbf{i}}}{dt} = \frac{-v_x \cos \phi}{\rho} \hat{\mathbf{i}} + \frac{v_x}{\rho} \hat{\mathbf{i}}.$$

Substituting this into the equation for **a**:

$$\mathbf{a} = \left(\frac{dv_\rho}{dt} - \frac{v_\rho v_x}{\rho} \cos \phi\right)\hat{\mathbf{i}} + \left(\frac{dv_x}{dt} + \frac{v_\rho v_x}{\rho}\right)\hat{\mathbf{i}}$$

Exercises 1.1

1. The direction cosines of the line OP in Fig. E1.1 (1) are:

$$\cos \alpha = \frac{-2}{\sqrt{14}}$$

$$\cos \beta = \frac{1}{\sqrt{14}}$$

and its length is 10 in. Locate the point P in the following coordinate systems:

a. Rectangular Cartesian coordinates.
b. Spherical coordinates.
c. Cylindrical coordinates.

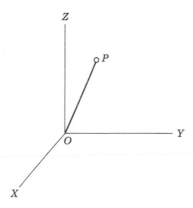

Fig. E1.1 (1)

2. Describe the surfaces generated for constant r, θ, and ϕ in spherical coordinates, and find the curves produced by the intersection of any two of the surfaces.

3. Determine the transformation formulas from cylindrical to spherical coordinates.

4. Evaluate

$$\iiint_v (x^2 + y^2 + z^2)\, dx\, dy\, dz$$

where v is the volume of the sphere having its center at the origin and radius equal to a. Use any coordinate system that is convenient.

Answer. $4\pi a^5/5$.

5. The coordinate of a body moving along the X-axis is given by $x = 5t^2$ where x is in inches and t is in seconds. Compute the average speed and average acceleration over the following time intervals:

a. 2 to 2.1 sec.
b. 2 to 2.001 sec.

Determine the instantaneous speed and absolute acceleration at exactly 2 sec by using the definition of the derivative.

6. A point moving along a horizontal line has the following positions at various instants of time:

x (in inches)	0.07	0.04	0.03	0.04
t (in seconds)	0	1	2	3

a. Plot displacement versus time.
b. Find the average speed of the point in the intervals 0 to 1 sec, 1 to 2 sec, 2 to 3 sec.
c. Find the instantaneous speeds at times $t = 1, 2, 3$ sec from part (*a*) and plot them versus time.
d. From the curve of part (*c*) determine the absolute acceleration of the point at time $t = 2$ sec.

7. A disk starts spinning from rest and attains a maximum angular speed of 2 revolutions per minute in 4 min.

a. What information would be needed to determine the instantaneous angular speed at any particular instant during this interval?
b. Assuming constant absolute angular acceleration during the interval, determine the number of revolutions made within the first minute.

Answer. $\frac{1}{4}$ revolution.

8. An automobile travels 4 mi north, then 6 mi northeast. Represent these displacements and determine the resultant displacement:

a. Graphically.
b. Analytically.

Find the unit vector in the direction of the resultant displacement.

Answer. 9.268 mi; $\hat{\mathbf{r}} = 0.457\hat{\mathbf{i}} + 0.89\hat{\mathbf{j}}$.

9. Prove $m(\mathbf{A} + \mathbf{B}) = m\mathbf{A} + m\mathbf{B}$ graphically, where m is a scalar constant.

10. If

$$A = \hat{i} + \hat{j} + \hat{k}$$
$$B = 2\hat{i} - 4\hat{j} + 7\hat{k}$$
$$C = 10\hat{i} + 5\hat{m} + \hat{k},$$

where $\phi = 60°$,
find: **a.** $A + B + C$.
   b. $A - C$.
   c. $|A + B|$.
   d. The unit vector in the direction of $(A + B + C)$.
   e. The direction cosines of $(A + B + C)$.

Answer
(a) $3.67\hat{i} + 8.16\hat{j} + 9\hat{k}$.
(b) $0.33\hat{i} - 10.16\hat{j}$.
(c) 9.0554.
(d) $0.291\hat{i} + 0.643\hat{j} + 0.71\hat{k}$.

11. The following vectors are functions of time:

$$A = 3t\hat{i} - (2t^2 + 3)\hat{j}, \qquad B = -t^3\hat{i} + 6\hat{k}.$$

Find: **a.** The time derivative of the difference of these vectors.
   b. The integral of the sum of the vectors.

Answer
(a) $3(1 + t^2)\hat{i} - 4t\hat{j}$.

(b) $(-\frac{1}{4}t^4 + \frac{3}{2}t^2 + C_1)\hat{i} - (\frac{2}{3}t^3 + 3t + C_2)\hat{j} + (6t + C_3)\hat{k}$.

12. A vector V has the form $V = \displaystyle\int_0^\tau x(t)\,dt$.

a. If $x(t) = \left(\dfrac{4}{\pi}\right)^3 t^2\hat{i} + \sin 2t\hat{j}$, calculate $V = V(\tau)$.

b. Evaluate V for $\tau = \dfrac{\pi}{4}$ and $\tau = \dfrac{\pi}{2}$.

Answer

(a) $V = \dfrac{1}{3}\left(\dfrac{4}{\pi}\right)^3 \tau^3\hat{i} + \dfrac{1}{2}(1 - \cos 2\tau)\hat{j}$.

(b) $V = \frac{1}{3}\hat{i} + \frac{1}{2}\hat{j}$, $V = \frac{8}{3}\hat{i} + \hat{j}$.

13. Derive the expression for the acceleration a in cylindrical coordinates, using the unit vectors $\hat{i}$, $\hat{m}$, and $\hat{k}$.

14. If $r = (\cos 3t)\hat{i} + e^t\hat{k}$, find v and a in cylindrical coordinates.

15. The rectangle shown in Fig. E1.1 (15) rotates in its plane about point A; the angular displacement of the line AC is given by $\phi = 3t$ rad. Determine the

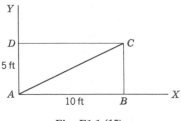

Fig. E1.1 (15)

magnitude of the linear velocity and acceleration of points B, C, and D, using polar coordinates.

Answer. v: 30, 33.57, 15 ft/sec; a: 90, 100.71, 45 ft/sec².

16. The vector $\mathbf{A} = x\hat{\mathbf{i}} - 3yz\hat{\mathbf{j}} + x^2\hat{\mathbf{k}}$ acts at a point P. The position vector of P has a magnitude of 10 in. and equal direction cosines with respect to the X-, Y-, and Z-axes. Represent $\mathbf{A}$ in cylindrical coordinates using the unit vectors $\hat{\mathbf{l}}$, $\hat{\mathbf{m}}$, and $\hat{\mathbf{k}}$.

Answer. $\mathbf{A} = -66.63\hat{\mathbf{l}} - 74.79\hat{\mathbf{m}} + 33.33\hat{\mathbf{k}}.$

1.2   Transformations in Space and Time

We have seen that directed line segments scaled in length can be used to represent vector quantities and that, in one sense at least, problems in point motion feature transformations of these line segments in space and time. In this section we consider these two types of transformations separately and from a more fundamental point of view, both to arrive at a more complete understanding of vector properties and to be able later to generalize to transformations of quadric surfaces and other geometrical forms, which will be useful in representing other types of quantities.

Because a physical magnitude is to be associated with the length of the vector, let us assume that it will remain constant and thus restrict our considerations to the effects of the inherent properties of space itself. There are only two modes of transformation of a vector of constant length: translation and rotation. That is, such a vector can be changed from any location and orientation in space to any other by first translating it to the new location and then carrying out the required rotation, or by first rotating it at the old location and then translating it to the new one.

The translation may be dealt with very easily. If any vector $\mathbf{u}$ is defined by its scalar components at any one location O, we can keep it fixed in this coordinate system and translate the entire system to any other location O' by means of a position vector $\mathbf{R}$ from O to O' (Fig. 1.22). Because the vector remains fixed in the system, its projections do not change. Consequently, its projections on the axes at the new location, $X'Y'Z'$, must equal its projections on the axes at the old location, XYZ:

$$u_x' = u_x \tag{2.1}$$

$$u_y' = u_y \tag{2.2}$$

$$u_z' = u_z \tag{2.3}$$

These are the transformation formulas that define the operation of translating a vector of constant length from one location to another in

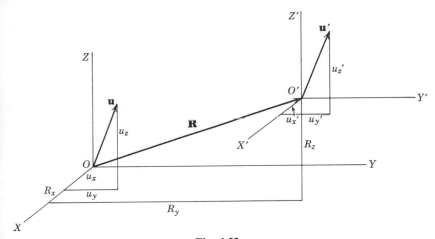

Fig. 1.22

Cartesian space. They tell us that we must proceed to the new location, defined by $\mathbf{R}$, construct a parallel coordinate system $X'Y'Z'$ there, and place the vector so that its projections in the new system satisfy (2.1) to (2.3). Of course, simply moving the vector in such a way that its tail ends at (R_x, R_y, R_z) and its tip at

$$x = R_x + u_x \tag{2.4}$$

$$y = R_y + u_y \tag{2.5}$$

$$z = R_z + u_z \tag{2.6}$$

in the original system is an entirely equivalent operation.

The rotation is more complicated. Suppose that we wish to rotate the vector $\mathbf{u}$ to a new orientation while it is at O, perhaps before translating it to some other location. Equivalently, we could hold the direction of the vector fixed in space and rotate the coordinate axes to new orientations X', Y', Z', while keeping them mutually perpendicular and their distance scales the same. For example, if the vector happened to lie in the XY-plane,

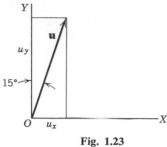

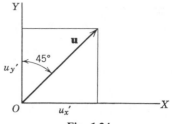

Fig. 1.23   **Fig. 1.24**

making an angle of 15° with the *Y*-axis (Fig. 1.23), and if we wanted to
rotate it clockwise 30° until it made an angle of 45° with this axis (Fig. 1.24),
we could instead hold the vector fixed in space and rotate the *X*- and *Y*-
axes 30° in a counterclockwise direction to achieve the same result
(Fig. 1.25). Evidently, the new coordinates would be given in terms of the
old coordinates by relations of the type:

$$u_x' = u_x \cos 30 + u_y \sin 30$$
$$= u_x \cos 30 + u_y \cos 60 \tag{2.7}$$

Thus, in general, to find the projections of the vector in the new coordinate system (u_x', u_y', u_z') in terms of its projections in the old system
(u_x, u_y, u_z), as was accomplished for translation in (2.1) to (2.3), we must
sum the projections of all of the scalar quantities u_x, u_y, u_z on each of the
axes X', Y', and Z' (Fig. 1.26). If we agree to describe the angle between
any two axes by their letter designations written in parentheses, for example,

$$(X, Y') = (Y', X) \tag{2.8}$$

for the angle between the *X*- and *Y'*-axes, it follows that:

$$u_x' = u_x \cos (X', X) + u_y \cos (X', Y) + u_z \cos (X', Z) \tag{2.9}$$
$$u_y' = u_x \cos (Y', X) + u_y \cos (Y', Y) + u_z \cos (Y', Z) \tag{2.10}$$
$$u_z' = u_x \cos (Z', X) + u_y \cos (Z', Y) + u_z \cos (Z', Z) \tag{2.11}$$

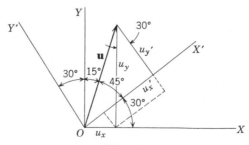

Fig. 1.25

These three equations are the required transformation formulas, defining the operation of rotating a vector of constant length from one direction to another in a fixed Cartesian coordinate system. However, by adopting a different way of labeling the coordinate axes we can write them more compactly. If we call the X'-axis the X_1'-axis, the Y'-axis the X_2'-axis, and so on,

$$X' = X_1' \qquad X = X_1$$
$$Y' = X_2' \qquad Y = X_2 \qquad (2.12)$$
$$Z' = X_3' \qquad Z = X_3,$$

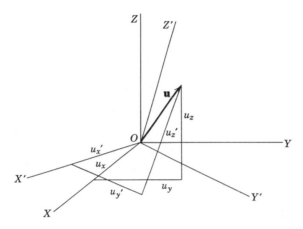

Fig. 1.26

we can represent the entire "new" set of axes by writing

$$X_i' \qquad \{i = 1, 2, 3 \qquad (2.13)$$

and the "old" set by writing

$$X_j \qquad \{j = 1, 2, 3. \qquad (2.14)$$

The subscripts i and j are called indices, and the notation built around their use is called indicial notation.

The cosines in (2.9) to (2.11) can also be written in indicial notation. For example, in

$$\cos{(X', Y)} = \cos{(X_1', X_2)} = c_{12} \qquad (2.15)$$

the subscript 1 represents the value of i, the index of the new axis, and the subscript 2 represents the value of j, the index of the old axis.

Applying the same ideas to projections on the axes, (2.9) can be written as

$$u_1' = \sum_{j=1}^{3} c_{1j} u_j = c_{11} u_1 + c_{12} u_2 + c_{13} u_3, \qquad (2.16)$$

and the three equations (2.9) to (2.11) can be written as

$$u_i' = \sum_{j=1}^{3} c_{ij} u_j \qquad \{i = 1, 2, 3. \qquad (2.17)$$

In expanding such an equation, the usual procedure is to carry out the summation as a preliminary step,

$$u_i' = c_{i1} u_1 + c_{i2} u_2 + c_{i3} u_3, \qquad (2.18)$$

and then give the remaining index its possible values one after the other in this equation:

$$u_1' = c_{11} u_1 + c_{12} u_2 + c_{13} u_3 \qquad (2.19)$$

$$u_2' = c_{21} u_1 + c_{22} u_2 + c_{23} u_3 \qquad (2.20)$$

$$u_3' = c_{31} u_1 + c_{32} u_2 + c_{33} u_3 \qquad (2.21)$$

Still another simplification is possible if we notice that the summation occurs over the only index that is repeated in (2.17). Consequently, the summation sign can be omitted if we adopt the convention, due to Einstein, that an index repeated in a single term means that we must sum that term over all possible values of the index, whose range can then be indicated in the same manner as previously:

$$u_i' = c_{ij} u_j \qquad \{i, j = 1, 2, 3 \qquad (2.22)$$

This equation is fully equivalent to the three equations (2.19) to (2.21) and, accordingly, to the three equations (2.9) to (2.11) defining the rotation of a constant length vector.

There are a few occasions when a summation is not needed, even though a repeated index is required, but in such a case we can agree to enclose the index in parentheses. This notation will be illustrated when the need arises. It is also common practice to omit writing the ranges for the indices, once they have been established in any particular context, for example 1, 2, and 3 in the present case. It is useful to remember that for an indicial equation to be valid the free indices in every term on both sides of the equation must be the same, and that the final number of equations will be equal to the range of the indices g raised to the power f, g^f, where f is the number of free indices.

To obtain the analogous set of relations for the unprimed projections in terms of the primed projections [(2.1) to (2.3) constitute both sets for the case of translation], we must consider the unprimed axes to be the "new" axes with the index i, X_i, and the primed axes the "old" axes with the index j, X_j'. Then we can proceed as before and write

$$u_x = u_x' \cos (X', X) + u_y' \cos (Y', X) + u_z' \cos (Z', X), \quad (2.23)$$

$$u_y = u_x' \cos (X', Y) + u_y' \cos (Y', Y) + u_z' \cos (Z', Y), \quad (2.24)$$

$$u_z = u_x' \cos (X', Z) + u_y' \cos (Y', Z) + u_z' \cos (Z', Z), \quad (2.25)$$

where the order of writing the axes in the direction cosines has been reversed to emphasize the identity of the angles appearing in (2.9) to (2.11); these reduce to

$$u_i = c_{ji} u_j' \qquad \{i, j = 1, 2, 3. \qquad (2.26)$$

The relative positions of the indices in this equation should be carefully noted and compared with those in (2.22). If we expand (2.26), the result is:

$$u_i = c_{1i} u_1' + c_{2i} u_2' + c_{3i} u_3'$$

$$u_1 = c_{11} u_1' + c_{21} u_2' + c_{31} u_3' \qquad (2.27)$$

$$u_2 = c_{12} u_1' + c_{22} u_2' + c_{32} u_3' \qquad (2.28)$$

$$u_3 = c_{13} u_1' + c_{23} u_2' + c_{33} u_3' \qquad (2.29)$$

Thus c_{ji} signifies the array of cosines,

$$
\begin{matrix}
c_{11} & c_{21} & c_{31} \\
c_{12} & c_{22} & c_{32} \\
c_{13} & c_{23} & c_{33}
\end{matrix}
\qquad (2.30)
$$

whereas c_{ij} in (2.22) represents the array:

$$
\begin{matrix}
c_{11} & c_{12} & c_{13} \\
c_{21} & c_{22} & c_{23} \\
c_{31} & c_{32} & c_{33}
\end{matrix}
\qquad (2.31)
$$

In (2.30) the element in the first row and second column, for example, is $c_{21} = \cos (X_2', X_1) = \cos (Y', X)$, whereas in (2.31) the element in the same row and column is $c_{12} = \cos (X_1', X_2) = \cos (X', Y)$. These are clearly cosines of different angles; it follows that in general

$$c_{ji} \neq c_{ij}. \qquad (2.32)$$

This simply means that, although the same direction cosines are required for a rotation of Cartesian axes, they appear in different positions in the corresponding arrays.

It is of special interest to note that each of the rows in c_{ij} (2.31), as well as each of the rows in c_{ji} (2.30), represents the direction cosines of a straight line with respect to three orthogonal axes. From (1.3), this must mean that, in the case of c_{ij},

$$c_{11}{}^2 + c_{12}{}^2 + c_{13}{}^2 = 1 \tag{2.33}$$

$$c_{21}{}^2 + c_{22}{}^2 + c_{23}{}^2 = 1 \tag{2.34}$$

$$c_{31}{}^2 + c_{32}{}^2 + c_{33}{}^2 = 1. \tag{2.35}$$

Expanding the equation

$$c_{ik}c_{jk} = 1 \quad \text{for} \quad i = j, \tag{2.36}$$

$$c_{i1}c_{j1} + c_{i2}c_{j2} + c_{i3}c_{j3} = 1 \quad \text{for} \quad i = j$$

$$c_{11}c_{11} + c_{12}c_{12} + c_{13}c_{13} = 1 \tag{2.37}$$

$$c_{21}c_{21} + c_{22}c_{22} + c_{23}c_{23} = 1 \tag{2.38}$$

$$c_{31}c_{31} + c_{32}c_{32} + c_{33}c_{33} = 1, \tag{2.39}$$

we see that it yields the same result; whereas if we had written $c_{ij}c_{ij} = 1$, which (2.33) to (2.35) seem to suggest, it would have appeared that a double summation was required. Of course, we could simply have used a different index for the second i and written, for example, $c_{ij}c_{kj} = 1$ for $i = k$ and obtained the same result. In any event, the repeated index will disappear in the preliminary equation of the expansion; therefore the preferred form is to use the new letter for this "dummy" index and retain i and j in the equation. No confusion should result as long as it is kept in mind that the repeated dummy index represents the old axes, whereas the other two indices represent the new axes.

Later we shall also prove that the sum of the products of the corresponding direction cosines of any two straight lines that are perpendicular will vanish; from this it follows that the sum of the products of the terms in any two rows of (2.31), or any two rows of (2.30), must be zero. From the first we obtain the equations:

$$c_{11}c_{21} + c_{12}c_{22} + c_{13}c_{23} = 0 \tag{2.40}$$

$$c_{21}c_{31} + c_{22}c_{32} + c_{23}c_{33} = 0 \tag{2.41}$$

$$c_{31}c_{11} + c_{32}c_{12} + c_{33}c_{13} = 0 \tag{2.42}$$

They may be represented in the same way as above by the single equation

$$c_{ik}c_{jk} = 0 \quad \text{for} \quad i \neq j \tag{2.43}$$

which yields only these three independent equations.

The equations represented by (2.43) are called the orthogonality conditions, whereas those given by (2.36) are called the normalization conditions. Actually, it is customary to combine these two equations by writing

$$c_{ik}c_{jk} = \begin{cases} 1 & \text{for} \quad i = j \\ 0 & \text{for} \quad i \neq j \end{cases} = \delta_{ij}, \tag{2.44}$$

where δ_{ij}, called Kronecker's delta, has the meaning specified in the brackets—that is, $\delta = 1$ when $i = j$ and $\delta = 0$ when $i \neq j$. In this form (2.44) is said to represent the orthonormality conditions.

Of course, the array (2.30) for c_{ji} also leads to a set of orthonormality conditions:

$$c_{ki}c_{kj} = \delta_{ij}; \qquad (2.45)$$

taking these into account, we can conclude that for any orthonormal transformation array c_{ij}:

(*a*) the sum of the squares of the elements in every row and column must be unity, and

(*b*) the sum of the products of the elements in every pair of rows and columns must vanish.

Because most of the rotational transformations commonly encountered are orthonormal, these are very useful relationships. They can be obtained in several other ways,[5,6] each of which has the advantage of illustrating different operations with indicial notation.

Evidently, (2.1) to (2.3) describing a translation could also be written in indicial notation if so desired, but because these will be trivially satisfied for any translation of the coordinate system by a vector **R**, we shall not bother to do so. The corresponding equations describing a rotation are (2.22) and (2.26):

$$\left. \begin{aligned} u_i' &= c_{ij}u_j \\ u_i &= c_{ji}u_j' \end{aligned} \right\} \qquad i, j = 1, 2, 3 \qquad (2.46)$$

This means that we have accomplished our original objective of developing a description for the two possible modes of transformation of a vector of constant length in Cartesian space, and we have also learned about the orthonormality properties of the rotational transformation arrays c_{ij} and c_{ji}. It is especially important to observe that the equations describing the rotation of a vector of constant length in this space are linear relations involving only the cosine array c_{ij} or c_{ji} and the scalar components of the vector. We shall return to this point later when we generalize to transformations of other geometrical objects. The implication is that equations involving vector quantities alone will have the same form regardless of the orientation of the coordinate system; they are said to be invariant.

[5] Long, R. R., *Engineering Science Mechanics*, pp. 16–19, Prentice-Hall, Englewood Cliffs, N.Y., 1963.
[6] Prager, W., *Introduction to Mechanics of Continua*, pp. 7, 8, Ginn, Boston, Mass., 1961.

To amplify, let us consider some of the operational properties that the foregoing transformation relations imply. It is desirable to emphasize that u_i is an entirely equivalent representation of the general vector quantity **u** in a space of established dimensionality, because the scalar quantities u_i completely determine the magnitude and direction of the directed line segment corresponding to **u** in this space. Thus to write

$$\mathbf{u} = \mathbf{v}, \tag{2.47}$$

where **v** is any other vector quantity, means

$$u_i = v_i \tag{2.48}$$

with i perhaps taking on the values 1, 2, 3 or equivalently x, y, z; according to (2.46) this implies that

$$c_{ji}u_j{}' = c_{ji}v_j{}' \tag{2.49}$$

so that

$$u_j{}' = v_j{}'. \tag{2.50}$$

Considered together, (2.48) and (2.50) mean that two vectors which are equal in one Cartesian coordinate system will remain equal in another such system rotated orthonormally relative to the first, although their projections may be different in the two systems. Similarly,

$$\mathbf{u} = \mathbf{0} \tag{2.51}$$

means

$$u_i = 0 \tag{2.52}$$

and implies that

$$c_{ji}u_j{}' = 0 \tag{2.53}$$

or

$$u_j{}' = 0. \tag{2.54}$$

It follows that to add two vector quantities,

$$\mathbf{u} + \mathbf{v}, \tag{2.55}$$

we must separately add their scalar components,

$$u_i + v_i. \tag{2.56}$$

We infer that this operation will produce a new vector **w**,

$$u_i + v_i = w_i, \tag{2.57}$$

and the transformation relations (2.46) can be used to prove that it will:

$$w_i = u_i + v_i = c_{ji}u_j{}' + c_{ji}v_j{}' = c_{ji}(u_j{}' + v_j{}') = c_{ji}w_j{}' \tag{2.58}$$

The new quantity transforms as a vector quantity should, so that we may conclude that it is a vector. It is just these transformation properties that

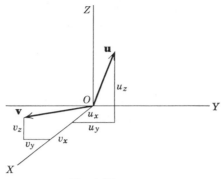

Fig. 1.27

constitute the basis for the definition of such quantities, as the preceding section suggests.

The easiest way to obtain this new vector is to translate the vectors to be added to a common origin O and express them both in terms of the unit vectors $\hat{\imath}$, $\hat{\jmath}$, and $\hat{k}$ (Figs. 1.27 and 1.28):

$$\mathbf{u} + \mathbf{v} = (u_x\hat{\imath} + u_y\hat{\jmath} + u_z\hat{k}) + (v_x\hat{\imath} - v_y\hat{\jmath} + v_z\hat{k})$$
$$= (u_x + v_x)\hat{\imath} + (u_y - v_y)\hat{\jmath} + (u_z + v_z)\hat{k} = \mathbf{w} \qquad (2.59)$$

Alternately, in the same way that we saw a vector like $\mathbf{u}$ to be the sum of the vectors $u_x\hat{\imath}$, $u_y\hat{\jmath}$, and $u_z\hat{k}$, we could translate one vector, $\mathbf{u}$, to the origin O and the other, $\mathbf{v}$, to act at the tip of $\mathbf{u}$; the vector from O to the tip of $\mathbf{v}$ would then be the new vector $\mathbf{w}$ (Fig. 1.29). Because $\mathbf{w}$ will always lie along the diagonal of the parallelogram that has $\mathbf{u}$ and $\mathbf{v}$ for adjoining sides, this is called the parallelogram rule for vector addition; of course it applies whether unit vectors are used or not.

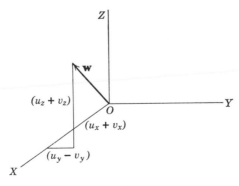

Fig. 1.28

The simplest kind of multiplication involving vector quantities is the kind that we have already utilized in forming products of $\hat{\imath}$, $\hat{\jmath}$, and $\hat{k}$ with scalar projections—multiplication of a vector $\mathbf{u}$ by a scalar quantity b. We have assumed that the result would be a new vector $\mathbf{w}$,

$$b\mathbf{u} = \mathbf{w}, \tag{2.60}$$

having the magnitude $|b|\,|\mathbf{u}|$, the direction of $\mathbf{u}$ if b is positive, and the opposite direction if b is negative. Let us test this assumption by seeing

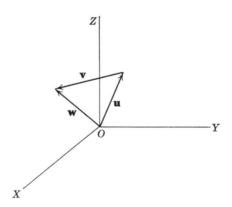

Fig. 1.29

if the new quantity transforms as a vector:

$$w_i = bu_i = bc_{ji}u_j' = c_{ji}(bu_j') = c_{ji}w_j', \tag{2.61}$$

which establishes that it does. It will be evident that this operation is closely related to addition as described above, since it may be regarded as producing a vector $\mathbf{w}$ which is the sum of $|b|$ vectors $\mathbf{u}$ in the direction indicated by the sign of b.

Now we can consider the result of forming the product of two vector quantities $\mathbf{u}$ and $\mathbf{v}$. If we simply write $u_i v_i$ and test this by the transformation formulas, we find that

$$u_i v_i = c_{ji}u_j' c_{ki}v_k' = c_{ji}c_{ki}u_j'v_k' \tag{2.62}$$

or, using (2.44),

$$u_i v_i = \delta_{jk}u_j'v_k' = u_j'v_j'. \tag{2.63}$$

In other words,

$$u_1 v_1 + u_2 v_2 + u_3 v_3 = u_1'v_1' + u_2'v_2' + u_3'v_3', \tag{2.64}$$

which shows that $u_i v_i$ is a scalar quantity that remains invariant in this kind of transformation.

Of course, we assumed that the indices of u and v were identical, and the result clearly depends on this being the case. If they had different indices, say $u_i v_l$, then instead of (2.62) we would obtain

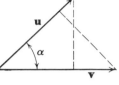

$$u_i v_l = c_{ji} u_j' c_{kl} v_k' = c_{ji} c_{kl} u_j' v_k' \quad (2.65)$$

and we could not reduce the product of the direction cosines in the same manner as above. We shall consider this case in more detail later, but for the moment we merely note that it constitutes

Fig. 1.30

a different way of forming a product of two vector quantities. In fact, the result represents a group of three vectors, which also must satisfy the transformation relations; this is why nine equations in the scalar quantities are required.

A product of the first kind, $u_i v_i$, is called a dot, scalar or sometimes inner product, and is usually indicated symbolically by

$$(u_i, v_i) \quad (2.66)$$

or

$$\mathbf{u} \cdot \mathbf{v}. \quad (2.67)$$

We shall adhere to the second representation for the present and write

$$\mathbf{u} \cdot \mathbf{v} = u_i v_i = u_x v_x + u_y v_y + u_z v_z, \quad (2.68)$$

or perhaps

$$u_i v_i = u_1 v_1 + u_2 v_2 + u_3 v_3 \quad (2.69)$$

if it is more convenient. Geometrically (Fig. 1.30), this implies

$$\mathbf{u} \cdot \mathbf{v} = |u| \, |v| \cos \alpha = \mathbf{v} \cdot \mathbf{u} \quad (2.70)$$

for then, because by (2.70)

$$\hat{\imath} \cdot \hat{\imath} = \hat{\jmath} \cdot \hat{\jmath} = \hat{k} \cdot \hat{k} = 1 \quad (2.71)$$

$$\hat{\imath} \cdot \hat{\jmath} = \hat{\jmath} \cdot \hat{k} = \hat{k} \cdot \hat{\imath} = 0, \quad (2.72)$$

it follows that if the dot product of two vectors is distributive,

$$\mathbf{u} \cdot \mathbf{v} = (u_x \hat{\imath} + u_y \hat{\jmath} + u_z \hat{k}) \cdot (v_x \hat{\imath} + v_y \hat{\jmath} + v_z \hat{k}) = u_x v_x + u_y v_y + u_z v_z$$

$$(2.73)$$

as required by (2.68). We see that the dot product of a vector with itself is simply the magnitude of the vector squared:

$$\mathbf{u} \cdot \mathbf{u} = u_x^2 + u_y^2 + u_z^2 = |u|^2 = u^2 \quad (2.74)$$

The earlier assertion that the sum of the products of the corresponding direction cosines of two perpendicular lines would vanish can easily be proved by means of the dot product. It is clear from (2.70) that this product will vanish for any two vectors that are perpendicular, and we can always describe the direction of a line by a unit vector directed along it (Fig. 1.31):

$$\hat{\mathbf{r}} = \cos(R, X)\hat{\mathbf{i}} + \cos(R, Y)\hat{\mathbf{j}} + \cos(R, Z)\hat{\mathbf{k}}. \tag{2.75}$$

Therefore, for lines R and S which are perpendicular,

$$\hat{\mathbf{r}} \cdot \hat{\mathbf{s}} = \cos(R, X)\cos(S, X) + \cos(R, Y)\cos(S, Y)$$
$$+ \cos(R, Z)\cos(S, Z) = 0. \tag{2.76}$$

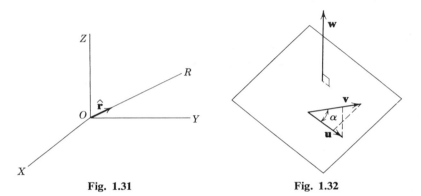

Fig. 1.31   **Fig. 1.32**

A product of the second kind, $u_i v_i$, is called a cross, vector, or outer product; we shall indicate it symbolically by

$$\mathbf{u} \times \mathbf{v}. \tag{2.77}$$

Corresponding to (2.70) for the dot product, it is defined in the following way:

$$\mathbf{u} \times \mathbf{v} = \hat{\mathbf{w}}\,|\mathbf{u}|\,|\mathbf{v}|\sin\alpha = \mathbf{w} \tag{2.78}$$

where $\hat{\mathbf{w}}$ is a unit vector that is perpendicular to the plane of $\mathbf{u}$ and $\mathbf{v}$ and in the direction of a right-hand screw for the rotation of $\mathbf{u}$ into $\mathbf{v}$ (Fig. 1.32).

It will be observed that $\mathbf{w}$ is a free vector and that

$$\mathbf{u} \times \mathbf{v} = \mathbf{w} \tag{2.79}$$

whereas

$$\mathbf{v} \times \mathbf{u} = -\mathbf{w}. \tag{2.80}$$

Also, because according to (2.78)

$$\hat{\mathbf{i}} \times \hat{\mathbf{j}} = \hat{\mathbf{k}}, \qquad \hat{\mathbf{j}} \times \hat{\mathbf{k}} = \hat{\mathbf{i}}, \qquad \hat{\mathbf{k}} \times \hat{\mathbf{i}} = \hat{\mathbf{j}} \tag{2.81}$$

$$\hat{\mathbf{j}} \times \hat{\mathbf{i}} = -\hat{\mathbf{k}}, \qquad \hat{\mathbf{k}} \times \hat{\mathbf{j}} = -\hat{\mathbf{i}}, \qquad \hat{\mathbf{i}} \times \hat{\mathbf{k}} = -\hat{\mathbf{j}} \tag{2.82}$$

$$\hat{\mathbf{i}} \times \hat{\mathbf{i}} = \hat{\mathbf{j}} \times \hat{\mathbf{j}} = \hat{\mathbf{k}} \times \hat{\mathbf{k}} = 0, \tag{2.83}$$

it follows that if the cross product of two vectors is distributive,

$$\mathbf{w} = \mathbf{u} \times \mathbf{v} = (u_x\hat{\mathbf{i}} + u_y\hat{\mathbf{j}} + u_z\hat{\mathbf{k}}) \times (v_x\hat{\mathbf{i}} + v_y\hat{\mathbf{j}} + v_z\hat{\mathbf{k}})$$

$$= \begin{vmatrix} \hat{\mathbf{i}} & \hat{\mathbf{j}} & \hat{\mathbf{k}} \\ u_x & u_y & u_z \\ v_x & v_y & v_z \end{vmatrix}$$

$$= (u_y v_z - u_z v_y)\hat{\mathbf{i}} + (u_z v_x - u_x v_z)\hat{\mathbf{j}} + (u_x v_y - u_y v_x)\hat{\mathbf{k}}. \quad (2.84)$$

This provides a convenient form for calculating a cross product, corresponding to (2.73) for a dot product.

Multiplication operations that involve the partial derivative vector operator del, defined as

$$\nabla = \hat{\mathbf{i}}\frac{\partial}{\partial x} + \hat{\mathbf{j}}\frac{\partial}{\partial y} + \hat{\mathbf{k}}\frac{\partial}{\partial z} = \hat{\mathbf{i}}_l\frac{\partial}{\partial x_l} \quad (2.85)$$

and often written symbolically simply as ∇, are especially important because of their physical applications. Each operation is given a name derived from these applications, and later we shall learn why the names are appropriate:

$$\nabla f = \hat{\mathbf{i}}\frac{\partial f}{\partial x} + \hat{\mathbf{j}}\frac{\partial f}{\partial y} + \hat{\mathbf{k}}\frac{\partial f}{\partial y} = \hat{\mathbf{i}}_l\frac{\partial f}{\partial x_l} = \text{grad } f = \text{gradient of } f \quad (2.86)$$

$$\nabla \cdot \mathbf{u} = \left(\hat{\mathbf{i}}\frac{\partial}{\partial x} + \hat{\mathbf{j}}\frac{\partial}{\partial y} + \hat{\mathbf{k}}\frac{\partial}{\partial z}\right) \cdot (u_x\hat{\mathbf{i}} + u_y\hat{\mathbf{j}} + u_z\hat{\mathbf{k}})$$

$$= \frac{\partial u_x}{\partial x} + \frac{\partial u_y}{\partial y} + \frac{\partial u_z}{\partial z} = \frac{\partial u_l}{\partial x_l} = \text{div } \mathbf{u} = \text{divergence of } \mathbf{u} \quad (2.87)$$

$$\nabla \times \mathbf{u} = \left(\hat{\mathbf{i}}\frac{\partial}{\partial x} + \hat{\mathbf{j}}\frac{\partial}{\partial y} + \hat{\mathbf{k}}\frac{\partial}{\partial z}\right) \times (u_x\hat{\mathbf{i}} + u_y\hat{\mathbf{j}} + u_z\hat{\mathbf{k}})$$

$$= \begin{vmatrix} \hat{\mathbf{i}} & \hat{\mathbf{j}} & \hat{\mathbf{k}} \\ \dfrac{\partial}{\partial x} & \dfrac{\partial}{\partial y} & \dfrac{\partial}{\partial z} \\ u_x & u_y & u_z \end{vmatrix} = \text{curl } \mathbf{u} = \text{curl of } \mathbf{u} \quad (2.88)$$

where, of course, f is some scalar function depending on x, y, and z, and $\mathbf{u}$ is a vector function depending on these same coordinates. The curl of $\mathbf{u}$ can also be expressed in indicial form, which we shall do when discussing the expansion of the product $u_i v_i$ appropriate to this kind of multiplication in a subsequent section.

Earlier we assumed without proof that a product of the first type could be differentiated in the same manner as a product of scalars,

$$\frac{d}{dt}(\mathbf{v}f) = \mathbf{v}\frac{df}{dt} + f\frac{d\mathbf{v}}{dt}; \tag{2.89}$$

it is also true that the other two types of products can be differentiated in the same way, provided that the order of the factors is preserved in the last:

$$\frac{d}{dt}(\mathbf{v}\cdot\mathbf{u}) = \mathbf{v}\cdot\frac{d\mathbf{u}}{dt} + \mathbf{u}\cdot\frac{d\mathbf{v}}{dt} \tag{2.90}$$

$$\frac{d}{dt}(\mathbf{v}\times\mathbf{u}) = \mathbf{v}\times\frac{d\mathbf{u}}{dt} + \frac{d\mathbf{v}}{dt}\times\mathbf{u} \tag{2.91}$$

Furthermore, except for the commutative law of multiplication, which must be modified for the cross product because of the relation shown in (2.79) and (2.80), all of the ordinary laws of algebra hold for operations with vector quantities.

Because the result of a dot product operation is a scalar, while the result of a cross product operation is a vector, it is possible for the product of three vectors to be taken in such a way that a scalar will be produced,

$$\mathbf{u}\times\mathbf{v}\cdot\mathbf{w}, \tag{2.92}$$

or in such a way that a vector will be produced,

$$\mathbf{u}\times(\mathbf{v}\times\mathbf{w}). \tag{2.93}$$

The first is called the scalar triple product and evidently may be calculated from:

$$\mathbf{u}\times\mathbf{v}\cdot\mathbf{w} = \begin{vmatrix} \hat{\mathbf{i}} & \hat{\mathbf{j}} & \hat{\mathbf{k}} \\ u_x & u_y & u_z \\ v_x & v_y & v_z \end{vmatrix} \cdot (w_x\hat{\mathbf{i}} + w_y\hat{\mathbf{j}} + w_z\hat{\mathbf{k}}) = \begin{vmatrix} w_x & w_y & w_z \\ u_x & u_y & u_z \\ v_x & v_y & v_z \end{vmatrix} \tag{2.94}$$

The second is called the vector triple product and may easily be shown to imply

$$\mathbf{u}\times(\mathbf{v}\times\mathbf{w}) = (\mathbf{u}\cdot\mathbf{w})\mathbf{v} - (\mathbf{u}\cdot\mathbf{v})\mathbf{w}. \tag{2.95}$$

Geometrically, the scalar triple product can be interpreted as the volume of the parallelepiped whose three adjacent sides are $\mathbf{u}$, $\mathbf{v}$, and $\mathbf{w}$. This follows directly from the definitions (2.78) and (2.70): it is evident from (2.78) and Fig. 1.32 that the magnitude of $(\mathbf{u}\times\mathbf{v})$ must equal the area of the parallelogram whose intersecting sides are $\mathbf{u}$ and $\mathbf{v}$, while according to (2.70) and Fig. 1.33, $(\mathbf{u}\times\mathbf{v})\cdot\mathbf{w}$ must give the volume of the parallelepiped whose base is this parallelogram and whose height is determined by the vector $\mathbf{w}$.

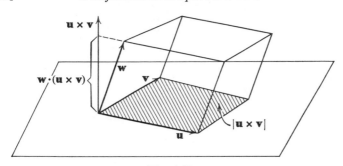

Fig. 1.33

This suggests, and it is easy to prove, that a cyclic interchange of the vectors **u**, **v**, and **w** will not affect the value of the triple scalar product:

$$\mathbf{u} \times \mathbf{v} \cdot \mathbf{w} = \mathbf{v} \times \mathbf{w} \cdot \mathbf{u} = \mathbf{w} \times \mathbf{u} \cdot \mathbf{v}. \qquad (2.96)$$

On the other hand, it is evident that the vectors cannot in general be interchanged in the vector triple product, because such products are non-commutative. In fact, it can even be proved that

$$\mathbf{u} \times (\mathbf{v} \times \mathbf{w}) = (\mathbf{u} \times \mathbf{v}) \times \mathbf{w} \qquad (2.97)$$

only if

$$\mathbf{v} \times (\mathbf{w} \times \mathbf{u}) = 0; \qquad (2.98)$$

thus it is not even possible to associate pairs of vectors freely in this kind of product.

It is also interesting to note that the vanishing of the dot product can be interpreted as defining a plane in space. If we regard one of the vectors $(\mathbf{u} - \mathbf{u}_0)$ as connecting a location $\mathbf{u}_0$ with any other location **u**, and the second vector **v** as being perpendicular to $(\mathbf{u} - \mathbf{u}_0)$ (see Fig. 1.34), the equation

$$(\mathbf{u} - \mathbf{u}_0) \cdot \mathbf{v} = 0 \qquad (2.99)$$

defines the plane containing all locations **u**.

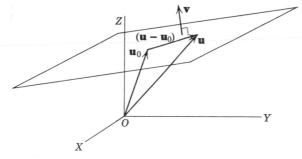

Fig. 1.34

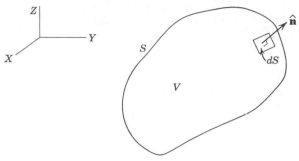

Fig. 1.35

The gradient of a scalar function should be interpreted as a vector corresponding both in length and in direction to the maximum rate of increase of the function from a given point. And although several interpretations of the divergence and curl of a vector function can be given,[7] the most useful of these are the two following geometrical theorems. Gauss' theorem states that, if S is a surface bounding a volume V and $\hat{\mathbf{n}}$ is an outward-directed unit vector normal to all elements dS of S (Fig. 1.35), then

$$\iiint_V \operatorname{div} \mathbf{u}\, dV = \iint_S \hat{\mathbf{n}} \cdot \mathbf{u}\, dS \qquad (2.100)$$

where $\mathbf{u} = \mathbf{u}(x, y, z)$ is some vector function defined in the region V and on the surface S. Stoke's theorem, on the other hand, states that if C is a curve bounding such a surface, and $d\mathbf{r}$ is an element of this curve taken in a counterclockwise sense from the average direction indicated by $\hat{\mathbf{n}}$ (Fig. 1.36), then

$$\iint_{S'} (\operatorname{curl} \mathbf{u}) \cdot \hat{\mathbf{n}}\, dS' = \int_C \mathbf{u} \cdot d\mathbf{r} \qquad (2.101)$$

where $\mathbf{u}(x, y, z)$ is now understood to be defined on S' and C. We shall not

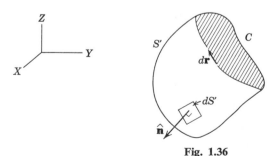

Fig. 1.36

[7] Hopf, L., *Differential Equations of Physics*, pp. 41–63, Dover, New York, 1948.

prove either of these theorems,[8] but several examples of their use in physical problems will be given later. No questions about integration procedure arise in (2.100) and (2.101) because of the dot products featured in each of the integrals, but it should be mentioned that integration of a vector quantity can usually be carried out by integrating the scalar coefficients of its unit vectors separately.

At this point it is worthwhile to note that the cross product operation makes it possible to relate linear and angular velocities in a more general

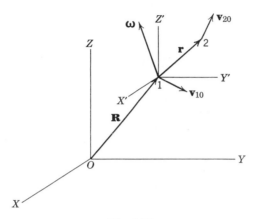

Fig. 1.37

way than was achieved in Section 1.1, where it was necessary to retain $\dot{\phi}$ and $\ddot{\phi}$ in the cylindrical and spherical coordinate expressions (1.50) to (1.53) instead of converting to ω and α. The relationship is based on Chasle's theorem, which states that if a point 2, located at a constant $|r|$ from a point 1 having the linear velocity v_{10} relative to the origin O of a fixed coordinate system XYZ, has an angular velocity ω about 1, its linear velocity v_{20} relative to O will be given by (see Fig. 1.37):

$$v_{20} = v_{10} + \omega \times r \qquad (2.102)$$

Even though **R** does not appear explicity in (2.102), it is of course true that

$$\dot{R} = v_{10}, \qquad (2.103)$$

where the components of **R** are computed in the XYZ-system and the components of **r** and ω are computed in the parallel $X'Y'Z'$-system by means of the unit vectors $\hat{i}$, $\hat{j}$, $\hat{k}$.

[8] Apostol, T. M., *Calculus*, Vol. 2, pp. 297–316, Blaisdell, New York, 1962.

It is easy to see that the last term in (2.102), $\boldsymbol{\omega} \times \mathbf{r}$, is the result of calculating $\dot{\mathbf{r}}$ when $|\mathbf{r}|$ must remain constant. We know that in general

$$\mathbf{v} = \frac{d\mathbf{r}}{dt} = v\hat{\mathbf{v}} = \frac{ds}{dt}\hat{\mathbf{v}}, \tag{2.104}$$

where s represents the path of the point in an arbitrary direction and $\hat{\mathbf{v}}$ is the unit velocity vector, tangent to the path at every instant. But from Fig. 1.38, describing the situation at some arbitrary time, it follows that

$$\frac{ds}{dt} = \omega \, |\mathbf{r}| \sin \beta . \tag{2.105}$$

Thus, using the definition (2.78) and observing that $\hat{\mathbf{v}}$ will be perpendicular

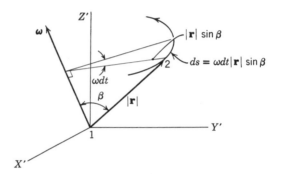

Fig. 1.38

to the plane containing $\boldsymbol{\omega}$ and $\mathbf{r}$ at all times, (2.104) becomes:

$$\dot{\mathbf{r}} = \mathbf{v} = \hat{\mathbf{v}} \, |\boldsymbol{\omega}| \, |\mathbf{r}| \sin \beta = \boldsymbol{\omega} \times \mathbf{r} \tag{2.106}$$

Differentiating (2.102) in accordance with the rule (2.91) to obtain the acceleration, we find

$$\dot{\mathbf{v}}_{20} = \dot{\mathbf{v}}_{10} + \boldsymbol{\omega} \times \dot{\mathbf{r}} + \dot{\boldsymbol{\omega}} + \mathbf{r}. \tag{2.107}$$

Thus, replacing $\dot{\mathbf{r}}$ by means of (2.106) and changing $\dot{\boldsymbol{\omega}}$ to $\boldsymbol{\alpha}$, we obtain:

$$\mathbf{a}_{20} = \mathbf{a}_{10} + \boldsymbol{\omega} \times (\boldsymbol{\omega} \times \mathbf{r}) + \boldsymbol{\alpha} \times \mathbf{r} \tag{2.108}$$

Equations (2.102) and (2.108) are more general than the relations of Section 1.1 in that they permit the origin 1 of $\mathbf{r}$ to have some linear velocity relative to a fixed origin O and allow for more latitude in the interpretation of the angular velocity $\boldsymbol{\omega}$ and angular acceleration $\boldsymbol{\alpha}$; they are less general in that they require $|\mathbf{r}|$ to remain constant. When

$$\mathbf{R} = 0 \tag{2.109}$$

$$\mathbf{v}_{10} = 0 \tag{2.110}$$

$$|\mathbf{r}| = |\boldsymbol{\rho}| = \rho\hat{\mathbf{l}} = \text{constant} \tag{2.111}$$

and

$$\boldsymbol{\omega} = \omega\hat{\mathbf{k}} = \text{constant}, \tag{2.112}$$

(2.102) reduces to

$$\mathbf{v}_{20} = \boldsymbol{\omega} \times \boldsymbol{\rho} = \omega\hat{\mathbf{k}} \times \rho\hat{\mathbf{l}} = \rho\omega\hat{\mathbf{m}} \tag{2.113}$$

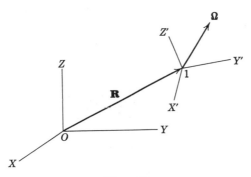

Fig. 1.39

and, with $\mathbf{a}_{10} = 0$, (2.108) reduces to

$$\mathbf{a}_{20} = \boldsymbol{\omega} \times (\boldsymbol{\omega} \times \boldsymbol{\rho}) = \omega\hat{\mathbf{k}} \times (\omega\hat{\mathbf{k}} \times \rho\hat{\mathbf{l}}) = -\rho\omega^2\hat{\mathbf{l}}, \tag{2.114}$$

which are the same results obtained in (1.48) and (1.49).

However, the constraint on $|\mathbf{r}|$ can be removed to achieve full generality. The principal problem is that, if both the orientation and the length of $\mathbf{r}$ can vary, $\dot{\mathbf{r}}$ may not be given simply by $\boldsymbol{\omega} \times \mathbf{r}$ as above. But it can be shown[9] that, if the $X'Y'Z'$-system as a whole has some angular velocity $\boldsymbol{\Omega}$ with respect to the fixed XYZ-system (Fig. 1.39), and $\mathbf{u}'$ is any vector defined in the primed system, then

$$\left(\frac{d\mathbf{u}'}{dt}\right)_{XYZ} = \left(\frac{d\mathbf{u}'}{dt}\right)_{X'Y'Z'} + \boldsymbol{\Omega} \times \mathbf{u}'. \tag{2.115}$$

Specifically, because $\mathbf{r}$ is defined in the primed system,

$$\left(\frac{d\mathbf{r}}{dt}\right)_{XYZ} = \left(\frac{d\mathbf{r}}{dt}\right)_{X'Y'Z'} + \boldsymbol{\Omega} \times \mathbf{r}. \tag{2.116}$$

[9] Shames, I. H., *Engineering Mechanics*, pp. 281–328, Prentice-Hall, Englewood Cliffs, N.J., 1960.

And if we construct a vector R^* to the tip rather than the tail of r (Fig. 1.40), so that

$$R^* = R + r \tag{2.117}$$

and

$$\left(\frac{dR^*}{dt}\right)_{XYZ} = \left(\frac{dR}{dt}\right)_{XYZ} + \left(\frac{dr}{dt}\right)_{XYZ}, \tag{2.118}$$

it follows that

$$v_{20} = v_{10} + v_{21} + \Omega \times r, \tag{2.119}$$

because the left-hand side of (2.118) defines v_{20} directly, whereas the first term on the right-hand side gives the $\dot{R}$ of (2.103) and the second term is given by (2.116).

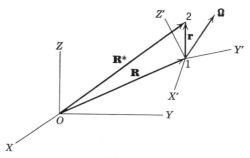

Fig. 1.40

By differentiating (2.119) again, and applying (2.115), it is not difficult to show that

$$a_{20} = a_{10} + a_{21} + \Omega \times (\Omega \times r) + 2\Omega \times v_{21} + A \times r \tag{2.120}$$

where $A = \dot{\Omega}$. The term $\Omega \times (\Omega \times r)$ represents the general form of the centripetal acceleration and the term $2\Omega \times v_{21}$ the general form of the Coriolis acceleration, special cases of which have been seen earlier. Also, the form of the last two equations should make it clear that, when $v_{21} = 0$ and Ω can be replaced by ω, (2.119) and (2.120) reduce, to (2.102) and (2.108), respectively.

Now we must also remove the constraint on time. We have, of course, implicitly assumed in all of the preceding work that time would transform into itself in a new reference system (shown primed except for an inverse transformation),

$$t = t'. \tag{2.121}$$

Basically, this is the reason why we have been able to neglect clock readings and observers and speak only of coordinate systems—although we were forced to recognize that observations could be made in both systems in the last development. Only under certain conditions, however, does time transform into itself, as will be made clear in the following paragraphs.

It is a fundamental assumption of modern mechanics that the velocity of light will have the same constant and finite value c in all reference systems that are at rest or moving with a constant linear velocity relative to one another. Nothing is said about systems which are accelerated relative to one another, and this fact should be especially noted.[10] If we adhere to the assumption, however, it follows that time cannot in general remain invariant in transformations between such systems.

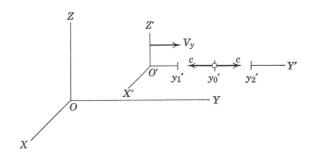

Fig. 1.41

Consider the arrival times of a light signal emitted at zero time from a point y_0' on the Y'-axis of a reference system $X'Y'Z'$, moving with a constant speed V_y relative to a fixed system XYZ, at points y_1' and y_2' equidistant on either side (Fig. 1.41). To an observer in the $X'Y'Z'$-system these arrival times must be equal,

$$t_{y_1'} = t_{y_2'}, \qquad (2.122)$$

whereas to an observer in the XYZ-system

$$t_{y_1'} < t_{y_2'}, \qquad (2.123)$$

because c is to remain constant in both systems.

To find how time transforms in general, it is convenient to imagine a four-dimensional space, presumed to result from superimposing the zero of the time axis on the combined zeros of the three Cartesian axes. In a fixed coordinate system of this kind, $XYZt$, it is clear that a distance

$$\Delta s = |(\Delta x^2 + \Delta y^2 + \Delta z^2)^{\frac{1}{2}}| \qquad (2.124)$$

[10] Bergmann, P. G., *Introduction to the Theory of Relativity*, pp. 8–10, Prentice-Hall, Englewood Cliffs, N.J., 1942.

will be traversed by a light ray in the time Δt,

$$|c \, \Delta t| = \Delta s; \qquad (2.125)$$

so that

$$|c \, \Delta t| = |(\Delta x^2 + \Delta y^2 + \Delta z^2)^{\frac{1}{2}}| \qquad (2.126)$$

or

$$c^2 \, \Delta t^2 - \Delta x^2 - \Delta y^2 - \Delta z^2 = 0. \qquad (2.127)$$

Furthermore, in another such system, $X'Y'Z't'$, moving with some constant linear velocity $\mathbf{V}$ relative to the first, it still must be true that

$$|c \, \Delta t'| = \Delta s' = |(\Delta x'^2 + \Delta y'^2 + \Delta z'^2)^{\frac{1}{2}}|; \qquad (2.128)$$

so that

$$c^2 \, \Delta t'^2 - \Delta x'^2 - \Delta y'^2 - \Delta z'^2 = 0. \qquad (2.129)$$

Of course, the points at the two ends of Δs and $\Delta s'$, described as "events," are of a rather special kind in this case, because they involve the transmission or reception of a light ray. This leads us to define the "interval" between any two events, not necessarily involving the propagation of light rays, as ΔS and write

$$\Delta S^2 = c^2 \, \Delta t^2 - \Delta x^2 - \Delta y^2 - \Delta z^2 \qquad (2.130)$$

or

$$\Delta S'^2 = c^2 \, \Delta t'^2 - \Delta x'^2 - \Delta y'^2 - \Delta z'^2 \qquad (2.131)$$

then to infer that in general it may be true that

$$\Delta S^2 = \Delta S'^2, \qquad (2.132)$$

because when $\Delta S^2 = 0$, $\Delta S'^2 = 0$.

In the limit of small quantities, (2.130) to (2.132) become:

$$dS^2 = c^2 \, dt^2 - dx^2 - dy^2 - dz^2 \qquad (2.133)$$

$$dS'^2 = c^2 \, dt'^2 - dy'^2 - dy'^2 - dz'^2 \qquad (2.134)$$

$$dS^2 = dS'^2; \qquad (2.135)$$

in fact, it can be proved[11] that (2.135) is the fundamental expression of the velocity of light remaining constant in such reference systems. It will not be difficult to see how important this relation is as we proceed and, actually, its implications are even broader than will appear; it means that the space-time continuum of our world has a special kind of mathematical structure, called Riemannian, whose properties are better known than most.[12]

[11] Landau, L. D., and E. M. Lifshitz, *The Classical Theory of Fields*, Vol. 2 of *Theoretical Physics*, pp. 1–15, Addison-Wesley, Reading, Mass., 1951.

[12] Wheeler, J. A., "The Dynamics of Space Time," *International Science and Technology*, No. 24, pp. 62–74, December 1963.

Suppose that an observer in the $X'Y'Z't'$-system reads his clock twice at the same location in his system, but at two distinct times separated by the interval $\Delta t'$. Let us calculate the time interval between these same two events for an observer in the fixed $XYZt$-system, that is, the time Δt that his clock would measure between them. We may anticipate that the latter will be somewhat longer, $\Delta t > \Delta t'$, because light, or some other type of electromagnetic signal with the velocity c will be required to compare the results of the readings.

In the primed system

$$\Delta s' = 0, \tag{2.136}$$

Because this observer's clock does not displace relative to him; therefore,

$$\Delta S'^2 = c^2 \, \Delta t'^2. \tag{2.137}$$

But to the observer in the unprimed system, the squared interval between the two events that occur in the moving system is

$$\Delta S^2 = c^2 \, \Delta t^2 - \Delta x^2 - \Delta y^2 - \Delta z^2. \tag{2.138}$$

Equation (2.135) tells us that, in the limit,

$$dS'^2 = dS^2;$$

so it follows that

$$c^2 \, dt'^2 = c^2 \, dt^2 - dx^2 - dy^2 - dz^2, \tag{2.139}$$

giving

$$dt'^2 = dt^2 - \frac{(dx^2 + dy^2 + dz^2)}{c^2} \tag{2.140}$$

or

$$dt' = dt \left[1 - \frac{dx^2 + dy^2 + dz^2}{c^2 \, dt^2} \right]^{\frac{1}{2}}. \tag{2.141}$$

However, it should be clear that in this case

$$\frac{dx^2 + dy^2 + dz^2}{dt^2} = \left(\frac{ds}{dt}\right)^2 = V^2, \tag{2.142}$$

where V is the speed of the primed system relative to the unprimed system. The final result is

$$dt = \frac{dt'}{\sqrt{1 - \dfrac{V^2}{c^2}}}. \tag{2.143}$$

The factor dividing dt' will appear often in our calculations, so we shall represent it by the script letter $\mathscr{S}$ and write (2.143) as

$$dt = \frac{dt'}{\mathscr{S}}. \tag{2.144}$$

Now $\mathscr{S}$ is understood to be positive and it can never be greater than one, because it approaches one as a maximum value as V becomes smaller relative to c. Furthermore, it approaches zero as V approaches c; and the smaller it becomes, the larger dt will be relative to dt'. To the observer in the fixed $XYZt$-system, the clock in the moving $X'Y'Z't'$-system will appear to run slower than his own clock.

The general rule is that clocks will appear to run slower as their velocity relative to the observer increases. They will always run at the fastest rate in the system in which they are at rest relative to the observer, called their proper system. To relate finite time increments in the two systems, of course, it is only necessary to integrate (2.144):

$$\int_{t_1'}^{t_2'} dt' = \int_{t_1}^{t_2} \mathscr{S}\, dt \tag{2.145}$$

$$(t_2' - t_1') = \mathscr{S}(t_2 - t_1) \tag{2.146}$$

Equation (2.146) is the result that we have been seeking, describing the way in which time transforms between two systems in relative motion. However, this result will also affect the transformation of other quantities such as lengths and velocities. To determine these effects, it is best to proceed in a more general way by attempting to establish the class of transformations in $XYZt$-space for which $dS^2 = dS'^2$.

Mathematically it is more convenient to work in an $XYZ\tau$-space, where

$$\tau = ict, \tag{2.147}$$

$$d\tau = ic\, dt, \qquad d\tau^2 = -c^2\, dt^2; \tag{2.148}$$

because then equations like (2.133) take the more symmetrical form of

$$dS^2 = -(d\tau^2 + dx^2 + dy^2 + dz^2). \tag{2.149}$$

The results obtained in this space can easily be converted to $XYZt$-space by means of the relations (2.147) and (2.148).

Just as every point in XYZ-space uniquely determines a vector with three components, we may imagine that every event in $XYZ\tau$-space uniquely determines a vector with four components; to ask what class of transformations will leave dS^2 unchanged is then equivalent to asking what class of transformations will leave the length of a four-vector unchanged. We know this class for three-vectors from our work at the beginning of the section; it consists of orthonormal translations and rotations. Therefore, we infer that the same will be true for four-vectors, and this can indeed be proved.[13]

[13] Einstein, A., *The Meaning of Relativity*, 3rd edition, pp. 24–39, Princeton University Press, Princeton, 1950.

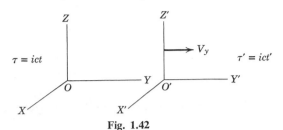

Fig. 1.42

We have seen that translations merely involve a change in the reference origin, generating relations that can be trivially satisfied; thus only rotations remain to be considered. Furthermore, it should be possible to replace every pure orthonormal rotation of the coordinate axes by component rotations of their projections in the original coordinate planes. For example, a general rotation of this kind in three-dimensional space (Fig. 1.26) could be reduced to three component rotations of the type shown in Fig. 1.25, with three primed axes appearing in each plane.

For purposes of simplicity, however, let us limit ourselves to a case similar to that shown in Fig. 1.41, where the $X'Y'Z't'$-system is moving with a constant velocity V_y relative to the $XYZt$-system and where it is assumed that O' coincided with O at $t' = 0$ and $t = 0$ (Fig. 1.42). Clearly, only the y- and τ-coordinates of an event can change in this situation. And it follows from the reasoning given above that y should be related to y' and τ to τ' as these coordinates are related to one another for a rotation of the reference axes in the YT-plane, as shown in Fig. 1.43, where U is understood to be a four-vector with the scalar components x, y, z, and τ in the unprimed system and x', y', z', and τ' in the primed system. Because we know that the x- and z-components do not change, it follows that

$$x = x' \tag{2.150}$$

and

$$z = z'; \tag{2.151}$$

whereas from the figure,

$$y = y' \cos \gamma - \tau' \sin \gamma \tag{2.152}$$

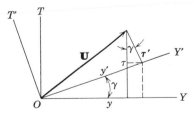

Fig. 1.43

and

$$\tau = y' \sin \gamma + \tau' \cos \gamma. \tag{2.153}$$

These are the transformation relations that we require, but the functions of the angle γ need to be expressed in terms of familar variables. To accomplish this, let us imagine that we are interested in an event which occurs at some time t' at the origin of the $X'Y'Z'$-system. Then

$$x' = y' = z' = 0, \qquad t' \neq 0, \tag{2.154}$$

and (2.150) through (2.153) become:

$$x = 0 \tag{2.155}$$

$$z = 0 \tag{2.156}$$

$$y = -\tau' \sin \gamma \tag{2.157}$$

$$\tau = \tau' \cos \gamma \tag{2.158}$$

Dividing (2.157) by (2.158), we obtain

$$\frac{y}{\tau} = -\frac{\sin \gamma}{\cos \gamma} = -\tan \gamma; \tag{2.159}$$

but because

$$\frac{y}{\tau} = \frac{y}{ict} = \frac{V_y}{ic} = -\frac{i}{c} V_y, \tag{2.160}$$

y/t being the velocity of the origin of the primed system relative to the unprimed origin, this reduces to

$$\tan \gamma = \frac{i}{c} V_y. \tag{2.161}$$

From (2.161) we can deduce $\cos \gamma$ and $\sin \gamma$ (Fig. 1.44):

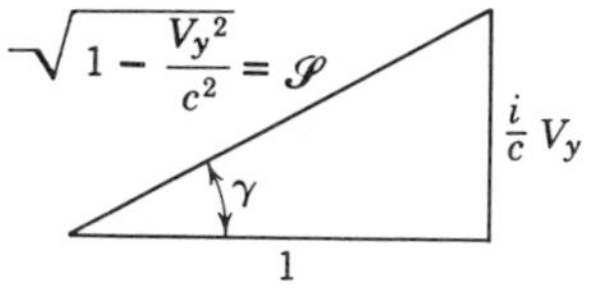

Fig. 1.44

$$\cos \gamma = \frac{1}{\mathscr{S}} \tag{2.162}$$

$$\sin \gamma = \frac{\frac{i}{c} V_y}{\mathscr{S}} \tag{2.163}$$

It is always possible to rotate the $XYZt$-system in such a way that the constant velocity $\mathbf{V}$ will become $\mathbf{V}_y$; thus there is no ambiguity in designating the factor $\sqrt{1 - (V_y^2/c^2)}$ as $\mathscr{S}$.

Substituting in (2.152) and (2.153) and making use of the fact that $\tau = ict$, $\tau' = ict'$, we obtain:

$$y = \frac{y' - \tau' \dfrac{i}{c} V_y}{\mathscr{S}} = \frac{y' + t' V_y}{\mathscr{S}} \tag{2.164}$$

$$\tau = \frac{y' \dfrac{i}{c} V_y + \tau'}{\mathscr{S}}, \qquad t = \frac{\dfrac{y'}{c^2} V_y + t'}{\mathscr{S}} \tag{2.165}$$

These, together with (2.150) and (2.151),

$$x = x'$$

$$z = z',$$

are called the Lorentz transformation equations. Evidently, the primed and unprimed coordinates can be exchanged to obtain the equations for the inverse transformation merely by replacing V_y with $-V_y$, this being the velocity of the unprimed relative to the primed system.

Our earlier result follows from them, for if we ask what period of time $(t_2 - t_1)$ a clock fixed in the $XYZt$-system would measure in relation to a period $(t_2' - t_1')$ measured on a clock moving with $X'Y'Z't'$-system, the last of equations in (2.165) yields (2.146) directly:

$$(t_2 - t_1) = \frac{\dfrac{y'}{c^2} V_y + t_2'}{\mathscr{S}} - \frac{\dfrac{y'}{c^2} V_y + t_1'}{\mathscr{S}} = \frac{(t_2' - t_1')}{\mathscr{S}}.$$

In addition, the equations enable us to predict how length measurements made in the two systems will be related. From the equation in (2.164) involving y and t' we see that

$$(y_2 - y_1) = \frac{y_2' + t' V_y}{\mathscr{S}} - \frac{y_1' + t' V_y}{\mathscr{S}} = \frac{(y_2' - y_1')}{\mathscr{S}}; \tag{2.166}$$

whereas (2.150) and (2.151) give

$$(x_2 - x_1) = (x_2' - x_1') \tag{2.167}$$

and

$$(z_2 - z_1) = (z_2' - z_1'). \tag{2.168}$$

In other words, because $\mathscr{S} < 1$, a rod of length $(y_2 - y_1)$ in the $XYZt$-system would seem to an observer in this system to be shortened by the factor $\mathscr{S}$ if it were moving with the $X'Y'Z't'$-system, although its dimensions in the X- and Z-directions would remain unchanged. Like the lag in a moving clock, this represents the result of the finite time required to compare the measurements between systems by means of electromagnetic signals of velocity c. As clocks will appear to run at their fastest rate in their proper system, rods will appear to have their greatest length in this system.[14]

Now let us see how measurements of the velocity of a point moving in the $X'Y'Z't'$-system, which is itself moving with the constant velocity V_y relative to the $XYZt$-system, transform. In the primed system the point displacements will be given by dx', dy', dz' in the time dt', whereas in the unprimed system its displacements dx, dy, dz in the time dt will not necessarily be the same as those of primed coordinate system. However, from the last equations in (2.164) and (2.165), together with (2.150) and (2.151), it follows that

$$dy = \frac{dy' + V_y\,dt'}{\mathscr{S}} \tag{2.169}$$

$$dt = \frac{\dfrac{V_y}{c^2}\,dy' + dt'}{\mathscr{S}} \tag{2.170}$$

$$dx = dx' \tag{2.171}$$

$$dz = dz'. \tag{2.172}$$

We can form the components of the velocity of the point in the unprimed system by dividing dy, dx, and dz by dt:

$$v_y = \frac{dy}{dt} = \frac{dy' + V_y\,dt'}{\dfrac{V_y}{c^2}\,dy' + dt'} \tag{2.173}$$

$$v_x = \frac{dx}{dt} = \frac{dx'\mathscr{S}}{\dfrac{V_y}{c^2}\,dy' + dt'} \tag{2.174}$$

$$v_z = \frac{dz}{dt} = \frac{dz'\mathscr{S}}{\dfrac{V_y}{c^2}\,dy' + dt'} \tag{2.175}$$

If we then divide the numerators and denominators on the right-hand sides

[14] Eisberg, R. M., *Fundamentals of Modern Physics*, pp. 3–30, Wiley, New York, 1963.

by dt', we obtain the transformation relations required:

$$v_y = \frac{v_y' + V_y}{\dfrac{V_y}{c^2} v_y' + 1} \tag{2.176}$$

$$v_x = \frac{v_x' \mathscr{S}}{\dfrac{V_y}{c^2} v_y' + 1} \tag{2.177}$$

$$v_z = \frac{v_z' \mathscr{S}}{\dfrac{V_y}{c^2} v_y' + 1} \tag{2.178}$$

When V_y is small relative to c, $\mathscr{S} \to 1$ and $V_y/c^2 \to 0$; thus it is easy to see that these equations reduce to those assumed in our earlier work:

$$v_y = v_y' + V_y \tag{2.179}$$

$$v_y = v_x' \tag{2.180}$$

$$v_z = v_z' \tag{2.181}$$

Of course, all four-vectors must satisfy transformation equations of the type (2.46):

$$x_i' = c_{ij} x_j \tag{2.182}$$

$$x_i = c_{ji} x_j' \tag{2.183}$$

where $i, j = 1, 2, 3, 4$, and in particular

$$x_1 = x, \qquad x_2 = y, \qquad x_3 = z, \qquad x_4 = \tau. \tag{2.184}$$

Thus we can state the Lorentz transformation equations simply by specifying c_{ij} or c_{ji}. For example, with c_{ji} given by the cosine array:

$$
\begin{array}{cccc}
1 & 0 & 0 & 0 \\[2ex]
0 & \dfrac{1}{\mathscr{S}} & 0 & -\dfrac{\dfrac{i}{c} V_y}{\mathscr{S}} \\[3ex]
0 & 0 & 1 & 0 \\[2ex]
0 & \dfrac{\dfrac{i}{c} V_y}{\mathscr{S}} & 0 & \dfrac{1}{\mathscr{S}}
\end{array}
\tag{2.185}
$$

then from (2.183):

$$x_i = c_{1i}x_1' + c_{2i}x_2' + c_{3i}x_3' + c_{4i}x_4'$$

$$x_1 = c_{11}x_1' + c_{21}x_2' + c_{31}x_3' + c_{41}x_4' \tag{2.186}$$

$$x_2 = c_{12}x_1' + c_{22}x_2' + c_{32}x_3' + c_{42}x_4' \tag{2.187}$$

$$x_3 = c_{13}x_1' + c_{23}x_2' + c_{33}x_3' + c_{43}x_4' \tag{2.188}$$

$$x_4 = c_{14}x_1' + c_{24}x_2' + c_{34}x_3' + c_{44}x_4' \tag{2.189}$$

or

$$x = x' + 0 \qquad + 0 + 0 \tag{2.190}$$

$$y = 0 + \frac{1}{\mathscr{S}}y' \; + 0 - \frac{\dfrac{i}{c}V_y}{\mathscr{S}}\tau' \tag{2.191}$$

$$z = 0 + 0 \qquad + z' + 0 \tag{2.192}$$

$$\tau = 0 + \frac{\dfrac{i}{c}V_y}{\mathscr{S}}y' + 0 + \frac{1}{\mathscr{S}}\tau' \tag{2.193}$$

which are the same as (2.150), (2.151) and the first equations of (2.164) and (2.165). This emphatically illustrates that these equations are the result of a rotational transformation carried out for a four-vector of constant length, and by applying (2.45) it is easy to show that the transformation is orthonormal.

It must be emphasized that as long as V_y remains so small relative to c that the latter may be considered infinite, these relations do not differ from those implicit in our earlier work; with $c = \infty$, $\mathscr{S} = 1$ and $\tau = ict$, $\tau' = ict$, (2.190) to (2.193) reduce to

$$x = x' \tag{2.194}$$

$$y = y' + V_yt \tag{2.195}$$

$$z = z' \tag{2.196}$$

$$t = t' \tag{2.197}$$

which are called the Galileo transformation equations. And although every case of physical motion should be given separate consideration for the importance of "relativistic" effects, it is useful to know that these can almost always be neglected if V_y is less than about 0.1 c.

Problems 1.2

1. The point P and the vector $\mathbf{R}$ [Fig. P1.2 (1)] are defined with respect to the XYZ-coordinate system as:

$$P(3, 3, 5)$$
$$\mathbf{R} = -2\hat{\mathbf{i}} + 5\hat{\mathbf{j}} + 8\hat{\mathbf{k}}$$

Locate P with respect to the parallel $X'Y'Z'$-coordinate system.

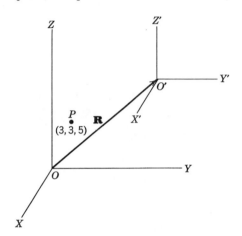

Fig. P1.2 (1)

Solution

$$\overrightarrow{OP} = 3\mathbf{i} + 3\hat{\mathbf{j}} + 5\hat{\mathbf{k}}$$
$$x = 3, \qquad y = 3, \qquad z = 5$$
$$R_x = -2, \qquad R_y = 5, \qquad R_z = 8$$
$$x' = x - R_x = 3 - (-2) = 5$$
$$y' = y - R_y = 3 - 5 = -2$$
$$z' = z - R_z = 5 - 8 = -3$$
$$\overrightarrow{O'P} = 5\hat{\mathbf{i}} - 2\hat{\mathbf{j}} - 3\hat{\mathbf{k}}$$

2. Write out the equations represented by:

a. $\quad t_{ij} = c_{ik}s_{jk} + \lambda\delta_{ij} \qquad \{i, j, k = 1, 2$

b. $\quad v_l = \dfrac{\partial t_{lm}}{\partial \theta_m} \qquad \{l, m = 1, 2, 3, 4$

c. $\quad s_{ij} = 2Ge_{ij} + 2Kd_{ij} \qquad \{i, j = 1, 2, 3$

d. $\quad \dfrac{\partial s_{ij}}{\partial x_i} + F_j = \rho a_j \qquad \{i, j = 1, 2, 3$

Solution

(a) $g = 2, f = 2$; hence $g^f = 2^2 = 4$ equations:

$$t_{ij} = c_{i1}s_{j1} + c_{i2}s_{j2} + \lambda\delta_{ij}$$
$$t_{11} = c_{11}s_{11} + c_{12}s_{12} + \lambda\delta_{11}$$
$$t_{12} = c_{11}s_{21} + c_{12}s_{22} + \lambda\delta_{12}$$
$$t_{21} = c_{21}s_{11} + c_{22}s_{12} + \lambda\delta_{21}$$
$$t_{22} = c_{21}s_{21} + c_{22}s_{22} + \lambda\delta_{22}$$

But

$$\delta_{11} = \delta_{22} = 1, \qquad \delta_{12} = \delta_{21} = 0;$$

therefore:

$$t_{11} = c_{11}s_{11} + c_{12}s_{12} + \lambda$$
$$t_{12} = c_{11}s_{21} + c_{12}s_{22}$$
$$t_{21} = c_{21}s_{11} + c_{22}s_{12}$$
$$t_{22} = c_{21}s_{21} + c_{22}s_{22} + \lambda$$

(b) $g = 4, f = 1$; hence $g^f = 4$ equations:

$$v_l = \frac{\partial t_{l1}}{\partial\theta_1} + \frac{\partial t_{l2}}{\partial\theta_2} + \frac{\partial t_{l3}}{\partial\theta_3} + \frac{\partial t_{l4}}{\partial\theta_4}$$

$$v_1 = \frac{\partial t_{11}}{\partial\theta_1} + \frac{\partial t_{12}}{\partial\theta_2} + \frac{\partial t_{13}}{\partial\theta_3} + \frac{\partial t_{14}}{\partial\theta_4}$$

$$v_2 = \frac{\partial t_{21}}{\partial\theta_1} + \frac{\partial t_{22}}{\partial\theta_2} + \frac{\partial t_{23}}{\partial\theta_3} + \frac{\partial t_{24}}{\partial\theta_4}$$

$$v_3 = \frac{\partial t_{31}}{\partial\theta_1} + \frac{\partial t_{32}}{\partial\theta_2} + \frac{\partial t_{33}}{\partial\theta_3} + \frac{\partial t_{34}}{\partial\theta_4}$$

$$v_4 = \frac{\partial t_{41}}{\partial\theta_1} + \frac{\partial t_{42}}{\partial\theta_2} + \frac{\partial t_{43}}{\partial\theta_3} + \frac{\partial t_{44}}{\partial\theta_4}$$

(c) $g = 3; f = 2$; hence $g^f = 9$ equations:

$$s_{11} = 2Ge_{11} + 2Kd_{11}$$
$$s_{12} = 2Ge_{12} + 2Kd_{12}$$
$$s_{13} = 2Ge_{13} + 2Kd_{13}$$
$$s_{21} = 2Ge_{21} + 2Kd_{21}$$
$$s_{22} = 2Ge_{22} + 2Kd_{22}$$
$$s_{23} = 2Ge_{23} + 2Kd_{23}$$
$$s_{31} = 2Ge_{31} + 2Kd_{31}$$
$$s_{32} = 2Ge_{32} + 2Kd_{32}$$
$$s_{33} = 2Ge_{33} + 2Kd_{33}$$

(d) $g = 3; f = 1$; hence $g^f = 3$ equations:

$$\frac{\partial s_{11}}{\partial x_1} + \frac{\partial s_{21}}{\partial x_2} + \frac{\partial s_{31}}{\partial x_3} + F_1 = \rho a_1$$

$$\frac{\partial s_{12}}{\partial x_1} + \frac{\partial s_{22}}{\partial x_2} + \frac{\partial s_{32}}{\partial x_3} + F_2 = \rho a_2$$

$$\frac{\partial s_{13}}{\partial x_1} + \frac{\partial s_{23}}{\partial x_2} + \frac{\partial s_{33}}{\partial x_3} + F_3 = \rho a_3$$

3. Using dummy index notation, prove that the length of the vector defined as $\sqrt{p_i p_i}$ is an invariant.

Solution

$$p_i = c_{ji} p_j'$$

$$p_i = c_{ki} p_k'$$

$$p_i p_i = c_{ji} c_{ki} p_j' p_k'$$

But

$$c_{ji} c_{kj} = \delta_{jk},$$

so that

$$p_i p_i = \delta_{jk} p_j' p_k';$$

and because

$$\delta_{jk} = \begin{cases} 1 & \text{if } j = k \\ 0 & \text{if } j \neq k, \end{cases}$$

$$p_i p_i = p_j' p_j' = p_k' p_k'.$$

Therefore, $\sqrt{p_i p_i}$ is also a scalar quantity, which cannot be affected by transformations of axes.

4. The components of a vector **v** in a coordinate system (X_1', X_2', X_3') are $(2, 2, 0)$. If a rotation to a new set of axes (X_1, X_2, X_3) is defined by

$$x_i = c_{ji} x_j'$$

where c_{ji} is the array:

$$\frac{\sqrt{2}}{2} \quad \frac{\sqrt{2}}{2} \quad 0$$

$$-\frac{\sqrt{2}}{2} \quad \frac{\sqrt{2}}{2} \quad 0$$

$$0 \quad \quad 0 \quad \quad 1$$

what are the components of **v** in the new system?

Solution

$$v_i = c_{ji} v_j'$$

where v_i is the ith component in the "new" (X_1, X_2, X_3) system. Expanding:

$$v_i = c_{1i}v_1' + c_{2i}v_2' + c_{3i}v_3'$$
$$v_1 = c_{11}v_1' + c_{21}v_2' + c_{31}v_3'$$
$$v_2 = c_{12}v_1' + c_{22}v_2' + c_{32}v_3'$$
$$v_3 = c_{13}v_1' + c_{23}v_2' + c_{33}v_3'$$

so

$$v_1 = \left(\frac{\sqrt{2}}{2}\right)(2) + \left(\frac{\sqrt{2}}{2}\right)(2) + (0)(0) = 2\sqrt{2}$$

$$v_2 = -\left(\frac{\sqrt{2}}{2}\right)(2) + \left(\frac{\sqrt{2}}{2}\right)(2) + (0)(0) = 0$$

$$v_3 = (0)(2) + (0)(2) + (1)(0) = 0$$

Thus, in the new coordinate system, $\mathbf{v}$ has the components $(2\sqrt{2}, 0, 0)$. As a check, we can see if the length of the vector remains invariant:

$$(v_1')^2 + (v_2')^2 + (v_3')^2 = (v_1)^2 + (v_2)^2 + (v_3)^2$$
$$(2)^2 + (2)^2 + (0)^2 = (0)^2 + (2\sqrt{2})^2 + (0)^2$$
$$8 = 8,$$

as it should be.

We can also analyze the transformation geometrically. Because both before and after the transformation the vector $\mathbf{v}$ lies in the XY-plane, a two-dimensional representation will suffice [Fig. P1.2 (4)]. This particular

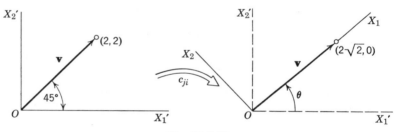

Fig. P1.2 (4)

transformation is one example of a rather important general type—a rotation of the $X'Y'$ (or $X_1'X_2'$)-plane about the Z' (or X_3)-axis through a counterclockwise angle θ; for a transformation of this kind c_{ji} always has the form:

$$\begin{matrix} \cos\theta & \sin\theta & 0 \\ -\sin\theta & \cos\theta & 0 \\ 0 & 0 & 1 \end{matrix}$$

Note that in the figure the vector itself, not just its magnitude, is invariant. We could just as well regard the transformation as rotating the vector $\mathbf{v}$ through a clockwise angle θ, leaving the axes unchanged. It is demonstrated below that such a transformation satisfies the orthonormality conditions.

Normality of rows:

$$c_{11}{}^2 + c_{21}{}^2 + c_{31}{}^2 = \cos^2 \theta + \sin^2 \theta + 0 = 1$$
$$c_{12}{}^2 + c_{22}{}^2 + c_{32}{}^2 = \sin^2 \theta + \cos^2 \theta + 0 = 1$$
$$c_{13}{}^2 + c_{23}{}^2 + c_{33}{}^2 = 0 + 0 + 1 = 1$$

Normality of columns:

$$c_{11}{}^2 + c_{12}{}^2 + c_{13}{}^2 = \cos^2 \theta + \sin^2 \theta + 0 = 1$$
$$c_{21}{}^2 + c_{22}{}^2 + c_{23}{}^2 = \sin^2 \theta + \cos^2 \theta + 0 = 1$$
$$c_{31}{}^2 + c_{32}{}^2 + c_{33}{}^2 = 0 + 0 + 1 = 1$$

Orthogonality of rows:

$$c_{11}c_{12} + c_{21}c_{22} + c_{31}c_{32} = -\cos \theta \sin \theta + \sin \theta \cos \theta + 0 = 0$$
$$c_{11}c_{13} + c_{21}c_{23} + c_{31}c_{33} = 0 + 0 + 0 = 0$$
$$c_{12}c_{13} + c_{22}c_{23} + c_{32}c_{33} = 0 + 0 + 0 = 0$$

Orthogonality of columns:

$$c_{11}c_{21} + c_{12}c_{22} + c_{13}c_{23} = \cos \theta \sin \theta - \sin \theta \cos \theta + 0 = 0$$
$$c_{11}c_{31} + c_{12}c_{32} + c_{13}c_{33} = 0 + 0 + 0 = 0$$
$$c_{21}c_{31} + c_{22}c_{32} + c_{23}c_{33} = 0 + 0 + 0 = 0$$

5. Complete the table of direction cosines for an orthonormal rotation of a right-handed coordinate system:

	x_1	x_2	x_3
x_1'	$\dfrac{1}{\sqrt{3}}$	$\dfrac{1}{\sqrt{6}}$	$\dfrac{1}{\sqrt{2}}$
x_2'	$\dfrac{1}{\sqrt{3}}$	$\dfrac{1}{\sqrt{6}}$	
x_3'			

Using the orthogonality condition for the first two rows, we obtain

$$\frac{1}{\sqrt{3}} \cdot \frac{1}{\sqrt{3}} + \frac{1}{\sqrt{6}} \cdot \frac{1}{\sqrt{6}} + \frac{1}{\sqrt{2}} \cos (x_2', x_3') = 0$$

$$\frac{1}{3} + \frac{1}{6} + \frac{1}{\sqrt{2}} \cos (x_2', x_3) = 0$$

$$\cos (x_2', x_3) = -\frac{1}{\sqrt{2}},$$

which makes it possible to utilize the normality of the third column:

$$\left(\frac{1}{\sqrt{2}}\right)^2 + \left(\frac{1}{\sqrt{2}}\right)^2 + [\cos (x_3', x_3)]^2 = 1$$

$$\cos (x_3', x_3) = 0$$

Applying the normality condition to the first two columns, we obtain:

$$\cos(x_3', x_1) = \sqrt{1 - 2(\tfrac{1}{3})} = \pm\sqrt{\tfrac{1}{3}}$$

$$\cos(x_3', x_2) = \sqrt{1 - 2(\tfrac{1}{6})} = \pm\sqrt{\tfrac{2}{3}}$$

The signs remain undetermined; but we may resort to geometry, as shown in Fig. P1.2 (5). Thus, for a right-handed coordinate system the direction

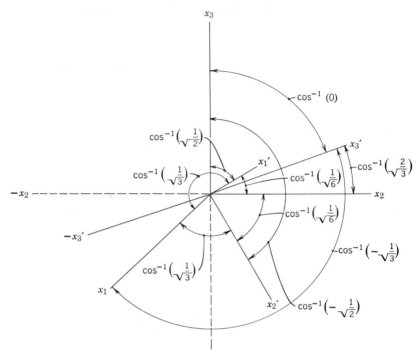

Fig. P1.2 (5)

cosines of x_3' should be $(-(1/\sqrt{3}),\ \sqrt{\tfrac{2}{3}},\ 0)$, giving finally:

	x_1	x_2	x_3
x_1'	$\dfrac{1}{\sqrt{3}}$	$\dfrac{1}{\sqrt{6}}$	$\dfrac{1}{\sqrt{2}}$
x_2'	$\dfrac{1}{\sqrt{3}}$	$\dfrac{1}{\sqrt{6}}$	$-\dfrac{1}{\sqrt{2}}$
x_3'	$-\dfrac{1}{\sqrt{3}}$	$\sqrt{\dfrac{2}{3}}$	0

6. Find the equation of the locus of all points (x, y, z) [Fig. P1.2 (6)] such that a vector from the point $(2, -1, 4)$ to the point (x, y, z) will always be perpendicular to the vector from $(2, -1, 4)$ to $(3, 3, 2)$.

$$\mathbf{A} = (x - 2)\hat{\mathbf{i}} + (y + 1)\hat{\mathbf{j}} + (z - 4)\hat{\mathbf{k}}$$
$$\mathbf{B} = \hat{\mathbf{i}} + 4\hat{\mathbf{j}} - 2\hat{\mathbf{k}}$$

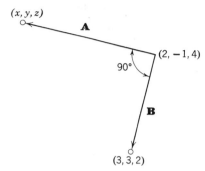

Fig. P1.2 (6)

Solution

The unit vectors in these directions are

$$\hat{\mathbf{a}} = \frac{1}{\sqrt{(x - 2)^2 + (y + 1)^2 + (z - 4)^2}} [(x - 2)\hat{\mathbf{i}} + (y + 1)\hat{\mathbf{j}} + (z - 4)\hat{\mathbf{k}}]$$

$$\hat{\mathbf{b}} = \frac{1}{\sqrt{1 + 16 + 4}} [\hat{\mathbf{i}} + 4\hat{\mathbf{j}} - 2\hat{\mathbf{k}}]$$

and their coefficients define the direction cosines. Using the fact that the sum of the products of corresponding direction cosines of any two straight lines which are perpendicular must vanish, we obtain

$$\frac{1}{\sqrt{(x - 2) + (y + 1) + (z - 4)}} \cdot \frac{1}{\sqrt{1 + 16 + 4}}$$
$$\times [(x - 2)1 + (y + 1)4 - (z - 4)2] = 0$$
$$x - 2 + 4y + 4 - 2z + 8 = 0$$
$$x + 4y - 2z + 10 = 0.$$

This is the equation of the solution plane.

7. Two vector functions are defined by:

$$\mathbf{A} = (x^3 y + z)\hat{\mathbf{i}} + x^2\hat{\mathbf{k}}$$
$$\mathbf{B} = (xy^2 - z)\hat{\mathbf{i}} + y^2\hat{\mathbf{j}}$$

Find: **a.** $\mathbf{A} \cdot \mathbf{B}$.
　　　b. $\mathbf{A} \times \mathbf{B}$.
　　　c. $\mathbf{B} \times \mathbf{A}$.

Solution

(a)　　　$$\mathbf{A} \cdot \mathbf{B} = A_x B_x + A_y B_y + A_z B_z$$
$$= (x^2 y + z)(xy^2 - z) + 0(y^2) + x^2(0)$$
$$= x^3 y^3 + z(xy^2 - x^2 y) - z^2.$$

(b)

$$\mathbf{A} \times \mathbf{B} = \begin{vmatrix} \hat{\mathbf{i}} & \hat{\mathbf{j}} & \hat{\mathbf{k}} \\ (x^2y + z) & 0 & x^2 \\ (xy^2 - z) & y^2 & 0 \end{vmatrix}$$

$$= \hat{\mathbf{i}}(-x^2y^2) + \hat{\mathbf{j}}x^2(xy^2 - z) + \hat{\mathbf{k}}(x^2y + z)y^2$$

$$= -x^2y^2\hat{\mathbf{i}} + x^2(xy^2 - z)\hat{\mathbf{j}} + y^2(x^2y + z)\hat{\mathbf{k}}$$

(c) $$\mathbf{B} \times \mathbf{A} = -\mathbf{A} \times \mathbf{B}$$

$$= -[x^2y^2\hat{\mathbf{i}} + x^2(xy^2 - z)\hat{\mathbf{j}} + y^2(x^2y + z)\hat{\mathbf{k}}]$$

$$= x^2y^2\hat{\mathbf{i}} + x^2(z - xy^2)\hat{\mathbf{j}} - y^2(x^2y + z)\hat{\mathbf{k}}$$

8. Find the angle between the vectors

$$\mathbf{A} = 2\hat{\mathbf{i}} + 2\hat{\mathbf{j}} - \hat{\mathbf{k}}$$

and

$$\mathbf{B} = 6\hat{\mathbf{i}} - 3\hat{\mathbf{j}} + 2\hat{\mathbf{k}}$$

Solution

$$\mathbf{A} \cdot \mathbf{B} = AB \cos \theta = A_x B_x + A_y B_y + A_z B_z$$

$$= (2)(6) + (2)(-3) + (-1)(2)$$

$$= 12 - 6 - 2 = 4$$

$$A = |\mathbf{A}| = \sqrt{2^2 + 2^2 + (-1)^2} = 3$$

$$B = |\mathbf{B}| = \sqrt{(6)^2 + (-3)^2 + (2)^2} = 7$$

Thus

$$\cos \theta = \frac{\mathbf{A} \cdot \mathbf{B}}{AB} = \frac{4}{(3)(7)} = 0.1905$$

and

$$\theta = 79°.$$

9. Determine the unit perpendicular to the plane of the vectors

$$\mathbf{A} = 2\hat{\mathbf{i}} - 6\hat{\mathbf{j}} - 3\hat{\mathbf{k}}$$

and

$$\mathbf{B} = 4\hat{\mathbf{i}} + 3\hat{\mathbf{j}} - \hat{\mathbf{k}}.$$

Solution

Let the vector

$$\mathbf{C} = C_1\hat{\mathbf{i}} + C_2\hat{\mathbf{j}} + C_3\hat{\mathbf{k}}$$

be perpendicular to the plane of **A** and **B**; then

$$\mathbf{C} \cdot \mathbf{A} = 2C_1 - 6C_2 - 3C_3 = 0,$$

$$2C_1 - 6C_2 = 3C_3$$

and

$$\mathbf{C} \cdot \mathbf{B} = 4C_1 + 3C_2 - C_3 = 0,$$

$$4C_1 + 3C_2 = C_3.$$

Solving these two equations simultaneously, we obtain

$$C_1 = \tfrac{1}{2}C_3$$

and

$$C_2 = -\tfrac{1}{3}C_3;$$

therefore,

$$\mathbf{C} = C_3[\tfrac{1}{2}\hat{\mathbf{i}} - \tfrac{1}{3}\hat{\mathbf{j}} + \hat{\mathbf{k}}].$$

The unit vector in the direction of **C** must be given by

$$\hat{c} = \frac{\mathbf{C}}{|\mathbf{C}|} = \frac{C_3[\frac{1}{2}\hat{i} - \frac{1}{3}\hat{j} + \hat{k}]}{\sqrt{C_3^2[(\frac{1}{2})^2 + (-\frac{1}{3})^2 + (1)^2]}}$$

$$= \pm(\tfrac{3}{7}\hat{i} - \tfrac{2}{7}\hat{j} + \tfrac{6}{7}\hat{k})$$

Alternate Solution

$$\mathbf{C} = \mathbf{A} \times \mathbf{B} = \begin{vmatrix} \hat{i} & \hat{j} & \hat{k} \\ 2 & -6 & -3 \\ 4 & 3 & -1 \end{vmatrix}$$

$$= 15\hat{i} - 10\hat{j} + 30\hat{k}.$$

The unit vector parallel to **A** × **B** consequently will be given by:

$$\frac{\mathbf{A} \times \mathbf{B}}{|\mathbf{A} \times \mathbf{B}|} = \frac{15\hat{i} - 10\hat{j} + 30\hat{k}}{\sqrt{(15)^2 + (-10)^2 + (30)^2}}$$

$$= \tfrac{3}{7}\hat{i} - \tfrac{2}{7}\hat{j} + \tfrac{6}{7}\hat{k}$$

But because **B** × **A** will also give a vector perpendicular to the plane containing **A** and **B**,

$$\hat{c} = \pm(\tfrac{3}{7}\hat{i} - \tfrac{2}{7}\hat{j} + \tfrac{6}{7}\hat{k}).$$

10. Prove that the cylindrical coordinate system is orthogonal.

Solution [See Fig. P1.2 (10)]

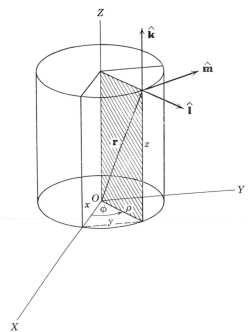

Fig. P1.2 (10)

The unit vectors in the ρ-, ϕ-, and z-directions are given by:

$$\hat{\mathbf{l}} = \cos \phi \hat{\mathbf{i}} + \sin \phi \hat{\mathbf{j}}$$
$$\hat{\mathbf{m}} = -\sin \phi \hat{\mathbf{i}} + \cos \phi \hat{\mathbf{j}}$$
$$\hat{\mathbf{k}} = \hat{\mathbf{k}}$$

Hence

$$\hat{\mathbf{l}} \cdot \hat{\mathbf{m}} = (\cos \phi \hat{\mathbf{i}} + \sin \phi \hat{\mathbf{j}}) \cdot (-\sin \phi \hat{\mathbf{i}} + \cos \phi \hat{\mathbf{j}}) = 0$$
$$\hat{\mathbf{l}} \cdot \hat{\mathbf{n}} = (\cos \phi \hat{\mathbf{i}} + \sin \phi \hat{\mathbf{j}}) \cdot (\hat{\mathbf{k}}) = 0$$
$$\hat{\mathbf{m}} \cdot \hat{\mathbf{n}} = (-\sin \phi \hat{\mathbf{i}} + \cos \phi \hat{\mathbf{j}}) \cdot (\hat{\mathbf{k}}) = 0$$

showing that $\hat{\mathbf{l}}$, $\hat{\mathbf{m}}$, and $\hat{\mathbf{k}}$ must be mutually perpendicular.

11. A scalar function $\phi(x, y, z)$ has the form

$$\phi = \tfrac{1}{2}k_1 x^2 + \tfrac{1}{2}k_2 y^2 + gz.$$

Find

a. grad $\phi = \nabla \phi$
b. curl grad $\phi = \nabla x (\nabla \phi)$

and show that

c. $\nabla x (\nabla \phi) = 0$, regardless of the form of ϕ.

Solution

(a)
$$\nabla \phi = \left(\frac{\partial}{\partial x} \hat{\mathbf{i}} + \frac{\partial}{\partial y} \hat{\mathbf{j}} + \frac{\partial}{\partial z} \hat{\mathbf{k}} \right) \phi$$

$$= \frac{\partial \phi}{\partial x} \hat{\mathbf{i}} + \frac{\partial \phi}{\partial y} \hat{\mathbf{j}} + \frac{\partial \phi}{\partial z} \hat{\mathbf{k}}$$

$$= k_1 x \hat{\mathbf{i}} + k_2 y \hat{\mathbf{j}} + g \hat{\mathbf{k}}$$

(b)
$$\nabla x (\nabla \phi) = \begin{vmatrix} \hat{\mathbf{i}} & \hat{\mathbf{j}} & \hat{\mathbf{k}} \\ \dfrac{\partial}{\partial x} & \dfrac{\partial}{\partial y} & \dfrac{\partial}{\partial z} \\ k_1 x & k_2 y & g \end{vmatrix}$$

$$= \left(\frac{\partial g}{\partial y} - \frac{\partial(k_2 y)}{\partial z} \right) \hat{\mathbf{i}} + \left(\frac{\partial(k_1 x)}{\partial z} - \frac{\partial g}{\partial x} \right) \hat{\mathbf{j}}$$
$$+ \left(\frac{\partial(k_2 y)}{\partial x} - \frac{\partial(k_1 x)}{\partial y} \right) \hat{\mathbf{k}} = 0$$

(c) Since $\phi = \phi(x, y, z)$ only,

$$\nabla x (\nabla \phi) = \begin{vmatrix} \hat{\mathbf{i}} & \hat{\mathbf{j}} & \hat{\mathbf{k}} \\ \dfrac{\partial}{\partial x} & \dfrac{\partial}{\partial y} & \dfrac{\partial}{\partial z} \\ \dfrac{\partial \phi}{\partial x} & \dfrac{\partial \phi}{\partial y} & \dfrac{\partial \phi}{\partial z} \end{vmatrix}$$

$$= \left[\frac{\partial^2 \phi}{\partial y \, \partial z} - \frac{\partial^2 \phi}{\partial z \, \partial y} \right] \hat{\mathbf{i}} + \left[\frac{\partial^2 \phi}{\partial z \, \partial x} - \frac{\partial^2 \phi}{\partial x \, \partial z} \right] \hat{\mathbf{j}} + \left[\frac{\partial^2 \phi}{\partial x \, \partial y} - \frac{\partial^2 \phi}{\partial y \, \partial x} \right] \hat{\mathbf{k}}.$$

But, provided that ϕ is an analytic function,

$$\frac{\partial^2 \phi}{\partial y\,\partial z} = \frac{\partial^2 \phi}{\partial z\,\partial y}, \qquad \frac{\partial^2 \phi}{\partial z\,\partial x} = \frac{\partial^2 \phi}{\partial x\,\partial z}, \qquad \frac{\partial^2 \phi}{\partial x\,\partial y} = \frac{\partial^2 \phi}{\partial y\,\partial x};$$

so that $\nabla x(\nabla \phi) = 0$.

12. Show that $\nabla \cdot (\nabla \times \mathbf{u}) \equiv 0$ for all $\mathbf{u}$.

Solution

$$\nabla \cdot (\nabla \times \mathbf{u}) = \nabla \cdot \begin{vmatrix} \hat{\mathbf{i}} & \hat{\mathbf{j}} & \hat{\mathbf{k}} \\ \dfrac{\partial}{\partial x} & \dfrac{\partial}{\partial y} & \dfrac{\partial}{\partial z} \\ u_1 & u_2 & u_3 \end{vmatrix}$$

$$= \nabla \cdot \left[\left(\frac{\partial u_3}{\partial y} - \frac{\partial u_2}{\partial z} \right)\hat{\mathbf{i}} + \left(\frac{\partial u_1}{\partial z} - \frac{\partial u_3}{\partial x} \right)\hat{\mathbf{j}} + \left(\frac{\partial u_2}{\partial x} - \frac{\partial u_1}{\partial y} \right)\hat{\mathbf{k}} \right]$$

$$= \frac{\partial}{\partial x}\left(\frac{\partial u_3}{\partial y} - \frac{\partial u_2}{\partial z} \right) + \frac{\partial}{\partial y}\left(\frac{\partial u_1}{\partial z} - \frac{\partial u_3}{\partial x} \right) + \frac{\partial}{\partial z}\left(\frac{\partial u_2}{\partial x} - \frac{\partial u_1}{\partial y} \right)$$

$$= \frac{\partial^2 u_3}{\partial x\,\partial y} - \frac{\partial^2 u_2}{\partial x\,\partial z} + \frac{\partial^2 u_1}{\partial y\,\partial z} - \frac{\partial^2 u_3}{\partial y\,\partial x} + \frac{\partial^2 u_2}{\partial z\,\partial x} - \frac{\partial^2 u_1}{\partial z\,\partial y} = 0.$$

13. Show that

$$\nabla \cdot (\phi \mathbf{u}) = (\nabla \phi) \cdot \mathbf{u} + \phi(\nabla \cdot \mathbf{u}).$$

Solution

$$\nabla \cdot (\phi \mathbf{u}) = \nabla \cdot (\phi u_1 \hat{\mathbf{i}} + \phi u_2 \hat{\mathbf{j}} + \phi u_3 \hat{\mathbf{k}})$$

$$= \frac{\partial}{\partial x}(\phi u_1) + \frac{\partial}{\partial y}(\phi u_2) + \frac{\partial}{\partial z}(\phi u_3)$$

$$= \frac{\partial \phi}{\partial x} u_1 + \phi \frac{\partial u_1}{\partial x} + \frac{\partial \phi}{\partial y} u_2 + \phi \frac{\partial u_2}{\partial y} + \frac{\partial \phi}{\partial z} u_3 + \phi \frac{\partial u_3}{\partial z}$$

$$= \frac{\partial \phi}{\partial x} u_1 + \frac{\partial \phi}{\partial y} u_2 + \frac{\partial \phi}{\partial z} u_3 + \phi \left(\frac{\partial u_1}{\partial x} + \frac{\partial u_2}{\partial y} + \frac{\partial u_3}{\partial z} \right)$$

$$= \left(\frac{\partial \phi}{\partial x}\hat{\mathbf{i}} + \frac{\partial \phi}{\partial y}\hat{\mathbf{j}} + \frac{\partial \phi}{\partial z}\hat{\mathbf{k}} \right) \cdot (u_1 \hat{\mathbf{i}} + u_2 \hat{\mathbf{j}} + u_3 \hat{\mathbf{k}})$$

$$+ \phi \left(\frac{\partial}{\partial x}\hat{\mathbf{i}} + \frac{\partial}{\partial y}\hat{\mathbf{j}} + \frac{\partial}{\partial z}\hat{\mathbf{k}} \right) \cdot (u_1 \hat{\mathbf{i}} + u_2 \hat{\mathbf{j}} + u_3 \hat{\mathbf{k}})$$

$$= (\nabla \phi) \cdot \mathbf{u} + \phi(\nabla \cdot \mathbf{u}).$$

14. Prove that
$$\mathbf{a} \times (\mathbf{b} \times \mathbf{c}) + \mathbf{b} \times (\mathbf{c} \times \mathbf{a}) + \mathbf{c} \times (\mathbf{a} \times \mathbf{b}) = 0$$
Solution

Since in general
$$\mathbf{u} \times (\mathbf{v} \times \mathbf{w}) = (\mathbf{u} \cdot \mathbf{w})\mathbf{v} - (\mathbf{u} \cdot \mathbf{v})\mathbf{w},$$
$$\mathbf{a} \times (\mathbf{b} \times \mathbf{c}) = (\mathbf{a} \cdot \mathbf{c})\mathbf{b} - (\mathbf{a} \cdot \mathbf{b})\mathbf{c}$$
$$\mathbf{b} \times (\mathbf{c} \times \mathbf{a}) = (\mathbf{b} \cdot \mathbf{a})\mathbf{c} - (\mathbf{b} \cdot \mathbf{c})\mathbf{a}$$
$$\mathbf{c} \times (\mathbf{a} \times \mathbf{b}) = (\mathbf{c} \cdot \mathbf{b})\mathbf{a} - (\mathbf{c} \cdot \mathbf{a})\mathbf{b}.$$

Adding these three equations gives
$$\mathbf{a} \times (\mathbf{b} \times \mathbf{c}) + \mathbf{b} \times (\mathbf{c} \times \mathbf{a}) + \mathbf{c} \times (\mathbf{a} \times \mathbf{b}) = \mathbf{b}(\mathbf{a} \cdot \mathbf{c} - \mathbf{c} \cdot \mathbf{a})$$
$$+ \mathbf{c}(\mathbf{b} \cdot \mathbf{a} - \mathbf{a} \cdot \mathbf{b}) + \mathbf{a}(\mathbf{c} \cdot \mathbf{b} - \mathbf{b} \cdot \mathbf{c}) = 0,$$

because the dot product is commutative.

15. Write the equation for the plane determined by the three points
$$P_1(0, 1, 2), \qquad P_2(-3, 2, 1), \qquad P_3(1, 0, -1).$$
Solution

The position vectors of P_1, P_2, and P_3 are
$$\mathbf{r}_1 = \hat{\mathbf{j}} + 2\hat{\mathbf{k}}$$
$$\mathbf{r}_2 = -3\hat{\mathbf{i}} + 2\hat{\mathbf{j}} + \hat{\mathbf{k}}$$
$$\mathbf{r}_3 = \hat{\mathbf{i}} - \hat{\mathbf{k}},$$

and the position vector of an arbitrary point $P(x, y, z)$ in this plane will be
$$\mathbf{r} = x\hat{\mathbf{i}} + y\hat{\mathbf{j}} + z\hat{\mathbf{k}}.$$
Then
$$\mathbf{r} - \mathbf{r}_1 = x\hat{\mathbf{i}} + (y - 1)\hat{\mathbf{j}} + (z - 2)\hat{\mathbf{k}}$$
$$\mathbf{r}_2 - \mathbf{r}_1 = -3\hat{\mathbf{i}} + \hat{\mathbf{j}} - \hat{\mathbf{k}}$$
$$\mathbf{r}_3 - \mathbf{r}_1 = \hat{\mathbf{i}} - \hat{\mathbf{j}} - 3\hat{\mathbf{k}};$$

but because these three vectors must all lie in the same plane,
$$(\mathbf{r} - \mathbf{r}_1) \cdot (\mathbf{r}_2 - \mathbf{r}_1) \times (\mathbf{r}_3 - \mathbf{r}_1) = 0.$$
Substitution gives
$$[x\hat{\mathbf{i}} + (y - 1)\hat{\mathbf{j}} + (z - 2)\hat{\mathbf{k}}] \cdot (-3\hat{\mathbf{i}} + \hat{\mathbf{j}} - \hat{\mathbf{k}}) \times (\hat{\mathbf{i}} - \hat{\mathbf{j}} - 3\hat{\mathbf{k}}) = 0.$$

When the cross product is reduced, we obtain
$$(-3\hat{\mathbf{i}} + \hat{\mathbf{j}} - \hat{\mathbf{k}}) \times (\hat{\mathbf{i}} - \hat{\mathbf{j}} - 3\hat{\mathbf{k}})$$
$$= \begin{vmatrix} \hat{\mathbf{i}} & \hat{\mathbf{j}} & \hat{\mathbf{k}} \\ -3 & 1 & -1 \\ 1 & -1 & -3 \end{vmatrix}$$
$$= \hat{\mathbf{i}}(-3 - 1) + \hat{\mathbf{j}}(-1 - 9) + \hat{\mathbf{k}}(+3 - 1)$$
$$= -4\hat{\mathbf{i}} - 10\hat{\mathbf{j}} + 2\hat{\mathbf{k}};$$

the equation of the plane must be

$$[x\hat{\mathbf{i}} + (y - 1)\hat{\mathbf{j}} + (z - 2)\hat{\mathbf{k}}] \cdot (-4\hat{\mathbf{i}} - 10\hat{\mathbf{j}} + 2\hat{\mathbf{k}}) = 0$$

or

$$4x + 10y - 2z - 6 = 0.$$

16. Using their transformation properties, prove that the addition of two vectors gives a new vector.

Solution

If **a** and **b** are the vectors to be added, they must obey the transformation relations

$$a_i' = c_{ij}a_j$$

and

$$b_i' = c_{ij}b_j$$

where a_j and b_j are the components in the old coordinate system and a_i' and b_i' are the components in the new one, the c_{ij} being the direction cosines between the new and old sets of axes. Now

$$a_j + b_j = d_j$$

means that

$$a_1 + b_1 = d_1$$
$$a_2 + b_2 = d_2$$
$$a_3 + b_3 = d_3$$

which should be true in the new as well as the old coordinate system:

$$a_i' + b_i' = d_i'$$

Substituting for a_i' and b_i' from the transformation relations, we obtain

$$d_i' = a_i' + b_i' = c_{ij}a_j + c_{ij}b_j$$
$$= c_{i1}a_1 + c_{i2}a_2 + c_{i3}a_3 + c_{i1}b_1 + c_{i2}b_2 + c_{i3}b_3$$
$$= c_{i1}(a_1 + b_1) + c_{i2}(a_2 + b_2) + c_{i3}(a_3 + b_3)$$

or

$$d_i' = c_{i1}d_1 + c_{i2}d_2 + c_{i3}d_3$$
$$d_1' = c_{11}d_1 + c_{12}d_2 + c_{13}d_3$$
$$d_2' = c_{21}d_1 + c_{22}d_2 + c_{23}d_3$$
$$d_3' = c_{31}d_1 + c_{32}d_2 + c_{33}d_3,$$

which can be written in indicial notation as

$$d_i' = c_{ij}d_j.$$

Therefore, the d_j transform as the components of a vector should.

17. Evaluate $\int_S \hat{\mathbf{n}} \cdot \mathbf{u} \, dS$, where $\mathbf{u} = \hat{\mathbf{r}}/r$, over the surface of a sphere of radius a centered on the origin.

Solution

Because of the singularity at the origin, which affects the volume integral, Gauss' theorem can only be applied by breaking the integral into two parts and deleting a small sphere of radius ε, surface S', and volume V' centered on the singular point:

$$\int_S \hat{\mathbf{n}} \cdot \mathbf{u}\, dS = \int_S \frac{\hat{\mathbf{r}}}{r} \cdot \hat{\mathbf{n}}\, dS - \int_{S'} \frac{\hat{\mathbf{r}}}{r} \cdot \hat{\mathbf{n}}\, dS'$$

$$= \int_V \nabla \cdot \frac{\mathbf{r}}{r^2}\, dV - \int_{V'} \nabla \cdot \frac{\mathbf{r}}{r^2}\, dV'$$

Making use of the relation proved in Problem 1.2 (13), we have

$$\nabla \cdot (\phi \mathbf{A}) = (\nabla \phi) \cdot \mathbf{A} + \phi(\nabla \cdot \mathbf{A})$$

$$\nabla \cdot \frac{\mathbf{r}}{r^2} = \nabla\left(\frac{1}{r^2}\right) \cdot \mathbf{r} + \frac{1}{r^2}(\nabla \cdot \mathbf{r})$$

$$= \left[x\frac{\partial}{\partial x}\left(\frac{1}{r^2}\right) + y\frac{\partial}{\partial y}\left(\frac{1}{r^2}\right) + z\frac{\partial}{\partial z}\left(\frac{1}{r^2}\right) \right] + \frac{1}{r^2}(1 + 1 + 1)$$

$$= \left[x\frac{\partial}{\partial x}\left(\frac{1}{x^2 + y^2 + z^2}\right) + y\frac{\partial}{\partial y}\left(\frac{1}{x^2 + y^2 + z^2}\right) \right.$$

$$\left. + z\frac{\partial}{\partial z}\left(\frac{1}{x^2 + y^2 + z^2}\right) + \frac{3}{r^2} \right]$$

$$= \frac{3}{r^2} - \left[\frac{2x^2}{(x^2 + y^2 + z^2)^2} + \frac{2y^2}{(x^2 + y^2 + z^2)^2} + \frac{2z^2}{(x^2 + y^2 + z^2)^2} \right]$$

$$= \frac{3}{r^2} - \frac{2(x^2 + y^2 + z^2)}{r^4} = \frac{3}{r^2} - \frac{2}{r^2} = \frac{1}{r^2}.$$

Therefore, since in spherical coordinates

$$dv = r^2 \sin\theta\, d\theta\, d\phi\, dr,$$

$$\int_V \nabla \cdot \frac{\mathbf{r}}{r^2}\, dV = \int_V \frac{1}{r^2} r^2 \sin\theta\, d\theta\, d\phi\, dr$$

$$= \int_0^\pi \sin\theta\, d\theta \int_0^{2\pi} d\phi \int_0^a dr$$

$$= 4\pi a.$$

Similarly,

$$\int_{V'} \nabla \cdot \frac{\mathbf{r}}{r^2}\, dV' = 4\pi\varepsilon;$$

therefore,

$$\int_S \mathbf{u} \cdot \hat{\mathbf{n}}\, dS = 4\pi a - 4\pi\varepsilon,$$

and as $\varepsilon \to 0$ this simplifies to $4\pi a$.

18. Using Stoke's theorem, evaluate

$$\int_C (x^2y \ dx \ + 5xy^2 \ dy),$$

where the curve C is a circle of 2 in. radius centered on the origin in the XY-plane.

Solution

$$\iint_{S'} (\text{curl } \mathbf{u}) \cdot \hat{\mathbf{n}} \ dS' = \int_C \mathbf{u} \cdot d\mathbf{r}$$

$$d\mathbf{r} = dx\hat{\mathbf{i}} + dy\hat{\mathbf{j}}$$

But

$$\mathbf{u} \cdot d\mathbf{r} = x^2y \ dx \ + 5xy^2 \ dy,$$

so that

$$\mathbf{u} = (x^2y)\hat{\mathbf{i}} + (5xy^2)\hat{\mathbf{j}}.$$

Now

$$(\text{curl } \mathbf{u}) \cdot \hat{\mathbf{n}} = (\nabla x \mathbf{u}) \cdot \hat{\mathbf{k}} = \begin{vmatrix} 0 & 0 & 1 \\ \dfrac{\partial}{\partial x} & \dfrac{\partial}{\partial y} & \dfrac{\partial}{\partial z} \\ x^2y & 5xy^2 & 0 \end{vmatrix} = 5y^2 - x^2.$$

Changing to polar coordinates,

$$x = \rho \cos \phi$$
$$y = \rho \sin \phi$$
$$dS' = \rho \ d\phi \ d\rho,$$

$$\iint_{S'} (\text{curl } \mathbf{u}) \cdot \hat{\mathbf{n}} \ dS' = \int_{\phi=0}^{2\pi} \int_{\rho=0}^{2} \rho^3(5 \sin^2 \phi - \cos^2 \phi) \ d\rho \ d\phi$$

$$= 4 \int_0^{2\pi} (5 \sin^2 \phi - \cos^2 \phi) \ d\phi$$

$$= 20 \int_0^{2\pi} \sin^2 \phi \ d\phi - 4 \int_0^{2\pi} \cos^2 \phi \ d\phi$$

$$= 20 \left[\frac{\phi}{2} - \frac{1}{4} \sin 2\phi \right]_0^{2\pi} - 4 \left[\frac{\phi}{2} + \frac{1}{4} \sin 2\phi \right]_0^{2\pi}$$

$$= 20[\pi] - 4[\pi] = 16\pi.$$

Hence

$$\int_C (x^2y \ dx \ + 5xy^2 \ dy) = 16\pi.$$

19. Consider the equilateral triangle shown in Fig. P1.2 (19) and assume that point B can move only in a vertical line and point A only in a horizontal line in the XY-plane. If point A is given a constant velocity of 8 ft/sec, as shown, determine the angular velocity and acceleration of the edge BC and the linear velocity and acceleration of point B at the instant when $\theta = 45°$.

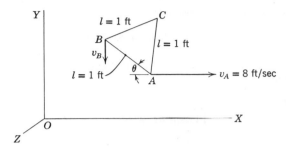

Fig. P1.2 (19)

Solution

$$\mathbf{v}_{20} = \mathbf{v}_{10} + \boldsymbol{\omega} \times \mathbf{r}; \qquad \mathbf{v}_{BO} = \mathbf{v}_{AO} + \boldsymbol{\omega}_{BA} \times \mathbf{r}_{AB}$$

Since when $\theta = 45°$,

$$\mathbf{r}_{AB} = \frac{1}{\sqrt{2}}(-\hat{\mathbf{i}} + \hat{\mathbf{j}}),$$

$$v_{BO}\hat{\mathbf{j}} = 8\hat{\mathbf{i}} + \omega\hat{\mathbf{k}} \times \left(-\frac{1}{\sqrt{2}}\hat{\mathbf{i}} + \frac{1}{\sqrt{2}}\hat{\mathbf{j}}\right)$$

$$= 8\hat{\mathbf{i}} - \frac{\omega}{\sqrt{2}}\hat{\mathbf{j}} - \frac{\omega}{\sqrt{2}}\hat{\mathbf{i}} = \left(8 - \frac{\omega}{\sqrt{2}}\right)\hat{\mathbf{i}} - \frac{\omega}{\sqrt{2}}\hat{\mathbf{j}}.$$

Thus

$$\omega = 8\sqrt{2} \text{ rad/sec},$$

and

$$\mathbf{v}_{BO} = -\frac{\omega}{\sqrt{2}}\hat{\mathbf{j}} = -\frac{8\sqrt{2}}{\sqrt{2}}\hat{\mathbf{j}} = -8\hat{\mathbf{j}} \text{ ft/sec}.$$

Also

$$\mathbf{a}_{BO} = \overset{0}{\overset{\uparrow}{\mathbf{a}_{AO}}} + \boldsymbol{\omega}_{AB} \times \mathbf{r}_{AB} + \boldsymbol{\omega}_{BA} \times (\boldsymbol{\omega}_{BA} \times \mathbf{r}_{AB})$$

$$= \dot{\omega}\hat{\mathbf{k}} \times \left(-\frac{1}{\sqrt{2}}\hat{\mathbf{i}} + \frac{1}{\sqrt{2}}\hat{\mathbf{j}}\right) + \omega\hat{\mathbf{k}} \times \left(-\frac{\omega}{\sqrt{2}}\hat{\mathbf{j}} - \frac{\omega}{\sqrt{2}}\hat{\mathbf{i}}\right)$$

$$= -\frac{1}{\sqrt{2}}\dot{\omega}\hat{\mathbf{j}} - \frac{\dot{\omega}}{\sqrt{2}}\hat{\mathbf{i}} + \frac{\omega^2}{\sqrt{2}}\hat{\mathbf{i}} - \frac{\omega^2}{\sqrt{2}}\hat{\mathbf{j}}$$

$$= -\frac{1}{\sqrt{2}}\dot{\omega}\hat{\mathbf{j}} - \frac{\dot{\omega}}{\sqrt{2}}\hat{\mathbf{i}} + \frac{128}{\sqrt{2}}\hat{\mathbf{i}} - \frac{128}{\sqrt{2}}\hat{\mathbf{j}},$$

giving

$$a_{BO}\hat{\mathbf{j}} = \left(\frac{128}{\sqrt{2}} - \frac{\dot{\omega}}{\sqrt{2}}\right)\hat{\mathbf{i}} - \left(\frac{128}{\sqrt{2}} + \frac{\dot{\omega}}{\sqrt{2}}\right)\hat{\mathbf{j}};$$

therefore,

$$\dot{\omega} = 128 \text{ rad/sec}^2$$

and

$$\mathbf{a}_{BO} = -\frac{256}{\sqrt{2}}\hat{\mathbf{j}} \text{ ft/sec}^2.$$

20. End B of the rod shown in Fig. P1.2 (20a) has a speed of 15 ft/sec in the X-direction; what is the velocity of point A of the rod?

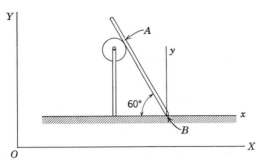

Fig. P1.2 (20a)

Solution

$$\mathbf{v}_{20} = \mathbf{v}_{10} + \boldsymbol{\omega} \times \mathbf{r}, \qquad \text{point 2 = point } A, \text{ point 1 = point } B,$$

where $\mathbf{r}$ is the vector from 1 to 2 [Fig. 1.2 (20b)]:

$$\mathbf{r} = -\frac{r}{2}\hat{\imath} + \frac{\sqrt{3}}{2} r \hat{\jmath}$$

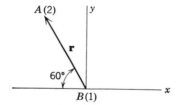

Fig. P1.2 (20b)

Also,

$$\boldsymbol{\omega} = \omega_z \hat{\mathbf{k}},$$

because $\boldsymbol{\omega}$ must point in the Z-direction. Then:

$$\boldsymbol{\omega} \times \mathbf{r} = \begin{vmatrix} \hat{\imath} & \hat{\jmath} & \hat{\mathbf{k}} \\ 0 & 0 & \omega_z \\ -\dfrac{r}{2} & \dfrac{\sqrt{3}}{2} r & 0 \end{vmatrix} = \left(-\frac{\sqrt{3}}{2}\omega_z r\right)\hat{\imath} + \left(-\frac{\omega_z r}{2}\right)\hat{\jmath};$$

therefore, with $\mathbf{v}_{10} = 15\hat{\imath}$ as given,

$$\mathbf{v}_{20} = 15\hat{\imath} + \left(-\frac{\sqrt{3}}{2}\omega_z r\right)\hat{\imath} + \left(-\frac{\omega_z r}{2}\right)\hat{\jmath}$$

$$= \left(15 - \frac{\sqrt{3}}{2}\omega_z r\right)\hat{\imath} - \frac{\omega_z r}{2}\hat{\jmath}.$$

We may also regard $\mathbf{v}_{20}$ as having the components $\mathbf{v}_R$, directed along the rod, and $\mathbf{v}_N$, normal to the rod:

$$\mathbf{v}_{20} = \mathbf{v}_N + \mathbf{v}_R$$

However,

$$\mathbf{v}_N = 0,$$

because $A(2)$ is the point of support; therefore,

$$\mathbf{v}_{20} = \mathbf{v}_R,$$

or in terms of x- and y-components,

$$\mathbf{v}_{20} = v_{20_x}\hat{\mathbf{i}} - v_{20_y}\hat{\mathbf{j}} = \tfrac{1}{2}v_{20}\hat{\mathbf{i}} - \frac{\sqrt{3}}{2}v_{20}\hat{\mathbf{j}}.$$

Substituting the first expression obtained for $\mathbf{v}_{20}$, we have

$$\left(15 - \frac{\sqrt{3}}{2}\,\omega_z r\right)\hat{\mathbf{i}} - \frac{\omega_z r}{2}\hat{\mathbf{j}} = \frac{v_{20}}{2}\hat{\mathbf{i}} - \frac{\sqrt{3}}{2}v_{20}\hat{\mathbf{j}};$$

therefore,

$$\frac{1}{2}v_{20} = 15 - \frac{\sqrt{3}}{2}\,\omega_z r$$

and

$$\frac{\sqrt{3}}{2}v_{20} = \frac{\omega_z r}{2}.$$

Multiplying the second equation by $\sqrt{3}$ and adding the two gives

$$v_{20} = \frac{15}{2};$$

so

$$\mathbf{v}_{20} = \frac{15}{4}(\hat{\mathbf{i}} - \sqrt{3}\hat{\mathbf{j}})\ \text{ft/sec}.$$

21. A guided missile moving at 300 ft/sec in the X-direction of a coordinate system fixed in the surface of the earth is also rolling clockwise at 4 rad/min. If a small rocket is fired with a speed of 10 ft/sec in the Y-direction from a point 3 ft above the center line of the missile, what will its velocity be relative to the earth? [See Fig. P1.2 (21).]

Solution

Fixing the $X'Y'Z'$-system in the missile as shown, we obtain:

$$\mathbf{v}_{20} = \mathbf{v}_{10} + \mathbf{v}_{21} + \mathbf{\Omega} \times \mathbf{r}$$

But

$$\mathbf{v}_{10} = 300\hat{\mathbf{i}}\ \text{ft/sec}$$

$$\mathbf{v}_{21} = 10\hat{\mathbf{j}}\ \text{ft/sec}$$

and

$$\mathbf{\Omega} = 4\hat{\mathbf{i}}\ \text{rad/min} = \frac{1}{15}\hat{\mathbf{i}}\ \text{rad/sec}$$

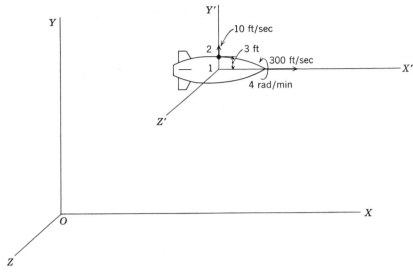

Fig. P1.2 (21)

with

$$\mathbf{r} = 3\hat{\mathbf{j}} \text{ ft.}$$

Thus

$$\boldsymbol{\Omega} \times \mathbf{r} = \begin{vmatrix} \hat{\mathbf{i}} & \hat{\mathbf{j}} & \hat{\mathbf{k}} \\ \frac{1}{15} & 0 & 0 \\ 0 & 3 & 0 \end{vmatrix} = \tfrac{1}{5}\hat{\mathbf{k}},$$

and

$$\mathbf{v}_{20} = 300\hat{\mathbf{i}} + 10\hat{\mathbf{j}} + \frac{\hat{\mathbf{k}}}{5}.$$

22. A bar 4 ft long [Fig. P1.2 (22)] rotates in the XY-plane about one of its end points O with an angular speed of 3 rad/sec, which is changing at the rate of 2 rad/sec². A disk is attached to the free end of the bar and rotates perpendicular to its axis at a constant angular speed of 5 rad/sec. Determine the velocity and acceleration of a point B on the rim of the disk with respect to the fixed XYZ-coordinate system.

Solution

Fixing the $X'Y'Z'$-system in the disk as indicated, so that it rotates with it, we have

$$\mathbf{v}_{20} = \mathbf{v}_{10} + \mathbf{v}_{21} + \boldsymbol{\Omega} \times \mathbf{r}; \qquad \text{point } 2 = \text{point } B, \text{ point } 1 = \text{point } A.$$

$$\mathbf{v}_{21} = 0$$

$$\mathbf{v}_{10} = \dot{\mathbf{R}} = \boldsymbol{\omega}_1 \times \mathbf{R} = -3\hat{\mathbf{k}} \times 4\hat{\mathbf{i}} = -12\hat{\mathbf{j}},$$

and

$$\boldsymbol{\Omega} = \boldsymbol{\omega}_1 + \boldsymbol{\omega}_2 = -3\hat{\mathbf{k}} + 5\hat{\mathbf{i}},$$

$$\boldsymbol{\Omega} \times \mathbf{r} = (-3\hat{\mathbf{k}} + 5\hat{\mathbf{k}}) \times \tfrac{1}{2}\hat{\mathbf{i}} = \tfrac{3}{2}\hat{\mathbf{j}} + \tfrac{5}{2}\hat{\mathbf{k}};$$

Introduction

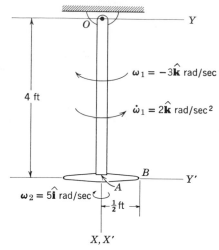

Fig. P1.2 (22)

therefore,

$$\mathbf{v}_{20} = \tfrac{3}{2}\hat{\mathbf{i}} - 12\hat{\mathbf{j}} + \tfrac{5}{2}\hat{\mathbf{k}}.$$

Furthermore,

$$\mathbf{a}_{20} = \mathbf{a}_{10} + \mathbf{a}_{21} + \mathbf{\Omega} \times (\mathbf{\Omega} \times \mathbf{r}) + 2\mathbf{\Omega} \times \mathbf{v}_{21} + \mathbf{A} \times \mathbf{r}.$$

But

$$\mathbf{a}_{10} = \mathbf{\omega}_1 \times (\mathbf{\omega}_1 \times \mathbf{R}) + \mathbf{\alpha} \times \mathbf{R}$$
$$= (-3\hat{\mathbf{k}}) \times (-12\hat{\mathbf{j}}) + 2\hat{\mathbf{k}} \times 4\hat{\mathbf{i}}$$
$$= -36\hat{\mathbf{i}} + 8\hat{\mathbf{j}},$$

$$\mathbf{a}_{21} = 0,$$

and

$$\mathbf{\Omega} \times (\mathbf{\Omega} \times \mathbf{r}) = (-3\hat{\mathbf{k}} + 5\hat{\mathbf{i}}) \times (\tfrac{3}{2}\hat{\mathbf{i}} + \tfrac{5}{2}\hat{\mathbf{k}})$$
$$= -\tfrac{9}{2}\hat{\mathbf{j}} - \tfrac{25}{2}\hat{\mathbf{j}}$$
$$= -17\hat{\mathbf{j}};$$

whereas

$$\mathbf{A} = \dot{\mathbf{\Omega}} = 2\hat{\mathbf{k}} + \mathbf{\omega}_1 \times \mathbf{\omega}_2$$
$$= 2\hat{\mathbf{k}} - 3\hat{\mathbf{k}} \times 5\hat{\mathbf{i}} = 2\hat{\mathbf{k}} - 15\hat{\mathbf{j}},$$

$$\mathbf{A} \times \mathbf{r} = (2\hat{\mathbf{k}} - 15\hat{\mathbf{j}}) \times \tfrac{1}{2}\hat{\mathbf{j}} = -\hat{\mathbf{i}}.$$

Therefore,

$$\mathbf{a}_{20} = -36\hat{\mathbf{i}} - \hat{\mathbf{i}} + 8\hat{\mathbf{j}} - 17\hat{\mathbf{j}} = -37\hat{\mathbf{i}} - 9\hat{\mathbf{j}}.$$

23. It is determined that a group of cosmic-ray particles entering the earth's atmosphere have an average speed of $0.99c$ and a mean lifetime of 15.7 μsec for spontaneous decay. What would their mean lifetime be if they were at rest?

Solution

The mean lifetime of the particles in a frame of reference moving with their average speed will be given by

$$\Delta t' = \Delta t \, \mathcal{S},$$

where

$$\Delta t = 15.7 \ \mu\text{sec}$$

and

$$\mathcal{S} = \sqrt{1 - \left(\frac{V}{c}\right)^2}$$

with

$$V = 0.99c.$$

Thus

$$\Delta t' = 15.7 \sqrt{1 - (0.99)^2} = 15.7 \sqrt{1 - 0.98}$$
$$= 15.7 \sqrt{0.02} = 1.57 \times 1.414 = 2.22 \ \mu\text{sec}.$$

24. A man in a spaceship moving with a constant velocity **V** relative to the planet Mars, as shown in Fig. P1.2 (24a), makes an observation of the planet at point A. What must be the speed of the spaceship so that Mars will appear to him as an ellipsoid having a major axis five times the minor axis?

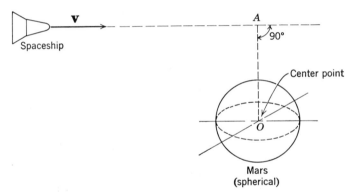

Fig. P1.2 (24a)

Solution

Establishing the coordinate systems shown in Fig. P1.2 (24b),

$$x' = x = d$$

$$z' = z = d,$$

with d representing the diameter of the planet, and

$$y' = y \mathcal{S};$$

therefore,

$$d' = d\mathcal{S},$$

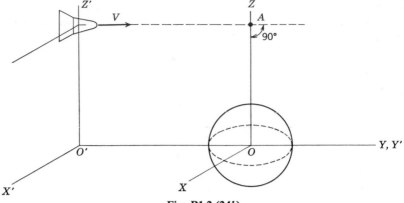

Fig. P1.2 (24b)

where d' will be the minor axis and d the major axis of the ellipsoid. Evidently

$$\frac{d'}{d} = \sqrt{1 - \frac{V^2}{c^2}} = \tfrac{1}{5};$$

therefore,

$$1 - \frac{V^2}{c^2} = \frac{1}{25}$$

$$\frac{V^2}{c^2} = \left[1 - \frac{1}{25}\right]$$

$$\frac{V}{c} = \sqrt{\frac{24}{25}}$$

$$V = \sqrt{\frac{24}{25}}\, c = 0.9798c.$$

An observer sees two particles traveling in opposite directions [Fig.P1.2 (25a)], each with a speed of 0.99c. What is the speed of one particle relative to the other?

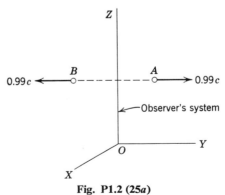

Fig. P1.2 (25a)

Solution
Because for V_y negative we know that

$$v_y' = \frac{v_y - V_y}{1 - \frac{V_y}{c^2}v_y},$$

the relative speed may be obtained directly by making the coordinate iden-
ifications suggested in Fig. P1.2(25b):

$$v_y' = \frac{0.99c - (-0.99c)}{1 - \frac{(-0.99c)(0.99c)}{c^2}}$$

$$= \frac{0.99 + 0.99}{1 + (0.99)^2} c$$

$$= 0.99995c.$$

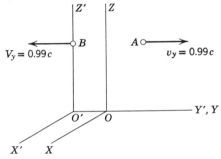

Fig. P1.2 (25b)

26. An observer in an interplanetary vehicle is approaching a light-emitting
object in space with a speed of $c/2$. If he measures the speed of the light
reaching him from the object with his own instruments, show that he should
find it to be c.

Solution
Fixing the unprimed coordinate system in the object and the primed
system in the vehicle means that v_y will be c and V_y will equal $-(c/2)$ [see
Fig. P1.2 (26)].

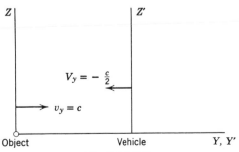

Fig. P1.2 (26)

Therefore, applying the Lorentz transformation relations,

$$v_y' = \frac{v_y - V_y}{1 - \frac{V_y}{c^2}v_y}$$

$$= \frac{c - \left(-\frac{c}{2}\right)}{1 - \left(-\frac{c}{2} \cdot \frac{c}{2}\right)}$$

$$= \frac{c[1 + \frac{1}{2}]}{[1 + \frac{1}{2}]}$$

$$= c.$$

Of course, the velocity of light will remain invariant in all inertial systems. Had we tried to use a Galilean transformation, we would have obtained a experimentally inconsistent result:

$$v_y' = v_y - V_y$$

$$= c - \left(-\frac{c}{2}\right)$$

$$= \tfrac{3}{2}c.$$

Exercises 1.2

1. The vectors **r**, **R**, and **A** are expressed in the XYZ-coordinate system as:

$$\mathbf{r} = -\hat{\mathbf{i}} + \hat{\mathbf{j}} + 2\hat{\mathbf{k}}$$
$$\mathbf{R} = 4\hat{\mathbf{j}} + 2\hat{\mathbf{k}}$$
$$\mathbf{A} = 2\hat{\mathbf{i}} + \hat{\mathbf{j}} + \hat{\mathbf{k}}$$

Locate P and express **r**′ and **A** in the $X'Y'Z'$-coordinate system [Fig. E1.2 (1)].

Answer. $\mathbf{r}' = -\hat{\mathbf{i}} - 3\hat{\mathbf{j}}; \mathbf{A} = 2\hat{\mathbf{i}} + \hat{\mathbf{j}} + \hat{\mathbf{k}}.$

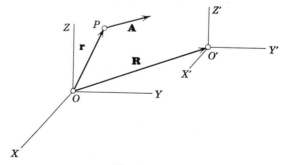

Fig. E1.2 (1)

2. The vector $\mathbf{d}$ in one system of coordinates (X, Y, Z) goes from point P_1 $(1, 3, 5)$ to point P_2 $(5, 8, 10)$; a rotation to a new system of axes (X', Y', Z') is defined by

$$x_i' = c_{ij}x_j$$

where c_{ij} is the array of direction cosines:

$$
\frac{1}{\sqrt{3}} \quad \sqrt{\frac{2}{3}} \quad 0
$$

$$
-\sqrt{\frac{2}{3}} \quad \frac{1}{\sqrt{3}} \quad 0
$$

$$
0 \quad 0 \quad 1
$$

a. Locate the points P_1 and P_2 with respect to the transformed coordinate system.

b. Express $\mathbf{d}$ in the transformed coordinate system.

Answer.

(a) $P_1(3.02, 0.92, 5)$; $P_2(9.4, 0.536, 10)$.

(b) $\mathbf{d} = 6.4\hat{\mathbf{i}}' - 0.38\hat{\mathbf{j}}' + 5\hat{\mathbf{k}}'$.

3. By translation in a plane of a pair of coordinate axes to a new origin $(1, 1)$, followed by an orthonormal rotation through a counterclockwise angle of $45°$, the equation of a certain locus is transformed into $x''^2 - 2y''^2 = 2$. Find the equation of the locus with respect to the original axes.

Answer. $x_1^2 + x_2^2 - 6x_1x_2 + 4x_1 + 4x_2 = 0$.

4. Complete the following table of direction cosines for an orthonormal rotation of a right-handed Cartesian coordinate system:

	X	Y	Z
X'			1
Y'			
Z'	$\frac{3}{5}$	$-\frac{4}{5}$	

Answer. $-\frac{4}{5}, -\frac{3}{5}, 0$.

5. New X'-, Y'-, and Z'-axes are chosen so that the X'-axis makes equal angles with the positive X- and Y-axes and the negative Z-axis, whereas the Y'-axis lies in the XZ-plane and bisects the angle between the X- and Z-axes. Show that the X'- and Y'-axes are perpendicular, and find the direction cosines of the Z'-axis that completes a right-handed rectangular system.

Answer. $\dfrac{1}{\sqrt{6}}, -\dfrac{2}{\sqrt{6}}, -\dfrac{1}{\sqrt{6}}$.

6. A rotation of a Cartesian coordinate system is defined by the equation

$$x_1' = c_{ij}x_j$$

where the c_{ij} satisfy the orthonormality conditions

$$c_{ik}c_{jk} = \delta_{ij}.$$

Which of the following is an acceptable form for c_{ij}?

a.

$$\begin{array}{ccc} \frac{1}{2} & \frac{1}{2} & 0 \\ -\frac{1}{2} & \frac{1}{2} & 0 \\ 0 & 0 & 1 \end{array}$$

b.

$$\begin{array}{ccc} \frac{3}{5} & \frac{4}{5} & 0 \\ -\frac{4}{5} & \frac{3}{5} & 0 \\ 0 & 0 & 1 \end{array}$$

c.

$$\begin{array}{ccc} 0 & 0 & 1 \\ \frac{1}{2} & \sqrt{\frac{3}{2}} & 0 \\ \sqrt{\frac{3}{2}} & \frac{1}{2} & 0 \end{array}$$

7. Write out the equations represented by
a. $c_k = a_k - b_k$
b. $T = S_{kk}$
c. $2W = s_{ij}e_{ij}$
where k, i, j run from 1 through 3, and
d. $T = \dfrac{m}{2} c_{ij}c_{ik}\dot{\theta}_j\dot{\theta}_k$
where i, j, k run from 1 through 2.

8. Show that the orthonormality conditions of a coordinate rotation can take the form:

$$c_{ki}c_{kj} = \delta_{ij}$$

9. Two vectors $\mathbf{u}$ and $\mathbf{v}$ are given by:

$$\mathbf{u} = 2\hat{\mathbf{i}} - 3\hat{\mathbf{j}} + \hat{\mathbf{k}}$$
$$\mathbf{v} = 4\hat{\mathbf{i}} + 2\hat{\mathbf{j}} + 2\hat{\mathbf{k}}$$

Find: **a.** $\mathbf{u} \cdot \mathbf{v}$
  b. $\mathbf{u} \times \mathbf{v}$
  c. $\mathbf{v} \times \mathbf{u}$

Answer
(a) 4.
(b) $-8\hat{\mathbf{i}} + 16\hat{\mathbf{k}}$.
(c) $8\hat{\mathbf{i}} - 16\hat{\mathbf{k}}$.

10. A vector **v** has rectangular components (3, 4, 0). Find expressions in terms of the unit vectors $\hat{\imath}, \hat{\jmath}, \hat{k}$ for the following:

a. A unit vector $\hat{v}$ in the direction of **v**.

b. A unit vector $\hat{u}$ perpendicular to **v** and in the XY-plane.

Answer

(a) $\frac{3}{5}\hat{\imath} + \frac{4}{5}\hat{\jmath}$.

(b) $-\frac{4}{5}\hat{\imath} + \frac{3}{5}\hat{\jmath}$.

11. Determine the area of a parallelogram formed on two vectors v_1 and v_2 having components (1, 0, 1) and (1, 1, 1), respectively.

Answer. $\sqrt{2}$.

12. Given a vector **f** (x, y, z) defined by

$$\mathbf{f} = \frac{F_0}{2}(x^2 + y^2)^{-\frac{1}{2}}(\hat{\imath} + \hat{\jmath}),$$

where F_0 is a scalar constant, solve the following set of equations for the components of the vector $\mathbf{r} \approx (r_x, r_y, r_z)$:

$$\mathbf{r} \times \mathbf{f} = \hat{k}F_0(x^2 + y^2)^{-\frac{1}{2}} \sinh{(ay)}$$

$$\mathbf{r} \cdot \mathbf{f} = 0$$

Answer. $\mathbf{r} \approx [\sinh{(ay)}, -\sinh{(ay)}, 0]$.

13. A scalar function $u(x, y, z)$ has the form

$$u = \frac{x^2}{2} - 2xy + \frac{y^2}{2} - \frac{2}{z}.$$

Find the vector function $\mathbf{f}(x, y, z)$ defined by

$$\mathbf{f} = -\text{grad } u = -\nabla u.$$

Answer. $\mathbf{f} = -(x - 2y)\hat{\imath} - (y - 2x)\hat{\jmath} - \frac{2}{z^2}\hat{k}$.

14. A vector **v** is defined by

$$\mathbf{v} = (ay \sin bz)\hat{\imath} + (ax \sin bz)\hat{\jmath} + (cx^2y^2)\hat{k}$$

where a, b, and c are scalar constants.

a. Find $\mathbf{s} = \text{curl } \mathbf{v} = \nabla \times \mathbf{v}$.

b. Find $u = \text{div } \mathbf{s} = \nabla \cdot (\nabla \times \mathbf{v})$.

Answer

(a) $(2cx^2y - abx \cos bz)\hat{\imath} + (aby \cos bz - 2cxy^2)\hat{\jmath}$.

(b) 0.

15. Verify:

a. $\nabla \cdot (\mathbf{u} \times \mathbf{v}) = \mathbf{v} \cdot (\nabla \times \mathbf{u}) - \mathbf{u} \cdot (\nabla \times \mathbf{v})$

b. $\mathbf{u} \cdot \mathbf{v} \times \mathbf{w} = \mathbf{v} \cdot \mathbf{w} \times \mathbf{u}$

c. $\mathbf{u} \times (\mathbf{v} \times \mathbf{w}) = (\mathbf{u} \cdot \mathbf{w})\mathbf{v} - (\mathbf{u} \cdot \mathbf{v})\mathbf{w}$

16. Find the volume of the parallelepiped whose sides are given by the vectors

$$\mathbf{a} = 3\hat{\mathbf{i}} + \hat{\mathbf{j}} + \hat{\mathbf{k}}$$
$$\mathbf{b} = \hat{\mathbf{i}} - \hat{\mathbf{j}}$$
$$\mathbf{c} = 2\hat{\mathbf{j}} - \hat{\mathbf{k}}$$

Answer.   6.

17. Using Stoke's theorem, evaluate the linear integral of the vector function $\mathbf{w} = x\hat{\mathbf{k}}$ around the closed curve *ABC* shown in Fig. E1.2 (17).

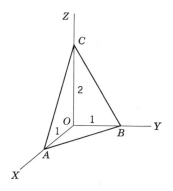

Fig. E1.2 (17)

Answer.   1.

18. If **r** is the position vector of a point *P* on a closed surface *S*, show that the volume *V* of the enclosed region is given by

$$V = \tfrac{1}{3} \int_S \mathbf{r} \cdot d\mathbf{S}.$$

19. A body is spinning about an axis having direction cosines $c_{lx} = 0.5$, $c_{ly} = 0.5$, $c_{lz} = 0.707$ with an angular speed of 50 rad/sec. What is the linear velocity of a point in the body having a position vector $\mathbf{r} = 6\hat{\mathbf{i}} + 4\hat{\mathbf{j}}$ ft?

Answer. $\mathbf{v} = -141.4\hat{\mathbf{i}} + 212.1\hat{\mathbf{j}} - 50.0\hat{\mathbf{k}}$ ft/sec.

20. What is the linear velocity of the center of a wheel 4 ft in diameter if a point 1 ft below the center has a velocity of 10 ft/sec in the *X*-direction and there is no slipping?

Answer. $20\hat{\mathbf{i}}$.

21. A capsule is suspended 4 ft from the center of a balloon. Find the total linear velocity of the capsule if the velocity of the center of the balloon is $10\hat{\mathbf{j}}$ and it is rotating with an angular velocity of $\tfrac{1}{2}\hat{\mathbf{i}}$ when the capsule is at the following points:
   a. $-4\hat{\mathbf{j}}$
   b. $+4\hat{\mathbf{j}}$
   c. $+4\hat{\mathbf{i}}$
   d. $2\hat{\mathbf{i}} + 2\hat{\mathbf{j}} + 2\sqrt{2}\hat{\mathbf{k}}$.

Answer
(a) $10\hat{\mathbf{i}} - 2\hat{\mathbf{k}}$.
(b) $10\hat{\mathbf{j}} + 2\hat{\mathbf{k}}$.
(c) $10\hat{\mathbf{j}}$.
(d) $(10 - \sqrt{2})\hat{\mathbf{j}} + \hat{\mathbf{k}}$.

22. Develop the expression

$$\mathbf{a}_{20} = \mathbf{a}_{20} + \mathbf{a}_{21} + \boldsymbol{\Omega} \times (\boldsymbol{\Omega} \times \mathbf{r}) + 2\boldsymbol{\Omega} \times \mathbf{v}_{21} + \mathbf{A} \times \mathbf{r}$$

with proper identification of all terms.

23. The disk shown in Fig. E1.2 (23) rotates at a constant angular speed ω_1 while the mass m rotates at a constant angular speed ω_2. Compute the velocity $\mathbf{v}$ and acceleration $\mathbf{a}$ with respect to the fixed coordinate system $X_0 Y_0 Z_0$ by:
    a. letting the $X'Y'Z'$-system be fixed to the disk.
    b. letting the $X'Y'Z'$-system rotate with the mass.

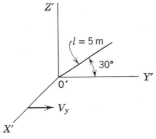

Fig. E1.2 (23)

Answer
$\mathbf{v} = \omega_1 d\hat{\mathbf{i}} + l\omega_2\hat{\mathbf{j}} - l\omega_1\hat{\mathbf{k}}; \; \mathbf{a} = -l(\omega_1^2 + \omega_2^2)\hat{\mathbf{i}} - \omega_1^2 d\hat{\mathbf{k}}$.

24. Solve the Lorentz transformation equations for the primed coordinates, thus showing that the inverse transformations are obtained by changing V to $-V$ and interchanging the primed and unprimed coordinates.

25. A rod 5 m long [Fig. E1.2 (25)] makes an angle of 30° in the $Y'Z'$-plane with respect to the positive Y'-axis. The primed axes are attached to the rod and

Fig. E1.2 (25)

are moving at a velocity $V_y = 0.8c$ with respect to an unprimed reference system. What is the length and angle of the rod as measured by an observer in the unprimed system?

Answer. 3.6 m; 43.9°.

26. A cube has a volume of 1 ft³ when situated with respect to the unprimed reference system as shown in Fig. E1.2 (26). How fast must the cube travel

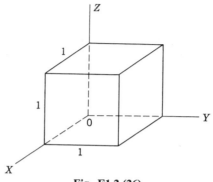

Fig. E1.2 (26)

in the Y-direction for its volume to be measured as $\frac{1}{2}$ft³ by an observer at rest in the unprimed system?

Answer. 0.866c.

27. Two rockets approach each other with speeds of 0.6c and 0.7c, measured with respect to the surface of the earth. What is the velocity of one rocket relative to the other?

Answer. 0.9154c.

1.3 Indicial Matrix Equations

We shall often encounter systems of simultaneous algebraic equations of the form

$$a_{ij}x_j = x_i' \qquad i, j = 1, 2, 3, 4, \ldots, n; \tag{3.1}$$

it is, therefore, desirable to consider some of their more important characteristics. The foregoing discussion shows that the x_i' can be the x_j components of a three- or four-vector transformed to a coordinate space with a new basis, when the a_{ij} are an ordered array of direction cosines specifying how to convert the old basis to the new one by an orthonormal rotation of axes. It is not difficult to see that this concept can be extended to n-dimensional vector spaces, where n represents any finite number of dimensions.

However, only a few vector quantities have been identified so far, and we must recognize that in general x_j can represent any quantity consisting of a number of scalar components which satisfy the proper algebraic rules. Furthermore, many different sets of constants a_{ij} can be thought of as arrays of direction cosines specifying rotations between multidimensional spaces. Of course, systems of algebraic equations can be written in which the coefficients of the x_j are variables, but these are excluded from present

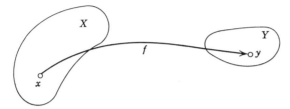

Fig. 1.45

considerations. We shall assume that the a_{ij} are constants; clearly then, every x_i' will vary linearly with each x_j and thus, with their sum as specified by (3.1):

$$a_{i1}x_1 + a_{i2}x_2 + \cdots + a_{in}x_n = x_i'$$

$$a_{11}x_1 + a_{12}x_2 + \cdots + a_{1n}x_n = x_1'$$

$$a_{21}x_1 + a_{22}x_2 + \cdots + a_{2n}x_n = x_2' \qquad (3.2)$$

$$\cdot$$
$$\cdot$$
$$\cdot$$

$$a_{n1}x_1 + a_{n2}x_2 + \cdots + a_{nn}x_n = x_n'$$

Nevertheless, it is worthwhile to recognize that in principle we could continue to broaden a_{ij} until we arrived at some very general operator f and, restricting j and i to single nonidentical values for simplicity, finally write

$$f(x) = y \qquad (3.3)$$

The y-values could still be interpreted as the x-coordinates transformed to a new space by the action of the operator f (Fig. 1.45). This is the modern concept of a functional relationship between two variables.[15,16]

Returning to the special linear form (3.1), it is important to observe that this can also be interpreted as a matrix equation. Any array of elements μ_{kl}, usually scalar quantities, ordered in such a way that the first subscript

[15] Apostol, T. M., *Calculus*, Vol. 1, pp. 40–50, Blaisdell, New York, 1961.
[16] Dieudonne, J., *Foundations of Modern Analysis*, pp. 5, 6, New York, Academic, 1960.

indicates the row of the element and the second its column, can be called a matrix:

$$[\mu_{kl}] = \begin{bmatrix} \mu_{11} & \mu_{12} & \cdots & \mu_{1n} \\ \mu_{21} & \mu_{22} & \cdots & \mu_{2n} \\ \vdots & & & \vdots \\ \mu_{n1} & \mu_{n2} & \cdots & \mu_{nn} \end{bmatrix} = \mathscr{M} \tag{3.4}$$

As shown, the elements are often enclosed in square brackets and sometimes indicated as a whole by a single script capital letter.

The array given in (3.4) is square and, to begin with, we shall assume that this is what is meant when two unspecified subscripts are used. When a row or column matrix is intended, the number one will replace the appropriate subscript. Although later we shall encounter quantities that can carry more than two subscripts, for present purposes it will be assumed that only two are possible.

Equation (3.1) evidently can be written as

$$\mathscr{A}\mathscr{X} = \mathscr{X}', \tag{3.5}$$

where

$$\mathscr{A} = \begin{bmatrix} a_{11} & a_{12} & \cdots & a_{1n} \\ a_{21} & a_{22} & \cdots & a_{2n} \\ \vdots & & & \vdots \\ a_{n1} & a_{n2} & \cdots & a_{nn} \end{bmatrix} = [a_{ij}] \tag{3.6}$$

$$\mathscr{X} = \begin{bmatrix} x_1 \\ x_2 \\ \vdots \\ x_n \end{bmatrix} = [x_{j1}] \tag{3.7}$$

$$\mathscr{X}' = \begin{bmatrix} x_1' \\ x_2' \\ \vdots \\ x_n' \end{bmatrix} = [x_{i1}'], \tag{3.8}$$

provided matrix multiplication is defined by the indicial operations suggested by this equation, that is, if we place

$$[a_{ij}][x_{j1}] = [a_{ij}x_{j1}], \tag{3.9}$$

and if matrix equality means that corresponding elements are equal,

$$[a_{ij}x_{j1}] = [x_{i1}'] \tag{3.10}$$

meaning

$$a_{ij}x_{j1} = x_{i1}'. \tag{3.11}$$

For then, suppressing the subscript indicating a column matrix during the expansion process,

$$\mathscr{A}\mathscr{X} = [a_{ij}][x_{j1}] = [a_{ij}x_j]$$
$$= [a_{i1}x_1 + a_{i2}x_2 + \cdots a_{in}x_n]$$

$$= \begin{bmatrix} (a_{11}x_1 + a_{12}x_2 + \cdots a_{1n}x_n) \\ (a_{21}x_1 + a_{22}x_2 + \cdots a_{2n}x_n) \\ \cdot \\ \cdot \\ \cdot \\ (a_{n1}x_1 + a_{n2}x_2 + \cdots a_{nn}x_n) \end{bmatrix} = [x_{i1}] = \begin{bmatrix} x_1' \\ x_2' \\ \cdot \\ \cdot \\ x_n' \end{bmatrix} = X'. $$

$$\tag{3.12}$$

Therefore, according to (3.10) and (3.11), we arrive by matrix operations at the set of equations (3.2), originally written by indicial expansion. It follows that, subject to the foregoing limitations, the indicial equation (3.1) can be regarded as a matrix equation.

Equation (3.9) or, more generally, for matrices $\mathscr{M}$ and $\mathscr{N}$ where $\mathscr{N}$ also has several columns,

$$\mathscr{M}\mathscr{N} = [\mu_{kl}][\nu_{mn}] = [\mu_{kl}\nu_{ln}] = [\kappa_{kn}] = \mathscr{K}, \tag{3.13}$$

is therefore a logical definition of the multiplication operation for matrices. Reference to the arrays of elements (3.6) and (3.7) for $\mathscr{A}$ and $\mathscr{X}$ and the array of elements in (3.12) for $\mathscr{A}\mathscr{X}$ will establish that this operation consists of multiplying the elements of the first row of $\mathscr{M}$ by the corresponding elements of the first column of $\mathscr{N}$ and summing, then multiplying the elements of the second row of $\mathscr{M}$ by the corresponding elements of the first column of $\mathscr{N}$ and summing, an so on for all rows. If several columns are present in $\mathscr{N}$, the entire process must be repeated for each one. Thus a given row of $\mathscr{M}$ must have the same number of elements as a given column of $\mathscr{N}$, which is to say that the number of columns in $\mathscr{M}$ must equal the number of rows in $\mathscr{N}$ for multiplication of the two to be possible. Matrices that satisfy this requirement are said to be conformable.

It is evident that the elements resulting from multiplying rows of $\mathscr{M}$ by columns of $\mathscr{N}$ and summing would not in general be equal to the elements obtained by multiplying rows of $\mathscr{N}$ by columns of $\mathscr{M}$ and summing; matrix multiplication is noncommutative,

$$\mathscr{M}\mathscr{N} \neq \mathscr{N}\mathscr{M}. \tag{3.14}$$

However, it is not difficult to show that all of the other fundamental laws of algebra apply to matrix operations.[17] They are associative and commutative for addition:

$$(\mathscr{M} + \mathscr{N}) + \mathscr{K} = \mathscr{M} + (\mathscr{N} + \mathscr{K}) \tag{3.15}$$

$$\mathscr{M} + \mathscr{N} = \mathscr{N} + \mathscr{M} \tag{3.16}$$

as well as associative and distributive for multiplication:

$$\mathscr{M}\mathscr{N}(\mathscr{K}) = \mathscr{M}(\mathscr{N}\mathscr{K}) \tag{3.17}$$

$$\mathscr{M}(\mathscr{N} + \mathscr{K}) = \mathscr{M}\mathscr{N} + \mathscr{M}\mathscr{K} \tag{3.18}$$

$$(\mathscr{N} + \mathscr{K})\mathscr{M} = \mathscr{N}\mathscr{M} + \mathscr{K}\mathscr{M} \tag{3.19}$$

In a particular case (Equation 3.10) it has already been indicated that for two matrices to be equal their corresponding elements must be equal; this is also true in general:

$$\mathscr{M} = \mathscr{N}, \qquad \mu_{kl} = \nu_{kl} \tag{3.20}$$

Also, when two matrices are added, their corresponding elements must be added:

$$\mathscr{M} + \mathscr{N}, \qquad \mu_{kl} + \nu_{kl} \tag{3.21}$$

$$\mathscr{M} - \mathscr{N}, \qquad \mu_{kl} - \nu_{kl} \tag{3.22}$$

A zero matrix $\mathscr{O}$, all of whose elements are zero, and a unit matrix

$$\mathscr{I} = [\delta_{kl}], \tag{3.23}$$

all of whose elements are zero except those on the principal diagonal, which are unity, are also defined so that we may write expressions such as:

$$\mathscr{M} - \mathscr{M} = \mathscr{O} \tag{3.24}$$

$$\mathscr{O}\mathscr{M} = \mathscr{M}\mathscr{O} = \mathscr{O} \tag{3.25}$$

$$\mathscr{I}\mathscr{M} = \mathscr{M}\mathscr{I} = \mathscr{M} \tag{3.26}$$

[17] Vulikh, B. Z., *Introduction to Functional Analysis*, pp. 13–36, Addison-Wesley, Reading, Mass., 1963.

The transpose $\tilde{\mathscr{M}}$ (or M^T) of a matrix $\mathscr{M} = [\mu_{kl}]$ is defined in the following way:

$$\tilde{\mathscr{M}} = [\mu_{lk}], \tag{3.27}$$

that is, the rows and columns of $\mathscr{M}$ are interchanged; if a matrix is equal to its own transpose, it is said to be symmetric:

$$\mathscr{M} = \tilde{\mathscr{M}}, \qquad \mu_{kl} = \mu_{lk} \tag{3.28}$$

Similarly, if a matrix is equal to the negative of its transpose and

$$\mu_{kl} = 0 \qquad \text{for} \quad k = l \tag{3.29}$$

it is said to be antisymmetric or skew-symmetric:

$$\mathscr{M} = -\tilde{\mathscr{M}}, \qquad \mu_{kl} = -\mu_{lk} \tag{3.30}$$

If this relation holds but $\mu_{kl} \neq 0$ for $k = l$, it is called simply a skew matrix. Of course, the elements of a matrix may also be complex numbers; and the matrix whose elements are the conjugates of the elements of $\mathscr{M}$, if these are complex, is indicated by $\mathscr{M}^*$. Matrices that are equal to their own transposed conjugate complex are called Hermitian,

$$\mathscr{M} = \tilde{\mathscr{M}}^*; \tag{3.31}$$

those that are equal to the negative of their transposed conjugate complex are called anti-Hermitian,

$$\mathscr{M} = -\tilde{\mathscr{M}}^*. \tag{3.32}$$

Clearly (3.31) and (3.32) reduce to the first expression in (3.28) and (3.30) if the matrices are real.

Calculations with matrices are much simpler if the matrices involved are symmetric or antisymmetric, Hermitian or anti-Hermitian; many important physical problems, some of which we shall encounter later, do feature matrices of this kind. Calculations are even easier if one or more of the matrices is diagonal, that is, with zero elements everywhere except on the principal diagonal (uppermost left to lower-right), because all such matrices commute with each other in multiplication and lead to simpler results in the remaining cases. Often matrix problems can effectively be solved by transforming certain of the matrices to their diagonal form, and eventually we shall learn the techniques for accomplishing this.

It will be evident that a column matrix can be converted to a row matrix by taking its transpose, and vice versa. This fact greatly facilitates computations with vectors in matrix algebra. If, for example, we wish to calculate the scalar product of the column vector $\mathscr{U} = [u_{i1}]$ with the column vector $\mathscr{V} = [v_{j1}]$, we can merely take the transpose of $\mathscr{U}$ and apply the definition (3.13) of matrix multiplication:

$$\tilde{\mathscr{U}}\mathscr{V} = [u_{1i}][v_{ji}] = [u_i v_i]; \tag{3.33}$$

thus,

$$\tilde{\mathscr{U}}\mathscr{V} = [u_1 \, u_2 \cdots u_n] \begin{bmatrix} v_1 \\ v_2 \\ \cdot \\ \cdot \\ \cdot \\ v_n \end{bmatrix} = [(u_1 v_1 + u_2 v_2 + \cdots + u_n v_n)]. \tag{3.34}$$

Alternatively, by taking the transpose of $\mathscr{V}$:

$$\tilde{\mathscr{V}}\mathscr{U} = [v_{1j}][u_{i1}] = [v_j u_j]$$

$$= [v_1 \, v_2 \cdots v_n] \begin{bmatrix} u_1 \\ u_2 \\ \cdot \\ \cdot \\ \cdot \\ u_n \end{bmatrix}$$

$$= [(v_1 u_1 + v_2 u_2 + \cdots + v_n u_n)] \tag{3.35}$$

Of course, this process is equivalent to the dot product operation for three-dimensional vectors (2.69):

$$\mathbf{u} \cdot \mathbf{v} = u_i v_i = u_1 v_1 + u_2 v_2 + u_3 v_3 \tag{3.36}$$

Because matrix multiplication is generally noncommutative, we should expect that multiplication by the reciprocal of a given matrix will not always be possible, which means that not every matrix $\mathscr{M}$ will possess a reciprocal or inverse matrix $\mathscr{M}^{-1}$. To establish a rule for determining when an inverse will exist and calculating it if it does, the concept of the cofactor M_{kl} of an element μ_{kl} must be used. This is defined in the following way:

$$M_{kl} = (-1)^{k+l} |m_{kl}| \tag{3.37}$$

where $|m_{kl}|$ is the determinant of the minor of the element μ_{kl}, obtained by crossing out the kth row and lth column of the determinant $|\mathscr{M}|$ of the matrix $\mathcal{M}$. For example, if $k, l = 1, 2, 3, 4$ so that

$$\mathcal{M} = \begin{bmatrix} \mu_{11} & \mu_{12} & \mu_{13} & \mu_{14} \\ \mu_{21} & \mu_{22} & \mu_{23} & \mu_{24} \\ \mu_{31} & \mu_{32} & \mu_{33} & \mu_{34} \\ \mu_{41} & \mu_{42} & \mu_{43} & \mu_{44} \end{bmatrix}, \tag{3.38}$$

the determinant of the minor of the element μ_{23} is

$$|m_{23}| = \begin{vmatrix} \mu_{11} & \mu_{12} & \mu_{14} \\ \mu_{31} & \mu_{32} & \mu_{34} \\ \mu_{41} & \mu_{42} & \mu_{44} \end{vmatrix} \tag{3.39}$$

and the cofactor of μ_{23} is

$$M_{23} = (-1)^5 |m_{23}| = - \begin{vmatrix} \mu_{11} & \mu_{12} & \mu_{14} \\ \mu_{31} & \mu_{32} & \mu_{34} \\ \mu_{41} & \mu_{42} & \mu_{44} \end{vmatrix} \tag{3.40}$$

It can easily be established[18] that the product of a matrix $\mathcal{M}$ with its transposed cofactor matrix $[\widetilde{M_{kl}}]$, called the adjoint of $\mathcal{M}$, produces a special diagonal matrix all of whose nonzero elements are the determinant $|\mathcal{M}|$:

$$\mathcal{M}[\widetilde{M_{kl}}] = |\mathcal{M}| [\delta_{kl}] \tag{3.41}$$

If $|\mathcal{M}| \neq 0$, this can be written as

$$\mathcal{M} \frac{[\widetilde{M_{kl}}]}{|\mathcal{M}|} = [\delta_{kl}] = \mathcal{I} \tag{3.42}$$

Therefore, since if $\mathcal{M}^{-1}$ exists it must be true that

$$\mathcal{M} \mathcal{M}^{-1} = \mathcal{I}, \tag{3.43}$$

it follows that

$$\mathcal{M}^{-1} = \frac{[\widetilde{M_{kl}}]}{|\mathcal{M}|}. \tag{3.44}$$

The inverse of the matrix $\mathcal{M}$ can be calculated from this, and we see that it will exist only if $|\mathcal{M}| \neq 0$. If the inverse does exist, $\mathcal{M}$ is said to be non-singular, and division by $\mathcal{M}$, or multiplication by $\mathcal{M}^{-1}$, is possible. It should be noted, however, that although $\mathcal{M}^{-1}\mathcal{M} = \mathcal{M}\mathcal{M}^{-1}$, it is not necessarily true that $\mathcal{M}^{-1}\mathcal{N} = \mathcal{N}\mathcal{M}^{-1}$; thus one must either premultiply or postmultiply by $\mathcal{M}^{-1}$.

[18] Dettman, J. W., *Mathematical Methods in Physics and Engineering*, pp. 5–18, McGraw-Hill, New York, 1962.

Unitary and orthogonal matrices are especially useful.[19] The former is defined as a matrix that satisfies the relation

$$\tilde{\mathcal{M}}^* = \mathcal{M}^{-1} \tag{3.45}$$

and the latter as one which satisfies

$$\tilde{\mathcal{M}} = \mathcal{M}^{-1}. \tag{3.46}$$

Evidently, real unitary matrices will always be orthogonal, whereas if a unitary matrix is Hermitian, then from (3.31) and (3.45),

$$\mathcal{M} = \mathcal{M}^{-1}; \tag{3.47}$$

so,

$$\mathcal{M}\mathcal{M} = \mathcal{M}^2 = \mathcal{I}. \tag{3.48}$$

Returning to the set of linear equations (3.1) or (3.5),

$$a_{ij}x_j = y_i \tag{3.49}$$

or, alternatively,

$$\mathcal{A}\mathcal{X} = \mathcal{Y} \tag{3.50}$$

where x_i' and $\mathcal{X}'$ have been replaced by y_i and $\mathcal{Y}$ for greater generality, we can now see that as long as the matrix $\mathcal{A}$ is nonsingular, the equations can be solved explicitly for the unknown x_j's. In our earlier language this is equivalent to asserting that a set of coordinates x_j will always exist in the j-space, which can be exactly transformed into the coordinates y_i in the i-space by the action of the linear operator a_{ij}. Conversely, for $\mathcal{A}$ to be singular, with $|\mathcal{A}| = 0$, implies that no such set of x_j's will exist in general, although certain special sets may exist. It should be evident that the transformation matrices of the first case will often be unitary, orthogonal, or both, like the matrix of an orthonormal rotation, whereas the transformation matrices of the second case usually will not possess such simple physical properties.

If $\mathcal{A}$ is nonsingular, we can simply premultiply (3.50) by $\mathcal{A}^{-1}$ and obtain the solutions as

$$\mathcal{X} = \mathcal{A}^{-1}\mathcal{Y}. \tag{3.51}$$

For example, if $i, j = 1, 2$ and $y_i = k_i$, a set of constants, then the result is

$$\begin{bmatrix} x_1 \\ x_2 \end{bmatrix} = \begin{bmatrix} a_{11} & a_{12} \\ a_{21} & a_{22} \end{bmatrix}^{-1} \begin{bmatrix} k_1 \\ k_2 \end{bmatrix}. \tag{3.52}$$

[19] Jeffreys, H., and B. S. Jeffreys, *Methods of Mathematical Physics*, pp. 114–127, Cambridge, 1962.

But when we apply (3.44), we obtain

$$\mathscr{A}^{-1} = \frac{\widetilde{[A_{ij}]}}{|\mathscr{A}|} = \frac{\begin{bmatrix} a_{22} & -a_{12} \\ -a_{21} & a_{11} \end{bmatrix}}{(a_{11}a_{22} - a_{12}a_{21})} ; \qquad (3.53)$$

(3.52) thus becomes

$$\begin{bmatrix} x_1 \\ x_2 \end{bmatrix} = \frac{\begin{bmatrix} a_{22} & -a_{12} \\ -a_{21} & a_{11} \end{bmatrix}\begin{bmatrix} k_1 \\ k_2 \end{bmatrix}}{(a_{11}a_{22} - a_{12}a_{21})} = \frac{\begin{bmatrix} (a_{22}k_1 - a_{12}k_2) \\ (-a_{21}k_1 + a_{11}k_2) \end{bmatrix}}{(a_{11}a_{22} - a_{12}a_{21})} \qquad (3.54)$$

giving:

$$x_1 = \frac{(a_{22}k_1 - a_{12}k_2)}{(a_{11}a_{22} - a_{12}a_{21})} \qquad (3.55)$$

$$x_2 = \frac{(a_{11}k_2 - a_{21}k_1)}{(a_{11}a_{22} - a_{12}a_{21})} \qquad (3.56)$$

Of course, this is an especially simple case. For larger systems where $\mathscr{A}$ is nonsingular and the y_i's are a set of constants k_i, it is usually easier[20] to apply Cramer's rule, which can be derived from the general relation (3.41). This rule states that even if $i, j = 1, 2, 3, \ldots, n$

$$x_1 = \frac{|\mathscr{A}_1(k_i)|}{|\mathscr{A}|}$$

$$x_2 = \frac{|\mathscr{A}_2(k_i)|}{|\mathscr{A}|} \qquad (3.57)$$

$$\begin{matrix} \cdot & & \cdot \\ \cdot & & \cdot \\ \cdot & & \cdot \end{matrix}$$

$$x_n = \frac{|\mathscr{A}_n(k_i)|}{|\mathscr{A}|}$$

where $|\mathscr{A}_1(k_i)|$ is formed by replacing the first column of $|\mathscr{A}|$ by the column of k_i's, $|\mathscr{A}_2(k_i)|$ by replacing the second column, and so on. Hence the

[20] Pipes, L. A., *Applied Mathematics for Engineers and Physicists*, pp. 84–90, McGraw-Hill, New York, 1946.

preceding example gives directly:

$$x_1 = \frac{\begin{vmatrix} k_1 & a_{12} \\ k_2 & a_{22} \end{vmatrix}}{\begin{vmatrix} a_{11} & a_{12} \\ a_{21} & a_{22} \end{vmatrix}} = \frac{(a_{22}k_1 - a_{12}k_2)}{(a_{11}a_{22} - a_{12}a_{21})} \tag{3.58}$$

$$x_2 = \frac{\begin{vmatrix} a_{11} & k_1 \\ a_{21} & k_2 \end{vmatrix}}{(a_{11}a_{22} - a_{12}a_{21})} = \frac{(a_{11}k_2 - a_{21}k_1)}{(a_{11}a_{22} - a_{12}a_{21})} \tag{3.59}$$

which are identical to the results (3.55) and (3.56).

There is one case when $|\mathscr{A}| = 0$ which is of special importance; that is when all of the k_i are zero:

$$\mathscr{A}\mathscr{X} = 0. \tag{3.60}$$

It can be proved[21] that the necessary and sufficient condition for a nonzero solution x_j of this equation to exist is exactly that

$$|\mathscr{A}| = 0. \tag{3.61}$$

We shall make extensive use of this fact in our later work.

For the sake of simplicity the preceding discussion has been restricted to matrices that are either of the row or column type or square ($k, l = 1, 2, \ldots, n$). Actually, matrices in which $k = 1, 2, \ldots, n$ and $l = 1, 2, \ldots, m$ where $m \neq n$ are not uncommon; and many of the principles that we have developed for square matrices continue to apply to these. The obvious exceptions are those that feature the symmetry, diagonal, and inverse concepts. In our sense of the definitions, nonsquare matrices cannot possess an inverse and can be neither symmetrical, antisymmetrical, nor diagonal.[22]

Operations involving matrices with large numbers of elements can often be simplified by partitioning certain of the matrices. As an illustration, with $\mathscr{M}$ and $\mathscr{N}$ given by

$$\mathscr{M} = \left[\begin{array}{cc:c} \mu_{11} & \mu_{12} & \mu_{13} \\ \mu_{21} & \mu_{22} & \mu_{23} \\ \hdashline \mu_{31} & \mu_{32} & \mu_{33} \end{array} \right] \tag{3.62}$$

$$\mathscr{N} = \left[\begin{array}{cc:c} \nu_{11} & \nu_{12} & \nu_{13} \\ \nu_{21} & \nu_{22} & \nu_{23} \\ \hdashline \nu_{31} & \nu_{32} & \nu_{33} \end{array} \right] \tag{3.63}$$

[21] Courant, R., and D. Hilbert, *Methods of Mathematical Physics*, Vol. 1, pp. 1–16, Interscience, New York, 1953.

[22] Irving, J., and N. Mullineux, *Mathematics in Physics and Engineering*, pp. 250–308, Academic Press, New York, 1959.

and partitioned as indicated, so that

$$\mathscr{M}_1 = \begin{bmatrix} \mu_{11} & \mu_{12} \\ \mu_{21} & \mu_{22} \end{bmatrix}, \quad \mathscr{M}_2 = \begin{bmatrix} \mu_{13} \\ \mu_{23} \end{bmatrix}, \quad \mathscr{M}_3 = [\mu_{31} \quad \mu_{32}], \quad \mathscr{M}_4 = [\mu_{33}]$$

(3.64)

and

$$\mathscr{N}_1 = \begin{bmatrix} \nu_{11} & \nu_{12} \\ \nu_{21} & \nu_{22} \end{bmatrix}, \quad \mathscr{N}_2 = \begin{bmatrix} \nu_{13} \\ \nu_{23} \end{bmatrix}, \quad \mathscr{N}_3 = [\nu_{31} \quad \nu_{32}], \quad \mathscr{N}_4 = [\nu_{33}],$$

(3.65)

we could calculate $\mathscr{M} + \mathscr{N}$ and $\mathscr{M}\mathscr{N}$ in the following way:

$$\mathscr{M} + \mathscr{N} = \begin{bmatrix} (\mathscr{M}_1 + \mathscr{N}_1) & (\mathscr{M}_2 + \mathscr{N}_2) \\ (\mathscr{M}_3 + \mathscr{N}_3) & (\mathscr{M}_4 + \mathscr{N}_4) \end{bmatrix}$$

(3.66)

$$\mathscr{M}\mathscr{N} = \begin{bmatrix} \mathscr{M}_1 & \mathscr{M}_2 \\ \mathscr{M}_3 & \mathscr{M}_4 \end{bmatrix} \begin{bmatrix} \mathscr{N}_1 & \mathscr{N}_2 \\ \mathscr{N}_3 & \mathscr{N}_4 \end{bmatrix}$$

$$= \begin{bmatrix} (\mathscr{M}_1 \mathscr{N}_1 + \mathscr{M}_2 \mathscr{N}_3) & (\mathscr{M}_1 \mathscr{N}_2 + \mathscr{M}_2 \mathscr{N}_4) \\ (\mathscr{M}_3 \mathscr{N}_1 + \mathscr{M}_4 \mathscr{N}_3) & (\mathscr{M}_3 \mathscr{N}_2 + \mathscr{M}_4 \mathscr{N}_4) \end{bmatrix}$$

(3.67)

When the matrices contain more elements, the partitioning can be carried out in other ways and perhaps even repeated to achieve the desired simplification. Furthermore, the same method can sometimes be applied to convert operations with nonsquare matrices to suboperations with square, row, and column matrices.[23] It is only necessary to make certain that the general rules of matrix algebra are obeyed and, especially, that the requirement of conformability is satisfied if the matrices are to be multiplied.

Problems 1.3

1. Calculate $\mathscr{A}\mathscr{B}$ if

$$\mathscr{A} = \begin{bmatrix} 1 & 3 \\ -2 & 0 \\ 4 & 4 \end{bmatrix} \quad \text{and} \quad \mathscr{B} = \begin{bmatrix} s_{11} & s_{12} \\ s_{21} & s_{22} \end{bmatrix}$$

Solution

$$\mathscr{A}\mathscr{B} = \begin{bmatrix} (1s_{11} + 3s_{21}) & (1s_{12} + 3s_{22}) \\ (-2s_{11} + 0) & (-2s_{12} + 0) \\ (4s_{11} + 4s_{21}) & (4s_{12} + 4s_{22}) \end{bmatrix}$$

[23] Hohn, F. E., *Elementary Matrix Algebra*, pp. 77–87, Macmillan, New York, 1958.

2. Show by example that in general:
  a. $\mathscr{A}\mathscr{B} \neq \mathscr{B}\mathscr{A}$.
  b. $\mathscr{C}\mathscr{D} = 0$ does not imply either that $\mathscr{C} = 0$ or $\mathscr{D} = 0$.

Solution

(a) Let

$$\mathscr{A} = \begin{bmatrix} 3 & -1 \\ 2 & -4 \end{bmatrix} \quad \text{and} \quad \mathscr{B} = \begin{bmatrix} 1 & -1 \\ 2 & 2 \end{bmatrix}.$$

Then

$$\mathscr{A}\mathscr{B} = \begin{bmatrix} 1 & -5 \\ -6 & -10 \end{bmatrix} \quad \text{whereas} \quad \mathscr{B}\mathscr{A} = \begin{bmatrix} 1 & 3 \\ 10 & -10 \end{bmatrix};$$

therefore,

$$\mathscr{A}\mathscr{B} \neq \mathscr{B}\mathscr{A}.$$

(b) Let

$$\mathscr{C} = \begin{bmatrix} 3 & 2 & 0 \\ 1 & -1 & 0 \\ 5 & 6 & 0 \end{bmatrix} \quad \text{and} \quad \mathscr{D} = \begin{bmatrix} 0 & 0 & 0 \\ 0 & 0 & 0 \\ 8 & -1 & 6 \end{bmatrix}.$$

Then

$$\mathscr{C}\mathscr{D} = \begin{bmatrix} 0 & 0 & 0 \\ 0 & 0 & 0 \\ 0 & 0 & 0 \end{bmatrix};$$

but $\mathscr{C} \neq 0$ and $\mathscr{D} \neq 0$.

3. Show by example that $\mathscr{A}\mathscr{B} = \mathscr{A}\mathscr{C}$ does not necessarily imply that $\mathscr{B} = \mathscr{C}$.

Solution

Let

$$\mathscr{A} = \begin{bmatrix} 2 & 1 & 0 \\ 1 & -1 & 0 \\ 3 & 2 & 0 \end{bmatrix}, \quad \mathscr{B} = \begin{bmatrix} 1 & -1 & 2 \\ 2 & 2 & 3 \\ 7 & 6 & 8 \end{bmatrix} \quad \text{and} \quad \mathscr{C} = \begin{bmatrix} 1 & -1 & 2 \\ 2 & 2 & 3 \\ 1 & 2 & -1 \end{bmatrix}.$$

Then

$$\mathscr{A}\mathscr{B} = \begin{bmatrix} 4 & 0 & 7 \\ -1 & -3 & -1 \\ 7 & 1 & 12 \end{bmatrix} = \mathscr{A}\mathscr{C};$$

but $\mathscr{B} \neq \mathscr{C}$.

4. Show by example that $(\mathscr{A}\mathscr{B})^T = \mathscr{B}^T\mathscr{A}^T$.

Solution

Let

$$\mathscr{A} = \begin{bmatrix} 3 & -1 \\ 2 & 5 \end{bmatrix} \quad \text{and} \quad \mathscr{B} = \begin{bmatrix} 1 & 2 \\ 3 & 4 \end{bmatrix}.$$

Then

$$\mathscr{A}\mathscr{B} = \begin{bmatrix} 0 & 2 \\ 17 & 24 \end{bmatrix};$$

therefore,

$$(\mathscr{A}\mathscr{B})^T = \begin{bmatrix} 0 & 17 \\ 2 & 24 \end{bmatrix}.$$

Also,

$$\mathscr{B}^T = \begin{bmatrix} 1 & 3 \\ 2 & 4 \end{bmatrix} \quad \text{and} \quad \mathscr{A}^T = \begin{bmatrix} 3 & 2 \\ -1 & 5 \end{bmatrix};$$

thus:

$$\mathscr{B}^T \mathscr{A}^T = \begin{bmatrix} 0 & 17 \\ 2 & 24 \end{bmatrix} = (\mathscr{A}\mathscr{B})^T$$

5. Any matrix can be written as the sum of a symmetric and a skew-symmetric matrix. Show that this is true for the matrices

$$\begin{bmatrix} \dfrac{\partial u_x}{\partial x} & \dfrac{\partial u_x}{\partial y} \\[2ex] \dfrac{\partial u_y}{\partial x} & \dfrac{\partial u_y}{\partial y} \end{bmatrix} \quad \text{and} \quad \begin{bmatrix} 0.1 & 0.04 & 0 \\ 0.02 & 0.1 & 0 \\ 0 & 0 & 0.1 \end{bmatrix}$$

Solution

$$\begin{bmatrix} \dfrac{\partial u_x}{\partial x} & \dfrac{\partial u_x}{\partial y} \\[2ex] \dfrac{\partial u_y}{\partial x} & \dfrac{\partial u_y}{\partial y} \end{bmatrix} = \begin{bmatrix} \dfrac{\partial u_x}{\partial x} & \dfrac{1}{2}\left(\dfrac{\partial u_x}{\partial y} + \dfrac{\partial u_y}{\partial x}\right) \\[2ex] \dfrac{1}{2}\left(\dfrac{\partial u_y}{\partial x} + \dfrac{\partial u_x}{\partial y}\right) & \dfrac{\partial u_y}{\partial y} \end{bmatrix} + \begin{bmatrix} 0 & \dfrac{1}{2}\left(\dfrac{\partial u_x}{\partial y} - \dfrac{\partial u_y}{\partial x}\right) \\[2ex] \dfrac{1}{2}\left(\dfrac{\partial u_y}{\partial x} - \dfrac{\partial u_x}{\partial y}\right) & 0 \end{bmatrix}$$

where the first term is symmetric and the second term is skew-symmetric. Similarly:

$$\begin{bmatrix} 0.1 & 0.04 & 0 \\ 0.02 & 0.1 & 0 \\ 0 & 0 & 0.1 \end{bmatrix} = \begin{bmatrix} 0.1 & 0.03 & 0 \\ 0.03 & 0.1 & 0 \\ 0 & 0 & 0.1 \end{bmatrix} + \begin{bmatrix} 0 & 0.01 & 0 \\ -0.01 & 0 & 0 \\ 0 & 0 & 0 \end{bmatrix}.$$

6. Calculate the cofactors A_{12} and A_{13} for the following matrix:

$$\mathscr{A} = \begin{bmatrix} 3 & 1 & 2 & -1 \\ 5 & 1 & 2 & 1 \\ 1 & -1 & 1 & 2 \\ 2 & 2 & 2 & 2 \end{bmatrix}$$

Solution

$$A_{12} = (-1)^{1+2} \begin{vmatrix} 5 & 2 & 1 \\ 1 & 1 & 2 \\ 2 & 2 & 2 \end{vmatrix} = 6$$

$$A_{13} = (-1)^{1+3} \begin{vmatrix} 5 & 1 & 1 \\ 1 & -1 & 2 \\ 2 & 2 & 2 \end{vmatrix} = -24$$

7. Compute the adjoint of the matrix

$$\mathscr{A} = \begin{bmatrix} 1 & -1 & 2 \\ 3 & 2 & 0 \\ 1 & 2 & 1 \end{bmatrix}$$

Solution

$$[A_{ij}] = \begin{bmatrix} 2 & -3 & 4 \\ 5 & -1 & -3 \\ -4 & 6 & 5 \end{bmatrix}$$

$$\text{Adjoint of } \mathscr{A} = [A_{ji}] = \begin{bmatrix} 2 & 5 & -4 \\ -3 & -1 & 6 \\ 4 & -3 & 5 \end{bmatrix}$$

8. Calculate the inverse of the matrix

$$\mathscr{A} = \begin{bmatrix} 1 & 2 & 3 \\ 2 & -1 & 0 \\ 1 & 1 & 1 \end{bmatrix}$$

Solution

$$|\mathscr{A}| = 1(-1 - 0) + 2(0 - 2) + 3(2 + 1) = 4;$$

therefore, A^{-1} exists:

$$[A_{ij}] = \begin{bmatrix} -1 & -2 & 3 \\ 1 & -2 & 1 \\ 3 & 6 & -5 \end{bmatrix}$$

$$A^{-1} = \frac{[A_{ji}]}{|\mathscr{A}|} = \begin{bmatrix} -\frac{1}{4} & \frac{1}{4} & \frac{3}{4} \\ -\frac{1}{2} & -\frac{1}{2} & \frac{3}{2} \\ \frac{3}{4} & \frac{1}{4} & -\frac{5}{4} \end{bmatrix}$$

9. Using the data in the last problem, show that $\mathscr{A}\mathscr{A}^{-1} = \mathscr{I}$, the unit matrix.

Solution

$$\mathscr{A} = \begin{bmatrix} 1 & 2 & 3 \\ 2 & -1 & 0 \\ 1 & 1 & 1 \end{bmatrix}, \qquad \mathscr{A}^{-1} = \begin{bmatrix} -\frac{1}{4} & \frac{1}{4} & \frac{3}{4} \\ -\frac{1}{2} & -\frac{1}{2} & \frac{3}{2} \\ \frac{3}{4} & \frac{1}{4} & -\frac{5}{4} \end{bmatrix}$$

$$\mathscr{A}\mathscr{A}^{-1} = \begin{bmatrix} (-\frac{1}{4} - \frac{4}{4} + \frac{9}{4}) & 0 & 0 \\ 0 & (\frac{2}{4} + \frac{2}{4} + 0) & 0 \\ 0 & 0 & (\frac{3}{4} + \frac{6}{4} - \frac{5}{4}) \end{bmatrix}$$

$$= \begin{bmatrix} 1 & 0 & 0 \\ 0 & 1 & 0 \\ 0 & 0 & 1 \end{bmatrix} = \mathscr{I}$$

10. A set of quantities x_i are related to another set y_i by the matrix equation

$$x_i = a_{ij}y_j \qquad \{i, j = 1, 2, 3.$$

Express y_2 as a function of the quantities x_i and the coefficients a_{ij}.

Solution

Premultiplying by the inverse of a_{ij} gives

$$a_{ij}^{-1}x_i = \alpha_{ki}x_i = \mathscr{I}y_j = y_k.$$

Therefore,

$$y_2 = \alpha_{21}x_1 + \alpha_{22}x_2 + \alpha_{23}x_3,$$

where, because $\alpha_{ki} = [A_{ji}]/|\mathscr{A}|$,

$$\alpha_{21} = -\frac{\begin{vmatrix} a_{21} & a_{23} \\ a_{31} & a_{33} \end{vmatrix}}{|\mathscr{A}|}, \qquad \alpha_{22} = \frac{\begin{vmatrix} a_{11} & a_{13} \\ a_{31} & a_{33} \end{vmatrix}}{|\mathscr{A}|}, \qquad \alpha_{23} = -\frac{\begin{vmatrix} a_{11} & a_{13} \\ a_{21} & a_{23} \end{vmatrix}}{|\mathscr{A}|}.$$

Note that the same results follow directly from relations of the type:

$$\alpha_{21} = \frac{\begin{vmatrix} a_{11} & 1 & a_{13} \\ a_{21} & 0 & a_{23} \\ a_{31} & 0 & a_{33} \end{vmatrix}}{|\mathscr{A}|} \qquad \alpha_{22} = \frac{\begin{vmatrix} a_{11} & 0 & a_{13} \\ a_{21} & 1 & a_{23} \\ a_{31} & 0 & a_{33} \end{vmatrix}}{|\mathscr{A}|} \qquad \alpha_{23} = \frac{\begin{vmatrix} a_{11} & 0 & a_{13} \\ a_{21} & 0 & a_{23} \\ a_{31} & 1 & a_{33} \end{vmatrix}}{|\mathscr{A}|}$$

11. Solve the following set of equations using Cramer's rule:

$$x + by = 1$$
$$bz + y = 2$$
$$z + bx = 3$$

Solution

$$\begin{vmatrix} 1 & b & 0 \\ 0 & 1 & b \\ b & 0 & 1 \end{vmatrix} = 1 + b^3$$

Assuming that this does not vanish, we have

$$x = \frac{\begin{vmatrix} 1 & b & 0 \\ 2 & 1 & b \\ 3 & 0 & 1 \end{vmatrix}}{1 + b^3} = \frac{1 - 2b + 3b^2}{1 + b^3}$$

$$y = \frac{\begin{vmatrix} 1 & 1 & 0 \\ 0 & 2 & b \\ b & 3 & 1 \end{vmatrix}}{1 + b^3} = \frac{2 - 3b + b^2}{1 + b^3}$$

$$z = \frac{\begin{vmatrix} 1 & b & 1 \\ 0 & 1 & 2 \\ b & 0 & 3 \end{vmatrix}}{1 + b^3} = \frac{3 + 2b^2 - b}{1 + b^3}$$

Exercises 1.3

1.

$$\mathcal{A} = \begin{bmatrix} 15 & 6 & -7 \\ 3 & -8 & 8 \\ 1 & 4 & -4 \end{bmatrix} \qquad \mathcal{B} = \begin{bmatrix} 2 & -1 & 1 \\ 5 & 13 & -7 \\ 8 & 0 & -12 \end{bmatrix}$$

$$\mathcal{C} = \begin{bmatrix} 2 \\ -5 \\ 20 \end{bmatrix} \qquad \mathcal{D} = [-8 \quad 1 \quad 2]$$

Calculate:

a. $\mathcal{A} + \mathcal{B}$.
b. $\mathcal{B} - \mathcal{A}$.
c. $\mathcal{A}\mathcal{C}$.
d. $\mathcal{C}\mathcal{D}$.
Show that:
e. $\mathcal{A}\mathcal{C} \neq \mathcal{C}\mathcal{A}$.
f. $\mathcal{D}(\mathcal{A} + \mathcal{B}) = \mathcal{D}\mathcal{A} + \mathcal{D}\mathcal{B}$.

2. Write matrix $\mathscr{A}$ of Problem 1.3 (1) as the sum of two matrices, one symmetric and one skew-symmetric.

3. Compute the transpose of the matrix $\mathscr{B}$ of Problem 1.3 (1).

4. Compute the inverse of matrix $\mathscr{A}$ of Problem 1.3 (1).

Answer.
$$\begin{bmatrix} 0 & 0.2 & 0.4 \\ -1 & 2.65 & 7.05 \\ -1 & 2.7 & 6.9 \end{bmatrix}$$

5. Solve the following set of equations using Cramer's rule:
$$3x + 2y - z = 2$$
$$2x - y + 3z = -4$$
$$x + y + z = 5$$

Answer. $-\frac{29}{13}, \frac{69}{13}, \frac{25}{13}$

6. A set of quantities y_i are related to another set x_j by the matrix equation $\mathscr{Y} = \mathscr{A}\mathscr{X}$, where
$$\mathscr{A} = [a_{ij}] = \begin{bmatrix} \frac{3}{5} & \frac{4}{5} & 0 \\ -\frac{4}{5} & \frac{3}{5} & 0 \\ 0 & 0 & 1 \end{bmatrix}.$$

Express x_1 as a function of quantities y_i.

Answer. $x_1 = \frac{3}{5}y_1 - \frac{4}{5}y_2$

2

Physical Laws for a Point Object

2.1 Newton's Equations, Related Concepts, and Relativistic Extensions

Fortunately, the behavior of objects in our world is of such a nature that we can do more than merely describe the motion of points located on them. General laws can be formulated that enable us to predict this motion with acceptable accuracy for a given object from a knowledge of its physical properties and environment. And although these laws can be cast in several different mathematical forms, each of which is best suited to certain types of problems, all are necessarily equivalent because they represent abstractions from the same observational facts.

The best known form, and probably the one with the most intuitive appeal, follows from Newton's three laws. However, the very terms that give this statement its intuitive plausibility, such as mass and force, are the ones most lacking in logical clarity. Considerable effort is required to define them in a precise way;[1] but we shall circumvent such difficulties, insofar as possible, by stressing the mathematical content of the laws.

The objects featured in this formulation are physical points; that is, it is assumed in the beginning that all of the pertinent physical properties of a real object can be concentrated at a single mathematical point of the type already considered, so that the motion of this point will accurately describe the motion of the object. In effect, then, the first law states that a reference system exists with respect to which a physical point isolated

[1] Lindsay, R. B., and H. Margenau, *Foundations of Physics*, pp. 59–98, Dover, New York, 1957.

108

from other such points, so that it is uninfluenced by its environment, will be unaccelerated,

$$\ddot{x} = 0, \qquad \ddot{y} = 0, \qquad \ddot{z} = 0, \qquad (1.1)$$

the coordinates of the point in this system being x, y, and z. Of course, this means that if the point has some linear velocity $\dot{x}_0$, $\dot{y}_0$, $\dot{z}_0$, it will continue to move with the same velocity,

$$\dot{x} = \dot{x}_0, \qquad \dot{y} = \dot{y}_0, \qquad \dot{z} = \dot{z}_0, \qquad (1.2)$$

or if it is at rest, $\dot{x}_0 = \dot{y}_0 = \dot{z}_0 = 0$, it will remain at rest in this system,

$$\dot{x} = 0, \qquad \dot{y} = 0, \qquad \dot{z} = 0. \qquad (1.3)$$

Because they behave this way, objects are said to possess inertia, and the foregoing law is sometimes called the law of inertia. It should also be noted that if a physical point is unaccelerated with respect to one reference system, it will remain unaccelerated with respect to all other reference systems which are moving with a constant linear velocity relative to the first. Accordingly, such systems are called inertial references, and it will be clear that the relativistic transformation relations developed earlier pertain to just this kind of reference systems.

It is observed, however, that objects whose only significant physical property is that they contain a certain amount of matter, will nevertheless accelerate each other's motion if they are brought close enough together in a given reference system. Furthermore, it can be demonstrated by actual measurements that the accelerations of every such pair of objects, considered as physical points, will be directed toward one another and will form a constant ratio, while the ratio of certain pairs of these constants for three objects will be equal to one of the others. As an illustration, for three physical points 1, 2, and 3 it would be found in part that

$$\frac{a_{12}}{-a_{21}} = m_{21}, \qquad \frac{a_{23}}{-a_{32}} = m_{32}, \qquad \frac{a_{13}}{-a_{31}} = m_{31}, \qquad (1.4)$$

where the first subscript indicates the point under consideration and the second subscript the point affecting it, with the a's representing accelerations and the m's constants; furthermore,

$$\frac{m_{31}}{m_{21}} = m_{32}. \qquad (1.5)$$

The minus signs are used to show that the accelerations in each pair are oppositely directed.

Substituting for m_{32} above, we see that

$$m_{21}a_{23} = -m_{31}a_{32}; \qquad (1.6)$$

in other words, the acceleration of point 2 due to point 3 and that of 3 due to 2 are related to one another through constants which depend on the acceleration of each by point 1. This means that if we select 1 as a standard physical point and evaluate m for all other physical points relative to it, as

$$m_2, \qquad m_3, \qquad m_4, \ldots \tag{1.7}$$

where 1 is understood to be the last subscript, then we can relate the accelerations of any pair of these in the given reference system by expressions of the form:

$$m_2 a_{23} = -m_3 a_{32} \tag{1.8}$$

$$m_3 a_{34} = -m_4 a_{43} \tag{1.9}$$

$$\begin{array}{cc} . & . \\ . & . \\ . & . \end{array}$$

The constants $m_2, m_3, m_4, \ldots$ are taken to provide a measure of the amount of matter in the objects 2, 3, 4, ... and are called their masses. Clearly, it is the mass of an object that is its only pertinent physical property in these circumstances; therefore, we shall refer to its representative point as a point mass from now on. Of course, objects can possess other physical properties which will cause them to accelerate relative to one another, electrical charge, for example. We are simply suppressing these for the present in the interests of simplicity.

Newton's second law consists, first, in assuming that quantities such as $m_2 a_{23}$ in (1.8) will be equal to some function F_{23} of the distance between the interacting particles, their relative velocity, and time,

$$m_2 \mathbf{a}_{23} = \mathbf{F}_{23}(\mathbf{r}, \dot{\mathbf{r}}, t) \tag{1.10}$$

where the point mass 3 is located at the origin of coordinates and the vector character of a_{23}, r, $\dot{r}$, and thus F_{23}, is recognized. The function $\mathbf{F}_{23}$ is called the force acting on point mass 2 due to point mass 3; this is about the most satisfactory definition of force that can be obtained, if we allow that the function can be generalized to include the accelerating effects of other physical properties and thus can be "repulsive" as well as "attractive." Later we shall adopt a sign convention to distinguish between these two types of forces.

The second law also assumes that all of the accelerations of a point mass produced by others will be additive; for example,

$$m_2(\mathbf{a}_{23} + \mathbf{a}_{24} + \cdots) = \mathbf{F}_{23} + \mathbf{F}_{24} + \cdots \tag{1.11}$$

or simply

$$\mathbf{F}(\mathbf{r}, \dot{\mathbf{r}}, t) = m\mathbf{a}, \tag{1.12}$$

where **F** is understood to be the resultant force acting on the point whose mass is m, whose position coordinates and velocity at the time t are given by **r** and **ṙ**, and whose acceleration will therefore be **a**. Notice that if we replace the $m\mathbf{a}$ products in (1.8) and (1.9) with their equivalent forces we obtain:

$$\mathbf{F}_{23} = -\mathbf{F}_{32} \tag{1.13}$$

$$\mathbf{F}_{34} = -\mathbf{F}_{43} \tag{1.14}$$

$$\begin{matrix} \cdot & \cdot \\ \cdot & \cdot \\ \cdot & \cdot \end{matrix}$$

This is the content of Newton's third law, stating that every point mass acted on by a force from another will react with an opposing force of the same magnitude. These ideas can also easily be generalized to include other physical effects.

Equation (1.12) offers a convenient way of determining masses. If at some point the acceleration of an object due to the earth's gravitational field is known to be **g**, and its weight in pounds on a spring scale at the same point is known to be **W**, then assuming no other forces are involved (1.12) gives

$$W = mg, \qquad m = \frac{W}{g}, \tag{1.15}$$

because **W** and **g** are both in the same direction. It is known that the vacuum value of g near the earth's surface is approximately 32.2 ft/sec² for all objects; therefore, m (in slugs if the stated units are used, although several other systems of units are also in common use) can easily be evaluated for any given object by establishing its weight in the same region.[2]

Equation (1.12) can also be written as a first order differential equation,

$$\mathbf{F}(\mathbf{r}, \dot{\mathbf{r}}, t) = m\frac{d\mathbf{v}}{dt}; \tag{1.16}$$

this suggests that the quantity $m\mathbf{v}$ will be of special importance in predicting the motions of physical objects, a more general form of (1.16) being

$$\mathbf{F}(\mathbf{r}, \dot{\mathbf{r}}, t) = \frac{d}{dt}m\mathbf{v} \tag{1.17}$$

with the special form depending on the mass remaining constant in time.

[2] Halliday, D., and R. Resnick, *Physics for Students of Science and Engineering*, pp. 66–89, Wiley, New York, 1960.

It is customary to call this quantity the linear momentum and indicate it by

$$\mathbf{p} = m\mathbf{v}. \tag{1.18}$$

Notice that the first and second laws require $\mathbf{p}$ to remain constant for an isolated object ($\mathbf{F} = 0$) regardless of the values of m and $\mathbf{v}$; the usual statement is that $\mathbf{p}$ will be conserved in the absence of applied forces. It follows from (1.18) that

$$p_x = m\dot{x}, \qquad p_y = m\dot{y}, \qquad p_z = m\dot{z}. \tag{1.19}$$

Of course, (1.16) can also be written as three first or second order scalar differential equations:

$$F_x(x, y, z, \dot{x}, \dot{y}, \dot{z}, t) = m\frac{d\dot{x}}{dt} = m\frac{d^2x}{dt^2} \tag{1.20}$$

$$F_y(x, y, z, \dot{x}, \dot{y}, \dot{z}, t) = m\frac{d\dot{y}}{dt} = m\frac{d^2y}{dt^2} \tag{1.21}$$

$$F_z(x, y, z, \dot{x}, \dot{y}, \dot{z}, t) = m\frac{d\dot{z}}{dt} = m\frac{d^2z}{dt^2} \tag{1.22}$$

Sometimes one of these various forms will be found to be the most convenient, sometimes another.

The last equations also suggest certain other quantities and another conservation principle of great importance in predicting the motions of objects. If, for example, we multiply the first of these by $\dot{x}$, the result is

$$\dot{x}F_x = m\dot{x}\ddot{x} = \frac{m}{2}\frac{d}{dt}(\dot{x}\dot{x}) = \frac{d}{dt}\left(\frac{m\dot{x}^2}{2}\right),$$

or multiplying through by dt,

$$F_x\,dx = d\left(\frac{m\dot{x}^2}{2}\right). \tag{1.23}$$

Because $F_x\,dx$ is the quantity commonly defined as the work, W_x, the inference is that quantities like $m\dot{x}^2/2$ will have special importance; they are, of course, called the components of the total kinetic energy, usually indicated by the letter T:

$$T = \frac{m}{2}\mathbf{v}\cdot\mathbf{v} = \frac{mv^2}{2} = \frac{m\dot{x}^2}{2} + \frac{m\dot{y}^2}{2} + \frac{m\dot{z}^2}{2} = T_x + T_y + T_z \tag{1.24}$$

Now, if we imagine a point mass to move from one position x_1 on the X-axis along any path whatsoever to another such position x_2 while acted on by the force F_x, and integrate (1.23) between these two positions, we obtain

$$\int_{x_1}^{x_2} F_x \, dx = (T_x)_{x_2} - (T_x)_{x_1},$$ (1.25)

the right-hand side being the integral of a perfect differential. Because in general

$$F_x = F_x(x, y, z, \dot{x}, \dot{y}, \dot{z}, t),$$ (1.26)

the value of the integral on the left-hand side will depend on the path that the point mass takes between the positions x_1 and x_2; however, if it happens that F_x depends only on the position coordinate x,

$$F_x = F_x(x),$$ (1.27)

another quantity, called the potential energy in the x-direction and indicated by $V_x(x)$ is suggested,[3]

$$V_x(x) = \int_x^{x_s} F_x(x) \, dx = - \int_{x_s}^x F_x(x) \, dx$$ (1.28)

where x_s is selected as a standard reference point. For then, according to (1.25),

$$(T_x)_{x_2} - (T_x)_{x_1} = \int_{x_1}^{x_s} F_x(x) \, dx + \int_{x_s}^{x_2} F_x(x) \, dx$$

$$= - \int_{x_s}^{x_1} F_x(x) \, dx + \int_{x_s}^{x_2} F_x(x) \, dx$$

$$= (V_x)_{x_1} - (V_x)_{x_2};$$ (1.29)

therefore,

$$(T_x)_{x_1} + (V_x)_{x_1} = (T_x)_{x_2} + (V_x)_{x_2} = T_x + V_x = E_x$$ (1.30)

where E_x is a constant, called the total mechanical energy for motion in the x-direction. With

$$F_y = F_y(y)$$ (1.31)

and

$$F_z = F_z(z)$$ (1.32)

similar relations can be obtained for the other two directions. Moreover, if we define the total potential energy as

$$V = V_x + V_y + V_z$$ (1.33)

[3] Houston, W. V., *Principles of Mathematical Physics*, pp. 20–24, McGraw-Hill, New York, 1948.

and the total mechanical energy as

$$E = E_x + E_y + E_z, \tag{1.34}$$

it follows that the latter will also be conserved:

$$T + V = E \tag{1.35}$$

Actually, the concept of a potential function can be generalized beyond the definition given in (1.28) and (1.33), or equivalently

$$F_x(x) = -\frac{dV_x}{dx}, \quad F_y = -\frac{dV_y}{dy}, \quad F_z = -\frac{dV_z}{dz} \tag{1.36}$$

where

$$V = V_x(x) + V_y(y) + V_z(z). \tag{1.37}$$

If more generally

$$V = V(x, y, z), \tag{1.38}$$

as long as

$$F_x = -\frac{\partial V}{\partial x}, \quad F_y = -\frac{\partial V}{\partial y}, \quad F_z = -\frac{\partial V}{\partial z}, \tag{1.39}$$

or what is the same thing,

$$\mathbf{F} = -\nabla V, \tag{1.40}$$

the total mechanical energy will still be conserved. For since the curl of a gradient always vanishes, (1.40) implies that

$$\nabla \times \mathbf{F} = 0; \tag{1.41}$$

and Stokes' theorem (1.2.101) makes it plain that around any closed curve

$$\int_C \mathbf{F} \cdot d\mathbf{r} = 0. \tag{1.42}$$

Thus the work done by the force as the point mass moves between any two positions (x_1, y_1, z_1) and (x_2, y_2, z_2) will be independent of the path,[4] which means that we may also write

$$T + V(x, y, z) = E. \tag{1.43}$$

Equation (1.41) is the necessary and sufficient condition for the existence of such a potential function, and forces that satisfy it are therefore said to be conservative.

[4] Symon, K. R., *Mechanics*, 2nd edition, pp. 112–118, Addison-Wesley, Reading, Mass., 1960.

In any event, the equation

$$\int_1^2 \mathbf{F} \cdot d\mathbf{r} = T_2 - T_1 \tag{1.44}$$

is called the work-energy relation, and the three scalar equations like (1.25) are of considerable utility in their own right. It is interesting to note that an analogous set of equations exist for the other conserved quantity. If we multiply (1.20) by dt,

$$F_x \, dt = m \frac{d\dot{x}}{dt} \, dt = d(m\dot{x}) = dp_x, \tag{1.45}$$

and integrate between two times, t_1 and t_2, the result is:

$$\int_{t_1}^{t_2} F_x \, dt = (p_x)_{t_2} - (p_x)_{t_1} \tag{1.46}$$

The value of the integral is called the impulse delivered by the force F_x between the times t_1 and t_2; this evidently produces a change in the linear momentum of the point mass in the x-direction in the same way that the work done by F_x between the points x_1 and x_2 produces a change in its kinetic energy in this direction according to (1.25). All three equations like (1.46) can be expressed by writing a single vector equation called the impulse-momentum relation:

$$\int_{t_1}^{t_2} \mathbf{F} \, dt = \mathbf{p}_{t_2} - \mathbf{p}_{t_1} \tag{1.47}$$

Of course, the work-energy relation (1.44) is inherently a scalar equation.

Another conservation principle of much utility features angular momentum, instead of linear momentum, and depends on the total moment of force, instead of the total force, being zero. Because angular velocity measures the rate of rotation of a position vector to a point having a certain linear velocity, angular momentum must involve this position vector and, in fact, is defined as

$$\mathbf{l} = \mathbf{r} \times m\mathbf{v} = \mathbf{r} \times \mathbf{p} \tag{1.48}$$

where $\mathbf{r}$ extends from the fixed origin of coordinates to the point mass m with the linear velocity $\mathbf{v}$. In expanded form this becomes

$$l_x\hat{\mathbf{i}} + l_y\hat{\mathbf{j}} + l_z\hat{\mathbf{k}} = \begin{vmatrix} \hat{\mathbf{i}} & \hat{\mathbf{j}} & \hat{\mathbf{k}} \\ x & y & z \\ p_x & p_y & p_z \end{vmatrix}$$

$$= (yp_z - zp_y)\hat{\mathbf{i}} + (zp_x - xp_z)\hat{\mathbf{j}} + (xp_y - yp_x)\hat{\mathbf{k}} \tag{1.49}$$

or

$$l_x = yp_z - zp_y \tag{1.50}$$

$$l_y = zp_x - xp_z \tag{1.51}$$

$$l_z = xp_y - yp_x. \tag{1.52}$$

In the same way the moment of force is defined as

$$\mathbf{M} = \mathbf{r} \times \mathbf{F}, \tag{1.53}$$

where $\mathbf{F}$ is the total force acting on the point at $\mathbf{r}$, and expands to:

$$M_x = yF_z - zF_y \tag{1.54}$$

$$M_y = zF_x - xF_z \tag{1.55}$$

$$M_z = xF_y - yF_x \tag{1.56}$$

Of course, both l and $\mathbf{M}$ are with respect to the origin, and it is easy to see from the scalar equations that they consist of all the contributions from

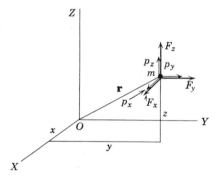

Fig. 2.1

the components $p_x = mv_x$, $p_y = mv_y$, $p_z = mv_z$, or F_x, F_y, F_z times their respective perpendicular distances from the origin, with appropriate signs attached (Fig. 2.1). The arrowheads shown on the scalar components of $\mathbf{p}$ and $\mathbf{F}$ merely emphasize the orientation of these vectors, which are omitted in the figure for the sake of clarity. On the other hand, because both l and $\mathbf{M}$ are free vectors[5] like $\boldsymbol{\omega}$, their components along any of the axes can easily be written as, for example,

$$M_x = \mathbf{M} \cdot \hat{\mathbf{i}}. \tag{1.57}$$

From this we may infer that, in general, the moment of a force $\mathbf{F}$ about any line n will be

$$M_n = \mathbf{M}_1 \cdot \hat{\mathbf{n}} = (\mathbf{r}_{1 \text{ to } 2} \times \mathbf{F}) \cdot \hat{\mathbf{n}}, \tag{1.58}$$

[5] Synge, J. L., and B. A. Griffith, *Principles of Mechanics*, 3rd edition, pp. 118–135, McGraw-Hill, New York, 1959.

where 1 is any point on the line with unit vector $\hat{\mathbf{n}}$ and 2 is any point on the line of action of the force (Fig. 2.2). Notice especially that the moment of force or angular momentum about a line is a scalar, even though with respect to any point on the line it is a vector.

Now, if we form the cross product of $\mathbf{r}$ with both sides of (1.17),

$$\mathbf{r} \times \mathbf{F} = \mathbf{r} \times \frac{d}{dt}\, m\mathbf{v} = \frac{d}{dt}(\mathbf{r} \times m\mathbf{v}), \qquad (1.59)$$

using the fact that

$$\frac{d}{dt}(\mathbf{r} \times m\mathbf{v}) = \mathbf{r} \times \frac{d}{dt}\, m\mathbf{v} + \underbrace{\mathbf{v} \times m\mathbf{v}}_{0}, \qquad (1.60)$$

it follows from the above definitions that

$$\mathbf{M} = \frac{d}{dt}\,\mathbf{l}. \qquad (1.61)$$

Clearly, when $\mathbf{M} = 0$, $\mathbf{l} = $ constant; in other words, when the total moment of force acting on a point mass around a given origin vanishes, its angular momentum with respect to that origin will be conserved. Multiplying (1.61) through by dt and integrating from t_1 to t_2, we can also obtain the angular momentum counterpart of the impulse-momentum relations (1.47):

$$\int_{t_1}^{t_2} \mathbf{M}\, dt = \mathbf{l}_{t_2} - \mathbf{l}_{t_1} \qquad (1.62)$$

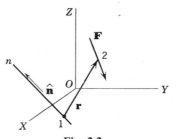

Fig. 2.2

It should be evident from the preceding development that the potential energy function V, if it can be mapped for a given region by applying the three equations resembling (1.28) to the displacements of a test mass, will in itself contain much information about the possible accelerations of any point mass in that region. Later we shall see that the concept of potential energy can be broadened to correspond to the generalization of the force concept and learn that many problems in mechanics derive their uniqueness largely from the form in which V enters them. As an illustration within the limitations of our present definition, consider the motions possible for a point mass with the energies E_0, E_1, E_2, and E_3 in a region where the potential varies as shown schematically in Fig. 2.3. From (1.30),

$$E_x = T_x + V_x,$$

and the related definition of T_x we know it must be true that

$$\dot{x} = \pm\sqrt{\frac{2}{m}\,[E_x - V(x)]}; \qquad (1.63)$$

thus we see that the motion of the point mass must be confined to those portions of the X-axis where

$$V(x) \le E_x. \qquad (1.64)$$

This means that with the energy E_0 it could only remain at $x = d$, whereas with the energy E_1 it could oscillate around $x = d$ between $x = c$ and

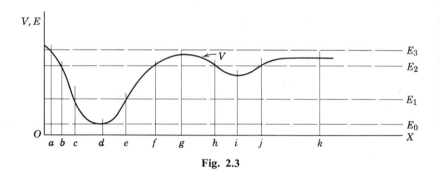

Fig. 2.3

$x = e$, and with the energy E_2 either around $x = d$ between $x = b$ and $x = f$ or around $x = i$ between $x = h$ and $x = j$. If it were moving in the negative X-direction with the energy E_3, it would have to turn at $x = a$ and move off in the positive X-direction.

Because

$$-\frac{dV(x)}{dx} = 0 = F_x \qquad (1.65)$$

at the points $x = d$, $x = g$, $x = i$, and $x = k$, they are called points of force equilibrium; the shape of the curve itself, if we imagine the motion of the point mass to resemble that of a ball subject to this potential rolling ideally along the curve, suggests why the first is called a point of stable equilibrium, the second a point of unstable equilibrium, the third a point of metastable equilibrium, and the fourth a point of neutral equilibrium. At these locations all elemental forces balance in such a way that the point mass can remain at rest in the given reference system. This idea will be found especially useful when we come to deal with large groups of point masses; we shall also learn later that it can be generalized even further than can the idea of a force.

Implicit in the preceding discussion of point mass motion is the assumption that the reference system involved is the proper system; so it is clear that, relative to other inertial systems, the Lorentz transformation relations, (2.150), (2.151) and (2.164), (2.165), will have to be satisfied. But because a point mass unaccelerated in this reference system will remain unaccelerated in all inertial systems, and because an observer in any of these could presumably define mass as we have done, let us assume that Newton's equation (1.17),

$$\mathbf{F} = \frac{d}{dt}\, m\mathbf{v},$$

will have the same form in all such systems.[6]

If we want to generalize this equation so that it will apply between inertial systems, then, the inference is that time must be transformed according to (2.144) in Chapter 1,

$$dt = \frac{dt'}{\mathscr{S}},$$

and that mass will become a variable. The latter follows from considering that lengths must be transformed according to (2.166) to (2.168) of Chapter 1:

$$(y_2 - y_1) = \frac{(y_2' - y_1')}{\mathscr{S}}$$

$$(x_2 - x_1) = (x_2' - x_1')$$

$$(z_2 - z_1) = (z_2' - z_1')$$

For evidently volumes in the two systems must be related by

$$(x_2 - x_1)(y_2 - y_1)(z_2 - z_1) = (x_2' - x_1')\frac{(y_2' - y_1')}{\mathscr{S}}(z_2' - z_1'), \quad (1.66)$$

and the amount of matter an object can contain at a given density depends on its volume.[7]

Let us agree to call the mass of an object its rest mass m_0 in its proper system, where it is at rest relative to the observer, and m elsewhere. Now, if we define the four-vector velocity

$$\mathscr{V} = \mathscr{V}_1 \hat{\mathbf{i}}_1 + \mathscr{V}_2 \hat{\mathbf{i}}_2 + \mathscr{V}_3 \hat{\mathbf{i}}_3 + \mathscr{V}_4 \hat{\mathbf{i}}_4, \quad (1.67)$$

---

[6] Wigner, E. P., "Symmetry and Conservation Laws," *Physics Today*, pp. 34–40, March 1964.

[7] Oliver, B. M., "The View From the Starship Bridge and Other Observations," *IEEE Spectrum*, pp. 86–92, January 1961.

where the subscripts refer to the X, Y, Z, and τ-axes and

$$\mathscr{V}_1 = \frac{dx}{dt'} = \frac{dx}{dt}\frac{dt}{dt'} = \frac{v_1}{\mathscr{S}} \tag{1.68}$$

$$\mathscr{V}_2 = \frac{dy}{dt'} = \frac{dy}{dt}\frac{dt}{dt'} = \frac{v_2}{\mathscr{S}} \tag{1.69}$$

$$\mathscr{V}_3 = \frac{dz}{dt'} = \frac{dz}{dt}\frac{dt}{dt'} = \frac{v_3}{\mathscr{S}} \tag{1.70}$$

$$\mathscr{V}_4 = \frac{d\tau}{dt'} = \frac{d\tau}{dt}\frac{dt}{dt'} = \frac{ic}{\mathscr{S}}, \tag{1.71}$$

using (2.144) of Chapter 1 and the fact that $\tau = ict$, as well as the four-vector force

$$\mathbf{F} = F_1\hat{\mathbf{i}}_1 + F_2\hat{\mathbf{i}}_2 + F_3\hat{\mathbf{i}}_3 + F_4\hat{\mathbf{i}}_4, \tag{1.72}$$

we can write the Newtonian equation in this space as

$$\mathbf{F} = \frac{d}{dt'}m_0\mathscr{V}. \tag{1.73}$$

Expanding in accordance with the preceding definitions,

$$F_1\hat{\mathbf{i}}_1 + F_2\hat{\mathbf{i}}_2 + F_3\hat{\mathbf{i}}_3 + F_4\hat{\mathbf{i}}_4 = \frac{d}{dt'}\frac{m_0}{\mathscr{S}}(v_1\hat{\mathbf{i}}_1 + v_2\hat{\mathbf{i}}_2 + v_3\hat{\mathbf{i}}_3 + ic\hat{\mathbf{i}}_4), \tag{1.74}$$

we see that it can be separated into one vector equation,

$$\mathbf{F}_{1,2,3} = \frac{d}{dt'}\frac{m_0\mathbf{v}}{\mathscr{S}} = \frac{1}{\mathscr{S}}\frac{d}{dt}\frac{m_0\mathbf{v}}{\mathscr{S}}, \tag{1.75}$$

and one scalar equation,

$$F_4 = \frac{d}{dt'}\frac{m_0}{\mathscr{S}}ic. \tag{1.76}$$

The latter reflects the time transformation requirement and the former the transformation requirements imposed on lengths. Thus, if (1.17) is to apply to all inertial systems, it must be true that

$$\mathbf{F} = \mathbf{F}(x, y, z) = \mathbf{F}_{1,2,3} = \mathscr{S}\mathbf{F}_{1,2,3} \tag{1.77}$$

and

$$m\mathbf{v} = \frac{m_0}{\mathscr{S}}\mathbf{v} \tag{1.78}$$

or

$$m = \frac{m_0}{\mathscr{S}}. \tag{1.79}$$

Considering that

$$\mathbf{F}_{1,2,3} = F_x \hat{\mathbf{i}} + F_y \hat{\mathbf{j}} + F_z \hat{\mathbf{k}}, \tag{1.80}$$

(1.77) makes it plain that conservative forces are intended; of course, (1.78) can also be written in the form

$$\mathbf{p} = \frac{\mathbf{p_0}}{\mathscr{S}}. \tag{1.81}$$

Equation (1.79) defines the way in which the mass of an object will vary; we see that it will appear to increase as the velocity of the object relative to the observer increases, because in this case $\mathscr{S}$ will approach zero.

Another important implication of these results follows immediately from the work-energy equation (1.44). If we write this equation in the form

$$\int dT = \int \mathbf{F} \cdot d\mathbf{r} \tag{1.82}$$

and substitute for $\mathbf{F}$ from (1.17) with m replaced by $m_0/\mathscr{S}$ as indicated by (1.79),

$$\int dT = m_0 \int \left(\frac{d}{dt} \frac{\mathbf{v}}{\mathscr{S}}\right) \cdot d\mathbf{r}, \tag{1.83}$$

the resulting expression can be integrated[8] to obtain

$$T = \frac{m_0 c^2}{\mathscr{S}} + \text{constant}. \tag{1.84}$$

Now, if we were to identify the constant with the negative potential energy and further choose this to be zero, it would follow from (1.43) and (1.79) that

$$E = T = \frac{m_0 c^2}{\mathscr{S}} = mc^2. \tag{1.85}$$

The implication is that, independent of the potential energy, there will always be an amount of energy mc^2 associated with a mass m. When $V_y = v_y \ll c$, so that

$$\mathscr{S}^{-1} = \left(1 - \frac{v_y^2}{c^2}\right)^{-\frac{1}{2}} \simeq 1 + \frac{1}{2}\frac{v_y^2}{c^2}, \tag{1.86}$$

(1.85) reduces to

$$E \simeq m_0 c^2 \left(1 + \frac{1}{2}\frac{v_y^2}{c^2}\right) = m_0 c^2 + \frac{m_0 v_y^2}{2}, \tag{1.87}$$

which clearly reveals the presence of an intrinsic component of the specified form, over and above the usual kinetic energy. This fact was first pointed

[8] Lindsay, R. B., and H. Margenau, *Foundations of Physics*, pp. 347–355, Dover, New York, 1957.

out by Einstein; it has also been demonstrated by him that a quantity of pure radiation, like a light photon, with the energy E must also be assigned an inertia with the mass equivalent E/c^2.

If we square both sides of (1.79) and solve for mv_y,

$$m^2 = \frac{m_0{}^2}{\mathscr{S}^2} = \frac{m_0{}^2}{1 - \dfrac{v_y{}^2}{c^2}} \tag{1.88}$$

$$m^2(c^2 - v_y{}^2) = m_0{}^2c^2 \tag{1.89}$$

$$m^2v_y{}^2 = m^2c^2 - m_0{}^2c^2 \tag{1.90}$$

$$mv_y = (m^2c^2 - m_0{}^2c^2)^{1/2}, \tag{1.91}$$

the result is called the relativistic linear momentum. Because v_y can be identified with v, this is usually written simply as

$$mv = p = (m^2c^2 - m_0{}^2c^2)^{1/2}. \tag{1.92}$$

A corresponding expression for the relativistic kinetic energy can be derived from (1.84),

$$T = \frac{m_0c^2}{\mathscr{S}} + \text{constant} = \frac{m_0c^2}{\sqrt{1 - \dfrac{v_y{}^2}{c^2}}} + \text{constant},$$

by assuming that T will be zero when $v_y \ll c$, for then the constant must equal $-m_0c^2$, and

$$T = \frac{m_0c^2}{\mathscr{S}} - m_0c^2 = mc^2 - m_0c^2. \tag{1.93}$$

Squaring both sides of (1.92), we see that

$$p^2 = m^2c^2 - m_0{}^2c^2, \tag{1.94}$$

$$m^2c^4 = p^2c^2 + m_0{}^2c^4, \tag{1.95}$$

$$mc^2 = E = (p^2c^2 + m_0{}^2c^4)^{1/2}; \tag{1.96}$$

therefore, (1.93) can also be written in the form

$$T = (p^2c^2 + m_0{}^2c^4)^{1/2} - m_0c^2. \tag{1.97}$$

These expressions for the momentum and kinetic energy are of special interest because, by using them, the conservation principles developed earlier can still be applied in relativistic situations.

Problems 2.1

1. Is the force

$$\mathbf{F} = \sin y \hat{\mathbf{i}} + x(1 + \cos y)\hat{\mathbf{j}}$$

conservative? Calculate $\int_C \mathbf{F} \cdot d\mathbf{r}$ around a circle of radius a in the XY-plane.

Solution

$$\nabla \times \mathbf{F} = \begin{vmatrix} \hat{\mathbf{i}} & \hat{\mathbf{j}} & \hat{\mathbf{k}} \\ \dfrac{\partial}{\partial x} & \dfrac{\partial}{\partial y} & \dfrac{\partial}{\partial z} \\ \sin y & x(1 + \cos y) & 0 \end{vmatrix}$$

$$= \hat{\mathbf{k}}[1 + \cos y - \cos y]$$
$$= \hat{\mathbf{k}};$$

thus **F** is nonconservative.

Stoke's theorem is:

$$\iint_{S'} (\text{curl } \mathbf{u}) \cdot \hat{\mathbf{n}} \, dS' = \int_C \mathbf{u} \cdot d\mathbf{r}$$

This gives

$$\iint_{S'} \hat{\mathbf{k}} \cdot \hat{\mathbf{k}} \, dS' = \iint_{S'} dS' = \int_C \mathbf{F} \cdot d\mathbf{r};$$

consequently,

$$\int_C \mathbf{F} \cdot d\mathbf{r} = \iint_{S'} dS' = \pi a^2,$$

the area of the circle of radius a.

2. Consider Atwood's machine, shown in Fig. P2.1 (2), where the pulley is assumed to be frictionless and of negligible mass. If an additional mass of 1 g

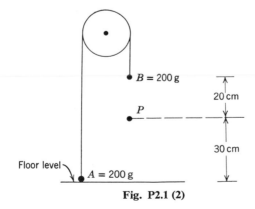

Fig. P2.1 (2)

is placed on the mass B and removed after a travel of 20 cm to point P, which is 30 cm above the floor level, calculate the following:

a. The time of travel of the mass B to the point P.
b. The time of travel of the mass B to the ground from point P.

Solution

Since the masses A and B are equal, there will be no motion until the additional mass is placed on B. Then the resultant force acting will be

$$F = 1 \times 980 \text{ dynes,}$$

because the acceleration due to gravity is 980 cm/sec². The total mass in motion will be

$$(200 + 200 + 1) = 401 \text{ g;}$$

so its acceleration can be calculated from

$$a = \frac{F}{m}$$

$$= \frac{980}{401} \simeq \frac{98}{40} = 2.45 \text{ cm/sec}^2.$$

Because the initial velocity is zero, the distance of travel will be

$$x = \tfrac{1}{2}at_1^2;$$

thus with

$$x = 20 \text{ cm}$$

and

$$a = 2.45 \text{ cm/sec}^2,$$

$$t_1 = \sqrt{\frac{2 \times 20}{2.45}} = \sqrt{16} = 4 \text{ sec.}$$

After the 1 g mass is removed, the two masses will move with uniform speed because no force will be acting:

$$v = at = \frac{98}{40} \times 4 = 9.8 \text{ cm/sec}$$

Therefore, the time of travel to the ground will be

$$t_2 = \frac{d}{v} = \frac{30}{9.8} = 3.06 \text{ sec.}$$

3. A 2000 lb load is placed in an 8000 lb barge, which is equipped with a winch for pulling the load across its smooth deck [Fig. P2.1 (3)]. Initially both the barge and the load are at rest with respect to the water.

    a. Using the principle of conservation of momentum, determine the velocity of the barge and the velocity of the load when the winch is drawing the load toward it at the rate of 10 ft/sec.

    b. What is the final position of the barge after 50 ft of rope has been drawn in by the winch?

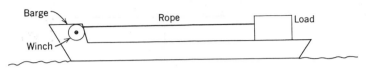

Fig. P2.1 (3)

Solution

(a) Mass of barge $= M_B = 8000/g$; mass of load $= M_L = 2000/g$. Calling the velocity of the barge v_B, the velocity of the load v_L, and the velocity of the load with respect to the barge $v_{L/B} = -10$ ft/sec,

$$v_L = v_B + v_{L/B} = v_B - 10.$$

Then conservation of momentum gives

$$v_B \frac{8000}{g} + (v_B - 10)\frac{2000}{g} = 0;$$

therefore,

$$4v_B + v_B - 10 = 0,$$

$$5v_B = 10,$$

and

$$v_B = 2 \text{ ft/sec}$$

$$v_L = -8 \text{ ft/sec}.$$

(b) $t = \dfrac{l}{v_{L/B}} = \dfrac{50}{10} = 5 \text{ sec};$

thus the barge will move a total distance of

$$d = v_B t = (2)(5) = 10 \text{ ft}.$$

4. A bullet weighing 2 oz is fired into a pendulum of length l which weighs 50 lb, causing the pendulum to swing through an arc of 45°. What was the velocity of the bullet just before it entered the pendulum?

Solution

Let the potential energy $V_1 = 0$ initially [Fig. P2.1 (4)]. The final kinetic energy $T_2 = 0$, whereas

$$T_1 = \frac{1}{2}\left(\frac{50 + 0.125}{32.2}\right)v_1{}^2$$

and

$$V_2 = 50.125[l - l \cos 45°] = 50.125(l)(0.293).$$

Now, applying conservation of energy,

$$V_1 + T_1 = V_2 + T_2$$

$$\frac{1}{2}\left(\frac{50.125}{32.2}\right)v_1{}^2 = 50.125(l)(0.293)$$

$$v_1{}^2 = 64.4(l)(0.293) = 18.7l$$

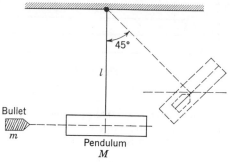

Fig. P2.1 (4)

and

$$v_1 = 4.31\sqrt{l}.$$

From conservation of momentum,

$$mv_0 = (m + M)v_1;$$

therefore

$$\tfrac{1}{8}v_0 = (50.125)(4.31)\sqrt{l},$$

giving

$$v_0 = 1728\sqrt{l}\,\text{ft/sec}.$$

5. Determine the total moment of the forces $\mathbf{F}_1$ and $\mathbf{F}_2$ shown in Fig. P2.1 (5):

   a. About the point A.
   b. About the line AB.

Solution

(a) $$\sum \mathbf{M}_A = \mathbf{r}_1 \times \mathbf{F}_1 + \mathbf{r}_2 \times \mathbf{F}_2$$

But

$$\mathbf{r}_1 = -2\hat{\mathbf{i}} - 2\hat{\mathbf{j}}, \qquad \mathbf{F}_1 = 3\hat{\mathbf{j}} + 5\hat{\mathbf{k}}$$

$$\mathbf{r}_1 \times \mathbf{F}_1 = \begin{vmatrix} \hat{\mathbf{i}} & \hat{\mathbf{j}} & \hat{\mathbf{k}} \\ -2 & -2 & 0 \\ 0 & 3 & 5 \end{vmatrix} = -10\hat{\mathbf{i}} + 10\hat{\mathbf{j}} - 6\hat{\mathbf{k}}$$

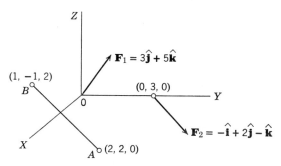

Fig. P2.1 (5)

and

$$r_2 = -2\hat{i} + \hat{j}, \qquad F_2 = -\hat{i} + 2\hat{j} - \hat{k}$$

$$r_2 \times F_2 = \begin{vmatrix} \hat{i} & \hat{j} & \hat{k} \\ -2 & 1 & 0 \\ -1 & 2 & -1 \end{vmatrix} = -\hat{i} - 2\hat{j} - 3\hat{k};$$

therefore,

$$\sum M_A = -11\hat{i} + 8\hat{j} - 9\hat{k} \text{ lb ft.}$$

(b)

$$\sum M_{AB} = \sum \mathbf{M}_A \cdot \widehat{\mathbf{AB}}$$

But

$$\mathbf{AB} = -\hat{i} - 3\hat{j} + 2\hat{k} \quad \text{and} \quad |\mathbf{AB}| = \sqrt{14};$$

so

$$\widehat{\mathbf{AB}} = -\frac{1}{\sqrt{14}}\hat{i} - \frac{3}{\sqrt{14}}\hat{j} + \frac{2}{\sqrt{14}}\hat{k}.$$

Therefore,

$$M_{AB} = \frac{11}{\sqrt{14}} - \frac{24}{\sqrt{14}} - \frac{18}{\sqrt{14}} = \frac{-31}{\sqrt{14}} \text{ lb ft.}$$

6. A point mass rotates at 20 rad/sec on a frictionless disk at a distance of 5 ft from the center; a string is attached to the point mass and passes through a hole in the center of the disk. If the string is pulled downward with a constant velocity of 4 ft/sec, what will the magnitude of the total velocity of the point mass be when it is $\frac{1}{2}$ ft from the center? [See Fig. P2.1 (6).]

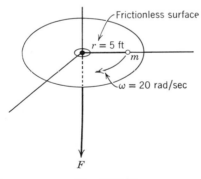

Fig. P2.1 (6)

Solution

Since $\mathbf{M} = \mathbf{r} \times \mathbf{F} = 0$, $\mathbf{l} = \mathbf{r} \times m\mathbf{v} = \text{constant} = \mathbf{C}$, from $\mathbf{M} = (d\mathbf{l}/dt)$. Using polar coordinates, we have

$$\boldsymbol{\rho} \times m(v_r\hat{\mathbf{l}} + v_\phi\hat{\mathbf{m}}) = \mathbf{C},$$

which implies

$$\rho v_\phi = \text{constant};$$

but

$$v_\phi = \omega\rho,$$

so
$$\rho^2\omega = \text{constant.}$$

Therefore, we can say that
$$\rho_1{}^2\omega_1 = \rho_2{}^2\omega_2;$$

substituting, we obtain
$$(5)^2 20 = (\tfrac{1}{2})^2\omega_2,$$

$$\omega_2 = 2000 \text{ rad/sec.}$$

Then
$$(v_\phi)_2 = \omega_2\rho_2 = (2000)\tfrac{1}{2} = 1000 \text{ ft/sec}$$

and
$$v^2 = (1000)^2 + (4)^2,$$

giving
$$v \simeq 1000 \text{ ft/sec.}$$

7. A billiard ball weighing $\frac{1}{4}$ lb is struck a blow, lasting 0.01 sec, with a cue. If its velocity is 2 ft/sec immediately after being struck, what was the impulse of the blow? Also, calculate the force exerted by the cue on the ball, neglecting friction.

Solution

Because the ball was initially at rest, its change in momentum must be equal to its final momentum:
$$mv - mv_0 = \left(\frac{1}{4 \times 32}\right) 2 = \frac{1}{64} \text{ slug-ft/sec}$$

But the change in momentum is numerically equal to the impulse of the blow:
$$\text{Impulse} = F(t - t_0) = \frac{1}{64} \text{ lb sec.}$$

The force then follows from dividing the impusle by the time over which it was delivered:
$$\frac{1}{64} \times \frac{1}{0.01} = \frac{100}{64} = 1.56 \text{ lb.}$$

8. Consider the impact of a quantum of radiation with a free electron that is at rest. Let p be the initial and p' the final momentum of the quantum of radiation, and p_e the momentum of the electron after the collision. Show that
$$\cos \phi = \frac{p_e{}^2 + p^2 - p'^2}{2pp_e}$$

$$\cos \theta = \frac{p'^2 + p^2 - p_e{}^2}{2pp'}$$

where θ and ϕ are the angles shown in Fig. P2.1 (8).

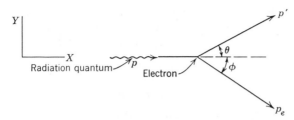

Fig. P2.1 (8)

Solution

Equating the initial and final momenta in the X- and Y-direction, we have

$$p = p_e \cos \phi + p' \cos \theta$$
$$0 = p' \sin \theta - p_e \sin \phi.$$

Therefore,

$$\cos \phi = \frac{p - p' \cos \theta}{p_e}$$

and

$$\sin \phi = \frac{p' \sin \theta}{p_e} = \sqrt{1 - \cos^2 \phi};$$

so,

$$\frac{p'^2 \sin^2 \theta}{p_e^2} = 1 - \cos^2 \phi = 1 - \left(\frac{p - p' \cos \theta}{p_e}\right)^2$$

$$= \frac{p_e^2 - p^2 - p'^2 \cos^2 \theta + 2pp' \cos \theta}{p_e^2}$$

and

$$p'^2(\sin^2 \theta + \cos^2 \theta) - p_e^2 + p^2 = 2pp' \cos \theta,$$

from which it follows that

$$\cos \theta = \frac{p'^2 + p^2 - p_e^2}{2pp'}.$$

Similarly:

$$p' \cos \theta = p - p_e \cos \phi$$
$$p' \sin \theta = p_e \sin \phi$$

$$1 - \cos^2 \theta = \frac{p_e^2}{p'^2} \sin^2 \phi = 1 - \frac{(p - p_e \cos \phi)^2}{p'^2}$$

$$p'^2 - p^2 - p_e^2 \cos^2 \phi + 2pp_e \cos \phi - p_e^2 \sin^2 \phi$$

$$\cos \phi = \frac{p_e^2 + p^2 - p'^2}{2pp_e}$$

9. What is the rest energy of one atomic mass unit?

Solution

One atomic mass unit (amu) is defined as $\frac{1}{16}$ the mass of a neutral oxygen atom, and Avogadro's number $N = 6.023 \times 10^{23}$ gives the number of atoms present in a gram molecular volume. Thus there will be 6.023×10^{23} atoms in 16 g of atomic oxygen, and

$$1 \text{ amu} = \frac{1}{16} \left(\frac{16}{6.023 \times 10^{23}} \right)$$

$$= 1.6660 \times 10^{-24} \text{ g.}$$

Applying the relation

$$E = mc^2$$

we can now express this in units of energy;

$$E_{\text{amu}} = \frac{(1.666 \times 10^{-24} \text{ g}) \left(3 \times 10^{10} \frac{\text{cm}}{\text{sec}} \right)^2}{\left(1.6 \times 10^{-12} \frac{\text{erg}}{\text{eV}} \right)}$$

$$= 9.34 \times 10^8 \text{ eV}$$

$$= 934 \text{ MeV.}$$

10. What will be the kinetic energy of a proton, whose rest energy is 938 MeV, if its momentum is $(1000 \text{ MeV})/c$?

Solution

The result follows directly from the relation

$$T = (p^2 c^2 + m_0^2 c^4)^{1/2} - m_0 c^2.$$

Because

$$m_0 c^2 = 938 \text{ MeV and } p = \frac{1000}{c},$$

$$T = \left[\left(\frac{1000}{c} c \right)^2 + (938)^2 \right]^{1/2} - 938$$

$$= [10^6 + 879844]^{1/2} - 938$$

$$= 433 \text{ MeV.}$$

11. A particle comes to rest with a mass of m_1 and disintegrates into two particles, one having a rest mass of m_2 and the other a gamma ray photon with a zero

$$m_2 \longleftarrow \underset{m_1}{\xrightarrow{\hspace{3cm}}} \overset{\gamma}{\longrightarrow}$$

Fig. P2.1 (11)

rest mass [Fig. P2.1 (11)]. Show that the kinetic energy of the particle with mass m_2 will be

$$T_{m_2} = \frac{(m_1 - m_2)^2}{2m_1} c^2.$$

Solution

The total energy will be conserved; therefore, we may write

$$m_1 c^2 = \sqrt{p_{m_2}^2 c^2 + m_2^2 c^4} + T_\gamma$$

where T_γ indicates the kinetic energy of the γ photon. But momentum will also be conserved, which means that

$$p_{m_2} = \frac{T_\gamma}{c}$$

or

$$T_\gamma = p_{m_2}c.$$

Accordingly, we have

$$m_1c^2 - p_{m_2}c = \sqrt{p_{m_2}^2c^2 + m_2^2c_4};$$

squaring both sides then gives

$$m_1^2c^4 - 2m_1p_{m_2}c^3 + p_{m_2}^2c^2 = p_{m_2}^2c^2 + m_2^2c^4,$$

$$m_1^2c - 2m_1p_{m_2} = m_2^2c,$$

or

$$p_{m_2} = \frac{(m_1^2 - m_2^2)c}{2m_1}.$$

The kinetic energy of the particle with this momentum will therefore be:

$$\begin{aligned}
T_{m_2} &= \sqrt{p_{m_2}^2c^2 + m_2^2c_4} - m_2c^2 \\
&= m_1c^2 - T_\gamma - m_2c^2 \\
&= m_1c^2 - p_{m_2}c - m_2c^2 \\
&= m_1c^2 - \frac{(m_1^2 - m_2^2)}{2m_1}c^2 - m_2c^2 \\
&= c^2\frac{(2m_1^2 - m_1^2 + m_2^2 - 2m_1m_2)}{2m_1} \\
&= c^2\frac{(m_1^2 + m_2^2 - 2m_1m_2)}{2m_1} \\
&= \frac{(m_1 - m_2)^2}{2m_1}c^2.
\end{aligned}$$

Exercises 2.1

1. The following forces are important physical quantities:
   a. $F_x\hat{\imath} = -kx\hat{\imath}$ the force exerted by a linear spring.

   b. $W\hat{\jmath} = -mg\hat{\jmath}$, the force due to the acceleration of gravity.

   Show that these forces are conservative and find the potential energy associated with each. Determine the reference point for which the potential energy is zero.

2. A point mass m starts from rest at A [Fig. E2.1 (2)] and slides down an inclined frictionless track that contains a circular loop of radius r. Calculate the force exerted by the track on the mass at the points B and C on the horizontal and vertical diameters.

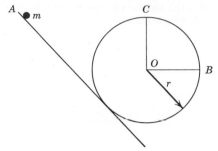

Fig. E2.1 (2)

Answer. $\dfrac{2mgh}{r}$ at B; $\dfrac{2mg(h-r)}{r} - mg$ at C.

3. Two blocks are connected by an inextensible cord over a frictionless pulley of negligible mass, as shown in Fig. E2.1 (3). Ignoring friction, what will be the velocity of block B after it has travelled 5 ft, if it starts from rest?

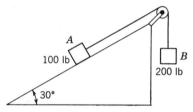

Fig. E2.1 (3)

Answer. $v = 12.69$ ft/sec.

4. A bullet of mass $m = 20$ g is fired into a ballistic pendulum of mass $M = 5$ kg, and the center of gravity of the pendulum rises 10 cm after it is struck [Fig. E2.1 (4)]. Find the initial velocity of the bullet.

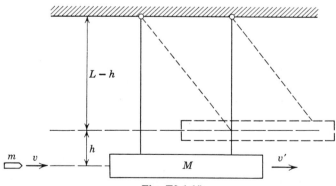

Fig. E2.1 (4)

Answer. $v_0 = 350$ m/sec.

5. A rocket with its fuel has an initial mass of M_0. After it is fired, the total mass is given by the expression

$$M = \frac{M_0}{2}(1 + e^{-kt}),$$

where k is a constant, the mass varying with time because of the consumption of the fuel. If the velocity is given as $v = 300t^2$ ft/sec in a straight line, determine the propulsion force F exerted on the rocket after 1 sec has elapsed.

Answer. $F = -150M_0 ke^{-k} + 300M_0(1 + e^{-k})$.

6. A point mass located at the point (1, 2, 3) has a velocity **c**, given in Fig. E2.1 (6). Determine the locus of all points for which its angular momentum will be conserved.

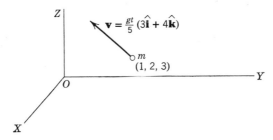

Fig. E2.1 (6)

Answer. $y = 2; 4x - 3z = -5$.

7. A point mass initially at rest is acted upon by a rectilinear force $F = 3t^2$ lb for a duration of 5 sec. If the mass weighs 128.8 lb, what will its velocity be after 10 sec? [See Fig. E21. (7).]

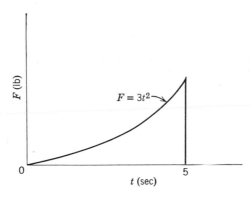

Fig. E2.1 (7)

Answer.   31.25 ft/sec.

8. Show that the force field

$$\mathbf{F} = yz^2\hat{\mathbf{i}} + (xz^2 - 1)\hat{\mathbf{j}} + 2(xyz - 1)\hat{\mathbf{k}}$$

is conservative. Determine the potential energy of the field and compute the work done on a point mass which moves from point (1, 2, 1) to point (3, 1, 2) in the field.

Answer. 9.

9. A force $\mathbf{F} = 3\hat{\mathbf{i}} - 4\hat{\mathbf{j}} + \hat{\mathbf{k}}$ acts at point B [Fig. E2.1 (9)]. The moment of this force about point A is given as $\mathbf{M} = 5\hat{\mathbf{i}} + 2\hat{\mathbf{j}} - 7\hat{\mathbf{k}}$. What is the shortest position vector from point A to the line of action of the force $\mathbf{F}$?

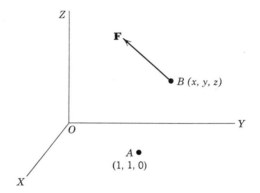

Fig. E2.1 (9)

Answer. $\mathbf{r} = \hat{\mathbf{i}} + \hat{\mathbf{j}} + \hat{\mathbf{k}}$.

10. For the case of a point mass moving in the X-direction in a conservative force field, energy is conserved, and we have the relationship

$$\tfrac{1}{2}mv_x^2 + V(x) = E_x = \text{constant}.$$

From this equation, develop a relationship between displacement and time, neglecting relativistic considerations.

Answer. $\displaystyle\int_{x_0}^{x} dx \Big/ \sqrt{\frac{2}{m}(E - V)} = t - t_0.$

11. A particle of mass m moves in one dimension under the influence of a potential

$$V(x) = \frac{K}{x^4}$$

where K is a constant.

a. What is the force acting on the particle?
b. Find $\dot{x}$ as a function of x.

Answer.

(a) $F = \dfrac{4K}{x^5}$.

(b) $\dot{x} = \sqrt{\dfrac{2}{m}\left(E - \dfrac{K}{x^4}\right)}$.

12. Assume that the two atoms of a diatomic molecule are point masses and that the potential energy function related to their mutual attractive and repulsive force fields is given by

$$V(r) = \frac{a}{r^{12}} - \frac{b}{r^6},$$

where a and b are constants and r is the separation distance.

a. Sketch both $V(r)$ and $F(r)$ versus r.
b. Determine the values of r for which $V(r) = 0$ and $V(r)$ is a minimum.

Answer.

(b) $r = 6\sqrt{\dfrac{a}{b}}$; $r = 6\sqrt{\dfrac{2a}{b}}$.

13. The potential curve shown for $V(\rho)$ in Fig. E2.1 (13) is symmetrical about the Z-axis and ρ lies in the XY-plane. Describe the possible motions of a point mass moving in space under the influence of this potential.

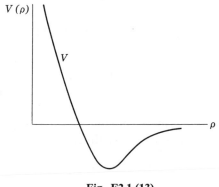

Fig. E2.1 (13)

14. If an electron is moving with a speed of 1.8×10^8 m/sec, what is its mass?

Answer. 11.385×10^{-31} kg.

15. Calculate the rest energies of an electron and a proton.

Answer.   0.511 MeV; 938 MeV.

16. What is the speed of a 5 MeV electron?

Answer. 0.996c.

17. What is the momentum of a 2 MeV electron?

Answer. $\dfrac{2.5 \text{ MeV}}{c}$.

2.2 The Lagrangian and Hamiltonian Equations

The full functional dependence of the force components in the Newtonian equations (1.20) to (1.22),

$$F_x = F_x(x, y, z, \dot{x}, \dot{y}, \dot{z}, t) \tag{2.1}$$

$$F_y = F_y(x, y, z, \dot{x}, \dot{y}, \dot{z}, t) \tag{2.2}$$

$$F_z = F_z(x, y, z, \dot{x}, \dot{y}, \dot{z}, t), \tag{2.3}$$

suggests that the restricted definition of the potential energy utilized in the preceding section,

$$V = V(x, y, z), \tag{2.4}$$

should be generalized if these equations are to be fully exploited. We should expect this to result in broadened ideas of energy conservation; indeed, such broadening seems called for, because many natural processes are observed in which the sum of kinetic and potential energy does not remain constant.

Probably the best procedure, largely because it permits coordinates to be separated in a more general way and thus preserves many of the desirable features of the preceding development, is to recognize that certain well-defined constraints may be imposed on the motion of a point mass. For example, it may be constrained to move on a particular curve, like a ball swung on a string, or some special surface, like a ball rolled on a table. An unconstrained point mass moving in real space would have three positional degrees of freedom at any time,

$$\mathbf{r} = \mathbf{r}(x, y, z, t); \tag{2.5}$$

however, if a constraint existed such that an independent equation

$$f(x, y, z, t) = 0 \tag{2.6}$$

could be written, it should be possible to form two independent "generalized" position coordinates q_j incorporating this requirement and to describe the constrained motion as a two-degree-of-freedom system with

$$\mathbf{r} = \mathbf{r}(q_1, q_2, t). \tag{2.7}$$

In fact, it can be established[9] that if n point masses are present in three-dimensional space and k constraint equations can be written, $3n - k$ independent generalized coordinates will exist in terms of which the motion of the system can be described. Sometimes these are not difficult to discover. For example, consider the motion of two masses m_1 and m_2, connected by a rigid rod of length r_0, with respect to a fixed origin, as shown in Fig. (2.4). Making no use of the constraint imposed by the rod, the six position coordinates associated with $\mathbf{r}_1$, and $\mathbf{r}_2$ $(x_1, y_1, z_1, x_2, y_2, z_2)$ would

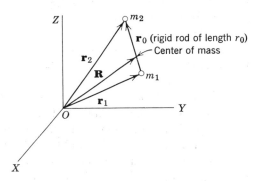

Fig. 2.4

be required to describe the motion of the masses; however, incorporating the condition that

$$[(x_2 - x_1)^2 + (y_2 - y_1)^2 + (z_2 - z_1)^2]^{1/2} = r_0, \qquad (2.8)$$

we should be able to describe this same motion with five independent position coordinates.

Defining the center of mass by the equation

$$(m_1 + m_2)\mathbf{R} = m_1\mathbf{r}_1 + m_2\mathbf{r}_2, \qquad (2.9)$$

or

$$\mathbf{R} = \frac{m_1\mathbf{r}_1 + m_2\mathbf{r}_2}{m_1 + m_2}, \qquad (2.10)$$

and noting that

$$\mathbf{r}_0 = \mathbf{r}_2 - \mathbf{r}_1, \qquad (2.11)$$

we see that one way of accomplishing the conversion to independent generalized coordinates is to describe the motion of m_2 relative to m_1 with $\mathbf{r}_0$ and the motion of the center of mass with $\mathbf{R}$. Three coordinates (X, Y, Z) will determine the latter, and only two will be required to determine the

[9] Goldstein, H., *Classical Mechanics*, pp. 10–26, Addison-Wesley, Reading, Mass., 1959.

former because the magnitude r_0 of the vector is known (ϕ and θ using spherical coordinates). Thus the components of $\mathbf{R}$ and $\mathbf{r}_0$ are independent generalized coordinates, and (2.10) and (2.11) show how these are related to the nonindependent Cartesian coordinate components of $\mathbf{r}_1$ and $\mathbf{r}_2$. Both sets qualify as generalized coordinates, since the only overall requirement for such coordinates is that they locate the point masses uniquely, but only the former are independent.

More often, because they are frequently composite variables with units other than simple units of length, independent generalized coordinates are hard to express in terms of Cartesian coordinates. Accomplishing this may amount to achieving a solution of the problem. In many cases, however, such relations do not have to be determined in advance; the important thing is that the generalized coordinates themselves exist and, for so-called holonomic systems, are independent. Such systems either have constraint equations of the type (2.6), which must be integrable if differentials are involved, or have no constraints at all, in which case application of the above concepts is trivial. Nonholonomic systems, with constraint equations that cannot be put in the form (2.6) and for which generalized coordinates are not necessarily independent, can also be defined; they are of limited usefulness, however, and we shall not consider them further.[10]

If $\mathbf{r}_i$ represents the position vector of either of the two point masses m_i in Fig. (2.4), then with

$$\mathbf{r}_i = \mathbf{r}_i(q_1, q_2, \ldots, q_5, t) \tag{2.12}$$

it follows that, if the system is in static equilibrium and remains so ($\mathbf{F}_i = 0$), we can define a small arbitrary "virtual" displacement $\delta\mathbf{r}_i(q_1, q_2, \ldots, q_5)$, valid for any time, and write the principle of virtual work:

$$\sum_{i=1}^{2} \mathbf{F}_i \cdot \delta\mathbf{r}_i = 0. \tag{2.13}$$

Because indices will not always refer to axes as before, the summation convention will not be employed in the following development in order to avoid confusion. And although only two masses will be used to assist visualization, it must be emphasized that the conclusions will apply to a system containing any number.

By separating the total force into the contribution from the constraints (superscript C) and all other applied forces (superscript A),

$$\mathbf{F}_i = \mathbf{F}_i^{C} + \mathbf{F}_i^{A}, \tag{2.14}$$

---

[10] Long, R. R., *Engineering Science Mechanics*, pp. 90–94, Prentice-Hall, Englewood Cliffs, N.J., 1963.

we can express (2.13) in the modified form,

$$\sum_{i=1}^{2} \mathbf{F}_i^C \cdot \delta\mathbf{r}_i + \sum_{i=1}^{2} \mathbf{F}_i^A \cdot \delta\mathbf{r}_i = 0. \tag{2.15}$$

When we restrict ourselves to cases in which the constraint forces do no work, such as those from the rigid rod in the present case, this becomes

$$\sum_{i=1}^{2} \mathbf{F}_i^A \cdot \delta\mathbf{r}_i = 0. \tag{2.16}$$

Hereafter we shall assume the superscript A and simply write:

$$\sum_{i=1}^{2} \mathbf{F}_i \cdot \delta\mathbf{r}_i = 0. \tag{2.17}$$

Now, a moving point mass may be imagined to be in a state of static equilibrium under the force

$$\mathbf{F}_i - m_i\ddot{\mathbf{r}}_i, \tag{2.18}$$

since we know from the Newtonian equations that

$$\mathbf{F}_i - m_i\ddot{\mathbf{r}}_i = 0; \tag{2.19}$$

therefore, we may allow our system to be in motion by expressing (2.17) in the form

$$\sum_{i=1}^{2} (\mathbf{F}_i - m_i\ddot{\mathbf{r}}_i) \cdot \delta\mathbf{r}_i = 0, \tag{2.20}$$

called d'Alembert's principle.

Let us rewrite the last equation as

$$\sum_{i=1}^{2} m_i\ddot{\mathbf{r}}_i \cdot \delta\mathbf{r}_i - \sum_{i=1}^{2} \mathbf{F}_i \cdot \delta\mathbf{r}_i = 0 \tag{2.21}$$

and analyze the two left-hand terms separately. To begin with, a virtual displacement can be interpreted as a first variation of the function $\mathbf{r}_i$, and this in turn is equivalent to the first differential of the function.[11] No variation in time is allowed in a virtual displacement, so that when we use (2.12) it follows that

$$\delta\mathbf{r}_i = \frac{\partial\mathbf{r}_i}{\partial q_1}\delta q_1 + \frac{\partial\mathbf{r}_i}{\partial q_2}\delta q_2 + \cdots + \frac{\partial\mathbf{r}_i}{\partial q_5}\delta q_5 = \sum_{j=1}^{5}\frac{\partial\mathbf{r}_i}{\partial q_j}\delta q_j; \tag{2.22}$$

we see that the first term becomes:

$$\sum_{i=1}^{2} m_i\ddot{\mathbf{r}}_i \cdot \delta\mathbf{r}_i = \sum_{i=1}^{2}\sum_{j=1}^{5} m_i\ddot{\mathbf{r}}_i \cdot \frac{\partial\mathbf{r}_i}{\partial q_j}\delta q_j. \tag{2.23}$$

[11] Dettman, J. W., *Mathematical Methods in Physics and Engineering*, pp. 68–70, McGraw-Hill, New York, 1962.

If, however, aiming toward the construction of an equivalent form in which the derivatives of the $\mathbf{r}_i$ are replaced by derivatives of the q_j, we now form

$$\sum_{i=1}^{2} \sum_{j=1}^{5} \frac{d}{dt}\left(m_i\dot{\mathbf{r}}_i \cdot \frac{\partial \mathbf{r}_i}{\partial q_j}\right) = \sum_{i=1}^{2} \sum_{j=1}^{5} m_i\dot{\mathbf{r}}_i \cdot \frac{d}{dt}\left(\frac{\partial \mathbf{r}_i}{\partial q_j}\right) + \sum_{i=1}^{2} \sum_{j=1}^{5} \frac{\partial \mathbf{r}_i}{\partial q_j} \cdot m_i\ddot{\mathbf{r}}_i \quad (2.24)$$

and isolate the term corresponding to (2.23), except for its multiplication by δq_j, the result is:

$$\sum_{i=1}^{2} \sum_{j=1}^{5} m_i\ddot{\mathbf{r}}_i \cdot \frac{\partial \mathbf{r}_i}{\partial q_j} = \sum_{i=1}^{2} \sum_{j=1}^{5} \frac{d}{dt}\left(m_i\dot{\mathbf{r}}_i \cdot \frac{\partial \mathbf{r}_i}{\partial q_j}\right) - \sum_{i=1}^{2} \sum_{j=1}^{5} m_i\dot{\mathbf{r}}_i \cdot \frac{d}{dt}\left(\frac{\partial \mathbf{r}_i}{\partial q_j}\right) \quad (2.25)$$

But utilizing the fact that

$$\dot{\mathbf{r}}_i = \frac{d}{dt}\,\mathbf{r}_i(q_1, q_2, \ldots, q_{3n-k}, t) = \sum_{j=1}^{5} \frac{\partial \mathbf{r}_i}{\partial q_j} \frac{dq_j}{dt} + \frac{\partial \mathbf{r}_i}{\partial t} \frac{dt}{dt}$$

$$= \sum_{j=1}^{5} \frac{\partial \mathbf{r}_i}{\partial q_j} \dot{q}_j + \frac{\partial \mathbf{r}_i}{\partial t}, \quad (2.26)$$

where the $\dot{q}_j$ are called generalized velocities, we see by direct differentiation of this expression that the following equalities hold:

$$\frac{\partial \dot{\mathbf{r}}_i}{\partial \dot{q}_j} = \frac{\partial \mathbf{r}_i}{\partial q_j} \quad (2.27)$$

and

$$\frac{\partial \dot{\mathbf{r}}_i}{\partial q_j} = \sum_{l=1}^{5} \frac{\partial^2 \mathbf{r}_i}{\partial q_j \, \partial q_l} \dot{q}_l + \frac{\partial^2 \mathbf{r}_i}{\partial q_j \, \partial t} = \frac{d}{dt}\left(\frac{\partial \mathbf{r}_i}{\partial q_j}\right). \quad (2.28)$$

This means that we can replace the terms corresponding to the right-hand sides of these relations with terms involving $\dot{\mathbf{r}}_i$ in (2.25), thereby completing scalar products in $\dot{\mathbf{r}}_i$ to yield v_i^2 and permit a conversion to kinetic energy in both cases:

$$\sum_{i=1}^{2} \sum_{j=1}^{5} m_i\ddot{\mathbf{r}}_i \cdot \frac{\partial \mathbf{r}_i}{\partial q_j} = \sum_{i=1}^{2} \sum_{j=1}^{5} \frac{d}{dt}\left(m_i\dot{\mathbf{r}}_i \cdot \frac{\partial \dot{\mathbf{r}}_i}{\partial \dot{q}_j}\right) - \sum_{i=1}^{2} \sum_{j=1}^{5} m_i\dot{\mathbf{r}}_i \cdot \frac{\partial \dot{\mathbf{r}}}{\partial q_j}$$

$$= \sum_{j=1}^{5} \frac{d}{dt}\left(\frac{\partial}{\partial \dot{q}_j} \sum_{i=1}^{2} \frac{m_i v_i^2}{2}\right) - \sum_{j=1}^{5} \frac{\partial}{\partial q_j} \sum_{i=1}^{2} \frac{m_i v_i^2}{2} \quad (2.29)$$

since, for example,

$$\frac{\partial}{\partial \dot{q}_j} \frac{m_i v_i^2}{2} = \frac{\partial}{\partial \dot{q}_j} \frac{m_i}{2} \dot{\mathbf{r}}_i \cdot \dot{\mathbf{r}}_i = m_i\dot{\mathbf{r}}_i \cdot \frac{\partial \dot{\mathbf{r}}_i}{\partial \dot{q}_j}. \quad (2.30)$$

It follows that the first term of (2.21) can be written as

$$\sum_{i=1}^{2} m_i \ddot{\mathbf{r}}_i \cdot \delta\mathbf{r}_i = \sum_{j=1}^{5} \left(\frac{d}{dt} \frac{\partial T}{\partial \dot{q}_j} - \frac{\partial T}{\partial q_j} \right) \delta q_j \tag{2.31}$$

in terms of the total kinetic energy T and the generalized coordinates q_j and $\dot{q}_j$.

When we apply (2.22) again, the second term of (2.21) becomes

$$\sum_{i=1}^{2} \mathbf{F}_i \cdot \delta\mathbf{r}_i = \sum_{i=1}^{2} \sum_{j=1}^{5} \mathbf{F}_i \cdot \frac{\partial \mathbf{r}_i}{\partial q_j} \delta q_j; \tag{2.32}$$

but if we define the generalized forces

$$\sum_{i=1}^{2} \mathbf{F}_i \cdot \frac{\partial \mathbf{r}_i}{\partial q_j} = Q_j, \tag{2.33}$$

corresponding to the generalized coordinates q_j, this takes the form

$$\sum_{i=1}^{2} \mathbf{F}_i \cdot \delta\mathbf{r}_i = \sum_{j=1}^{5} Q_j \, \delta q_j. \tag{2.34}$$

Like the other generalized quantities, the Q_j need not have units of force, but, as (2.32) suggests, $Q_j \, \delta q_j$ will always have units of work.

Substituting the reduced terms of (2.31) and (2.34) back in (2.21), we obtain:

$$\sum_{j=1}^{5} \left(\frac{d}{dt} \frac{\partial T}{\partial \dot{q}_j} - \frac{\partial T}{\partial q_j} - Q_j \right) \delta q_j = 0 \tag{2.35}$$

But for holonomic systems the q_j will be independent; therefore, the δq_j must also be independent and remain entirely arbitrary. This means that the bracketed coefficient of each of the δq_j's must vanish in order to satisfy (2.35); thus we conclude that:

$$\frac{d}{dt} \frac{\partial T}{\partial \dot{q}_j} - \frac{\partial T}{\partial q_j} = Q_j \qquad \{ j = 1, 2, \ldots, 5 \tag{2.36}$$

These are the Lagrangian equations; and even though there will only be five in this case, it should be evident that the preceding method can easily be generalized and $3n - k$ such equations written for a holonomic system involving n masses and k constraint equations in three-dimensional space.

Because equations (2.33) do not require the existence of a potential function of the form (2.4),

$$V = V(x, y, z),$$

equations (2.36) are not restricted to systems that are conservative in the earlier sense, even though we have utilized the usual definition of kinetic energy (2.30). Thus the possibility now exists of creating more general potential functions and broadening the concept of energy conservation. We shall pursue this further later, but first let us observe that if a potential function of the form (2.4) or, even more generally,

$$V = V(q_1, q_2, \ldots, q_n) \tag{2.37}$$

does exist, the Lagrangian equations take an especially simple form.

Since we may then write

$$\mathbf{F}_i = -\nabla_i V, \tag{2.38}$$

(2.33) will yield

$$Q_j = -\sum_{i=1}^{2} \left(\frac{\partial V}{\partial x_i} \frac{\partial x_i}{\partial q_j} + \frac{\partial V}{\partial y_i} \frac{\partial y_i}{\partial q_j} + \frac{\partial V}{\partial z_i} \frac{\partial z_i}{\partial q_j} \right) \tag{2.39}$$

or, written as a single partial derivative,

$$Q_j = -\frac{\partial}{\partial q_j} V(q_1, q_2, \ldots, q_5). \tag{2.40}$$

Therefore, (2.36) becomes

$$\frac{d}{dt} \frac{\partial T}{\partial \dot{q}_j} - \frac{\partial}{\partial q_j} (T - V) = 0; \tag{2.41}$$

but T does not depend explicitly on q_j and V does not depend on $\dot{q}_j$, which suggests that we define a function

$$T(\dot{q}_1, \dot{q}_2, \ldots, \dot{q}_5) - V(q_1, q_2, \ldots, q_5) = L \tag{2.42}$$

and write simply:

$$\frac{d}{dt} \frac{\partial L}{\partial \dot{q}_j} - \frac{\partial L}{\partial q_j} = 0 \qquad \{j = 1, 2, \ldots, 5 \tag{2.43}$$

As defined in (2.42), L is called the Lagrangian function for a conservative system, and (2.43) are the Lagrangian equations[12] for such a system in the particular case when $3n - k = 5$. It is important to note that they will remain invariant in form under all coordinate transformations, because only independent generalized coordinates are involved and L is necessarily a scalar function.[13]

---

[12] Not uncommonly, partial derivatives are indicated merely by subscripting the independent variable. For example, these equations are sometimes written in the form: $\dot{L}_{\dot{q}_j} = L_{q_j}$; however, we shall not use this convention until second order partial derivatives become important.

[13] Lanczos, C., *The Variational Principles of Mechanics*, pp. 115–119, 193–201, Univ. of Toronto Press, Toronto, 1960.

It is easy to see that these reduce to the Newtonian equations in their earlier form if no constraints are present and if the generalized coordinates are merely the Cartesian coordinates. For example, suppose that

$$q_1 = x_1, \qquad \dot{q}_1 = \dot{x}_1; \tag{2.44}$$

then

$$\frac{d}{dt}\frac{\partial L}{\partial \dot{x}_1} = \frac{d}{dt}\left(\frac{\partial}{\partial \dot{x}_1}\frac{m_1 \dot{x}_1^2}{2}\right) = \frac{d}{dt} m_1 \dot{x}_1 \tag{2.45}$$

and

$$\frac{\partial L}{\partial x} = -\frac{\partial V}{\partial x_1} = F_{x_1}; \tag{2.46}$$

thus the first of equations (2.43) would become

$$m_1 \ddot{x}_1 - F_{x_1} = 0. \tag{2.47}$$

In the same way, with

$$q_2 = y_1, \qquad \dot{q}_2 = \dot{y}_1$$

$$\begin{matrix} \cdot & & \cdot \\ \cdot & & \cdot \\ \cdot & & \cdot \end{matrix} \tag{2.48}$$

$$q_6 = z_2, \qquad \dot{q}_6 = \dot{z}_2$$

the remaining equations will become:

$$m_1 \ddot{y}_1 - F_{y_1} = 0$$

$$\begin{matrix} \cdot & & \cdot \\ \cdot & & \cdot \\ \cdot & & \cdot \end{matrix} \tag{2.49}$$

$$m_2 \ddot{z}_2 - F_{z_2} = 0$$

and we may summarize them all by writing

$$\mathbf{F}_i = m\ddot{\mathbf{r}}_i \tag{2.50}$$

as in (2.19).

The Lagrangian equations (2.43) also suggest another useful form of the equations of motion. Because these are effectively ordinary differential equations of the second order, like the Newtonian equations, and because any such equation can be rewritten as two first-order ordinary differential equations,[14] it is natural to expect a form of the latter kind to exist. This thought, and our experience with the importance of the momentum as a variable, leads us to define the generalized momenta

$$p_j = \frac{\partial L}{\partial \dot{q}_j} \qquad \{j = 1, 2, \ldots, 5, \tag{2.51}$$

[14] Sneddon, I. N., *Elements of Partial Differential Equations*, pp. 7–9; McGraw-Hill, New York, 1957.

implicitly assuming that the kinetic energy appearing in L will be quadratic in $\dot{q}_j$, as in (2.45), and that the potential energy will not depend on $\dot{q}_j$. Substituting in (2.43), we then obtain

$$\dot{p}_j = \frac{\partial L}{\partial q_j} \quad \{j = 1, 2, \ldots, 5; \tag{2.52}$$

and the two first-order equations (2.51) and (2.52) are evidently equivalent to the single second-order equation (2.43).

Actually, however, these are not the two first-order equations commonly used. Let us substitute these in the expression for the first variation of the Lagrangian function $L = L(q_1, q_2, \ldots, q_5, \dot{q}_1, \dot{q}_2, \ldots, \dot{q}_5)$:

$$\delta L = \sum_{j=1}^{5} \frac{\partial L}{\partial q_j} \delta q_j + \sum_{j=1}^{5} \frac{\partial L}{\partial \dot{q}_j} \delta \dot{q}_j$$

$$= \sum_{j=1}^{5} \dot{p}_j \, \delta q_j + \sum_{j=1}^{5} p_j \, \delta \dot{q}_j \tag{2.53}$$

where, for consistency with the preceding development, the summation convention has not been applied. This can be rewritten as

$$\delta L = \sum_{j=1}^{5} \dot{p}_j \, \delta q_j + \sum_{j=1}^{5} \delta(p_j \dot{q}_j) - \sum_{j=1}^{5} \dot{q}_j \, \delta p_j \tag{2.54}$$

or

$$\sum_{j=1}^{5} - \dot{p}_j \, \delta q_j + \sum_{j=1}^{5} \dot{q}_j \, \delta p_j = \sum_{j=1}^{5} \delta(p_j \dot{q}_j) - \delta L = \delta \left(\sum_{j=1}^{5} p_j \dot{q}_j - L \right). \tag{2.55}$$

The last bracketed quantity is called the Hamiltonian function for a conservative system, H; and, because no $\delta \dot{q}$'s appear on the left-hand side of the equation, it can be written as a function of the q's and p's only[15]:

$$\sum_{j=1}^{5} p_j \dot{q}_j - L = H = H(q_1, q_2, \ldots, q_5, p_1, p_2, \ldots, p_5) \tag{2.56}$$

Thus

$$\delta H = \sum_{j=1}^{5} \frac{\partial H}{\partial q_j} \delta q_j + \sum_{j=1}^{5} \frac{\partial H}{\partial p_j} \delta p_j \tag{2.57}$$

must correspond to (2.55),

$$\delta H = \sum_{j=1}^{5} - \dot{p}_j \, \delta q_j + \sum_{j=1}^{5} \dot{q}_j \, \delta p_j;$$

it follows that

$$\frac{\partial H}{\partial q_j} = -\dot{p}_j \tag{2.58}$$

[15] Corben, H. C., and P. Stehle, *Classical Mechanics*, 2nd edition, pp. 154–162, Wiley, New York, 1960.

and

$$\frac{\partial H}{\partial p_j} = \dot{q}_j \tag{2.59}$$

where, as before, $j = 1, 2, \ldots, 5$. These are the Hamiltonian equations for a conservative system. They too are quite general; but they may not retain their form under certain coordinate transformations, especially in relativistic situations, because the momentum is a vector quantity. Of course, they can be written for $j = 1, 2, \ldots, 3n - k$ degrees of freedom with no difficulty.

Using (2.51) and the related assumptions to replace p_j in the expression for the Hamiltonian function (2.56),

$$H = \sum_{j=1}^{5} \frac{\partial L}{\partial \dot{q}_j} \dot{q}_j - L = \sum_{j=1}^{5} \sum_{i=1}^{2} \left(\frac{\partial}{\partial \dot{q}_j} \frac{m_i}{2} \dot{q}_j \dot{q}_j \right) \dot{q}_j - L$$

$$= \sum_{j=1}^{5} \sum_{i=1}^{2} m_i \dot{q}_j \dot{q}_j - L, \tag{2.60}$$

we see that

$$H = 2T - T + V = T + V = E \tag{2.61}$$

in this case. In other words, the Hamiltonian H for a conservative system simply represents the total mechanical energy. And, it should be evident that the Hamiltonian equations will also reduce to the earlier form of the Newtonian equations in the absence of constraints. With the coordinate identifications of (2.44) to (2.46), for example, we obtain from (2.58)

$$\frac{\partial H}{\partial x_1} = \frac{\partial V}{\partial x_1} = -\dot{p}_1 = -\frac{d}{dt} m_1 \dot{x}_1 \tag{2.62}$$

or

$$\frac{d}{dt} m_1 \ddot{x}_1 + \frac{\partial V}{\partial x_1} = 0, \tag{2.63}$$

$$m_1 \ddot{x}_1 - F_{x_1} = 0 \tag{2.64}$$

as in (2.47). Here, this appears to be the full content of the corresponding Lagrangian equation; but the second Hamilton equation (2.59) actually is required to obtain the relation applied in (2.62),

$$\frac{\partial H}{\partial p_1} = \frac{\partial}{\partial p_1} \left(\frac{p_1^2}{2m_1} \right) = \frac{p_1}{m_1} = \dot{x}_1 \tag{2.65}$$

or

$$p_1 = m_1 \dot{x}_1. \tag{2.66}$$

Notice that the kinetic energy must be expressed in terms of the momentum p before the equation can be applied. In more complicated cases it is often this step that causes the greatest difficulties.

Problems 2.2

1. A transformation from a set of Cartesian coordinates $x_1, x_2 \cdots x_n$ to a set of generalized coordinates $q_1, q_2 \cdots q_m$, where $m < n$, is given:

$$x_1 = x_1(q_1, q_2 \cdots q_m)$$
$$x_2 = x_2(q_1, q_2 \cdots q_m)$$

$$\vdots$$

$$x_n = x_n(q_1, q_2 \cdots q_m)$$

$$x_i = x_i(q_j) \qquad \begin{cases} i = 1, 2 \cdots n \\ j = 1, 2 \cdots m < n \end{cases}$$

Show that the $\dot{x}_i$ can be expressed in terms of the $\dot{q}_j$ by means of a vector transformation.

Solution

Forming

$$dx_i = \frac{\partial x_i}{\partial q_1} dq_1 + \frac{\partial x_i}{\partial q_2} dq_2 \cdots + \frac{\partial x_i}{\partial q_m} dq_m = \frac{\partial x_i}{\partial q_j} dq_j$$

and dividing through by dt,

$$\frac{dx_i}{dt} = \frac{\partial x_i}{\partial q_j} \frac{dq_j}{dt},$$

we obtain

$$\dot{x}_i = \frac{\partial x_i}{\partial q_j} \dot{q}_j.$$

But because $\partial x_i / \partial q_j$ has two free indices, it may be expressed in matrix form as

$$\frac{\partial x_i}{\partial q_j} = c_{ij},$$

where:

$$c_{ij} = \begin{bmatrix} \dfrac{\partial x_1}{\partial q_1} & \dfrac{\partial x_1}{\partial q_2} & \cdots & \dfrac{\partial x_1}{\partial q_m} \\[2mm] \dfrac{\partial x_2}{\partial q_1} & \dfrac{\partial x_2}{\partial q_2} & \cdots & \dfrac{\partial x_2}{\partial q_m} \\[2mm] \vdots & & & \vdots \\[2mm] \dfrac{\partial x_n}{\partial q_1} & \dfrac{\partial x_n}{\partial q_2} & \cdots & \dfrac{\partial x_n}{\partial q_m} \end{bmatrix}$$

Then

$$\dot{x}_i = c_{ij} \dot{q}_j$$

has the form of a vector transformation.

2. A scalar function T is defined as

$$T = \frac{m}{2} (\dot{x}_i \dot{x}_i) \qquad \{i = 1, 2$$

where

$$x_i = c_{ij}\phi_j \qquad \{j = 1, 2$$

and the ϕ_j represent generalized coordinates.

a. Express T in terms of the c_{ij} and $\dot{\phi}_j$.
b. If the matrix c_{ij} may be expressed in the form $c_{ij} = \partial x_i / \partial \phi_j$, find its elements for the case when

$$x_1 = \phi_1 \cos \phi_2$$

$$x_2 = \phi_1 \sin \phi_2$$

c. Combine the results of (a) and (b) to obtain an expression for T involving only the ϕ_j and $\dot{\phi}_j$.

Solution

(a) Substituting, with the index j changed to k for its second appearance in order to avoid confusion,

$$T = \frac{m}{2} (c_{ij}\dot{\phi}_j c_{ik}\dot{\phi}_k)$$

$$= \frac{m}{2} c_{ij}c_{ik}\dot{\phi}_j\dot{\phi}_k$$

(b)

$$c_{11} = \frac{\partial x_1}{\partial \phi_1} = \frac{\partial}{\partial \phi_1}(\phi_1 \cos \phi_2) = \cos \phi_2$$

$$c_{12} = \frac{\partial x_1}{\partial \phi_2} = \frac{\partial}{\partial \phi_2}(\phi_1 \cos \phi_2) = -\phi_1 \sin \phi_2$$

$$c_{21} = \frac{\partial x_2}{\partial \phi_1} = \frac{\partial}{\partial \phi_1}(\phi_1 \sin \phi_2) = \sin \phi_2$$

$$c_{22} = \frac{\partial x_2}{\partial \phi_2} = \frac{\partial}{\partial \phi_2}(\phi_1 \sin \phi_2) = \phi_1 \cos \phi_2$$

Thus:

$$c_{ij} = \begin{bmatrix} \cos \phi_2 & -\phi_1 \sin \phi_2 \\ \sin \phi_2 & \phi_1 \cos \phi_2 \end{bmatrix}$$

(c) $T = \dfrac{m}{2} [c_{ij}c_{ik}\dot{\phi}_j\dot{\phi}_k + c_{2j}c_{2k}\dot{\phi}_j\dot{\phi}_k]$

$$= \frac{m}{2} [(c_{11}^2 + c_{21}^2)(\dot{\phi}_1)^2 + (c_{12}^2 + c_{22}^2)(\dot{\phi}_2)^2 + 2(c_{11}c_{12} + c_{21}c_{22})\dot{\phi}_1\dot{\phi}_2]$$

But

$$c_{11}^2 + c_{21}^2 = \cos^2 \phi_2 + \sin^2 \phi_2 = 1$$
$$c_{12}^2 + c_{22}^2 = \phi_1^2 \sin^2 \phi_2 + \phi_1^2 \cos^2 \phi_2 = \phi_1^2$$
$$c_{11}c_{12} + c_{21}c_{22} = -\phi_1 \cos \phi_2 \sin \phi_2 + \phi_1 \sin \phi_2 \cos \phi_2 = 0;$$

therefore,

$$T = \frac{m}{2} [\dot{\phi}_1^2 + (\phi_1\dot{\phi}_2)^2].$$

3. For the coplanar double pendulum shown in Fig. P2.2 (3a), which of the following sets of variables will serve as independent generalized coordinates:

$$(\theta, \phi), \qquad (\theta, \psi), \qquad (\theta, y_2), \qquad (x_1, x_2), \qquad (\phi, \psi), \qquad (y_1, y_2)$$

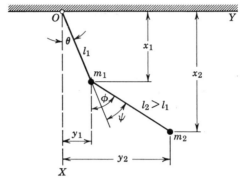

Fig. P2.2 (3a)

Solution

Because the problem is two-dimensional and there are two constraints, the number of independent generalized coordinates will be $(2 \times 2 - 2) = 2$. But the generalized coordinates must also specify the location of the two point masses uniquely. This last requirement rules out (x_1, x_2), because only they would permit various possible positions for m_1 and m_2, as shown in Figs. P2.2 (3b) and P2.2 (3c).

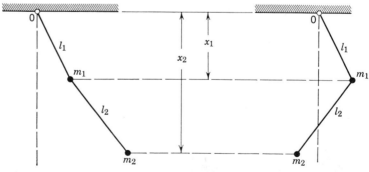

Fig. 2.2 (3b)

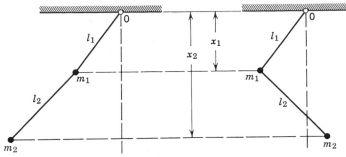

Fig. 2.2 (3c)

4. Using the method of virtual work, and neglecting all friction, calculate the value the angle θ must have for the system shown in Fig. P2.2 (4) to remain in equilibrium.

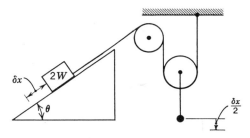

Fig. 2.2 (4)

Solution

Assume a virtual displacement of δx along the plane for the rectangular weight; then the circular weight will displace an amount $\delta x/2$, as shown in the figure. Accordingly, the work done by all of the forces of the system will be

$$W\frac{\delta x}{2} - 2W \sin \theta \, \delta x.$$

But the principle of virtual work tells us that this must vanish for the system to remain in equilibrium. Thus the virtual displacement cancels, and we obtain:

$$\frac{W}{2} = 2W \sin \theta$$

$$\sin \theta = \tfrac{1}{4}$$

$$\theta = \sin^{-1} 0.25$$

5. Calculate by the method of virtual work the force F necessary to maintain the pin-jointed weightless frame in equilibrium in the position shown in Fig. P2.2 (5a).

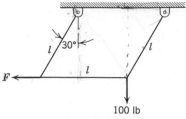

100 lb

Fig. 2.2 (5a)

Solution

Give the frame a virtual angular displacement $\delta\theta$ [Fig. P2.2 (5b)]. Then:

$$\text{Virtual work} = Fl\,\delta\theta\cos 30° - 100l\,\delta\theta\sin 30° = 0$$

$$F\cos 30° = 100\sin 30°$$

$$F = \frac{50}{0.866} = 57.7\text{ lb}$$

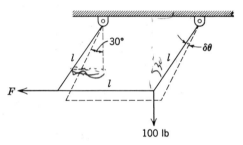

100 lb

Fig. 2.2 (5b)

6. Calculate the mechanical advantage W/F of the differential pulley system illustrated in Fig. P2.2 (6) using the method of virtual work.

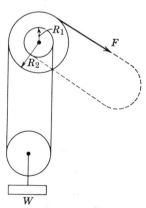

Fig. 2.2 (6)

Solution

A clockwise angular virtual displacement $\delta\theta$ of the upper pulley causes a virtual displacement of $[(R_2 - R_1)/2]\delta\theta$ for the weight W; then, because virtual work must vanish,

$$FR_2 \, \delta\theta - \frac{(R_2 - R_1)}{2} W\delta\theta = 0,$$

giving

$$\frac{W}{F} = \frac{2R_2}{R_2 - R_1}.$$

7. Neglecting friction and the inertial effects of the pulley, use d'Alembert's principle to determine the tension T in the rope of Fig. P2.2 (7a).

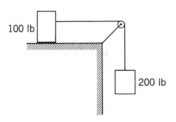

Fig. 2.2 (7a)

Solution

If we assume the 200 lb weight to be accelerating downward at a rate a_0, the magnitude of the acceleration of the 100 lb weight is also a_0; according to d'Alembert's principle we may consider both bodies to be in a state of

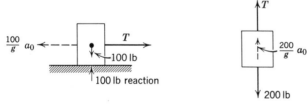

Fig. 2.2 (7b)

dynamic equilibrium under the forces shown in Fig. P2.2 (7b). Because the sum of the forces on each must vanish, this yields

$$T - \frac{100}{g} a_0 = 0$$

and

$$T + \frac{200}{g} a_0 = 200.$$

Subtracting the two equations then defines a_0,

$$\frac{300}{g} a_0 = 200, \qquad a_0 = \tfrac{2}{3}g,$$

and we see that

$$T = \frac{100}{g} \left(\frac{2}{3} g \right) = 66\tfrac{2}{3} \text{ lb.}$$

8. A point mass m slides down an inclined plane [Fig. P2.2 (8)]. Assume that its motion is opposed by a friction force of $f = \mu N$, where μ is a constant and N is the normal reaction exerted by the plane. If the one generalized coordinate required is taken to be the displacement of the mass along the plane, what generalized force will be acting on the mass?

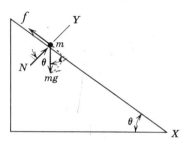

Fig. 2.2 (8)

Solution

Because no motion perpendicular to the plane occurs, the sum of the forces in that direction must equal zero; this defines N:

$$N - mg \cos \theta = 0, \qquad N = mg \cos \theta$$

We can now write the sum of the forces acting along the plane in the following way:

$$\sum F_x = mg \sin \theta - \mu N = mg \sin \theta - mg \cos \theta = mg (\sin \theta - \mu \cos \theta)$$

Our generalized coordinate is

$$q_j = q_1 = x;$$

therefore the definition of generalized force,

$$Q_j = \sum_i \mathbf{F}_i \cdot \frac{\partial \mathbf{r}_i}{\partial q_j},$$

reduces to

$$Q = \sum F_x \frac{\partial x}{\partial x} = \sum F_x,$$

which gives

$$Q = mg [\sin \theta - \mu \cos \theta].$$

9. Using the independent generalized coordinates θ and ϕ [Fig. P2.2 (3a)], calculate the generalized forces Q_θ and Q_ϕ for the double pendulum of Fig. P2.2 (9).

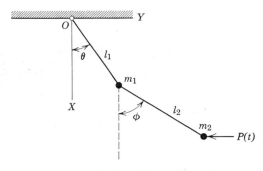

Fig. P2.2 (9)

Solution

To apply the relation

$$Q_j = \sum_i \mathbf{F}_i \cdot \frac{\partial \mathbf{r}_i}{\partial q_j}$$

let

$$\theta = q_1 \quad \text{and} \quad \phi = q_2.$$

Then, since

$$\mathbf{r}_1 = l_1 \cos \theta \hat{\mathbf{i}} + l_1 \sin \theta \hat{\mathbf{j}}$$

and

$$\mathbf{r}_2 = (l_1 \cos \theta + l_2 \cos \phi)\hat{\mathbf{i}} + (l_1 \sin \theta + l_2 \sin \phi)\hat{\mathbf{j}},$$

$$Q_\theta = \mathbf{F}_1 \cdot \frac{\partial \mathbf{r}_1}{\partial \theta} + \mathbf{F}_2 \cdot \frac{\partial \mathbf{r}_2}{\partial \theta},$$

with

$$\mathbf{F}_1 = m_1 g \hat{\mathbf{i}}$$

$$\mathbf{F}_2 = m_2 g \hat{\mathbf{i}} - P(t)\hat{\mathbf{j}}$$

and

$$\frac{\partial \mathbf{r}_1}{\partial \theta} = -l_1 \sin \theta \hat{\mathbf{i}} + l_1 \cos \theta \hat{\mathbf{j}}$$

$$\frac{\partial \mathbf{r}_2}{\partial \theta} = -l_1 \sin \theta \hat{\mathbf{i}} + l_1 \cos \theta \hat{\mathbf{j}},$$

gives

$$Q_\theta = -m_1 g l_1 \sin \theta - m_2 g l_1 \sin \theta - P(t)l_1 \cos \theta.$$

Similarly,

$$Q_\phi = \mathbf{F}_1 \cdot \frac{\partial \mathbf{r}_1}{\partial \phi} + \mathbf{F}_2 \cdot \frac{\partial \mathbf{r}_2}{\partial \phi},$$

with

$$\frac{\partial \mathbf{r}_1}{\partial \phi} = 0$$

$$\frac{\partial \mathbf{r}_2}{\partial \phi} = -l_2 \sin \phi \hat{\mathbf{i}} + l_2 \cos \phi \hat{\mathbf{j}},$$

yields

$$Q_\phi = -m_2 g l_2 \sin \phi - P(t) l_2 \cos \phi.$$

Note that in this case the units associated with the generalized forces are lb ft, units of work as required.

10. A point mass on a smooth plane tangent to the surface of the earth is located by its distance x from the point of tangency. Calculate the generalized force acting on the mass for the case when:

a. x is the generalized coordinate;
b. θ, shown in Fig. P2.2 (10), is the generalized coordinate.

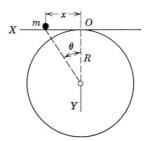

Fig. P2.2 (10)

Solution

In both cases

$$Q_j = \sum_i \mathbf{F}_i \cdot \frac{\partial \mathbf{r}_i}{\partial q_j},$$

$$\mathbf{F}_i = \mathbf{F} = -mg \sin \theta \hat{\mathbf{i}}$$

and

$$\mathbf{r}_i = x \hat{\mathbf{i}}.$$

(a) $$q_, = x, \qquad \frac{\partial \mathbf{r}_i}{\partial x} = \frac{\partial x}{\partial x} \hat{\mathbf{i}} = \hat{\mathbf{i}};$$

thus

$$Q_x = \mathbf{F} \cdot \hat{\mathbf{i}} = -mg \sin \theta$$

(b) $$q_j = \theta, \qquad \mathbf{r}_i = x \hat{\mathbf{i}} = R \tan \theta \hat{\mathbf{i}}, \qquad \frac{\partial \mathbf{r}_i}{\partial \theta} = \left(\frac{R}{\cos^2 \theta} \hat{\mathbf{i}} \right);$$

therefore,

$$Q_\theta = \mathbf{F} \cdot \frac{R}{\cos^2 \theta} \hat{\mathbf{i}} = -\frac{mgR \sin \theta}{\cos^2 \theta}.$$

11. If two masses $m_1 \neq m_2$ are connected by an inextensible rope of length l passing over a frictionless pulley [Fig. P2.2 (11)], find their equation of motion. The system, called Atwood's machine, is assumed to be in a uniform gravitational field g.

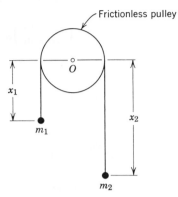

Fig. P2.2 (11)

Solution

The total kinetic energy is

$$T = \tfrac{1}{2}m_1\dot{x}_1^2 + \tfrac{1}{2}m_2\dot{x}_2^2$$

and the total potential energy may be written as

$$V = -m_1gx_1 - m_2gx_2;$$

hence the Lagrangian function takes the form:

$$L = \frac{m_1}{2}(\dot{x}_1)^2 + \frac{m_2}{2}(\dot{x}_2)^2 + g(m_1x_1 + m_2x_2)$$

But

$$x_1 + x_2 = l = \text{constant}, \qquad x_2 = l - x_1;$$

so

$$\dot{x}_2 = -\dot{x}_1,$$

and

$$L = \left(\frac{m_1}{2} + \frac{m_2}{2}\right)(\dot{x}_1)^2 + g(m_1x_1 - m_2x_1 + m_2l).$$

However, the last term is a constant and may be neglected. This gives

$$L = \left(\frac{m_1 + m_2}{2}\right)(\dot{x}_1)^2 + (m_1 - m_2)gx_1,$$

a Lagrangian that involves just one generalized coordinate, x_1 in this case. Therefore, applying the appropriate Lagrangian equation,

$$\frac{d}{dt}\frac{\partial L}{\partial \dot{x}_1} - \frac{\partial L}{\partial x_1} = 0,$$

we obtain

$$\frac{d}{dt}\left[(m_1 + m_2)\dot{x}_1\right] - (m_1 - m_2)g = 0$$

$$(m_1 + m_2)\ddot{x}_1 = (m_1 - m_2)g$$

$$\ddot{x}_1 = \left(\frac{m_1 - m_2}{m_2 + m_2}\right)g.$$

This is the differential equation of motion for the system; it can readily be integrated to give

$$\dot{x}_1 = \left(\frac{m_1 - m_2}{m_1 + m_2}\right)gt + \dot{x}_{1_0}$$

and

$$x_1 = \frac{1}{2}\left(\frac{m_1 - m_2}{m_1 + m_2}\right)gt^2 + \dot{x}_{1_0}t + x_{1_0},$$

where $\dot{x}_{1_0}$ and x_{1_0} indicate the initial velocity and displacement of m_1. Clearly, the factor $(m_1 - m_2)/(m_1 + m_2)$ represents the mass that m_1 would have to have to fall freely at the same rate as it would if connected to m_2. Of course, similar equations could have been obtained in the coordinate x_2.

12. Find the Lagrangian function for the double pendulum of Problem 2.2 (3), using θ and ϕ as independent generalized coordinates, and apply it to obtain the equations of motion [Fig. P2.2 (12)].

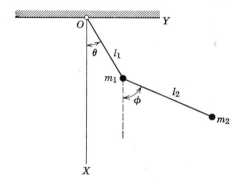

Fig. P2.2 (12)

Solution

Let the rectangular coordinates of m_1 and m_2 be (x_1, y_1) and (x_2, y_2); then:

$$y_1 = l_1 \sin \theta, \qquad x_1 = l_1 \cos \theta$$

$$y_2 = l_1 \sin \theta + l_2 \sin \phi, \qquad x_2 = l_1 \cos \theta + l_2 \cos \phi$$

$$\dot{y}_1 = l_1\dot{\theta} \cos \theta, \qquad \dot{x}_1 = -l_1\dot{\theta} \sin \theta$$

$$\dot{y}_2 = l_1\dot{\theta} \cos \theta + l_2\dot{\phi} \cos \phi, \qquad \dot{x}_2 = -l_1\dot{\theta} \sin \theta - l_2\dot{\phi} \sin \phi$$

Therefore, the total kinetic energy may be written as

$$T = \tfrac{1}{2}m_1(\dot{x}_1{}^2 + \dot{y}_1{}^2) + \tfrac{1}{2}m_2(\dot{x}_2{}^2 + \dot{y}_2{}^2)$$
$$= \tfrac{1}{2}m_1[l_1{}^2\dot{\theta}^2 \sin^2\theta + l_1{}^2\dot{\theta}^2 \cos^2\theta]$$
$$+ \tfrac{1}{2}m_2[(-l_1\dot{\theta}\sin\theta - l_2\dot{\phi}\sin\phi)^2 + (l_1\dot{\theta}\cos\theta + l_2\dot{\phi}\cos\phi)^2]$$
$$= \tfrac{1}{2}m_1[l_1{}^2\dot{\theta}^2] + \tfrac{1}{2}m_2[l_1{}^2\dot{\theta}^2 + l_2{}^2\dot{\phi}^2 + 2l_1l_2\dot{\theta}\dot{\phi}\cos(\theta - \phi)]$$
$$= \tfrac{1}{2}(m_1 + m_2)l_1{}^2\dot{\theta}^2 + \tfrac{1}{2}m_2l_2{}^2\dot{\phi}^2 + m_2l_1l_2\dot{\theta}\dot{\phi}\cos(\theta - \phi),$$

whereas the total potential energy will be given by

$$V = -m_1gx_1 - m_2gx_2 + \text{constant}$$
$$= -(m_1 + m_2)gl_1\cos\theta - m_2gl_2\cos\phi + \text{constant}.$$

Thus,

$$L = T - V$$
$$= \tfrac{1}{2}(m_1 + m_2)l_1{}^2\dot{\theta}^2 + \tfrac{1}{2}m_2l_2{}^2\dot{\phi}^2$$
$$+ m_2l_1l_2\dot{\theta}\dot{\phi}\cos(\theta - \phi) + (m_1 + m_2)gl_1\cos\theta$$
$$+ m_2gl_2\cos\phi + \text{constant}.$$

When we substitute the above value for L in the Lagrangian equations,

$$\frac{d}{dt}\frac{\partial L}{\partial \dot{q}_j} - \frac{\partial L}{\partial q_j} = 0 \qquad \{q_j = \theta, \phi,$$

with

$$(\theta - \phi) = \alpha$$

the equations of motion become

$$(m_1 + m_2)l_1\ddot{\theta} + m_2l_2(\ddot{\phi}\cos\alpha + \dot{\phi}^2\sin\alpha) + (m_1 + m_2)g\sin\theta = 0$$

and

$$l_2\ddot{\phi} + l_1\ddot{\theta}\cos\alpha - l_1\dot{\theta}^2\sin\alpha - g\sin\phi = 0.$$

13. Using x_1 and θ as independent generalized coordinates and assuming the potential energy of the spring to be $Kx_1{}^2/2$, where K is a constant, obtain the equations of motion for the two masses shown in Fig. P2.2 (13) by the Lagrangian and Hamiltonian methods.

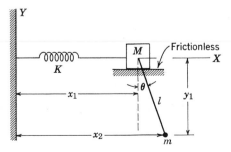

Fig. P2.2 (13)

Solution

In terms of x_1 and θ,

$$x_2 = x_1 + l \sin \theta$$
$$y_2 = -l \cos \theta;$$

Thus by differentiation

$$\dot{x}_2 = \dot{x}_1 + l\dot{\theta} \cos \theta$$
$$\dot{y}_2 = l\dot{\theta} \sin \theta$$

in terms of $\dot{x}_1$ and $\dot{\theta}$. This means that we can eliminate $\dot{x}_2$ and $\dot{y}_2$ in favor of $\dot{x}_1$ and $\dot{\theta}$ in the expression for the total kinetic energy. Dropping the subscript of x_1 to simplify the writing, we obtain

$$T = \tfrac{1}{2} M\dot{x}^2 + \tfrac{1}{2} m[(\dot{x} + l\dot{\theta} \cos \theta)^2 + (l\dot{\theta} \sin \theta)^2]$$
$$= \tfrac{1}{2}(M + m)\dot{x}^2 + \tfrac{1}{2} ml^2\dot{\theta}^2 + ml\dot{x}\dot{\theta} \cos \theta.$$

Furthermore, the total potential energy may be expressed as

$$V = \tfrac{1}{2} Kx^2 + mgl(1 - \cos \theta),$$

and we obtain the conservative Lagrangian function

$$L = T - V = \tfrac{1}{2}(m + M)\dot{x}^2 + \tfrac{1}{2} ml^2\dot{\theta}^2 + ml\dot{x}\dot{\theta} \cos \theta - \tfrac{1}{2} Kx^2$$
$$- mgl + mgl \cos \theta$$

Now, applying the Lagrangian equation,

$$\frac{d}{dt} \frac{\partial L}{\partial \dot{x}} - \frac{\partial L}{\partial x} = 0,$$

$$\frac{\partial L}{\partial \dot{x}} = (M + m)\dot{x} + ml\dot{\theta} \cos \theta$$

$$\frac{d}{dt} \frac{\partial L}{\partial \dot{x}} = (M + m)\ddot{x} + ml\ddot{\theta} \cos \theta - ml\dot{\theta}^2 \sin \theta$$

$$\frac{\partial L}{\partial x} = -Kx;$$

and the first equation of motion is

$$(M + m)\ddot{x} + ml\ddot{\theta} \cos \theta - ml\dot{\theta}^2 \sin \theta + Kx =)$$

Similarly with,

$$\frac{d}{dt} \frac{\partial L}{\partial \dot{\theta}} - \frac{\partial L}{\partial \theta} = 0,$$

$$\frac{\partial L}{\partial \dot{\theta}} = ml^2\dot{\theta} + ml\dot{x} \cos \theta$$

$$\frac{d}{dt} \frac{\partial L}{\partial \dot{\theta}} = ml^2\ddot{\theta} + ml\ddot{x} \cos \theta - ml\dot{x}\dot{\theta} \sin \theta$$

and

$$\frac{\partial L}{\partial \theta} = -ml\dot{x}\dot{\theta} \sin \theta - mgl \sin \theta$$

gives the second equation of motion:

$$l\ddot{\theta} + \ddot{x} \cos \theta + g \sin \theta = 0$$

If we used T and V in the form obtained above, the corresponding Hamiltonian function would be

$$H = T + V$$
$$= \tfrac{1}{2}(m + M)\dot{x}^2 + \tfrac{1}{2}ml^2\dot{\theta}^2 + ml\dot{x}\dot{\theta} \cos \theta + \tfrac{1}{2}Kx^2 + mgl - mgl \cos \theta;$$

however, this is expressed in terms of $\dot{x}$ and $\dot{\theta}$ instead of p_x and p_θ as required. We must apply the relations

$$p_x = \frac{\partial L}{\partial \dot{x}} = (M + m)\dot{x} + ml\dot{\theta} \cos \theta$$

$$p_\theta = \frac{\partial L}{\partial \dot{\theta}} = ml^2\dot{\theta} + ml\dot{x} \cos \theta$$

and solve these two equations simultaneously to determine $\dot{x}$ and $\dot{\theta}$ as functions of p_x and p_θ; the result is:

$$\dot{\theta} = \frac{1}{ml^2(\cos \theta - M - m)} [p_x ml \cos \theta - p_\theta(M + m)]$$

and

$$\dot{x} = \frac{1}{(M + m)} \left[p_x \left(1 - \frac{m \cos^2 \theta}{\cos \theta - M - m} \right) + \frac{p_\theta(M + m) \cos \theta}{l(\cos \theta - M - m)} \right].$$

Substituting for $\dot{x}$ and $\dot{\theta}$ in the above expression for H and applying Hamilton's equations will lead to the same equations of motion as those obtained above.

This example emphasizes the fact that certain problems can be solved more easily by Lagrange's method than by Hamilton's, because of algebraic complications. However, the reverse is also true and, in general, the choice of method must depend on the type of system being considered.

14. For the system of masses shown in Fig. P2.2 (14), S_1 and S_2 represent the lengths of inextensible cord from m_1 to m_2 and from m_3 to m_4. Choose q_1 and

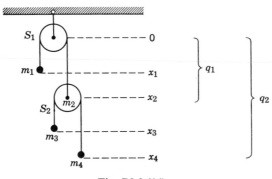

Fig. P2.2 (14)

q_2 as independent generalized coordinates, calculate the Lagrangian function, and from this determine the equations of motion.

Solution

The total kinetic energy will be

$$T = \sum_{i=1}^{4} \frac{m_i}{2} \dot{x}_i^2;$$

utilizing the constraints, however, we obtain

$$x_1 + x_2 = S_1$$

$$x_3 - x_2 + x_4 - x_2 = S_2$$

then, because

$$x_2 = q_1, \qquad \dot{x}_2 = \dot{q}_1$$

and

$$x_4 = q_2, \qquad \dot{x}_4 = \dot{q}_2,$$

$$x_1 = S_1 - q_1, \qquad \dot{x}_1 = -\dot{q}_1$$

and

$$x_3 = 2q_1 + S_2 - q_2, \qquad \dot{x}_3 = 2\dot{q}_1 - \dot{q}_2.$$

Hence,

$$T = \tfrac{1}{2}[(m_1 + 4m_3 + m_2)\dot{q}_1^2 + (m_3 + m_4)\dot{q}_2^2 - 4m_3\dot{q}_1\dot{q}_2].$$

Similarly, the total potential energy will be

$$V = -\sum_{i=1}^{4} m_i g x_i,$$

which becomes

$$V = -g[q_1(m_2 - m_1 + 2m_3) + q_2(m_4 - m_3) + m_1 S_1 + m_3 S_2].$$

Now we may write

$$L = T - V$$

and calculate

$$\frac{\partial L}{\partial \dot{q}_1} = (m_1 + m_2 + 4m_3)\dot{q}_1 - 2m_3\dot{q}_2,$$

$$\frac{\partial L}{\partial q_1} = g(m_2 - m_1 + 2m_3),$$

$$\frac{\partial L}{\partial \dot{q}_2} = (m_3 + m_4)\dot{q}_2 - 2m_3\dot{q}_1,$$

and

$$\frac{\partial L}{\partial q_2} = (gm_4 - m_3).$$

Application of the Lagrangian equations,

$$\frac{d}{dt}\frac{\partial L}{\partial \dot{q}_j} - \frac{\partial L}{\partial q_j} = 0 \qquad \{j = 1, 2,$$

then gives the equations of motion:

$$(m_1 + m_2 + 4m_3)\ddot{q}_1 - 2m_3\ddot{q}_2 - g(m_2 - m_1 + 2m_3) = 0$$

$$(m_3 + m_4)\ddot{q}_2 - 2m_3\ddot{q}_1 - g(m_4 - m_3) = 0$$

15. A mass m [Fig. P2.2 (15)] is placed on a frictionless plane that is tangent to the earth's surface, as in Problem 2.2 (10).

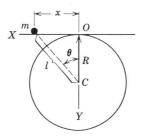

Fig. P2.2 (15)

a. Determine its equation of motion by Hamilton's method, Lagrange's method, and Newton's method, using x as the independent generalized coordinate.

b. Repeat the problem, this time choosing θ as the independent generalized coordinate.

(a) *Hamilton's method:*

$$H = T + V$$

is required, with T expressed in terms of p_x, since

$$q_j = x.$$

Clearly,

$$T = \frac{m}{2}\dot{x}^2$$

and

$$V = [l - R]mg = [(x^2 + R^2)^{\frac{1}{2}} - R]mg;$$

but also

$$p_x = \frac{\partial L}{\partial \dot{x}} = \frac{\partial}{\partial \dot{x}}(T - V) = m\dot{x},$$

and thus

$$\dot{x}^2 = \frac{p_x^2}{m^2}.$$

Therefore,

$$H = \frac{p_x^2}{2m} + [(x^2 + R^2)^{\frac{1}{2}} - R]mg;$$

and applying the Hamiltonian equations:

$$\dot{x} = \frac{\partial H}{\partial p_x} = \frac{p_x}{m}$$

$$\dot{p}_x = -\frac{\partial H}{\partial x} = -\frac{1}{2}(x^2 + R^2)^{-\frac{1}{2}}2xmg$$

$$= -\frac{mgx}{(x^2 + R^2)^{\frac{1}{2}}}$$

Lagrange's method:
From above,

$$L = \frac{m}{2}\dot{x}^2 - [(x^2 + R^2) - R]mg;$$

therefore, the Lagrangian equation

$$\frac{d}{dt}\frac{\partial L}{\partial \dot{x}} - \frac{\partial L}{\partial x} = 0$$

may be applied directly:

$$\ddot{x} + \frac{gx}{(x^2 + R^2)^{\frac{1}{2}}} = 0$$

Newton's method:
We must write

$$F_x = -\frac{dV}{dx} = -\frac{mgx}{(x^2 + R^2)^{\frac{1}{2}}} \; ;$$

hence the Newtonian equation

$$F_x = m\ddot{x}$$

gives:

$$-\frac{gx}{(x^2 + R^2)^{\frac{1}{2}}} = \ddot{x}$$

It is apparent that all three results are the same.
(b) Again,

$$H = T + V$$

is required, with T expressed as a function of p_θ; but because

$$l = \frac{R}{\cos \theta} = R \sec \theta$$

and

$$x = R \tan \theta,$$

it follows that for *Hamilton's method*

$$T = \frac{m}{2}\dot{x}^2 = \frac{m}{2}[R\dot{\theta} \sec^2 \theta]^2$$

and

$$V = [l - R]mg = [R \sec \theta - R]mg.$$

Also,

$$p_\theta = \frac{\partial L}{\partial \dot{\theta}} = \frac{\partial}{\partial \dot{\theta}}(T - V) = mR^2\dot{\theta} \sec^4 \theta,$$

giving

$$\dot\theta = \frac{p_\theta}{mR^2 \sec^4\theta}.$$

Therefore,

$$H = \frac{p_\theta{}^2}{2mR^2 \sec^4\theta} + [R \sec\theta - R]mg,$$

and Hamilton's equations give:

$$\dot\theta = \frac{\partial H}{\partial p_\theta} = \frac{p_\theta}{mR^2 \sec^4\theta}$$

$$\dot p_\theta = -\frac{\partial H}{\partial\theta} = -\frac{2p_\theta{}^2 \sin\theta}{mR^2 \sec^3\theta} - mgR \tan\theta \sec\theta$$

Lagrange's method:
From above,

$$L = \frac{m}{2} R^2\dot\theta^2 \sec^4\theta - mgR \sec\theta + mgR.$$

To apply the Lagrangian equation,

$$\frac{d}{dt}\frac{\partial L}{\partial\dot\theta} - \frac{\partial L}{\partial\theta} = 0,$$

we calculate

$$\frac{\partial L}{\partial\dot\theta} = mR^2\dot\theta \sec^4\theta,$$

$$\frac{d}{dt}\frac{\partial L}{\partial\dot\theta} = mR^2\ddot\theta \sec^4\theta + 4mR^2\dot\theta^2 \sec^4\theta \tan\theta,$$

and

$$\frac{\partial L}{\partial\theta} = 2mR^2\dot\theta^2 \sec^4\theta \tan\theta - mgR \sec\theta \tan\theta;$$

thus the equation of motion becomes

$$mR^2\ddot\theta \sec^4\theta + 4mR^2 \dot\theta^2 \sec^4\theta \tan\theta - 2mR^2\dot\theta^2 \sec^4\theta \tan\theta$$
$$+ mgR \sec\theta \tan\theta = 0$$

or

$$\ddot\theta + 2\dot\theta^2 \tan\theta + \frac{g \cos^2\theta \sin\theta}{R} = 0.$$

Newton's method:
To write the Newtonian equation,

$$F_x = m\ddot x,$$

in the proper form we must calculate from

$$x = R \tan\theta,$$

and

$$\dot x = R\dot\theta \sec^2\theta,$$

$$\ddot x = R\ddot\theta \sec^2\theta + 2R\dot\theta^2 \sec^2\theta \tan\theta.$$

Then because, as we have seen in Problem 2.2 (10),

$$F_x = -mg \sin \theta,$$

the equation of motion is

$$mR\ddot{\theta} \sec^2 \theta + 2mR\dot{\theta}^2 \sec^2 \theta \tan \theta + mg \sin \theta = 0$$

or

$$\ddot{\theta} + 2\dot{\theta}^2 \tan \theta + \frac{g \cos^2 \theta \sin \theta}{R} = 0.$$

Differentiating the first of the Hamiltonian equations once more with respect to time and substituting for $\dot{p}_\theta$ in the second equation, we obtain:

$$mR^2\ddot{\theta} \sec^4 \theta = -\frac{2p_\theta{}^2 \sin \theta}{mR^2 \sec^3 \theta} - mgR \tan \theta \sec \theta,$$

$$\ddot{\theta} + \frac{2p_\theta{}^2 \tan \theta}{(mR^2 \sec^4 \theta)^2} + \frac{g \tan \theta}{R \sec^3 \theta} = 0$$

or

$$\ddot{\theta} + 2\dot{\theta}^2 \tan \theta + \frac{g \cos^2 \theta \sin \theta}{R} = 0.$$

Again, therefore, all of the equations of motion are the same, as required because the motion of the mass is unique. But, clearly, the choice of the independent generalized coordinate and the method used to obtain the equation of motion seriously affects both the final form of the equation and the degree of difficulty involved in obtaining it.

Exercises 2.2

1. Use the principle of virtual work to determine the magnitude that the force P must have for the system of Fig. E2.2 (1) to remain in equilibrium. Neglect friction and the mass of the rod and the pulley.

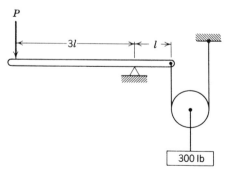

Fig. E2.2 (1)

Answer.   50 lb.

2. Neglecting frictional effects and the masses of the two rods, use the method of virtual work to calculate the magnitude of the force P necessary for equilibrium in Fig. E2.2 (2).

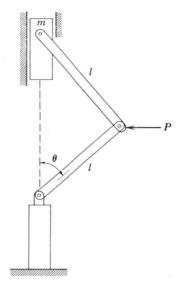

Fig. E2.2 (2)

Answer. $P = 2mg \tan \theta$.

3. Use d'Alembert's principle to determine the acceleration of both blocks and the tension in both ropes of Fig. E2.2 (3), neglecting friction and the masses of the pulleys.

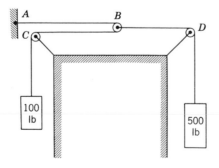

Fig. E2.2 (3)

Answer. $\frac{1}{3}g$, $\frac{2}{3}g$, 167 lb, 334 lb.

4. Calculate the generalized forces associated with the system shown in Fig. E2.2 (4), neglecting friction and the mass of the spring.

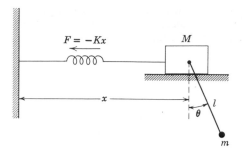

Fig. E2.2 (4)

Answer. $Q_1 = -Kx$; $Q_2 = -mgl \sin \theta$.

5. Determine the generalized force components associated with the independent generalized coordinates θ and ϕ for the spherical pendulum shown in Fig. E2.2 (5).

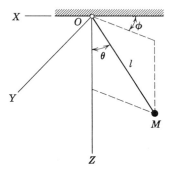

Fig. E2.2 (5)

Answer. $Q_\theta = -mgl \sin \theta$; $Q_\phi = 0$.

6. Make the following calculations:
   a. A point object is moving in a plane, subject to an inverse square attractive force; find the Lagrangian in polar coordinates.
   b. Find the Lagrangian in the case of a simple pendulum with a bob of mass m attached to a string of length l and negligible mass.

7. A particle of mass m moves in one dimension under the influence of a potential

$$V(x) = \frac{K}{x^4}.$$

Find x as a function of $\dot{x}$ using the Lagrangian equation.

Answer. $\dot{x} = \sqrt{\dfrac{2}{m}\left(E - \dfrac{K}{x^4}\right)}.$

8. Two point masses, m_1 and m_2, are connected by an inextensible string passing through a hole in a smooth table, so that m_1 slides on the table surface and m_2 hangs suspended. Assuming that m_2 moves only in a vertical line and that m_1 remains on the table, write down Lagrange's equation of motion for the system.

Answer. $\ddot{x} - \left(\dfrac{m_2}{m_1 + m_2} \right) g = 0.$

9. If $x = 0$ and $\dot{x} = x_0$ at time $t = 0$ for a point object, find x as a function of time using Lagrange's equation and the two following potentials:
a. $V = -mgx.$
b. $V = \frac{1}{2}kx^2.$

10. Find:

a. p_j for a point object whose Lagrangian has the form

$$L = \frac{m}{2}[(\dot{q}_1)^2 + (q_1\dot{q}_2)^2] - \frac{K}{2}(q_2)^2$$

b. The differential equations of motion for the same object, starting with Lagrange's equations.

11. Obtain the equation of motion for the simple pendulum [Fig. E2.2 (11)], using ϕ as the generalized coordinate, by Lagrange's method and Hamilton's method.

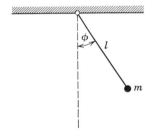

Fig. E2.2 (11)

Answer. $ml^2\ddot{\phi} + mgl \sin \phi = 0.$

12. Determine the equations of motion for the double pendulum of Problem 2.2 (12), using Hamilton's instead of Lagrange's method.

2.3 Time- and Velocity-Dependent Potentials

We shall soon see that the Hamiltonian function, like the Lagrangian function, can be expanded to include dependence on time for nonconservative systems; in fact, they can even be modified to include velocity-dependent potentials. But first it is desirable to consider one of the more important implications of requiring these functions to be time-independent for conservative systems. As in the preceding section we shall visualize the motion of two masses connected by a rigid rod, but bear in mind that the relations developed may be extended to any number of degrees of freedom.

The fact that (2.43) is the form of (2.36) applicable to such systems suggests that the conservative counterpart of equation (2.35) should be:

$$\sum_{j=1}^{5} \left(\frac{d}{dt} \frac{\partial L}{\partial \dot{q}_j} - \frac{\partial L}{\partial q_j} \right) \delta q_j = 0 \tag{3.1}$$

Now if, in view of the nature of virtual displacements, we require that

$$\delta q_j = 0 \quad \text{at} \quad t = t_1 \quad \text{and} \quad t = t_2 \tag{3.2}$$

and form

$$\int_{t_1}^{t_2} \delta L \, dt = \int_{t_1}^{t_2} \sum_{j=1}^{5} \frac{\partial L}{\partial \dot{q}_j} \delta \dot{q}_j \, dt + \int_{t_1}^{t_2} \sum_{j=1}^{5} \frac{\partial L}{\partial q_j} \delta q_j \, dt$$

$$= \sum_{j=1}^{5} \frac{\partial L}{\partial \dot{q}_j} \delta q_j \Big]_{t_1}^{t_2} - \int_{t_1}^{t_2} \sum_{j=1}^{5} \frac{d}{dt} \frac{\partial L}{\partial \dot{q}_j} \delta q_j \, dt + \int_{t_1}^{t_2} \sum_{j=1}^{5} \frac{\partial L}{\partial q_j} \delta q_j \, dt$$

$$= \int_{t_1}^{t_2} \sum_{j=1}^{5} \left(-\frac{d}{dt} \frac{\partial L}{\partial \dot{q}_j} + \frac{\partial L}{\partial q_j} \right) \delta q_j \, dt, \tag{3.3}$$

where an integration by parts has been carried out through use of the equivalence[16]

$$\delta \dot{q}_j = \frac{d}{dt}(q_j + \delta q_j) - \frac{d}{dt} q_j = \frac{d}{dt} \delta q_j, \tag{3.4}$$

we see these equations to assure that

$$\int_{t_1}^{t_2} \delta L \, dt = \delta \int_{t_1}^{t_2} L \, dt = \delta \int_{t_1}^{t_2} (T - V) \, dt = 0. \tag{3.5}$$

This is called Hamilton's variational principle for a conservative system. It states that the actual motion of the system between times t_1 and t_2 will be such that the integral

$$\int_{t_1}^{t_2} L(q_1, q_2, \ldots, q_5, \dot{q}_1, \dot{q}_2, \ldots, \dot{q}_5) \, dt$$

will be stationary with respect to independent virtual displacements vanishing at these two times. In physical terms this means that the real path will minimize the integral of the difference between the kinetic and

[16] Haar, D. ter, *Elements of Hamiltonian Mechanics*, pp. 34–37, North-Holland, Amsterdam, 1961.

potential energy between any two times and may in this sense be considered independent of time. It should be evident that, by proceeding in reverse, Lagrange's equations, and thus Newton's equations, for a conservative system could be derived from this principle.[17]

Hamilton's equations can also be derived from the same principle,[18] but in a way it is more satisfactory to base the derivation on the variational principle of least "action":

$$\delta \int_{t_1}^{t_2} \sum_{j=1}^{5} p_j \dot{q}_j \, dt = 0 \qquad (3.6)$$

where the virtual displacements must be carried out in such a way that the Hamiltonian H will remain constant, whether or not they vanish at t_1 and t_2. It will be noted that the action,

$$\int_{t_1}^{t_2} \sum_{j=1}^{5} p_j \dot{q}_j \, dt,$$

features the same quantity that distinguishes the Hamiltonian function from the Lagrangian function (2.56). However, we shall not make extensive use of this principle and, therefore, will not discuss it further at present.

Because in the general Lagrangian equations (2.36),

$$\frac{d}{dt} \frac{\partial T}{\partial \dot{q}_j} - \frac{\partial T}{\partial q_j} = Q_j \qquad \{j = 1, 2, \ldots, 5,$$

the generalized forces are defined by (2.33),

$$Q_j = \sum_{i=1}^{2} \mathbf{F}_i \cdot \frac{\partial \mathbf{r}_i}{\partial q_j},$$

there is no reason why we cannot now treat cases in which the force $\mathbf{F}_i$ or, what amounts to the same thing, the potential function V depends on the time t, or even on the generalized velocities $\dot{q}_j$. But, of course, if such dependence exists, equations like (1.28) can no longer be used; thus $\mathbf{F}_i \neq \nabla_i V$, and the system will not be conservative in the earlier sense.

It is worth noting that there is no question of T depending explicitly on time because the acceleration of the point mass, its rate of change of velocity with time, is already incorporated in the equations of motion; but the possibility exists that it may depend on the q_j (2.36). The implication

[17] Band, W., *Introduction to Mathematical Physics*, pp. 123–131; Van Nostrand, Princeton, N.J., 1959.
[18] Goldstein, H., *Classical Mechanics*, pp. 225–234, Addison-Wesley, Reading, Mass., 1959.

is that we may define a more general Lagrangian function than (2.42):

$$\mathscr{L} = T(q_1, q_2, \ldots, q_5, \dot{q}_1, \dot{q}_2, \ldots, \dot{q}_5)$$
$$- V(q_1, q_2, \ldots, q_5, \dot{q}_1, \dot{q}_2, \ldots, \dot{q}_5, t) \quad (3.7)$$

For then, parallel to the form of (2.43), we can write

$$\frac{d}{dt}\frac{\partial \mathscr{L}}{\partial \dot{q}_j} - \frac{\partial \mathscr{L}}{\partial q_j} = \frac{d}{dt}\frac{\partial T}{\partial \dot{q}_j} - \frac{d}{dt}\frac{\partial V}{\partial \dot{q}_j} - \frac{\partial T}{\partial q_j} + \frac{\partial V}{\partial q_j} = 0, \quad (3.8)$$

providing

$$\frac{d}{dt}\frac{\partial T}{\partial \dot{q}_j} - \frac{\partial T}{\partial q_j} = Q_j = \frac{d}{dt}\frac{\partial V}{\partial \dot{q}_j} - \frac{\partial V}{\partial q_j}. \quad (3.9)$$

It is immediately apparent that, if T does not depend on q_j and V depends on neither $\dot{q}_j$ nor t, in other words, if $\mathscr{L} = L$, (3.8) will reduce to

$$\frac{d}{dt}\frac{\partial T}{\partial \dot{q}_j} + \frac{\partial V}{\partial q_j} = 0, \quad (3.10)$$

which is essentially the same as (2.43). Stated another way, the generalized forces (3.9) reduce to

$$Q_i = - \frac{\partial V}{\partial q_j},$$

as in (2.40).

On the other hand, if $\mathscr{L}$ has the full dependence of (3.7), we can still write the Lagrangian equations in the form (3.8),

$$\frac{d}{dt}\frac{\partial \mathscr{L}}{\partial \dot{q}_j} - \frac{\partial \mathscr{L}}{\partial q_j} = 0 \quad \{j = 1, 2, \ldots, 5,$$

provided that the generalized forces are calculated from the right-hand equation in (3.9),

$$Q_j = \frac{d}{dt}\frac{\partial V}{\partial \dot{q}_j} - \frac{\partial V}{\partial q_j}. \quad (3.11)$$

Furthermore, examining equations (2.53) to (2.57) we see that if the Lagrangian depends on time, we must write

$$\delta \mathscr{L} = \sum_{j=1}^{5} \dot{p}_j \, \delta q_j + \sum_{j=1}^{5} p_j \, \delta \dot{q}_j + \frac{\partial \mathscr{L}}{\partial t} \delta t \quad (3.12)$$

and define the Hamiltonian from

$$\sum_{j=1}^{5} -\dot{p}_j \, \delta q_j + \sum_{j=1}^{5} \dot{q}_j \, \delta p_j - \frac{\partial \mathscr{L}}{\partial t} \delta t = \delta \left(\sum_{j=1}^{5} p_j \dot{q}_j - \mathscr{L} \right) = \delta \mathscr{H}. \quad (3.13)$$

Therefore,

$$\delta\mathscr{H}(q_1, q_2, \ldots, q_5, p_1, p_2, \ldots, p_5, t)$$

$$= \sum_{j=1}^{5} \frac{\partial\mathscr{H}}{\partial q_j} \delta q_j + \sum_{j=1}^{5} \frac{\partial\mathscr{H}}{\partial p_j} \delta p_j + \frac{\partial\mathscr{H}}{\partial t} \delta t; \quad (3.14)$$

and we conclude that, even if $\mathscr{H}$ depends on time, we can still write the Hamiltonian equations in the form

$$\frac{\partial\mathscr{H}}{\partial q_j} = -\dot{p}_j \qquad (3.15)$$

$$\frac{\partial\mathscr{H}}{\partial p_j} = \dot{q}_j, \qquad (3.16)$$

provided we also require that

$$\frac{\partial\mathscr{H}}{\partial t} = -\frac{\partial\mathscr{L}}{\partial t}. \qquad (3.17)$$

Often, in practice, the time dependence of $\mathscr{H}$ and $\mathscr{L}$ arises through the constraints of the system varying with time.

Because the conservative Hamiltonian is just the sum of the kinetic and potential energy, $H = T + V$, intuition suggests that it should be possible to equate the first variation of this quantity to the work done by the non-conservative forces alone. If we assume that the force function can be written as

$$\mathbf{F}_i = -\nabla_i V + \mathscr{N}_i, \qquad (3.18)$$

where $\mathscr{N}_i$ indicates the resultant of the nonconservative forces, then on physical grounds it is reasonable to suppose that

$$\delta H_i = dE_i = d(T + V)_i = \mathscr{N}_i \cdot d\mathbf{r}_i; \qquad (3.19)$$

this relation can be verified experimentally.[19] Sometimes (3.19) can be used to define the function $\mathscr{N}_i$, so that Newton's equation can be applied in the form

$$-\nabla_i V + \mathscr{N}_i = \frac{d}{dt} m\mathbf{v}_i. \qquad (3.20)$$

Obviously, both of these last relations will reduce to the usual conservative forms if $\mathscr{N}_i = 0$.

Of course, (3.8) and (3.11), (3.15) through (3.17), (3.19) and (3.20) all involve a broadening of the concept of energy conservation; and it may

[19] Shames, I. H., *Engineering Mechanics*, pp. 426–438, Prentice-Hall, Englewood Cliffs, N.J., 1960.

not always be possible to define an appropriate function $\mathscr{L}$, $\mathscr{H}$ or $\mathscr{N}$. We will consider below two important cases where it is possible to define such a function, but general principles are difficult to lay down. Nonconservative forces often involve heat flow, and later we will learn how the science of thermodynamics extends the conservation concept by recognizing heat as a form of energy and applying the idea expressed in (3.19). Actually, this is possible because, at least to first-order accuracy, a force can be associated with a temperature gradient just as with the type of potential gradient defined above. The same is true of various other kinds of gradients, a fact that is exploited in the modern disciplines of irreversible thermodynamics and systems analysis. Eventually we will consider both of these, and also learn how in certain fundamental particle processes conservation ideas can be extended even further.

Nevertheless, nonconservative forces can usually be recognized by the fact that they are not gradients of time-independent scalar potential functions. And in addition to the forces between point gravitational masses, any force that may be expressed as such a gradient can ordinarily be considered conservative—for example, electrostatic forces between point charges and linear spring forces between point inertial masses. Basically this is because we can then consider the associated physical properties to resemble the gravitational property closely enough to concentrate them all at the same point and simply extend the idea of mass, as developed in the beginning of Section 2.1. Although, in general, the force $\mathbf{F}_i$ can be any function relating the accelerations of objects due to any causes whatsoever, ordinarily only those functions that are gradients of scalar potentials will be conservative in the sense of (1.42),

$$\int_c \mathbf{F}_i \cdot d\mathbf{r}_i = 0.$$

Because gravitational forces are much weaker than all other types of forces known today, as the following table illustrates,[20] it might also be wondered whether the concept of conservative forces continues to apply over the entire range of strengths:

Fundamental particle interactions	Strength scale
Strong (nuclear)	~ 1
Moderately strong (electromagnetic)	$\sim 10^{-2}$
Weak (decay)	$\sim 10^{-5}$
Very weak (gravitational)	$\sim 10^{-40}$

[20] Feynman, R. P., R. B. Leighton, and M. Sands, *Lectures on Physics*, Vol. 1, pp. 2.1–2.11, Addison-Wesley, Reading, Mass., 1963.

A final answer to this question cannot be given yet, but the latest experiments with strongly interacting particles appear to confirm, as every other experiment has confirmed, the universal validity of the concept.[21]

As a first example of a nonconservative system for which an appropriate generalized force function can nevertheless be found, let us consider the case when friction forces proportional to the velocity in the three component directions are present:

$$\mathbf{f}_i = \sum_i (-C_x \dot{x}_i \hat{\mathbf{i}} - C_y \dot{y}_i \hat{\mathbf{j}} - C_z \dot{z}_i \hat{\mathbf{k}}) \tag{3.21}$$

where the C's are constants and the minus signs indicate opposition to the motion. Then, even though heat flow will occur and nonrecoverable work will be done, we can define the function

$$V_f = \tfrac{1}{2} \sum_i (C_x \dot{x}_i{}^2 + C_y \dot{y}_i{}^2 + C_z \dot{z}_i{}^2) \tag{3.22}$$

so that

$$\mathbf{f}_i = - \frac{\partial V_f}{\partial \dot{x}_i} \hat{\mathbf{i}} - \frac{\partial V_f}{\partial \dot{y}_i} \hat{\mathbf{j}} - \frac{\partial V_f}{\partial \dot{z}_i} \hat{\mathbf{k}}. \tag{3.23}$$

It follows from (2.33), (2.39), (2.40), and (2.27) that the generalized forces may be written as

$$Q_j = \sum_i \mathbf{F}_i \cdot \frac{\partial \mathbf{r}_i}{\partial q_j} = - \sum_i \left[\left(\nabla V \cdot \frac{\partial \mathbf{r}_i}{\partial q_j} \right) + \left(\frac{\partial V_f}{\partial \dot{x}_i} \hat{\mathbf{i}} + \frac{\partial V_f}{\partial \dot{y}_i} \hat{\mathbf{j}} + \frac{\partial V_f}{\partial \dot{z}_i} \hat{\mathbf{k}} \right) \cdot \frac{\partial \mathbf{r}_i}{\partial q_j} \right] \tag{3.24}$$

or

$$Q_j = - \frac{\partial V}{\partial q_j} - \frac{\partial V_f}{\partial \dot{q}_j}. \tag{3.25}$$

The equations of motion (2.36) then become

$$\frac{d}{dt} \frac{\partial T}{\partial \dot{q}_j} - \frac{\partial}{\partial q_j} (T - V) = - \frac{\partial V_f}{\partial \dot{q}_j}; \tag{3.26}$$

and using the form (2.43), we may write

$$\frac{d}{dt} \frac{\partial L}{\partial \dot{q}_j} - \frac{\partial L}{\partial q_j} = - \frac{\partial V_f}{\partial \dot{q}_j}. \tag{3.27}$$

Clearly, when no such frictional forces are present these equations reduce to the usual Lagrangian equations for a conservative system. It is often possible to express the generalized forces as a sum of conservative and

[21] Chew, G. F., M. Gell-Mann and A. H. Rosenfeld, "Strongly Interacting Particles," *Scientific American*, pp. 74–93, February 1964.

nonconservative parts, as in (3.25), so that the equations of motion can be obtained from the conservative Lagrangian equations by adding the proper correction terms.

Finally, we shall consider the case of an electron moving in an electromagnetic field. Because of its small size and the relative strength of electromagnetic interactions, we can assume that both the mass m and the charge e of the electron will be concentrated at a single point, and that gravitational forces will be negligible. Thus only the inertial effects of m will have to be taken into account[22]; otherwise, accelerations will be caused entirely by the effects of the electromagnetic field on the electron's charge.

If only an electrostatic field, which closely resembles a gravitational field except for possessing a repulsive capability, were present, it would be logical to apply the same reasoning as before and merely write m/e instead of m for the proportionality constants (1.7). The usual procedure, however, is to continue to write Newton's equation as in (1.16),

$$\mathbf{F} = m \frac{d\mathbf{v}}{dt},$$

but to express the force as

$$\mathbf{F}_E = e\mathbf{E} = -e\nabla\phi, \tag{3.28}$$

where $\mathbf{E} = \mathbf{E}(\mathbf{r})$ is the intensity of the electric field whose flux density is $\mathbf{D} = \mathbf{D}(\mathbf{r})$ and ϕ is a scalar potential function. In this case, of course, $\mathbf{F}_E$ would be conservative and we could proceed just as for pure gravitational forces.

On the other hand, if only a static magnetic field of intensity $\mathbf{H}(\mathbf{r})$ with the flux density $\mathbf{B}(\mathbf{r})$ were present, the situation would necessarily be different. Interactions involving magnetic forces, unlike gravitational and electrostatic forces, are inherently noncentral (Fig. 2.5). Magnetic properties cannot, therefore, be considered concentrated in a point, and the earlier reasoning breaks down. Stated another way, Newton's third law requiring equal and opposite reactions will not be satisfied.[23] Using Ampere's law it is not difficult to show[24] that the force exerted on such a charge by a pure magnetic field is

$$\mathbf{F}_B = e(\mathbf{v} \times \mathbf{B}) \tag{3.29}$$

[22] Dicke, R. H., P. G. Roll, and J. Weber, "Gravity Experiments," *International Science and Technology*, No. 29, pp. 50–64, May 1964.

[23] Symon, K. R., *Mechanics*, 2nd edition, pp. 139, 140, Addison-Wesley, Reading, Mass., 1960.

[24] Plonsey, R., and R. E. Collin, *Principles and Applications of Electromagnetic Fields*, pp. 198–204, McGraw-Hill, New York, 1961.

where **v** is the charge velocity and e, being a scalar quantity, can be either positive or negative. Evidently, this force will always act at right angles to **v** and **B**. However, precisely for this reason the force can do no work on the moving charge, and energy will continue to be conserved,

$$T + e\phi = E, \tag{3.30}$$

because (1.42),

$$\int_c \mathbf{F} \cdot d\mathbf{r} = 0,$$

will still be satisfied by the total force. Therefore, in this special case we can continue to regard the force (3.29) from a static magnetic field as pseudo-conservative and neglect the fact that the potential is velocity-dependent.

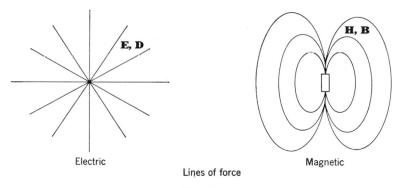

Electric   Magnetic

Lines of force

Fig. 2.5

Actually, though, electromagnetic fields usually vary in time in such a way as to satisfy Maxwell's equations:[25]

$$\nabla \times \mathbf{E} + \frac{\partial \mathbf{B}}{\partial t} = 0, \qquad \nabla \cdot \mathbf{B} = 0 \tag{3.31, 32}$$

$$\nabla \times \mathbf{H} - \frac{\partial \mathbf{D}}{\partial t} = \mathbf{J}, \qquad \nabla \cdot \mathbf{D} = \rho \tag{3.33, 34}$$

where ρ is the charge density and **J** is the density of the electric convection current, equal to $\rho\mathbf{v}$ plus the drift current density **j**. Thus the overall potential will vary with time, and the system will become nonconservative. As in the preceding example, however, we can compose this potential of a conservative and a nonconservative part.

[25] Holt, C. A., *Introduction to Electromagnetic Fields and Waves*, pp. 202, 203, 208, and 209, Wiley, New York, 1963.

According to (3.32), we should be able to express **B** as

$$\mathbf{B} = \nabla \times \mathbf{A} \tag{3.35}$$

where $\mathbf{A} = \mathbf{A}(\mathbf{r}, t)$ is a vector function, often called a vector potential. This is because writing E in the form

$$\mathbf{E} = -\nabla\phi - \frac{\partial\mathbf{A}}{\partial t} \tag{3.36}$$

satisfies (3.31),

$$\nabla \times \left(-\nabla\phi - \frac{\partial\mathbf{A}}{\partial t}\right) + \frac{\partial}{\partial t}(\nabla \times \mathbf{A}) = -\nabla \times \frac{\partial\mathbf{A}}{\partial t} + \nabla \times \frac{\partial\mathbf{A}}{\partial t} = 0,$$

$$\tag{3.37}$$

and suggests that $\mathbf{F}_E$ of (3.28) should be expanded to

$$\mathbf{F}_E = e\left(-\nabla\phi - \frac{\partial\mathbf{A}}{\partial t}\right). \tag{3.38}$$

Thus, we obtain the total Lorentz force

$$\mathbf{F} = \mathbf{F}_E + \mathbf{F}_B = e(\mathbf{E} + \mathbf{v} \times \mathbf{B}) = e\left[-\nabla\phi - \frac{\partial\mathbf{A}}{\partial t} + \mathbf{v} \times (\nabla \times \mathbf{A})\right]$$

$$\tag{3.39}$$

for use in Newton's equation. Evidently, the term $-\nabla\phi$ corresponds to $-\nabla V$ in (3.20),

$$-\nabla V + \mathcal{N} = \frac{d}{dt}m\mathbf{v},$$

while the remaining terms correspond to $\mathcal{N}$. Also, it can be shown[26] that the Lorentz force is just the generalized force Q_j of (3.11),

$$Q_j = \frac{d}{dt}\frac{\partial V}{\partial\dot{q}_j} - \frac{\partial V}{\partial q_j},$$

with $q_j = \mathbf{r}$ and the potential given by

$$V = e\phi - e\mathbf{A} \cdot \mathbf{v}. \tag{3.40}$$

The Lagrangian can then be formed as

$$\mathscr{L} = T - e\phi + e\mathbf{A} \cdot \mathbf{v}, \tag{3.41}$$

---

[26] Goldstein, H., *Classical Mechanics*, pp. 19–22, Addison-Wesley, Reading, Mass., 1959.

with $T = mv^2/2$ in the ordinary way, for use in (3.8). And, knowing $\mathscr{L}$, the Hamiltonian $\mathscr{H}$ may be written from the definition in (3.13),

$$\mathscr{H} = mv^2 - \mathscr{L}, \tag{3.42}$$

for use in (3.15) to (3.17).

Perhaps it is worth emphasizing that, even though the preceding discussion has been developed in terms of an electron moving in an electro-magnetic field, it applies equally as well to the motion of any charged point object in such a field, provided only that e and m are understood to represent that object's charge and mass.

Problems 2.3

1. Use Lagrange's equation to determine the equation of motion of the mass $2m$ after it is submerged in the liquid [Fig. P2.3 (1)]. Neglect the mass and frictional effects of the pulley, assume that the system starts from rest in the position shown, and that the liquid creates a frictional force proportional to the velocity of the mass.

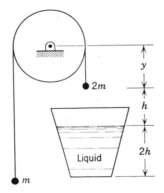

Fig. P2.3 (1)

Solution

After the mass has entered the liquid, we have

$$\frac{d}{dt}\frac{\partial L}{\partial \dot{y}} - \frac{\partial L}{\partial y} = -\frac{\partial V_f}{\partial \dot{y}}$$

where, applying the reasoning of Problem 2.2 (11),

$$L = T - V = \left(\frac{2m + m}{2}\right)\dot{y}^2 + (2m - m)gy = \tfrac{3}{2}m\dot{y}^2 + mgy$$

and, by assumption,

$$\frac{\partial V_f}{\partial \dot{y}} = k\dot{y}.$$

Substituting, we obtain

$$3m\ddot{y} + k\dot{y} - mg = 0$$

or

$$\ddot{y} + \frac{k}{3m}\dot{y} = \frac{g}{3}.$$

*The solution must be of the form

$$y = y_G + y_P;$$

but we can easily see that

$$\dot{y}_P = \frac{mg}{k}, \qquad y_P = \frac{mg}{k}t$$

and

$$\ddot{y}_G + \frac{k}{3m}\dot{y}_G = 0,$$

which, rewritten in the standard differential operator notation,

$$\left(D^2 + \frac{k}{3m}D\right)y_G = 0,$$

may be seen to have the solution

$$y_G = C_1 + C_2 e^{-\frac{k}{3m}t};$$

therefore,

$$y = C_1 + C_2 e^{-\frac{k}{3m}t} + \frac{mg}{k}t.$$

To evaluate C_1 and C_2, we must apply the initial conditions. First, it follows that if at $t = 0$, $y = 0$, then

$$0 = C_1 + C_2.$$

We also know that at $t = 0$, $\dot{y} = v_0$, being the velocity of the mass $2m$ just as it enters the liquid, However, from conservation of energy,

$$T_1 + V_1 = T_2 + V_2,$$

with

$$T_1 = 0, \qquad T_2 = \tfrac{3}{2}mv_0^2$$

and

$$V_1 = 0, \qquad V_2 = -mgh,$$

we obtain

$$v_0 = \sqrt{\tfrac{2}{3}gh}.$$

Now

$$\dot{y} = -C_2\frac{k}{3m}e^{-\frac{k}{3m}t} + \frac{mg}{k};$$

therefore,

$$\sqrt{\tfrac{2}{3}gh} = -C_2\frac{k}{3m} + \frac{mg}{k}$$

* Solutions of differential equations may be reserved for Section 3.1, if so desired.

and

$$C_2 = -\frac{m}{k}\sqrt{6gh} + \frac{3m^2g}{k^2},$$

which also defines

$$C_1 = \frac{m}{k}\sqrt{6gh} - \frac{3m^2g}{k^2}.$$

The final solution, therefore, is

$$y = \frac{m}{k}\sqrt{6gh} - \frac{3m^2g}{k^2} + \left(-\frac{m}{k}\sqrt{6gh} + \frac{3m^2g}{k^2}\right)e^{-\frac{k}{3m}t} + \frac{mg}{k}t.$$

2. Solve Problem 2.3 (1) using Newtonian methods.

Solution
   Calling the total tensile force in the cord T, it is easy to identify and sketch the forces acting on each mass [Fig. P2.3 (2)]. Thus Newton's equation may be written for each:

$$2mg - Tk\dot{y} = 2m\ddot{y}$$
$$T - mg = m\ddot{y}$$

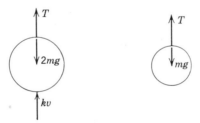

Fig. P2.3 (2)

Solving the second equation for T and substituting in the first then gives:

$$2mg - m(g + \ddot{y}) - k\dot{y} = 2m\ddot{y}$$
$$2mg - mg - k\dot{y} = 3m\ddot{y}$$
$$\ddot{y} + \frac{k}{3m}\dot{y} = \frac{g}{3}$$

3. Determine the equation of motion of an electron during and after its passage between the deflection plates of a two-dimensional cathode-ray oscilloscope, when a constant electric field E exists between the plates [Fig. P2.3 (3a)].

Solution
   Newton's equation of motion gives

$$\mathbf{F} = eE\hat{\mathbf{j}} = m\frac{d^2\mathbf{r}}{dt^2}$$

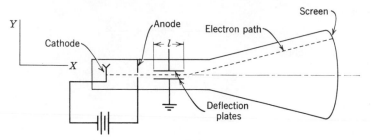

Fig. P2.3 (3a)

and the corresponding scalar equations are:

$$\ddot{x} = 0$$

$$\ddot{y} = \frac{e}{m} E$$

*Integration of the first equation yields

$$\dot{x} = C_1$$

and

$$x = C_1 t + C_2;$$

however, by locating the origin of coordinates at the start of the length l, we may use the initial conditions

$$\dot{x}(0) = v_0$$

and

$$x(0) = 0$$

to obtain

$$C_1 = v_0,$$

$$C_2 = 0;$$

hence

$$x = v_0 t.$$

Integration of the second equation of motion gives

$$\dot{y} = \frac{eE}{m} t + C_3$$

and

$$y = \frac{eE}{2m} t^2 + C_3 t + C_4.$$

However, using the initial conditions

$$\dot{y}(0) = 0$$

and

$$y(0) = 0,$$

we obtain

$$C_3 = 0,$$

$$C_4 = 0;$$

therefore,

$$y = \frac{eE}{2m} t^2.$$

This and the relation $x = v_0 t$ constitute the scalar equations of motion for the electron while it is between the plates of the oscilloscope. To determine the geometrical equation of its path, we can eliminate t between them to obtain

$$y = \frac{eEx^2}{2mv_0^2}, \qquad 0 < x < l,$$

the equation of a parabola. From then on the electron will move in a straight line until it strikes the phosphorescent screen, as shown in Fig. P2.3 (3b).

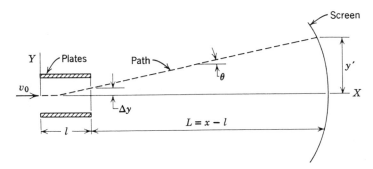

Fig. P2.3 (3b)

If we assume the curvature of the screen to be very small,

$$y' = L \tan \theta + \Delta y.$$

Placing $x = l$ in the above equation for y, we obtain

$$\Delta y = \frac{eE}{2m} \frac{l^2}{v_0^2}.$$

Also, the time that the electron remains between the plates follows from $x = v_0 t$; it is

$$t_l = \frac{l}{v_0}.$$

Therefore, using the foregoing expression for $\dot{y} = v_y$ with $C_3 = 0$, we have

$$v_y = \frac{eE}{m} \frac{l}{v_0},$$

and we can calculate

$$\tan \theta = \frac{v_y}{v_x} = \frac{eEl}{mv_0^2}.$$

Evidently, then,

$$y' = \frac{eElL}{mv_0^2} + \frac{eEl^2}{2mv_0^2}.$$

Of course, y' may be replaced by y if L is replaced by $x - l$, and the first term will vanish when $x = l$. Note that y' is a linear function of E and thus is proportional to the voltage applied across the plates.

4. A point object of charge e and mass m enters a constant magnetic field $-B\hat{\mathbf{k}}$. The velocity of the object just before entering the field is $\mathbf{v}_0$, a constant vector with a direction perpendicular to the field. Obtain the scalar equations of motion and prove that the path of the object inside the field will be circular, provided no other forces are acting.

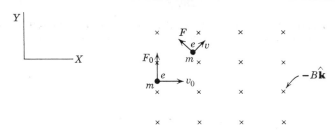

Fig. P2.3 (4)

Solution

Newton's equation for the motion of the object in the field [see Fig. P2.3 (4)] is

$$\mathbf{F} = e(\mathbf{v} \times \mathbf{B}) = \frac{d}{dt} m\mathbf{v}$$

or

$$-eB(\mathbf{v} \times \mathbf{k}) = m\mathbf{a},$$

$$-\frac{eB}{m}(\dot{x}\hat{\mathbf{i}} + \dot{y}\hat{\mathbf{j}} + \dot{z}\hat{\mathbf{k}}) \times \hat{\mathbf{k}} = \ddot{\mathbf{r}},$$

$$-\frac{eB}{m}(-\dot{x}\hat{\mathbf{j}} + \dot{y}\hat{\mathbf{i}}) = \ddot{x}\hat{\mathbf{i}} + \ddot{y}\hat{\mathbf{j}} + \ddot{z}\hat{\mathbf{k}};$$

therefore, the three scalar equations of motion must be:

$$\ddot{x} = -\frac{eB}{m}\dot{y}$$

$$\ddot{y} = \frac{eB}{m}\dot{x}$$

$$\ddot{z} = 0.$$

We need not solve these equations to determine the geometrical path. It is known that

$$\mathbf{F} = -eB(\mathbf{v} \times \hat{\mathbf{k}}),$$

so that

$$|\mathbf{F}| = eBv;$$

because B is constant and there is no change in potential energy, by conservation of energy we have

$$E = \frac{mv^2}{2}, \qquad v = \pm\sqrt{\frac{2E}{m}} = \text{constant} = v_0.$$

Thus **F** remains both constant in magnitude, with a value of F_0, and perpendicular to **v**. The point object must be experiencing a constant acceleration in a direction perpendicular to **v**, which can only occur if the motion is circular. Then, using the fact that $a = v_0^2/\rho$ from Section 1.1 and equating this to F_0/m, we obtain

$$\frac{v_0^2}{\rho} = \frac{eBv_0}{m}$$

or

$$\rho = \frac{mv_0}{eB} = \text{constant.}$$

5. A cyclotron has an oscillator frequency of 10^7 cps and a dee radius of 20 in. [Fig. P2.3 (5).]

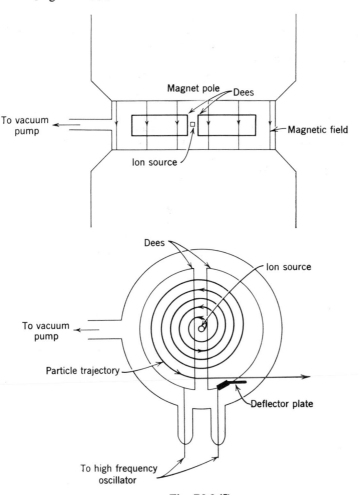

Fig. P2.3 (5)

a. What value of the magnetic induction B is needed to accelerate deuterons, which have the same charge but almost twice the mass of a proton?
b. What deuteron energy results?

Solution

The cyclotron accelerates charged particles by causing them to pass through a small potential difference many times. A magnetic field is used to bend the particle trajectories, and the two hollow *D*-shaped boxes in which the particles move are connected to a high frequency oscillator that changes the sign of their charge several million times per second. The charged particle source is in the center. If a particle finds that the dee facing it has an opposite charge, it will be accelerated toward it; but the magnetic field will cause it to follow a semicircular path in such a way that it will be accelerated again at the other side of the dee, provided the dees change sign as noted above.

Each time the particle is accelerated its energy is increased and it will describe a semicircle of slightly larger radius, but the period of revolution $\tau = 2\pi/\omega$ will remain the same, because it does not depend on the energy (or speed) of the charged particle:

$$\omega = \frac{v}{\rho} = \frac{qB}{m}, \qquad \tau = \frac{2\pi}{\omega} = \frac{2\pi m}{qB},$$

using results from Section 1.1 and the preceding problem with e replaced by q. Thus the particle will describe a spiral path, as shown in the figure, and may be removed from the dees by means of a charged deflector at the outer edge.

The angular frequency of the oscillation, ω_0, must equal the frequency with which the charged particle circulates in the magnetic field to achieve a resonant condition,

$$\omega_0 = \frac{qB}{m}.$$

The radius R of the dees determines the maximum particle energy; the speed of a particle moving at this radius will be given by

$$v = \frac{qBR}{m},$$

so that its kinetic energy will be

$$T = \tfrac{1}{2}mv^2 = \frac{(qBR)^2}{2m}.$$

Because $\omega_0 = 2\pi\nu_0$, where ν_0 is the oscillator frequency, it follows that

$$\nu_0 = \frac{qB}{2\pi m}$$

or

$$B = \frac{2\pi\nu_0 m}{q}.$$

Thus for (*a*) of this problem,

$$B = \frac{2\pi \times 10^7 (3.3 \times 10^{-27})}{1.6 \times 10^{-19}}$$

$$= 1.29 \text{ Wb/m}^2$$

while for (*b*):

$$T = \frac{(1.6 \times 10^{-19})^2 (1.29)^2 (20 \times 0.0254)^2}{2(3.3 \times 10^{-27})}$$

$$= 1.67 \times 10^{-12}$$

$$= 1.67 \times 10^{-12} \times \frac{10^{-6}}{1.6 \times 10^{-19}} = 10.4 \text{ MeV}$$

Exercises 2.3

1. A point mass is moving under the influence of a constant gravitational field $\mathbf{g} = (g_0/\sqrt{14})(\hat{\mathbf{i}} - 2\hat{\mathbf{j}} + 3\hat{\mathbf{k}})$. Assume that friction is present and that the frictional force can be obtained from a dissipation function $V_f = \frac{1}{2}kv^2$.
   a. Obtain the equation of motion for the point mass using the Lagrangian formulation.
   b. *Solve the equation in terms of displacement.
   c. Show that the maximum velocity which the point mass can attain is $\dot{q}_{max} = mg/k$.

Answer

(a) $\ddot{q} + \dfrac{k}{m} \dot{q} = g_0$, where q is the generalized coordinate in the direction of **g**.

(b) $q = -\dfrac{m^2 g}{k^2} + \dfrac{mg}{k} t + \dfrac{m^2 g}{k^2} e^{-\frac{k}{m}t}$.

2. Solve Problem 2.3 (1) using Newtonian methods.

3. A simple pendulum is submerged in a liquid which creates a frictional force that can be derived from a dissipation function $V_f = \frac{1}{2}kv^2$ [see Fig. E2.3 (3)].

   a. Use the Lagrangian formulation to determine the equation of motion.
   b. *Solve the equation of motion for the case when ϕ is very small.

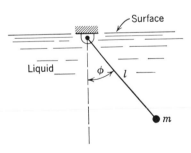

Fig. E2.3 (3)

Answer. $\ddot{\phi} + \dfrac{k}{m} \dot{\phi} + \dfrac{g}{l} \sin \phi = 0$.

4. Solve Problem 2.3 (3) using Newtonian methods.

* Solutions of differential equations may be reserved for Section 3.1, if so desired.

5. *An alpha particle of mass m and charge $2e$ is moving in a time-varying electric field given by

$$E = E_0 e^{-\alpha t} \cos \omega t.$$

If initially the particle has a velocity v_0, what is its velocity at time t?

Answer. $v = \dfrac{E_0 e}{m} e^{-\alpha t} \left[\dfrac{e^{i\omega t}}{i\omega - \alpha} - \dfrac{e^{-i\omega t}}{i\omega + \alpha} \right] + \dfrac{2\alpha E_0 e}{m(\omega^2 + \alpha^2)} + v_0.$

6. *A sinusoidal potential with a frequency of 1 million cps and a maximum amplitude of 10 V is applied to the plates of a parallel plate condenser, which are 2 cm apart. If an electron is released from one plate with an initial normal velocity of 10^8 cm/sec at an instant when the applied potential is zero, find the position of the electron at any subsequent time t.

Answer. $x = 1.5 \times 10^9 t - 223 \sin (6.28 \times 10^6 t)$.

7. A 10 eV electron is circulating in a plane at right angles to a uniform field whose magnetic induction is $B = 1.0 \times 10^{-4}$ Wb/m^2, or 1.0 G.

a. What is the radius of its orbit?
b. What is the period of its revolution?

Answer
(a) 10.8 cm.
(b) 3.6×10^{-7} sec.

8. A point object of mass m and charge e enters a region of constant electric field E with a constant velocity v_0 in the y-direction, as shown in Fig. E2.3 (8). Assuming that a constant gravitational force is acting in the negative y-direction, use Newton's equation to determine the equations of motion, *and solve for the distance L above the x-axis that the point object will travel before colliding with one of the plates.

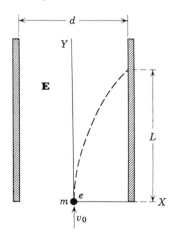

Fig. E2.3 (8)

Answer. $L = -\tfrac{1}{2} g \left(\dfrac{md}{eE} \right) + v_0 \sqrt{\dfrac{md}{eE}}.$

3

Point Object Motion

3.1 Equation Structure, Force Forms, and Solutions

If in a given problem the kinetic and potential energy are known or are easy to determine, it is probably simpler to obtain the working form of the equations of motion from the Lagrangian or Hamiltonian equations than from the Newtonian equations. However, if the applied force function is given, the opposite may be true, and it is this point of view that we shall adopt initially.

It is especially likely that the Newtonian formulation will be best if the force function can be written as a sum of functions of one coordinate variable, its first derivative and, possibly, time. For then the three equations (1.20) to (1.22) of Chapter 2, which are fully coupled and must be solved simultaneously, reduce to the three uncoupled equations,

$$F_x(x, \dot{x}, t) = m\ddot{x} \tag{1.1}$$

$$F_y(y, \dot{y}, t) = m\ddot{y} \tag{1.2}$$

$$F_z(z, \dot{z}, t) = m\ddot{z} \tag{1.3}$$

which can be solved separately. This will be recognized as a rather restricted class of motions, because in every case the actual three-dimensional motion of the point object must be such that its projections in the three coordinate directions will satisfy (1.1) to (1.3). Nevertheless, several important physical cases (especially motions along one of the coordinate axes) are included, and the mathematical problem is much simplified.

Let us select (1.1) as typical and start by recognizing that this is a second-order ordinary differential equation, which must be accompanied by two initial or boundary conditions if the two constants that will appear

187

when it is integrated are to be determined. Only then will it be possible to express the solution in the particular form

$$x = x(t) \tag{1.4}$$

and to obtain the velocity $\dot{x}$ and acceleration $\ddot{x}$ at any time t by direct differentiation. Of course, the integration itself may be difficult because (1.1) may be nonlinear—if $F_x(x, \dot{x}, t)$ contains powers of the dependent variable x, and/or $\dot{x}$, higher than the first—and will describe a nonconservative system, if it actually depends on t as shown.

Still without specifying the exact nature of the forces acting on the point object, let us further simplify by restricting ourselves to cases where (1.1) is linear and F_x does not depend explicitly on t, although implicit dependence through $\dot{x}$ is permissible. Then one general form of this equation will be

$$\alpha_1 \ddot{x} + \alpha_2 \dot{x} + \alpha_3 x = \alpha_4 \tag{1.5}$$

where α_1, α_2, and α_3 are positive constants. The implication is that, with

$$\alpha_1 = m, \tag{1.6}$$

the force function must be

$$F_x = -\alpha_2 \dot{x} - \alpha_3 x + \alpha_4. \tag{1.7}$$

When

$$\alpha_4 = 0 \tag{1.8}$$

the differential equation becomes homogeneous and is not very hard to solve, in spite of the fact that the system will be nonconservative because of the presence of the term involving $\dot{x}$ in the force. The general solution will contain two arbitrary constants. Thus two initial conditions, possibly of the type

$$x(t_0) = x_0 \tag{1.9}$$

$$\dot{x}(t_0) = \dot{x}_0 \tag{1.10}$$

where the subscript 0 indicates a definite numerical value, or perhaps two boundary conditions, such as (1.9) together with another relation of the type

$$x(t_1) = x_1 \tag{1.11}$$

where x_1 is some numerical value different from x_0, will be required to obtain a particular solution.[1] We will consider several such cases in the following section.

Furthermore, the theory of linear ordinary differential equations[1] tells us

---

[1] Hildebrand, F. B., *Advanced Calculus for Applications*, pp. 1–41, 187–189, Prentice-Hall, Englewood Cliffs, N.J., 1962.

that even if $\alpha_4 \neq 0$ and F_x contains an arbitrary function of t,

$$F_x = -\alpha_2 \dot{x} - \alpha_3 x + \alpha_4 + f(t), \tag{1.12}$$

the complete solution of the corresponding differential equation,

$$\alpha_1 \ddot{x} + \alpha_2 \dot{x} + \alpha_3 x = \alpha_4 + f(t), \tag{1.13}$$

can be obtained by finding any particular solution x_P of this equation and adding to it the general solution x_G of the corresponding homogeneous equation,

$$\alpha_1 \ddot{x} + \alpha_2 \dot{x} + \alpha_3 x = 0. \tag{1.14}$$

That is, the complete solution of (1.13) will be

$$x = x_G(t) + x_P(t), \tag{1.15}$$

where x_P needs contain no arbitrary constants because x_G will include two. The system will be nonconservative, both because of the term $-\alpha_2 \dot{x}$ and because of the function $f(t)$ appearing in the force (1.12), but this does not affect the linearity of the differential equation.

Actually, the α's may also become functions of the independent variable t without causing the equation to become nonlinear; this means that well-established solution techniques still exist.[2] They are often rather involved in practice, however; for the present time we shall avoid them, and all nonlinear cases as well.[3] Our procedure in the next section will be to keep the α's constant and build up solutions of (1.1) by considering one term at a time in (1.12) for F_x.

It is interesting to note that for a conservative system the homogeneous equation (1.14) reduces to

$$\alpha_1 \ddot{x} + \alpha_3 x = 0, \tag{1.16}$$

or

$$\alpha_1 \ddot{x} = -\alpha_3 x = F_x. \tag{1.17}$$

Thus a potential energy

$$V_x = \frac{\alpha_3 x^2}{2} \tag{1.18}$$

is implied, because

$$-\frac{dV_x}{dx} = -\alpha_3 x = F_x. \tag{1.19}$$

Assuming the kinetic energy to be

$$T_x = \frac{\alpha_1 \dot{x}^2}{2}, \tag{1.20}$$

[2] Whittaker, E. T., and G. N. Watson, *A Course of Modern Analysis*, 4th edition, pp. 194–208, Cambridge, 1958.
[3] Saaty, T. L., and J. Bram, *Nonlinear Mathematics*, pp. 175–275, McGraw-Hill, New York, 1964.

since the Cartesian coordinate is clearly an independent generalized coordinate, we see that both Lagrange's and Hamilton's equations return the result (1.16) for the equation of motion:

$$L = T_x - V_x = \frac{\alpha_1 \dot{x}^2}{2} - \frac{\alpha_3 x^2}{2}, \tag{1.21}$$

$$\frac{d}{dt}\frac{\partial L}{\partial \dot{x}} - \frac{\partial L}{\partial x} = \frac{d}{dt}\alpha_1 \dot{x} + \alpha_3 x = \alpha_1 \ddot{x} + \alpha_3 x = 0 \tag{1.22}$$

and

$$H = T_x + V_x = \frac{\alpha_1 \dot{x}^2}{2} + \frac{\alpha_3 x^2}{2}, \tag{1.23}$$

$$\frac{\partial H}{\partial x} = \alpha_3 x = -\dot{p}_x = -\alpha_1 \ddot{x}, \tag{1.24}$$

or

$$\alpha_1 \ddot{x} + \alpha_3 x = 0. \tag{1.25}$$

Of course, this is as it should be and only serves to emphasize that all three formalisms are equivalent. Regardless of which one we start with, or whether the system is conservative or nonconservative, we shall always come to the same working form of the equations of motion.

If the force function cannot be written as a sum of functions in which the coordinates are separated, so that in general

$$F_x(x, y, z, \dot{x}, \dot{y}, \dot{z}, t) = m\ddot{x}$$
$$F_y(x, y, z, \dot{x}, \dot{y}, \dot{z}, t) = m\ddot{y}$$
$$F_z(x, y, z, \dot{x}, \dot{y}, \dot{z}, t) = m\ddot{z}$$

as in (1.20) to (1.22) of Chapter 2, we must solve these equations simultaneously. Later we will learn that it is sometimes possible to uncouple the equations, so that each contains only one coordinate, by converting to so-called "normal" coordinates. They are also independent generalized coordinates, but such special ones that what amounts to a simultaneous solution must be carried out to identify them.

However, it is important to note that if the equations are linear and possess constant coefficients, the methods of solving systems of simultaneous linear algebraic equations that we have already learned (Section 1.3) can be adapted[4] to their solution without much difficulty. We shall consider a number of examples in the following sections, proceeding from completely uncoupled cases to systems containing more and more coupling, until we finally arrive at the case of motions in a fully-coupled continuous medium.

[4] Hochstadt, H., *Differential Equations, A Modern Approach*, pp. 37–81, Holt, Rinehart and Winston, New York, 1964.

3.2   One-Dimensional and Uncoupled Two- and Three-Dimensional Motions

For the reasons given in the preceding section, this topic can best be studied by analyzing the Newtonian equations that result from including only certain terms or combinations of terms in the expression (1.12) for F_x:

$$F_x = -\alpha_2 \dot{x} - \alpha_3 x + \alpha_4 + f(t)$$

All of the resulting differential equations will be linear, although some may be nonhomogeneous and some may describe nonconservative motions of point objects.

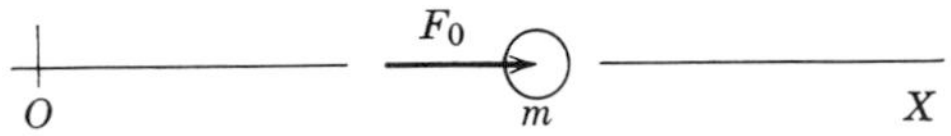

Fig. 3.1

First, let us consider the case when all of the terms in (1.12) are zero except α_4; that is,

$$F_x = \alpha_4 = \text{constant} = F_0. \tag{2.1}$$

Then Newton's equation (1.1) becomes

$$m\ddot{x} = F_0. \tag{2.2}$$

The physical system described is a point object of mass m accelerating uniformly in a positive direction along the X-axis under the influence of a constant force F_0 (Fig. 3.1). A body with an unchanging center of mass sliding along a very smooth track or falling freely toward the earth with almost no air resistance ($F_0 = -mg$, with the positive X-axis upward) would approximate this situation, as would a charged particle moving in a constant electric field. Obviously, the system would be conservative.

Equation (2.2) can immediately be integrated to obtain:

$$\dot{x} = \frac{F_0}{m} t + C_1 \tag{2.3}$$

$$x = \frac{F_0}{2m} t^2 + C_1 t + C_2 \tag{2.4}$$

The general solution is (2.4), and two initial or boundary conditions will be required to eliminate the arbitrary constants C_1 and C_2 and arrive at some particular solution. For example, with

$$x(0) = 0 \qquad (2.5)$$
$$\dot{x}(0) = 0, \qquad (2.6)$$

it follows from (2.3) and (2.6) that

$$C_1 = 0; \qquad (2.7)$$

and from this, (2.4) and (2.5) that

$$C_2 = 0. \qquad (2.8)$$

Thus, the particular solution for these initial conditions is

$$x = \frac{F_0 t^2}{2m}, \qquad (2.9)$$

with

$$\dot{x} = \frac{F_0 t}{m}. \qquad (2.10)$$

Next let us consider the case when all of the terms in (1.12) vanish but $-\alpha_3 x$:

$$F_x = -\alpha_3 x = -(\text{constant})x = -K_x x \qquad (2.11)$$

Newton's equation then is

$$m\ddot{x} + K_x x = 0. \qquad (2.12)$$

This force, proportional to the displacement and always acting in the opposite direction, is called a linear restoring force and is usually associated with an elastic spring. Hence we can imagine (2.12) to describe the oscillatory motion along the X-axis of a point object of mass m secured to a

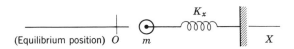

(Equilibrium position) O $\quad m$ $\qquad X$

Fig. 3.2

fixed linear spring, as shown in Fig. 3.2. Presumably some equilibrium position, at which the mass would rest and about which it would oscillate, exists; it is shown displaced from this position to emphasize that a condition of motion, arising from certain initial conditions, is assumed. This system too is conservative and, in fact, is perhaps the one best suited to measurements of inertial mass alone. A body oscillating on a smooth, horizontal track (so that both friction and gravity could be neglected), or possibly a charged particle bound to an equilibrium position by a linear electrical restoring force, would approximate the system. Notice that even if the spring is material, its mass is assumed to be negligible relative to that of the point object on which it acts. This is a common assumption, and we shall use it from this point onward unless specifically stated otherwise.

It is interesting to note that several springs secured to the mass in series or parallel can be reduced to a single equivalent spring with a constant K,

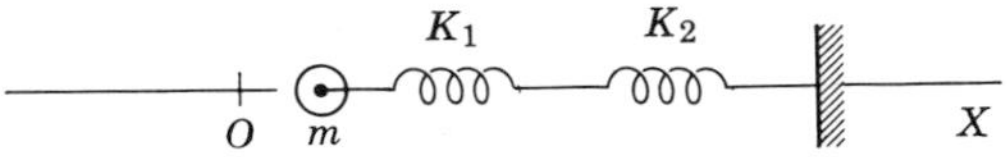

Fig. 3.3

consisting of a certain combination of the individual constants K_1, K_2, ... In the series case, for example (Fig. 3.3), calling the change in length of the first spring δ_1, with

$$F_1 = -K_1\delta_1, \qquad (2.13)$$

and the change in length of the second spring δ_2, with

$$F_2 = -K_2\delta_2, \qquad (2.14)$$

because of the necessity to make the system of Fig. (3.2) equivalent to that of Fig. (3.3) it must be true that

$$x = \delta_1 + \delta_2; \qquad (2.15)$$

and we conclude that

$$\frac{F_x}{K_x} = \frac{F_1}{K_1} + \frac{F_2}{K_2}. \qquad (2.16)$$

But each spring must also contain the same force,

$$F_1 = F_2 = F_x; \qquad (2.17)$$

therefore,

$$\frac{1}{K_x} = \frac{1}{K_1} + \frac{1}{K_2}$$

or

$$K_x = \frac{K_1 K_2}{K_1 + K_2}. \qquad (2.18)$$

For the parallel case (Fig. 3.4), we must have

$$F_x = F_1 + F_2; \qquad (2.19)$$

thus,

$$K_x x = K_1\delta_1 + K_2\delta_2. \qquad (2.20)$$

But the displacement of each spring must also be the same,

$$\delta_1 = \delta_2 = x, \tag{2.21}$$

so it follows that

$$K_x = K_1 + K_2. \tag{2.22}$$

We shall see later that even systems involving several masses coupled together with springs can be reduced to simpler equivalent systems by finding combined constants, although the procedure for finding them is more complicated than the present one. Actually, all such cases are analogous to those considered in Problems 2.2, where two masses were combined into one effective mass to simplify the equations of motion.

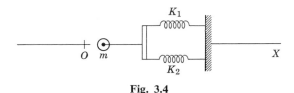

Fig. 3.4

Returning to the basic equation (2.12), which is identical in form to (1.16), we should begin by noting that, since the total mechanical energy is both conserved and separable, we should be able to achieve a preliminary analysis in the manner of (1.64) in Chapter 2 applied to Fig. 2.3. Comparing (1.16) and (2.12) we see that

$$\alpha_1 = m \tag{2.23}$$

and

$$\alpha_3 = K_x; \tag{2.24}$$

thus the kinetic and potential energy in the present instance must be [(1.20) and (1.18)]:

$$T_x = \frac{m\dot{x}^2}{2} \tag{2.25}$$

and

$$V_x = \frac{K_x x^2}{2}. \tag{2.26}$$

Furthermore, we know that

$$V_x \le E_x.$$

Conservation of energy also tells us [(1.63) in Chapter 2] that $\dot{x}$ may be either positive or negative but must remain proportional to $\sqrt{E_x - V_x}$; and, clearly, when $V_x = E_x$,

$$\frac{K_x x^2}{2} = E_x$$

or

$$x = \pm \sqrt{\frac{2}{K_x} E_x}, \tag{2.27}$$

at which points $\dot{x} = 0$. Plotting the parabola (2.26) in Fig. 3.5 and applying the above considerations, we see that our point object will

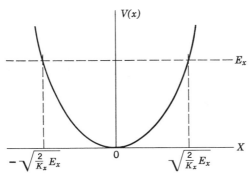

Fig. 3.5

indeed oscillate about some equilibrium position O, as suggested earlier, but in such a way that

$$\dot{x} = \pm \sqrt{\frac{2}{m} \left(E_x - \frac{K_x x^2}{2} \right)} \tag{2.28}$$

and

$$-\sqrt{\frac{2}{K_x} E_x} \leq x \leq \sqrt{\frac{2}{K_x} E_x}. \tag{2.29}$$

This is called a free vibration. Ordinarily such vibrations are required to be of small amplitude, so that the spring will remain elastic and therefore capable of providing the linear restoring force. Notice that the momentum of the object will be zero at its two turning points and that it will take on its maximum value when $x = 0$.

To obtain more details of the motion, we must solve (2.12),

$$m\ddot{x} + K_x x = 0.$$

The theory of solving second-order ordinary differential equations[5] suggests that we should try a solution of the form

$$x = e^{pt}, \tag{2.30}$$

where p is a parameter of the system. Substituting this in (2.12), we obtain

$$mp^2e^{pt} + K_xe^{pt} = 0$$
$$mp^2 + K_x = 0 \tag{2.31}$$

or

$$p = \pm\sqrt{-\frac{K_x}{m}} = \pm i\sqrt{\frac{K_x}{m}} = i\omega_0, \tag{2.32}$$

where

$$\omega_0 = \pm\sqrt{\frac{K_x}{m}} \tag{2.33}$$

is called the natural angular frequency of the system, for reasons that will become clear below. Hence (2.30) will be a solution of (2.12) if p has either of the values given by (2.32); we can constitute the general solution by associating an arbitrary constant with each of the two possible solutions and adding them:

$$x = A_1e^{i\omega_0 t} + A_2e^{-i\omega_0 t} \tag{2.34}$$

At this point it is worthwhile to observe that if the basic equation had a minus instead of a plus sign connecting the terms (the force could not then be interpreted as a restoring force),

$$\alpha_1\ddot{x} - \alpha_3 x = 0, \tag{2.35}$$

then corresponding to (2.31) we would obtain

$$\alpha_1 p^2 - \alpha_3 = 0.$$

Therefore,

$$p = \pm\sqrt{\frac{\alpha_3}{\alpha_1}} = \pm\beta, \tag{2.36}$$

and the solution corresponding to (2.34) would contain only real exponentials:

$$x = B_1e^{\beta t} + B_2e^{-\beta t} \tag{2.37}$$

We shall have occasion to use this equation and solution later, but it is a case of motion quite different from the present one.

Returning to the solution (2.34), it is desirable to understand that it can be written in several other equivalent ways. If A_1 and A_2 are selected as

[5] Apostol, T. M., *Calculus*, Vol. 1, pp. 217–245, Blaisdell, Waltham, Mass., 1961.

the complex number pair

$$A_1 = A_3 + iA_4 \tag{2.38}$$

$$A_2 = A_3 - iA_4, \tag{2.39}$$

then, by applying the well-known Euler relations to obtain

$$e^{i\omega_0 t} = \cos \omega_0 t + i \sin \omega_0 t \tag{2.40}$$

$$e^{-i\omega_0 t} = \cos \omega_0 t - i \sin \omega_0 t, \tag{2.41}$$

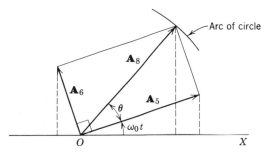

Fig. 3.6

(2.34) becomes

$$x = (A_3 + iA_4)(\cos \omega_0 t + i \sin \omega_0 t) + (A_3 - iA_4)(\cos \omega_0 t - i \sin \omega_0 t)$$

$$= A_3 \cos \omega_0 t + iA_3 \sin \omega_0 t + iA_4 \cos \omega_0 t - A_4 \sin \omega_0 t$$

$$+ A_3 \cos \omega_0 t - iA_3 \sin \omega_0 t - iA_4 \cos \omega_0 t - A_4 \sin \omega_0 t$$

$$= 2A_3 \cos \omega_0 t - 2A_4 \sin \omega_0 t, \tag{2.42}$$

or with

$$2A_3 = A_5 \tag{2.43}$$

$$2A_4 = A_6, \tag{2.44}$$

$$x = A_5 \cos \omega_0 t - A_6 \sin \omega_0 t. \tag{2.45}$$

Furthermore, if we regard A_5 and A_6 as the magnitudes of vectors, sometimes called phasors, rotating in a counterclockwise direction about their common origin with a constant angular velocity ω_0 (Fig. 3.6), it follows that the tip of their resultant $\mathbf{A}_8$ will rotate in a circle about O while its x-projection describes the actual (harmonic) motion of the object:

$$x = A_5 \cos \omega_0 t - A_6 \cos \left[\pi - \left(\frac{\pi}{2} + \omega_0 t \right) \right]$$

$$= A_5 \cos \omega_0 t - A_6 \cos \left(\frac{\pi}{2} - \omega_0 t \right)$$

$$= A_5 \cos \omega_0 t - A_6 \sin \omega_0 t$$

as in (2.45). With

$$-A_6 = A_7 \tag{2.46}$$

this can also be written as

$$x = A_5 \cos \omega_0 t + A_7 \sin \omega_0 t. \tag{2.47}$$

Additionally, it is clear that

$$x = A_8 \cos (\omega_0 t + \theta), \tag{2.48}$$

where

$$A_8 = \pm\sqrt{A_5^2 + A_6^2} \tag{2.49}$$

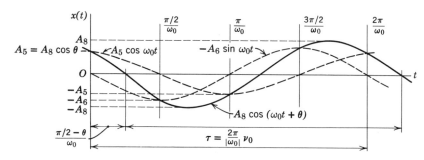

Fig. 3.7

and

$$\theta = \tan^{-1} A_6/A_5; \tag{2.50}$$

or, alternately, that

$$x = A_8 \sin \left[\frac{\pi}{2} - (\omega_0 t + \theta) \right]$$

$$= -A_8 \sin \left[\omega_0 t + \left(\theta - \frac{\pi}{2} \right) \right]$$

$$= A_9 \sin (\omega_0 t + \delta), \tag{2.51}$$

with

$$-A_8 = A_9 \tag{2.52}$$

and

$$\left(\theta - \frac{\pi}{2} \right) = \delta. \tag{2.53}$$

The angle θ is called the phase of the vibration, because it establishes the stage of the motion at $t = 0$; the angle δ is sometimes called the phase lag.

Plotting the separate components of (2.45), and their sum as well, we obtain the results shown in Fig. 3.7. This diagram makes it clear why ω_0

is called the natural angular frequency. Of course it is the angular speed of the tip of the resultant phasor, measured in radians per unit time, and ν_0 is the actual oscillation frequency of the object, measured in cycles per unit time. The period, or time required to complete one cycle, is indicated by τ; A_8 (or A_9) defines the maximum amplitude, usually designated simply by A, of the object's vibration. It is said to be performing a simple harmonic motion.

Suppose now that instead of (2.11) for F_x we had

$$F_x = -\alpha_2 \dot{x} - \alpha_3 x = -C_x \dot{x} - K_x x. \tag{2.54}$$

Newton's equation would then become

$$m\ddot{x} + C_x \dot{x} + K_x x = 0, \tag{2.55}$$

which corresponds to the complete homogeneous equation (1.14). However, the system represented is nonconservative because the force, and thus

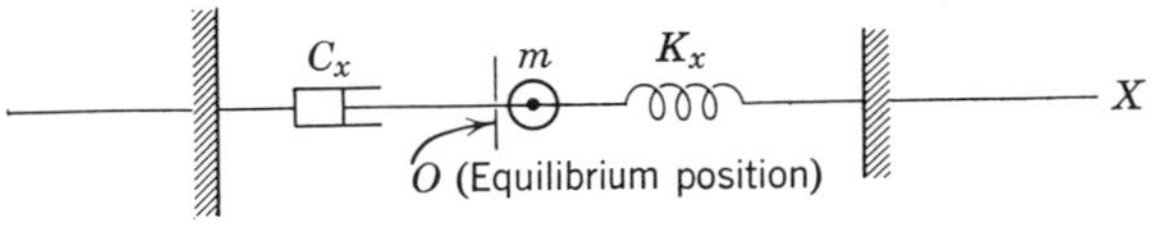

Fig. 3.8

the generalized potential energy, is velocity-dependent. Evidently we may identify the new term $-C_x \dot{x}$ with the special type of frictional forces discussed earlier [(3.21) to (3.27) in Chapter 2]; they are usually called linear damping forces and often represented by a dashpot (Fig. 3.8). It will be noted that this must act in parallel with the spring (both are connected to ground in the figure), because their displacements must be equal (2.21). Real systems in oscillatory motion are nearly always described more accurately by this equation than by (2.12), because frictional damping of some form will usually be present. Like that of the spring, the mass of the dashpot piston is ignored.

Proceeding to solve (2.55), we shall again try the solution (2.30),

$$x = e^{pt}.$$

This gives

$$mp^2 e^{pt} + C_x p e^{pt} + K_x e^{pt} = 0 \tag{2.56}$$

or

$$p^2 + \frac{C_x}{m} p + \frac{K_x}{m} = 0; \tag{2.57}$$

therefore,

$$p = \cfrac{-\cfrac{C_x}{m} \pm \sqrt{\left(\cfrac{C_x}{m}\right)^2 - \cfrac{4K_x}{m}}}{2}$$

$$= -\cfrac{C_x}{2m} \pm \sqrt{\left(\cfrac{C_x}{2m}\right)^2 - \cfrac{K_x}{m}}. \qquad (2.58)$$

We can construct the general solution in the same way as before, by associating an arbitrary constant with each of the particular solutions for the

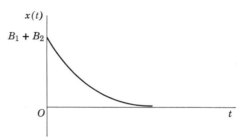

Fig. 3.9

two values of p and adding them, but now there are three different cases to consider.

If

$$\left(\frac{C_x}{2m}\right)^2 > \frac{K_x}{m}, \qquad (2.59)$$

the square root in (2.58) will be real, and the general solution will be:

$$x = e^{-\frac{C_x}{2m}t}\left[B_1 e^{\sqrt{\left(\frac{C_x}{2m}\right)^2 - \frac{K_x}{m}}\,t} + B_2 e^{-\sqrt{\left(\frac{C_x}{2m}\right)^2 - \frac{K_x}{m}}\,t}\right] \qquad (2.60)$$

Because

$$\frac{C_x}{2m} > \sqrt{\left(\frac{C_x}{2m}\right)^2 - \frac{K_x}{m}}, \qquad (2.61)$$

x will decrease exponentially with time (Fig. 3.9). The system represented will not oscillate at all and is said to be overdamped.

If

$$\left(\frac{C_x}{2m}\right)^2 < \frac{K_x}{m}, \qquad (2.62)$$

the square root in (2.58) will be imaginary, and for the general solution we will obtain

$$x = e^{-\frac{C_x}{2m}t}\left[A_i e^{i\sqrt{\frac{K_x}{m} - \left(\frac{C_x}{2m}\right)^2}\, t} + A_2 e^{-i\sqrt{\frac{K_x}{m} - \left(\frac{C_x}{2m}\right)^2}\, t} \right] \tag{2.63}$$

or, in the form (2.48),

$$x = A e^{-\frac{C_x}{2m}t} \cos\left(\sqrt{\frac{K_x}{m} - \left(\frac{C_x}{2m}\right)^2}\, t + \theta \right), \tag{2.64}$$

A and θ being the two arbitrary constants. In this case the system will oscillate in accordance with the cosine term, but the amplitude of its

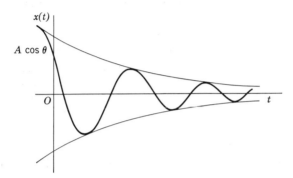

Fig. 3.10

oscillation will decrease exponentially with time, as shown in Fig. 3.10. It is said to be underdamped.

Finally, if

$$\left(\frac{C_x}{2m}\right)^2 = \frac{K_x}{m}, \tag{2.65}$$

the square root in (2.58) will vanish and we will be left with only one solution,

$$x_1 = C_1 e^{-\frac{C_x}{2m}t}. \tag{2.66}$$

However, the indication is that $-C_x/2m$ is a repeated root of (2.57), and it is well-known[6] that in this case we can obtain another solution by writing

$$x_2 = C_2 t e^{-\frac{C_x}{2m}t} \tag{2.67}$$

and construct the general solution by adding the two:

$$x = e^{-\frac{C_x}{2m}t}(C_1 + C_2 t) \tag{2.68}$$

[6] Apostol, T. M., *Calculus*, Vol. 2, pp. 330–333, Blaisdell, Waltham, Mass., 1962.

After a short interval, x will decrease even more rapidly with time than in (2.60), as shown in Fig. 3.11. This system is called critically damped, and from (2.65) we see that the critical damping constant

$$C_{x_{\text{crit}}} = 2\sqrt{K_x m}. \qquad (2.69)$$

Next, let us imagine that

$$F_x = -\alpha_3 x + f(t) \qquad (2.70)$$

or, in particular, that

$$F_x = -K_x x + F_0 \sin \omega t, \qquad (2.71)$$

where F_0 is a constant representing the maximum amplitude of an applied force varying periodically in time with an angular frequency ω. Of course,

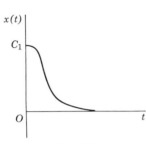

$f(t)$ could just as well be placed equal to $F_0 \cos \omega t$, but it should be noted that choosing between this and $F_0 \sin \omega t$ amounts to specifying a particular time scale. With F_x given by (2.71), the Newtonian equation is

$$m\ddot{x} + K_x x = F_0 \sin \omega t. \qquad (2.72)$$

Fig. 3.11

The system described is similar to the freely-vibrating system depicted in Fig. (3.2), except for the periodic force $F_0 \sin \omega t$ applied to the mass m (Fig. 3.12). However, such a force is enough to render the system nonconservative and the differential equation of motion (2.72) nonhomogeneous. Mechanical forces applied from a rotating part through a linear linkage and electrical forces associated with alternating current generators are both of this type. Also, as in the case of the dashpot and spring, the applied force and the spring must act in parallel on the mass because their displacements will be equal; the force is assumed to be connected to ground.

It follows from (1.15),

$$x = x_G(t) + x_P(t),$$

that we can obtain the complete solution of (2.72) by adding one particular solution of the full non-homogeneous form (2.72),

$$m\ddot{x} + K_x x = F_0 \sin \omega t,$$

Fig. 3.12

to the general solution of the homogeneous equation (2.12),

$$m\ddot{x} + K_x x = 0.$$

The latter we already know, and if we choose to write this in the form (2.51),

$$x_G = A \sin(\omega_0 t + \delta) \tag{2.73}$$

where A and δ are arbitrary constants, it only remains to find a particular solution.

Evidently, an expression of the form

$$x_P = D \sin \omega t \tag{2.74}$$

will satisfy (2.72) if D has the right value, since $\sin \omega t$ will appear in every term. Substituting to establish the value D should have, we see that

$$-mD\omega^2 \sin \omega t + K_x D \sin \omega t = F_0 \sin \omega t \tag{2.75}$$

or

$$D = \frac{F_0/m}{K_x/m - \omega^2} = \frac{F_0/m}{\omega_0^2 - \omega^2} = \frac{F_0/K_x}{1 - (\omega/\omega_0)^2}, \tag{2.76}$$

using the fact that $\omega_0^2 = K_x/m$. Therefore,

$$x_P = \frac{F_0/K_x}{1 - (\omega/\omega_0)^2} \sin \omega t, \tag{2.77}$$

and one of the forms of the complete solution of (2.72) must be:

$$x = A \sin(\omega_0 t + \delta) + \frac{F_0/K_x}{1 - (\omega/\omega_0)^2} \sin \omega t \tag{2.78}$$

As ω, the angular frequency of the applied force, approaches ω_0, the natural angular frequency of the system, the denominator of the last term in (2.78) will approach zero and x will increase without limit; this condition is called resonance. Clearly, the power delivered near resonance will be large, and use is often made of this fact in the design of oscillatory mechanical and electrical systems[7]. If damping actually were completely absent, the spring would ultimately break, or at least become nonlinear. But real systems always contain some damping; and in any event, various ways of introducing enough to limit displacements to predetermined safe values are known.

[7] Pipes, L. A., *Applied Mathematics for Engineers and Physicists*, pp. 141–151, 164–172, McGraw-Hill, New York, 1946.

Let us next consider the case in which a linear frictional damping force is present, that is, when

$$F_x = -\alpha_2 \dot{x} - \alpha_3 x + f(t), \tag{2.79}$$

or, specifically, when

$$F_x = -C_x \dot{x} - K_x x + F_0 \sin \omega t. \tag{2.80}$$

The corresponding Newtonian equation is

$$m\ddot{x} + C_x \dot{x} + K_x x = F_0 \sin \omega t, \tag{2.81}$$

and the resulting system resembles that of Fig. 3.8, except for the additional periodic applied force (Fig. 3.13). Evidently spring, dashpot, and applied

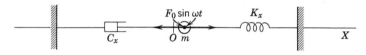

Fig. 3.13

force are all acting in parallel on the mass. Lacking only the constant term α_4, and with the general function $f(t)$ restricted to $F_0 \sin \omega t$, (2.81) is the complete linear but nonhomogeneous form (1.13), applicable to a non-conservative system. Clearly, if α_4 is included it must represent a constant force that will merely shift the equilibrium position one way or another, as the gravitational force would do if the system were turned vertically. Because this contributes nothing new physically, we shall confine our studies to (2.81).

Again we can obtain the complete solution by summing the general solution of the homogeneous equation (2.55),

$$m\ddot{x} + C_x \dot{x} + K_x x = 0,$$

and one particular solution of (2.81) in its extended form. From (2.60), (2.64), and (2.68) we know $x_G(t)$ for all three of the possibilities

$$\left(\frac{C_x}{2m}\right)^2 \gtreqless \frac{K_x}{m} \; ; \tag{2.82}$$

therefore, we need only to find a particular solution $x_P(t)$.

However, because (2.81) contains both first and second order derivatives of x with respect to t, it cannot be expected that either $D_1 \sin \omega t$ or $D_2 \cos \omega t$ separately will lead to a particular solution in the same way as before. Nevertheless, physical considerations suggest that we should be able to construct such a solution from their sum:

$$x_P = D_1 \sin \omega t + D_2 \cos \omega t \tag{2.83}$$

Substituting this in (2.81), we obtain:

$$-mD_1\omega^2 \sin \omega t - mD_2\omega^2 \cos \omega t + C_x D_1\omega \cos \omega t - C_x D_2\omega \sin \omega t$$
$$+ K_x D_1 \sin \omega t + K_x D_2 \cos \omega t = F_0 \sin \omega t \tag{2.84}$$

or

$$(-mD_1\omega^2 - C_x D_2\omega + K_x D_1 - F_0) \sin \omega t$$
$$+ (-mD_2\omega^2 + C_x D_1\omega + K_x D_2) \cos \omega t = 0. \tag{2.85}$$

Because neither $\sin \omega t$ nor $\cos \omega t$ can be zero in general, their coefficients must vanish to satisfy this equation; therefore,

$$\left(-\omega^2 + \frac{K_x}{m}\right) D_1 + \left(-\frac{C_x}{m}\omega\right) D_2 = \frac{F_0}{m} \tag{2.86}$$

$$\left(\frac{C_x}{m}\omega\right) D_1 + \left(-\omega^2 + \frac{K_x}{m}\right) D_2 = 0, \tag{2.87}$$

and this pair of simultaneous equations may be solved for D_1 and D_2.

If we make use of the fact that

$$\sqrt{K_x/m} = \omega_0$$

from (2.33) and, for convenience, place

$$C_x/m = \zeta_0 \tag{2.88}$$

and

$$F_0/m = \xi_0, \tag{2.89}$$

these equations become:

$$(\omega_0^2 - \omega^2)D_1 + (-\zeta_0\omega)D_2 = \xi_0 \tag{2.90}$$

$$(\zeta_0\omega)D_1 + (\omega_0^2 - \omega^2)D_2 = 0 \tag{2.91}$$

Applying Cramer's rule [(3.57) to (3.59) of Chapter 1], we see that

$$D_1 = \frac{\begin{vmatrix} \xi_0 & -\zeta_0\omega \\ 0 & \omega_0^2 - \omega^2 \end{vmatrix}}{\begin{vmatrix} \omega_0^2 - \omega^2 & -\zeta_0\omega \\ \zeta_0\omega & \omega_0^2 - \omega^2 \end{vmatrix}} = \frac{\xi_0(\omega_0^2 - \omega^2)}{(\omega_0^2 - \omega^2)^2 + (\zeta_0\omega)^2} \tag{2.92}$$

and

$$D_2 = \frac{\begin{vmatrix} \omega_0^2 - \omega^2 & \xi_0 \\ \zeta_0\omega & 0 \end{vmatrix}}{(\omega_0^2 - \omega^2)^2 + (\zeta_0\omega)^2} = \frac{-\xi_0\zeta_0\omega}{(\omega_0^2 - \omega^2)^2 + (\zeta_0\omega)^2}. \tag{2.93}$$

Hence (2.83) becomes

$$x_P = \frac{\xi_0}{(\omega_0^2 - \omega^2)^2 + (\zeta_0\omega)^2} [(\omega_0^2 - \omega^2)\sin\omega t - \zeta_0\omega\cos\omega t]. \tag{2.94}$$

We can now combine this particular solution with each of the $x_G(t)$ to obtain the complete solution of (2.81) for any system specified by definite values of ω_0, ζ_0, and ξ_0:

$$x = e^{-\frac{\zeta_0}{2}t}\left[B_1 e^{\sqrt{\left(\frac{\zeta_0}{2}\right)^2 - \omega_0^2}\,t} + B_2 e^{-\sqrt{\left(\frac{\zeta_0}{2}\right)^2 - \omega_0^2}\,t} \right]$$

$$+ \frac{\xi_0}{(\omega_0^2 - \omega^2)^2 + (\zeta_0\omega)^2}[(\omega_0^2 - \omega^2)\sin\omega t - \zeta_0\omega\cos\omega t],$$

$$\zeta_0^2 > 4\omega_0^2, \quad (2.95)$$

$$x = Ae^{-\frac{\zeta_0}{2}t}\cos\left[\sqrt{\omega_0^2 - \left(\frac{\zeta_0}{2}\right)^2}\,t + \theta \right]$$

$$+ \frac{\xi_0}{(\omega_0^2 - \omega^2)^2 + (\zeta_0\omega)^2}[(\omega_0^2 - \omega^2)\sin\omega t - \zeta_0\omega\cos\omega t],$$

$$\zeta_0^2 < 4\omega_0^2, \quad (2.96)$$

$$x = e^{-\frac{\zeta_0}{2}t}[C_1 + C_2 t]$$

$$+ \frac{\xi_0}{(\omega_0^2 - \omega^2)^2 + (\zeta_0\omega)^2}[(\omega_0^2 - \omega^2)\sin\omega t - \zeta_0\omega\cos\omega t],$$

$$\zeta_0^2 = 4\omega_0^2. \quad (2.97)$$

It should be clear from the earlier discussion of the $x_G(t)$ that in all three cases the first part of the solution, containing the two arbitrary constants, will die out exponentially with time. Thus, it is called the transient component of the vibration; and, of course, it is only this component that will be affected by the initial conditions. The other part of the solution, arising from $x_P(t)$, persists in time and is therefore called the steady-state component of the vibration. By writing the denominator of this part in a form parallel to the denominator of the last term in the solution (2.78) for the undamped forced oscillator,

$$\frac{1}{\left[\omega_0{}^2\left(\dfrac{\omega_0{}^2}{\omega_0{}^2} - \dfrac{\omega^2}{\omega_0{}^2}\right)\right]^2 + (\zeta_0\omega)^2} = \frac{1}{\omega_0{}^4[1 - (\omega/\omega_0)^2]^2 + (\zeta_0\omega)^2}, \quad (2.98)$$

it is easy to see that, although x may become large as ω approaches ω_0, it cannot increase without limit as before. In principle the mass will always be limited to some maximum displacement, although structural failure may occur before this is ever attained.

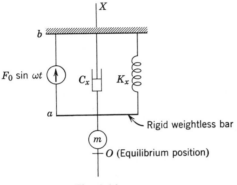

Fig. 3.14

Implicit in the preceding discussion is the possibility that (2.81), and thus the solutions (2.95) to (2.97), can be used to describe the motion of a point object that carries the charge e in addition to the mass m when the forces involved are electrical. Provided that we can interpret $-K_x x$ and $-C_x \dot{x}$ as electrical restoring and damping forces acting on the charge, we need only to replace F_0 by eE_0 (so that $\xi_0 = eE_0/m$) to describe its motion in an oscillating electric field of maximum amplitude E_0. As an example, these solutions can be used[8] to explain the opacity of dielectrics to electromagnetic radiation of certain frequencies; the material is imagined to contain a great many electrons which act as one-dimensional oscillators and absorb most of the incident radiation, if its frequency is close to their natural frequency.

Furthermore, rewriting (2.81) as a first order integrodifferential equation in the velocity $\dot{x}$,

$$m\frac{d\dot{x}}{dt} + C_x\dot{x} + K_x\int \dot{x}\, dt = F_0 \sin \omega t, \quad (2.99)$$

and redrawing Fig. 3.13 to emphasize its parallel character (Fig. 3.14),

[8] Symon, K. R., *Mechanics*, 2nd edition, pp. 50–58, Addison-Wesley, Reading, Mass., 1960.

suggests an interesting comparison with linear, lumped-parameter electrical circuit theory. Each of the terms in (2.99) represents a force. Thus, if we imagine a change of origin from the equilibrium position to ground and construct a schematic sketch (or linear graph) of the above system, assigning arrowheads to express the general case when the inertial, dashpot, and spring forces are all resisting the motion of the applied force (Fig. 3.15), it becomes clear this equation means that the sum of all such forces must always vanish at either of the vertices of the graph:

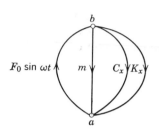

Fig. 3.15

$$F_m(t) + F_{C_x}(t) + F_{K_x}(t) = F_0 \sin \omega t \quad (2.100)$$

The circuit shown in Fig. 3.16, with i_0 representing maximum driver current, C capacitance, R resistance and L inductance, has a similar graph (Fig. 3.17); and according to Kirchhoff's current law, the sum of all the currents must also vanish at either vertex for all times:

$$i_C(t) + i_R(t) + i_L(t) = i_0 \sin \omega t \quad (2.101)$$

Additionally, it is well known[9] that each of the currents on the left is related to the voltage $v = v(t)$ across two terminals such as a and b by:

$$i_C(t) = C \frac{dv}{dt} \quad (2.102)$$

$$i_R(t) = R^{-1}v \quad (2.103)$$

$$i_L(t) = L^{-1} \int v \, dt \quad (2.104)$$

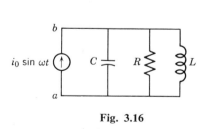

Fig. 3.16

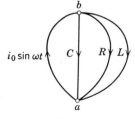

Fig. 3.17

[9] Holt, C. A., *Introduction to Electromagnetic Fields and Waves*, pp. 298–306, Wiley, New York, 1963.

Thus (2.101) becomes

$$C\frac{dv}{dt} + R^{-1}v + L^{-1}\int v\,dt = i_0 \sin \omega t, \qquad (2.105)$$

and a comparison of this with (2.99) suggests that, in addition to the general correspondence of $F(t)$ with $i(t)$ established by (2.100) and (2.101), the following specific quantities correspond:

$$m \sim C$$
$$C_x \sim R^{-1}$$
$$K_x \sim L^{-1} \qquad (2.106)$$
$$F_0 \sim i_0$$
$$\dot{x} \sim v$$

Because the solutions (2.95) to (2.97) can be applied to (2.99) merely by differentiating them to obtain $\dot{x}$, it follows that they may also be applied to (2.105) by writing v for $\dot{x}$ and interpreting

$$\omega_0{}^2 = 1/LC \qquad (2.107)$$
$$\zeta_0 = 1/RC \qquad (2.108)$$
$$\xi_0 = i_0/C \qquad (2.109)$$

on the basis of the above correspondences. However, first order differential equations of this type are especially easy to reduce to linear algebraic equations by the use of Laplace transforms; and although there is no great gain in doing so when only one equation is involved, simultaneous or coupled systems of such equations can most readily be solved by the matrix methods discussed in Section 1.3. Contemporary works on systems analysis develop these techniques in detail.[10]

In addition, they emphasize that the preceding development possesses an operational significance over and above its mathematical utility, pointing out that the force between two points (which, as we will later see, can be regarded as a momentum flux[11]) must be deduced from velocity measurements made at the points, in the same way that current (which can be considered a charge flux) must be deduced from two separated voltage measurements. This is also true of various other complementary variable pairs whose product is a measure of energy density, like fluid flux-pressure and heat flux-temperature. Thus, the inference is that the linear graph for a system in any one of the pairs of variables should describe corresponding

---

[10] Koenig, H. E., and W. A. Blackwell, *Electromechanical System Theory*, pp. 1–108, McGraw-Hill, New York, 1961.

[11] Rohsenow, W. M., and H. Y. Choi, *Heat, Mass and Momentum Transfer*, pp. 1–10, Prentice-Hall, Englewood Cliffs, N.J., 1961.

systems in all of the others, and that a single equation (or set of equations) of motion with a single solution exists for all.

On the surface, such an approach appears to neglect the physical content of the system. Equation (2.99) clearly applies to the small vibrations of a point object about its equilibrium position, whereas (2.105) describes the oscillatory flow of an electric current in the given circuit. The resistance R, the inductance L, and even the capacitance C may actually be distributed through an entire circuit of a real material, while by definition the dashpot C_x, the spring K_x and the mass m of the mechanical system are localized. However, lumping the parameters as in Fig. 3.16 usually amounts to replacing the real system with an equivalent fictitious one, in which the

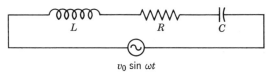

$v_0 \sin \omega t$

Fig. 3.18

active elements are localized. And, considering our earlier procedure of combining constants to obtain a simpler equivalent system, Fig. 3.14 evidently could be regarded as a lumped parameter representation of many smaller point masses vibrating in a medium with which they interact. In such a case the total mass, restoring force, and damping force (viscosity) would be distributed throughout the material "circuit."

Furthermore, the electric current consists of electrons, and resistance as well as induction must arise from interactions between these and charged particles of the conducting medium, just as viscosity must arise from particles interacting through their masses. Only the magnitude of the interactions need to be different. Even capacitance and mass are alike in one way: a capacitor is essentially a discontinuity in the electric field, and we shall learn later that the mass of a particle represents a discontinuity in an otherwise continuous "matter field." With this in mind, it is reasonable that Cv, where v represents the capacitor voltage, should correspond to the linear momentum $m\dot{x}$ and $Cv^2/2$ to the kinetic energy $m\dot{x}^2/2$, as suggested by the relations (2.106). Thus, physical aspects are not neglected in the systems approach; they are merely subordinated.

It should also be noted that, in addition to requiring the sum of the contributions to any "through" variable like current to vanish at a vertex, systems theory requires the sum of the contributions to any "across" variable like voltage to vanish around a closed circuit, on the basis of Kirchhoff's voltage law. Hence, if for the series arrangement in Fig. 3.18

we write the circuit equation,

$$v_L(t) + v_R(t) + v_C(t) = v_0 \sin \omega t, \tag{2.110}$$

and substitute from the terminal relations (2.102) to (2.104), we obtain:

$$L\frac{di}{dt} + Ri + C^{-1} \int i \, dt = v_0 \sin \omega t \tag{2.111}$$

Because it applies to a different type of circuit than that corresponding to Fig. 3.14, a comparison between this equation and (2.99) can have no operational or physical significance. In purely mathematical terms, however, the two equations have the same form; therefore, we may consider the following quantities to be mathematically analogous:

$$\begin{aligned}
m &\to L \\
C_x &\to R \\
K_x &\to C^{-1} \\
F_0 &\to v_0 \\
\dot{x} &\to i
\end{aligned} \tag{2.112}$$

Furthermore, because

$$i = \dot{q} \tag{2.113}$$

where q is the electric charge,

$$x \to q; \tag{2.114}$$

and we can rewrite (2.111) as

$$L\ddot{q} + R\dot{q} + C^{-1}q = v_0 \sin \omega t, \tag{2.115}$$

which has the same form as the original equation (2.81). Therefore, the solutions (2.95) to (2.97) can be applied to (2.115) by replacing x with q and taking:

$$\omega_0^2 = 1/CL \tag{2.116}$$

$$\zeta_0 = R/L \tag{2.117}$$

$$\xi_0 = v_0/L \tag{2.118}$$

Of course, either analogy can be used for electrical analog computations, but the former is preferred because it features identical mechanical and electrical circuits.

Two- and three-dimensional motions of a point object that nevertheless satisfy an uncoupled set of equations, like (1.1) to (1.3), may for the most part be treated by simple repetition of the one-dimensional solution procedure. We shall consider only two examples, both ultimately reducible to two-dimensional motions, but take special pains to look for new features. It may be anticipated that these will occur when we attempt to coordinate the separate solutions to generate the real motion from its projections.

For the first example, let us analyze the case of an object of mass m moving under the influence of a constant vector force,

$$\mathbf{F} = \text{constant,} \qquad (2.119)$$

which acts only on its mass. There will be little loss in generality if we assume specifically that

$$\mathbf{F} = -mg\hat{\mathbf{j}}, \qquad (2.120)$$

so that the three scalar equations of motion from the basic Newtonian equation [(1.12) of Chapter 2],

$$-mg\hat{\mathbf{j}} = m(\ddot{x}\hat{\mathbf{i}} + \ddot{y}\hat{\mathbf{j}} + \ddot{z}\hat{\mathbf{k}}), \qquad (2.121)$$

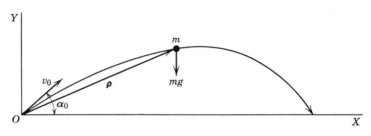

Fig. 3.19

are

$$\ddot{x} = 0 \qquad (2.122)$$
$$\ddot{y} = -g \qquad (2.123)$$
$$\ddot{z} = 0 \qquad (2.124)$$

And, if we assume the following initial conditions:

$$x(0) = 0, \quad \dot{x}(0) = \dot{x}_0 \qquad (2.125)$$
$$y(0) = 0, \quad \dot{y}(0) = \dot{y}_0 \qquad (2.126)$$
$$z(0) = 0, \quad \dot{z}(0) = 0 \qquad (2.127)$$

where

$$(\dot{x}_0^2 + \dot{y}_0^2)^{\frac{1}{2}} = v_0, \qquad (2.128)$$

the motion will be that of a point projectile of arbitrary mass m leaving an origin on a flat earth with an initial velocity $\mathbf{v}_0$ at time $t = 0$, subject to gravity but no air resistance. Because $\dot{z}(0) = 0$ and the system is conservative, the projectile will remain in the XY-plane, constituting a case of two-dimensional motion, as implied by the use of ρ for the position vector in Fig. 3.19.

The equations of motion that remain, (2.122) and (2.123), are clearly uncoupled; therefore, we may solve each one separately, in this case by direct integration:

$$\dot{x} = C_1, \qquad x = C_1 t + C_2 \tag{2.129}$$

$$\dot{y} = -gt + C_3, \qquad y = -\frac{gt^2}{2} + C_3 t + C_4 \tag{2.130}$$

Then, applying the initial conditions (2.125) and (2.126),

$$x(0) = 0 \rightarrow C_2 = 0 \tag{2.131}$$

$$\dot{x}(0) = \dot{x}_0 = v_0 \cos \alpha_0 \rightarrow C_1 = v_0 \cos \alpha_0 \tag{2.132}$$

$$y(0) = 0 \rightarrow C_4 = 0 \tag{2.133}$$

$$\dot{y}(0) = \dot{y}_0 = v_0 \sin \alpha_0 \rightarrow C_3 = v_0 \sin \alpha_0, \tag{2.134}$$

we obtain the particular solutions

$$x = (v_0 \cos \alpha_0)t, \qquad \dot{x} = v_0 \cos \alpha_0 \tag{2.135}$$

and

$$y = -\frac{gt^2}{2} + (v_0 \sin \alpha_0)t, \qquad \dot{y} = -gt + v_0 \sin \alpha_0. \tag{2.136}$$

These describe only the projections of the motion on the X- and Y-axes, but we can easily obtain the equation of the object's trajectory by solving the first of equations (2.135) and (2.136) simultaneously. Eliminating t, we obtain:

$$y = -\frac{g}{2} \frac{x^2}{(v_0 \cos \alpha_0)^2} + x \tan \alpha_0 \tag{2.137}$$

This parabola is the path along which the projectile must move with the velocity $\mathbf{v} = \dot{\boldsymbol{\rho}}$ in order for its projections to satisfy the equations of motion (2.122) and (2.123). Its angular momentum relative to the origin will be

$$\mathbf{l} = \boldsymbol{\rho} \times m\dot{\boldsymbol{\rho}} = (x\hat{\mathbf{i}} + y\hat{\mathbf{j}}) \times m(\dot{x}\hat{\mathbf{i}} + \dot{y}\hat{\mathbf{j}}) = m(x\dot{y} - y\dot{x})\hat{\mathbf{k}}, \tag{2.138}$$

and at all points along the path it will be acted on by the moment of force

$$\mathbf{M} = \boldsymbol{\rho} \times \mathbf{F} = (x\hat{\mathbf{i}} + y\hat{\mathbf{j}}) \times (-mg\hat{\mathbf{j}}) = -mgx\hat{\mathbf{k}}. \tag{2.139}$$

Any other information which might be desired, such as the maximum height attained (y_{max}) or the range (x_{max}) for a given initial velocity v_0, can now be calculated; but these aspects of the solution will be reserved for an illustrative problem.

Evidently, both of the preceding equations of motion are of the simple form (2.2). When air resistance is taken into account (at least approximately) by assuming a frictional force proportional to the velocity in each of the two component directions,

$$\mathbf{F} = -C_x \dot{x}\hat{\mathbf{i}} - (C_y \dot{y} + mg)\hat{\mathbf{j}}, \tag{2.140}$$

the system becomes nonconservative and the equations take a form related to (2.55), although lacking the restoring force provided by the spring and including a constant applied force in one case:

$$m\ddot{x} + C_x\dot{x} = 0 \tag{2.141}$$

$$m\ddot{y} + C_y\dot{y} + mg = 0 \tag{2.142}$$

Since they are still linear, with constant coefficients, they may be solved by the same methods as before and will also be reserved for the problems. But careful note should be taken of the fact that this represents

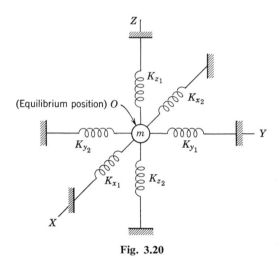

Fig. 3.20

a considerable idealization of reality. In practice it is often necessary to assign exponents other than unity to the force terms in $\dot{x}$ and $\dot{y}$, or to treat C_x and C_y as variables, thereby rendering the equations nonlinear.

Finally, consider the motion of a point mass subject to the force

$$\mathbf{F} = -K_x x\mathbf{i} - K_y y\mathbf{\hat{j}} - K_z z\mathbf{\hat{k}}. \tag{2.143}$$

This amounts to independent linear restoring forces in all three coordinate directions; therefore, the mass must be moving in such a way that its X, Y, and Z projections are separately performing simple harmonic oscillations. From the general Newtonian equation we can write the three scalar equations of motion:

$$m\ddot{x} + K_x x = 0 \tag{2.144}$$

$$m\ddot{y} + K_y y = 0 \tag{2.145}$$

$$m\ddot{z} + K_z z = 0 \tag{2.146}$$

With K_x, K_y, and K_z representing the sum of the constants indicated (2.22), we can represent the system as shown in Fig. 3.20.

Evidently, the general solution of each of the equations (2.144) to (2.146) will have one of the forms obtained for (2.12); let us select (2.48):

$$x = A_x \cos(\omega_{0_x} t + \theta_x) \tag{2.147}$$

$$y = A_y \cos(\omega_{0_y} t + \theta_y) \tag{2.148}$$

$$z = A_z \cos(\omega_{0_z} t + \theta_z) \tag{2.149}$$

Any particular solution will depend not only on the six initial conditions required to determine the six arbitrary constants A_x, A_y, A_z, θ_x, θ_y, and θ_z, but also on the relation of the three natural frequencies:

$$\omega_{0_x} = \sqrt{K_x/m} \tag{2.150}$$

$$\omega_{0_y} = \sqrt{K_y/m} \tag{2.151}$$

$$\omega_{0_z} = \sqrt{K_z/m} \tag{2.152}$$

For example, if it happened that

$$\omega_{0_x} = \omega_{0_y} = \omega_{0_z} = \omega_0, \tag{2.153}$$

and furthermore that

$$\theta_x = \theta_y = \theta_z = 0, \tag{2.154}$$

the time dependence of the solutions (2.147) to (2.149) could be eliminated, giving

$$\frac{x}{A_x} = \frac{y}{A_y} = \frac{z}{A_z} \tag{2.155}$$

and showing the path of the mass to be a straight line centered on the origin with a slope dependent on the specific values of the A's.

As a matter of fact, the force (2.143), being always directed toward the origin, is a special case of the so-called central force to be studied in the following section; we shall prove then that all of the motions possible under such a force lie in a plane. It can be shown[12] that as long as the condition (2.153) holds, the path of the mass will be an ellipse centered on the origin as the equilibrium position, simplifying to a circle when the difference between the phase angles of the component vibrations in the plane of motion equals $\pm\pi/2$ and the corresponding amplitudes are equal, and degenerating to a straight line when the difference between these phase angles is zero. All such oscillators are said to be isotropic.

More generally, if the natural frequencies satisfy relations of the type

$$\frac{\omega_{0_x}}{\alpha_x} = \frac{\omega_{0_y}}{\alpha_y} = \frac{\omega_{0_z}}{\alpha_z} \tag{2.156}$$

---

[12] Ames, J. S., and F. D. Murnaghan, *Theoretical Mechanics*, pp. 128–132, Dover, New York, 1958.

where the α's are integers, the path of the mass will at least be closed and its motion will be periodic, whatever the values of the θ's and A's. If the frequencies are not commensurable, in the sense of (2.156), the path will fill a rectangular box with the dimensions $2A_x \times 2A_y \times 2A_z$. It is interesting to note that two-dimensional paths of this kind will be traced on the screen of an oscilloscope by the electron beam when it is swept both horizontally and vertically by oscillating voltages. The patterns formed when the frequencies of these voltages are commensurable are called Lissajous figures, examples of which are shown in Fig. 3.21.

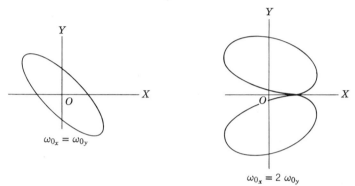

Fig. 3.21

Of course this relation, like all the preceding relations developed for electron motion, assumes that the velocity of the electrons is small enough for relativistic effects to be unimportant, and also that their wave properties are negligible. We will learn later under what conditions the latter must be taken into account.

Problems 3.2

1. A 16-lb weight placed carefully on the spring shown in Fig. P3.2 (1) extends it 4 ins. What is the natural angular frequency of the system? If the weight is suddenly given a velocity of 4.9 ft/sec downward from the equilibrium position, what is its displacement as a function of time?

Solution

The natural angular frequency of the system is defined as

$$\omega_0 = \sqrt{\frac{K_y}{m}} \; ;$$

in this case, however,

$$K_y = F/\delta = \frac{16 \text{ lb}}{4 \text{ in.}} = 4 \text{ lb/in.} ;$$

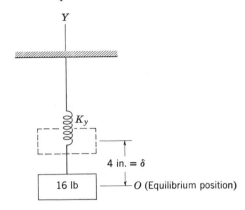

Fig. P3.2 (1)

therefore:

$$\omega_0 = \sqrt{\frac{4(\text{lb/in.})}{16(\text{lb})/32(\text{ft/sec}^2)}}$$

$$= \sqrt{\frac{4 \times 32}{16}\left(\frac{\text{ft}}{\text{in. sec}^2}\right)}$$

$$= \sqrt{\frac{4 \times 32 \times 12}{16}\left(\frac{\text{in.}}{\text{ft}}\right)\left(\frac{\text{ft}}{\text{in. sec}^2}\right)}$$

$$= 9.8 \text{ rad/sec}$$

The equation of motion is

$$\ddot{y} + \frac{K_y}{m}y = 0,$$

with the solution

$$y = B \cos \omega_0 t + C \sin \omega_0 t,$$

designating the two arbitrary constants required simply as B and C; hence

$$\dot{y} = -B\omega_0 \sin \omega_0 t + C\omega_0 \cos \omega_0 t.$$

But the specified initial conditions are

$$y = 0 \quad \text{and} \quad \dot{y} = 4.9 \text{ ft/sec} \quad \text{at} \quad t = 0.$$

Therefore

$$0 = B + 0,$$
$$B = 0,$$

and

$$4.9 = C\omega_0,$$

$$C = \frac{4.9}{\omega_0} = \frac{4.9}{9.8} = \frac{1}{2}.$$

It follows that the displacement of the center of the weight from the equilibrium position at any time will be given by

$$y = \tfrac{1}{2} \sin 9.8t \text{ ft.}$$

2. A point mass is mounted on a spring as shown in Fig. P3.2 (2), but the spring support is caused to vibrate harmonically so that $y' = A \cos \omega t$. If at $t = 0$ the mass is displaced downward a distance of 2 in. and is given a downward speed of 5 in./sec, and if $A = 2$ in., $\omega = 5$ rad/sec, $K_y = 400$ lb/ft, and $m = 1$ slug, what will the position of the mass be at $t = 10$ sec?

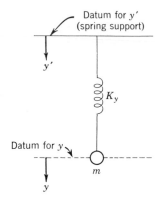

Fig. P3.2 (2)

Solution

The equation of motion will be

$$\ddot{y} + \frac{K_y}{m}(y - y') = 0$$

or, because $y' = 2 \cos 5t$,

$$\ddot{y} + \frac{K_y}{m}y = 2\frac{K_y}{m}\cos 5t;$$

we may infer this to have a general solution of the form

$$y = y_G + y_P$$
$$= B \cos \omega_0 t + C \sin \omega_0 t + \frac{F_0/K_y}{1 - \left(\dfrac{\omega}{\omega_0}\right)^2}\cos \omega t.$$

However, in this case

$$\omega_0 = \sqrt{\frac{K_y}{m}} = \sqrt{\frac{400}{1}\left(\frac{\text{lb}}{\text{ft}}\right)\left(\frac{\text{ft}}{\text{lb sec}^2}\right)} = 20 \text{ rad/sec}$$

and

$$\frac{F_0}{K_y} = 2 \text{ in.};$$

therefore,

$$\frac{F_0/K_y}{1 - \left(\dfrac{\omega}{\omega_0}\right)^2} = \frac{2}{1 - \left(\dfrac{5}{20}\right)^2} = 2.13.$$

Substituting numerical values,

$$y = B \cos 20t + C \sin 20t + 2.13 \cos 5t;$$

and, considering the initial conditions, we have:

$$2 = B + 2.13$$
$$B = -0.13,$$
$$5 = 20C$$
$$C = 0.25.$$

Hence,

$$y = 0.25 \sin 20t - 0.13 \cos 20t + 2.13 \cos 5t;$$

and when $t = 10$ sec, the position of the mass relative to the lower datum can be determined from this by subtracting the completed cycles and converting from radians to degrees:

$$y = 0.25 \sin 200 - 0.13 \cos 200 + 2.13 \cos 50$$
$$= 0.25 \sin [(200 - 198)57.3] - 0.13 \cos [(200 - 198)57.3]$$
$$+ 2.13 \cos [(50 - 47.2)57.3]$$
$$= 0.25(0.909) + 0.13(0.416) - 2.13(0.942) = -1.725 \text{ in.}$$

3. It is found experimentally that a spherical 6-lb weight stretches a spring $\frac{1}{2}$ ft [Fig. P3.2 (3)]. If a damping force numerically equal to three times the instantaneous velocity, acts on the weight in addition to the spring, and the weight is pulled $\frac{1}{3}$ ft below the equilibrium position before being released, find its displacement relative to the equilibrium position as a function of time.

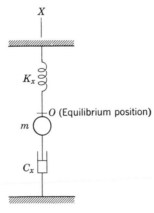

Fig. P3.2 (3)

Solution

The equation of motion must be

$$m\ddot{x} + C_x \dot{x} + K_x x = 0;$$

thus, we need only determine whether $(C_x/2m)^2$ is greater than, less than, or equal to K_x/m in order to write down the proper solution. Since

$$K_x = \frac{F}{\delta} = \frac{6}{6} = 1 \text{ lb/in.} = 12 \text{ lb/ft},$$

$$C_x \dot{x} = 3\dot{x} \text{ lb}$$

and

$$m = \frac{6}{32} \text{ slugs},$$

$$\left(\frac{C_x}{2m}\right)^2 = \left(\frac{3}{2} \times \frac{32}{6}\right)^2 = 64$$

and

$$\frac{K_x}{m} = 12 \times \frac{32}{6} = 64.$$

Therefore, the system is critically damped, and we know the general solution to be

$$x = e^{-\frac{C_x}{2m}t}[C_1 + C_2 t].$$

Now at

$$t = 0,$$

$$x = \tfrac{1}{3};$$

so,

$$C_1 = \tfrac{1}{3}.$$

Further,

$$\dot{x} = -\frac{C_x}{2m} e^{-\frac{C_x}{2m}t}\left(C_1 + C_2 e^{-\frac{C_x}{2m}t}\right) + C_2 e^{-\frac{C_x}{2m}t} t\left(-\frac{C_x}{2m}\right),$$

but at

$$\dot{x} = 0,$$

$$t = 0.$$

Thus,

$$0 = -\frac{C_x}{2m} C_1 + C_2$$

or

$$C_2 = \frac{C_x}{2m} C_1 = \frac{3}{2}\left(\frac{32}{6}\right)\frac{1}{3} = \frac{8}{3}.$$

The final result is

$$x = e^{-\frac{3}{2}\left(\frac{32}{6}\right)t}\left[\frac{1}{3} + \frac{8}{3}t\right] = \frac{1}{3} e^{-8t}[1 + 8t] \text{ ft}.$$

4. Calculate the effective spring constant of the system shown in Fig. P3.2 (4a). If a force $F(t) = 0$ for $t < 0$, $F(t) = F_0(t/T)$ for $0 < t < T$, and $F(t) = F_0$ for $t > T$ is applied to the system, which at $t = 0$ is at rest in the equilibrium position, obtain the solution for x as a function of time in the interval $0 < t < T$.

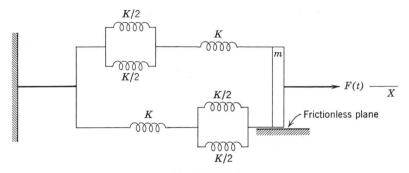

Fig. P3.2 (4a)

Solution

It is apparent from the symmetry of the system that m can be regarded as a point mass. Thus for either branch

$$\frac{1}{K_1} = \frac{1}{\frac{K}{2} + \frac{K}{2}} + \frac{1}{K},$$

$$K_1 = \frac{K}{2};$$

so the effective spring constant of the equivalent system must be

$$K_1 + K_2 = \frac{K}{2} + \frac{K}{2} = K.$$

The applied force varies with time as shown in Fig. P3.2 (4b). Therefore, in the interval $0 < t < T$, the equation of motion will be

$$\ddot{x} + \frac{K}{m}x = \frac{F_0}{mT}t.$$

The homogeneous equation is

$$\ddot{x} + \frac{K}{m}x = 0$$

which has the solution

$$x_G = B\cos\omega_0 t + C\sin\omega_0 t, \qquad \omega_0 = \sqrt{\frac{K}{m}}.$$

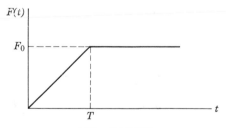

Fig. P3.2 (4b)

Let the particular solution be
$$x_P = At,$$
where A is a constant. Substituting in the equation of motion, we obtain
$$0 + \frac{K}{m} At = \frac{F_0}{mT} t$$
or
$$A = \frac{F_0}{KT}.$$

We conclude that the complete solution can be written as
$$x = x_G + x_P = B \cos \omega_0 t + C \sin \omega_0 t + \frac{F_0}{KT} t.$$

Applying the initial conditions, we have
$$x(0) = 0 = B;$$
$$\dot{x} = C\omega_0 \cos \omega_0 t + \frac{F_0}{KT},$$
$$\dot{x}(0) = 0 = C\omega_0 = \frac{F_0}{KT},$$
$$C = -\frac{F_0}{\omega_0 KT}.$$

Consequently, the required solution must be
$$x = \frac{F_0}{KT}\left[t - \frac{1}{\omega_0} \sin \omega_0 t \right].$$

5. Determine the equation of motion for the system shown in Fig. P3.2 (5a) if $F = F_0 \cos \omega t$ and the initial conditions are:
$$x(0) = 0$$
$$\dot{x}(0) = 0$$
Also, plot $x = x(t)$.

Solution

The force exerted by the single spring will be
$$F_1 = -K_1 x_1,$$

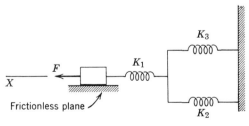

Fig. P3.2 (5a)

and the force due to the two springs in parallel will be

$$F_2 = -K_3 x_2 - K_2 x_2 = -(K_3 + K_2)x_2.$$

But

$$F_1 = F_2 = F'$$

and

$$x_1 + x_2 = x',$$

the total displacement; therefore,

$$x' = x_1 + x_2 = -\left(\frac{F'}{K_1} + \frac{F'}{K_3 + K_2}\right)$$

$$= -F'\left[\frac{(K_3 + K_2) + K_1}{K_1(K_3 + K_2)}\right]$$

or

$$F' = -\frac{K_1(K_3 + K_2)}{K_1 + K_2 + K_3} x'.$$

This may be written as

$$F' = -Kx', \qquad \text{where} \quad K = \frac{K_1(K_3 + K_2)}{K_1 + K_2 + K_3},$$

the spring constant of the equivalent spring.

The equation of motion then becomes

$$\ddot{x} + \frac{K}{m} x = \frac{F_0}{m} \cos \omega t.$$

We must first find a solution of the homogeneous equation,

$$\ddot{x} + \frac{K}{m} x = 0;$$

but one form of this is known to be

$$x_G = A \cos(\omega_0 t + \theta), \qquad \omega_0 = \sqrt{\frac{K}{m}}.$$

Also, we know that a particular solution of the nonhomogeneous equation is

$$x_P = \frac{F_0/m}{\omega_0{}^2 - \omega^2} \cos \omega t;$$

therefore, the complete solution must be

$$x = A \cos(\omega_0 t + \theta) + \frac{F_0/m}{\omega_0{}^2 - \omega^2} \cos \omega t.$$

The initial conditions are

$$\left.\begin{matrix} x = 0 \\ \dot{x} = 0 \end{matrix}\right\} \text{at } t = 0;$$

thus

$$x = A \cos \theta + \frac{F_0/m}{\omega_0{}^2 - \omega^2} = 0$$

$$\dot{x} = -A \sin \theta = 0.$$

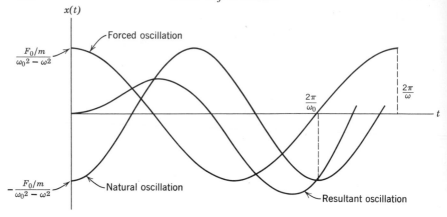

Fig. P3.2 (5b)

From the second condition either

$$A = 0$$

or

$$\theta = 0,$$

but if $A = 0$, the first condition cannot be satisfied. Hence we place $\theta = 0$, and the first condition becomes

$$A \cos (0) + \frac{F_0/m}{\omega_0^2 - \omega^2} = 0$$

or

$$A = - \frac{F_0/m}{\omega_0^2 - \omega^2} .$$

Accordingly, the required solution is:

$$x = \frac{F_0/m}{\omega_0^2 - \omega^2} (\cos \omega t - \cos\omega_0 t)$$

Forced oscillation   Free oscillation

This clearly represents the sum of two harmonic motions, one having the natural frequency of the system and the other the frequency of the driving force. If, for example, $\omega = \frac{2}{3}\omega_0$, we obtain the results shown in Fig. P3.2 (5b). The amplitude of the resultant motion will increase if ω is caused to approach ω_0, because the denominator of the amplitude factor

$$\frac{F_0/m}{\omega_0^2 - \omega^2}$$

will get smaller; for $\omega = \omega_0$, the system will resonate and the amplitude will in principle become infinite.

6. Sketch the electrical circuits that correspond physically to the mechanical systems shown in Figs. P3.2 (6a) and (6b). Also compare these with the circuits which would follow from pure mathematical analogy.

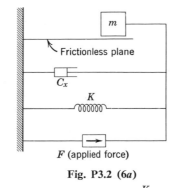

Fig. P3.2 (6a)

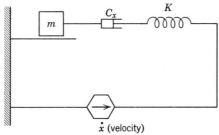

Fig. P3.2 (6b)

Solution

If we use the correspondences between constants accompanying the physical identification of force with current and velocity with voltage, (*a*) becomes as shown in Fig. P3.2 (6*c*), whereas (*b*) takes the form given in Fig. P3.2 (6*d*).

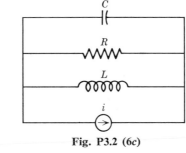

Fig. P3.2 (6c)

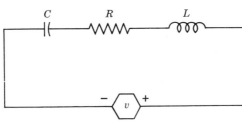

Fig. P3.2 (6d)

On the other hand, when force is treated as mathematically analogous to voltage and velocity as analogous to current, the two are reversed; that is, (*c*) applies to (*b*) and (*d*) to (*a*).

7. Draw the mechanical and electrical circuits corresponding to the mechanical system shown in Fig. P3.2 (7*a*).

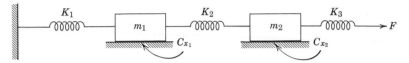

Fig. P3.2 (7*a*)

Solution

Figure P3.2 (7*a*) represents the mechanical circuit shown in Fig. P3.2 (7*b*); the physically equivalent electrical circuit is shown in Fig. P3.2 (7*c*).

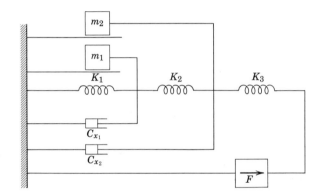

Fig. P3.2 (7*b*)

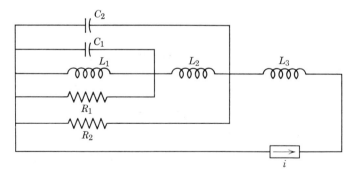

Fig. P3.2 (7*c*)

8. A train is made up of three units, the first of which is the engine. Each weighs 30,000 kg, and the springs that couple adjacent units have a reciprocal spring constant equal to 0.4×10^{-6} m/N (newton). On acceleration, the

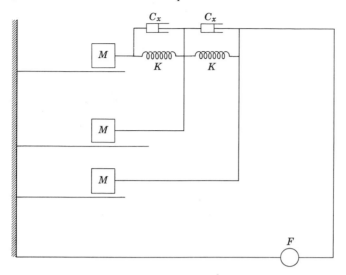

Fig. P3.2 (8a)

engine is capable of exerting a pull of 40,000 N. Draw the mechanical circuit and the physically corresponding electrical circuit analog for this system. Neglecting rolling resistance, discuss how to determine a suitable value of mechanical resistance for two identical shock absorbers to be placed between the units so that their relative motion will be satisfactorily damped.

Solution

The mechanical circuit is as shown in Fig. P3.2 (8a); therefore, the associated electrical circuit is of the form shown in Fig. P3.2 (8b).

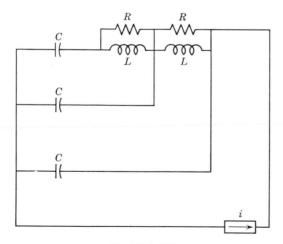

Fig. P3.2 (8b)

From the electrical circuit, the required value of R for given values of L and C may be determined. We can write

$$i = \beta_1 F$$

and

$$v = \beta_2 u$$

where β_1 and β_2 are scale factors having units of amperes/newton and volts/meter/second, respectively, and u represents velocity in the direction of the force F. Also, to establish a convenient time scale, we can use the relation

$$t_e = \beta_3 t_m$$

between times measured in the electrical system and times measured in the mechanical system.

Inductance, capacitance, and reciprocal resistance are related to the reciprocal spring constant, mass, and the damping coefficient in the following way:

$$L = \frac{v}{di/dt_e} = \frac{\beta_2 \beta_3}{\beta_1} \frac{u}{dF/dt_m} = \frac{\beta_2 \beta_3}{\beta_1} K^{-1} = \beta_4 K^{-1}$$

$$C = \frac{i}{dv/dt_e} = \frac{\beta_1 \beta_3}{\beta_2} \frac{F}{du/dt_m} = \frac{\beta_1 \beta_3}{\beta_2} m = \beta_5 m$$

$$R^{-1} = \frac{i}{v} = \frac{\beta_1}{\beta_2} \frac{F}{u} = \frac{\beta_1}{\beta_2} C_x = \beta_6 C_x$$

The units of β_4, β_5, and β_6, respectively, are henrys-newtons/meter, farads/kilogram, and mho/meter/newton-second.

Of the six scale factors, only three are independent. For example, β_1, β_2, and β_6 does not constitute an independent set, whereas β_1, β_4, and β_5 does. We can, therefore, choose any three independent values according to convenience. As an illustration, if we place

$$\beta_1 = 10^4 \text{ amperes/newton}$$
$$\beta_4 = 10^5 \text{ henrys-newtons/meter}$$
$$\beta_5 = 10^{-12} \text{ farads/kilogram}$$

then

$$i = 4 \text{ amperes}$$
$$L = 4 \times 10^{-2} \text{ henry}$$
$$C = 3 \times 10^{-8} \text{ farad}$$

which are satisfactory for electrical measurements. Of course, by choosing β_1, β_4, and β_5 we have also fixed β_2, β_3, and β_6:

$$\beta_2 = \frac{\beta_1}{\beta_6} = \frac{10^{-4}}{\sqrt{10}} \times 10^{-9} = \frac{1}{\sqrt{10}} \times 10^5$$

$$\beta_3 = \sqrt{\beta_4 \beta_5} = \sqrt{10^{-12} \times 10^5} = \sqrt{10} \times 10^4$$

$$\beta_6 = \sqrt{\frac{\beta_5}{\beta_4}} = \sqrt{\frac{10^{-12}}{10^5}} = \sqrt{10} \times 10^{-9}$$

Therefore,

$$v = 3.16 \times 10^4 u,$$

$$t_e = 3.16 \times 10^{-4} t_m,$$

$$R^{-1} = 3.16 \times 10^{-9} C_x.$$

9. The mechanical system shown in Fig. P3.2 (9a) could be used to protect a mass m during shipment. Determine the corresponding electrical circuit analog.

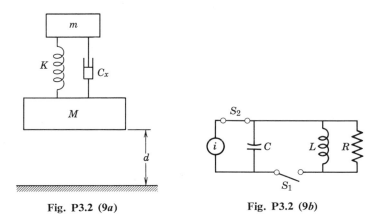

Fig. P3.2 (9a)   Fig. P3.2 (9b)

Solution

If the system is dropped a distance d and M collides plastically with the floor, the velocity of m at the instant of contact will be $u = \sqrt{2gd}$; also, the spring-dashpot system will be instantaneously activated.

The analogous circuit is shown in Fig. P3.2 (9b), with the switch S_1 being closed at the instant of contact and S_2 being opened at the same time. The important relationships for this problem are:

$$i = \beta_1 F = \beta_1 g$$

$$v = \beta_2 u$$

$$v_0 = \beta_2 u_0 = \beta_2 \sqrt{2gd}$$

$$t_e = \beta_3 t_m$$

$$L = \frac{\beta_2 \beta_3}{\beta_1} K^{-1} = \beta_4 K^{-1}$$

$$C = \frac{\beta_1 \beta_3}{\beta_2} m = \beta_5 m$$

$$R^{-1} = \frac{\beta_1}{\beta_2} C_x = \beta_6 C_x.$$

As before, any three independent β's can be chosen and the other three will be determined.

10. Construct the electrical circuit analog for the mechanical system shown in Fig. P3.2 (10*a*). Choosing appropriate values for the electrical circuit elements, solve the differential equation and obtain the expression corresponding to that for $x(t)$. Show that this yields the same result as solving the equation of motion for the mechanical system.

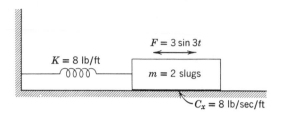

Fig. P3.2 (10*a*)

Solution

The mechanical circuit is of the form shown in Fig. P3.2 (10*b*); thus the electrical analog for this would be as shown in Fig. P3.2 (10*c*). Kirchhoff's current law, therefore, gives

$$C\frac{dv}{dt} + R^{-1}v + L^{-1}\int v\, dt = i_0 \sin \omega t,$$

the equation for a damped electrical oscillator.

By choosing appropriate values for the scale factors β_1, β_4, and β_5 we can evaluate the rest, as in the two preceding problems. Let

$$\beta_1 = 1 \text{ ampere/lb,}$$

$$\beta_4 = \tfrac{1}{10} \text{ henrys-lb/ft,}$$

$$\beta_5 = 10^{-6} \text{ farads/slug.}$$

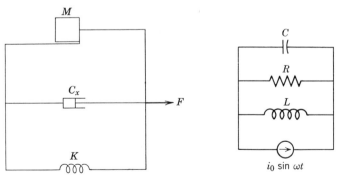

Fig. P3.2 (10*b*)   **Fig. P3.2 (10*c*)**

Then:

$$\beta_6 = \sqrt{\frac{\beta_5}{\beta_4}} = \sqrt{\frac{10^{-6}}{1/10}} = \sqrt{10} \times 10^{-3} \text{ mho/ft/lb-sec}$$

$$\beta_2 = \frac{\beta_1}{\beta_6} = \frac{1}{\sqrt{10} \times 10^{-3}} = \sqrt{10} \times 10^2 \text{ volts/ft/sec}$$

$$\beta_3 = \sqrt{\beta_4 \beta_5} = \sqrt{10^{-6} \times \tfrac{1}{10}} = \sqrt{10^{-7}}$$

Using these scale factors, we can choose the electrical circuit elements,

$$L = \beta_4 K^{-1} = \tfrac{1}{10} \times \tfrac{1}{8} = 0.0125 \text{ henrys}$$
$$C = \beta_5 m = 10^{-6} \times 2 = 2 \times 10^{-6} \text{ farads}$$
$$R^{-1} = \beta_6 R_m = 8 \times \sqrt{10} \times 10^{-3} \text{ mhos,}$$

and fix the parameter

$$i_0 = \beta_1 F_0 = 1 \times 3 = 3 \text{ amps.}$$

We can also see that voltage and velocity will be related as

$$v = \beta_2 u = \sqrt{10} \times 10^2 u$$

and times as

$$t_e = \beta_3 t_m = \sqrt{10^{-7}} \, t_m.$$

Evidently, the frequency of the current source should be $3\sqrt{10^7}$.
With these values the circuit equation becomes

$$2 \times 10^{-6} \frac{dv}{dt_e} + 8\sqrt{10} \times 10^{-3} v + \frac{1}{0.0125} \int v \, dt_e = 3 \sin 3\sqrt{10^7} \, t_e.$$

If we write this in the standard form

$$\alpha_1 \frac{d\dot{y}}{dt} + \alpha_2 \dot{y} + \alpha_3 \int \dot{y} \, dt = \alpha_4 \sin 3\sqrt{10^7} \, t_e$$

where, of course,

$$\alpha_1 = 2 \times 10^{-6}$$
$$\alpha_2 = 8 \times \sqrt{10} \times 10^{-3}$$
$$\alpha_3 = \frac{1}{0.0125}$$
$$\alpha_4 = 3,$$

the criterion $(C_x/2m)^2 \gtrless K_x/m$ becomes $(\alpha_2/2\alpha_1)^2 \gtrless \alpha_3/\alpha_1$. Thus, since

$$\left(\frac{\alpha_2}{2\alpha_1}\right)^2 = \left(\frac{8 \times \sqrt{10} \times 10^{-3}}{2 \times 2 \times 10^{-6}}\right)^2 = 40 \times 10^6$$

and

$$\frac{\alpha_3}{\alpha_1} = \frac{1/0.0125}{2 \times 10^{-6}} = 40 \times 10^6,$$

we see that the system is critically damped. The solution must therefore be:

$$y(t) = e^{-\frac{\zeta_0}{2}t}[C_1 + C_2 t] + \frac{\zeta_0}{(\omega_0'^2 - \omega'^2)^2 + (\zeta_0\omega')^2}$$

$$\times [(\omega_0'^2 - \omega'^2)\sin\omega't - \zeta_0\omega'\cos\omega't],$$

$$\zeta_0 = \frac{\alpha_2}{\alpha_1} = \frac{1}{RC} = \frac{8\sqrt{10}\times 10^{-3}}{2\times 10^{-6}} = 4\sqrt{10}\times 10^3$$

$$\xi_0 = \frac{\alpha_4}{\alpha_1} = \frac{i_0}{C} = \frac{3}{2\times 10^{-6}} = 1.5\times 10^6$$

$$\omega_0'^2 = \omega_0^2\times 10^7 = 4\times 10^7$$

$$\omega'^2 = \omega^2\times 10^7 = 9\times 10^7.$$

When we use these values, the solution for the electrical circuit equation becomes:

$$\int v\,dt_e = e^{-2\sqrt{10^7}t_e}\{C_1 + C_2 t_e\} + \frac{1.5}{169}\times 10^{-1}$$

$$\times \{-5\sin 3\sqrt{10^7}\,t_e - 12\cos 3\sqrt{10^7}\,t_e\}$$

The quantity $\int v\,dt_e$ is analogous to the displacement $x(t)$ in the mechanical system and is called the magnetic flux $\phi(t)$.

To obtain $x(t)$ from the above solution it becomes necessary to find the scale factor relating $\phi(t)$ and $x(t)$:

$$v = \beta_2 u$$

$$\frac{d\phi}{dt_e} = \beta_2 \frac{dx}{dt_m}$$

$$d\phi = \beta_2 \frac{dt_e}{dt_m}dx$$

$$= \beta_2\beta_3\,dx$$

$$= \sqrt{10}\times 10^2 \times \frac{1}{\sqrt{10}\times 10^3}\,dx$$

$$= 10^{-1}\,dx$$

$$\phi = 10^{-1}x$$

Applying this relation and the fact that $t_m = \sqrt{10^7}\,t_e$, we obtain

$$x(t) = e^{-2t_m}[C_3 + C_4 t_m] + \frac{1.5}{169}\{-5\sin 3t_m - 12\cos 3t_m\}.$$

This is exactly what follows from an analysis of the mechanical system:

$$m\ddot{x} + C_x\dot{x} + Kx = F_0 \sin \omega t$$

$$2\ddot{x} + 8\dot{x} + 8x = 3 \sin 3t$$

$$\left(\frac{C_x}{2m}\right)^2 = \left(\frac{8}{2 \times 2}\right)^2 = 4$$

$$\frac{K}{m} = \frac{8}{2} = 4$$

$$\left(\frac{C_x}{2m}\right)^2 = \frac{K_x}{m}$$

$$\zeta_0 = \frac{C_x}{m} = \frac{8}{2} = 4$$

$$\xi_0 = \frac{F_0}{m} = \frac{3}{2} = 1.5$$

$$\omega_0{}^2 = \frac{K}{m} = \frac{8}{2} = 4$$

$$x(t) = e^{-2t_m}[C_3 + C_4 t_m] + \frac{1.5}{169}[-5 \sin 3t_m - 12 \cos 3t_m]$$

Although a certain amount of labor is usually required to obtain the proper values for circuit elements and other parameters, it must be emphasized that electrical measurements are much to be preferred to any other kind.

11. A projectile of point mass m is fired with an initial speed v_0 at an angle of inclination α_0 [Fig. P3.2 (11)].

    a. For what angle α_0 will the range of the projectile be a maximum, assuming no air friction?

    b. If R_m is the maximum range, show that every $R < R_m$ can be reached by firing at two different angles.

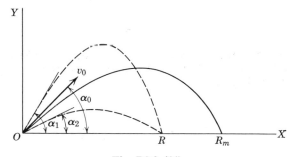

Fig. P3.2 (11)

Solution

(a) For comparison with the text method, we shall develop the solution by the Lagrangian technique. We know that

$$V = mgy$$

and

$$T = \frac{m}{2}(\dot{x}^2 + \dot{y}^2);$$

therefore,

$$L = \frac{m}{2}(\dot{x}^2 + \dot{y}^2) - mgy.$$

Applying

$$\frac{d}{dt}\frac{\partial L}{\partial \dot{q}_i} - \frac{\partial L}{\partial q_i} = 0 \qquad \{q_i = x, y$$

first to the y-coordinate, we obtain

$$\frac{d}{dt}(m\dot{y}) + mg = 0,$$

$$\ddot{y} = -g.$$

Then

$$\dot{y} = -gt + \dot{y}_0$$

and

$$y = -\tfrac{1}{2}gt^2 + \dot{y}_0 t + y_0,$$

where y_0 and $\dot{y}_0$ are constants of integration which have been shown to correspond to the suggested initial conditions. At $t = 0$ we know that $y = 0$ and $\dot{y} = v_0 \sin \phi_0$, so that

$$y_0 = 0$$

and

$$\dot{y}_0 = v_0 \sin \alpha_0;$$

thus

$$y = v_0 t \sin \alpha_0 - \tfrac{1}{2}gt^2.$$

Lagrange's equation applied to the x-coordinate gives

$$\frac{d}{dt}(m\dot{x}) = 0,$$

$$\dot{x} = \dot{x}_0.$$

Of course, this means that the momentum in the X-direction is constant, which is what we should expect since there is no force acting in that direction. Continuing, we have

$$x = \dot{x}_0 t + x_0;$$

but

$$x_0 = 0, \qquad \dot{x}_0 = v_0 \cos \alpha_0.$$

so

$$x = v_0 t \cos \alpha_0.$$

The total distance that the projectile will travel in the X-direction depends on the time required for it to return to the earth. If τ is the total travel time, then from the equation

$$y = (v_0 \sin \alpha_0 - \tfrac{1}{2}gt)t$$

and the fact that y must again be zero at any R, we have

$$v_0 \sin \alpha_0 - \tfrac{1}{2}g\tau = 0$$

or

$$\tau = \frac{2v_0 \sin \alpha_0}{g}.$$

Substituting this in

$$x = v_0 t \cos \alpha_0$$

gives, for $x = R$,

$$R = v_0 \tau \cos \alpha_0$$

or

$$R = \frac{2v_0{}^2 \cos \alpha_0 \sin \alpha_0}{g}.$$

Now the range R will be a maximum when

$$\frac{\partial R}{\partial \alpha_0} = 0.$$

Hence,

$$\frac{\partial R}{\partial \alpha_0} = \frac{2v_0{}^2}{g}\left[\cos \alpha_0 \frac{\partial(\sin \alpha_0)}{\partial \alpha_0} + \frac{\partial(\cos \alpha_0)}{\partial \alpha_0} \sin \alpha_0\right]$$

$$= \frac{2v_0{}^2}{g}[\cos^2 \alpha_0 - \sin^2 \alpha_0] = 0,$$

from which we see that

$$\cos^2 \alpha_0 - \sin^2 \alpha_0 = 0$$

or $\cos \alpha_0 = \sin \alpha_0$, showing that R will be a maximum for $\alpha_0 = 45°$

(b) To establish that every possible range R, except R_m, will have two different firing angles associated with it, let us place

$$\cos \alpha_0 \sin \alpha_0 = p$$

in the above relation for R. Then

$$R = \frac{2v_0{}^2 p}{g},$$

and it is easy to see that while, for given values of R and v_0, p will have a particular value, there will be two values of α associated with all but one particular value of p. By trigonometric identity,

$$\sin \alpha_0 \sqrt{1 - \sin^2 \alpha_0} = p;$$

and, squaring both sides, we obtain

$$\sin^2 \alpha_0(1 - \sin^2 \alpha_0) = p^2$$

or

$$\sin^4 \alpha_0 - \sin^2 \alpha_0 + p^2 = 0.$$

This is a quadratic equation in $\sin^2 \alpha_0$; hence

$$\sin^2 \alpha_0 = \frac{1 \pm \sqrt{1 - 4p^2}}{2}.$$

Clearly, we will have two roots; taking the subscript 0 for granted,

$$\sin^2 \alpha_1 = \frac{1}{2} + \frac{\sqrt{1 - 4p^2}}{2}$$

and

$$\sin^2 \alpha_2 = \frac{1}{2} - \frac{\sqrt{1 - 4p^2}}{2},$$

except when

$$1 - 4p^2 = 0.$$

In this case

$$p^2 = \tfrac{1}{4}$$

or

$$\cos \alpha_0 \sin \alpha_0 = \tfrac{1}{2},$$

which means that

$$\alpha_0 = 45°,$$

because then

$$\cos 45° \sin 45° = \frac{1}{\sqrt{2}} \times \frac{1}{\sqrt{2}} = \frac{1}{2}.$$

12. Two projectiles are fired from the same point with the initial speed v_0 but at angles α_1 and α_2, where $\alpha_1 > \alpha_2$. What must the time interval between the firings be to make the projectiles collide in the air?

Solution

We know that in general for either projectile

$$y = v_0 t \sin \alpha_0 - \tfrac{1}{2}g t^2$$

$$x = v_0 t \cos \alpha_0.$$

If the two projectiles are to collide, they must have the same x- and y-coordinates after times of flight t_1 and t_2. Therefore,

$$x = v_0 t_1 \cos \alpha_1$$

and

$$x = v_0 t_2 \cos \alpha_2,$$

or

$$t_1 = \frac{x}{v_0 \cos \alpha_1}$$

and

$$t_2 = \frac{x}{v_0 \cos \alpha_2},$$

giving

$$t_1 - t_2 = \frac{x}{v_0}\left(\frac{1}{\cos \alpha_1} - \frac{1}{\cos \alpha_2} \right)$$

or

$$\Delta t = \frac{x}{v_0}\left[\frac{\cos \alpha_2 - \cos \alpha_1}{\cos \alpha_1 \cos \alpha_2}\right].$$

Now we may use the other two equations to replace x with a function of α_1 and α_2.
Substituting for t from

$$x = v_0 t \cos \alpha_0, \qquad t = \frac{x}{v_0 \cos \alpha_0}$$

in

$$y = v_0 t \sin \alpha_0 - \tfrac{1}{2}gt^2,$$

we obtain

$$y = x \tan \alpha_0 - \frac{gx^2}{2v_0^2 \cos^2 \alpha}.$$

Therefore,

$$y = x \tan \alpha_1 - \frac{gx^2}{2v_0^2 \cos^2 \alpha_1}$$

and

$$y = x \tan \alpha_2 - \frac{gx^2}{2v_0^2 \cos^2 \alpha_2}.$$

It follows that

$$\tan \alpha_2 - \tan \alpha_1 = x\,\frac{g}{2v_0^2}\left[\frac{1}{\cos^2 \alpha_2} - \frac{1}{\cos^2 \alpha_1}\right]$$

or

$$x = \frac{2v_0^2\cos^2 \alpha_2 \cos^2 \alpha_1 (\tan \alpha_2 - \tan \alpha_1)}{g(\cos^2 \alpha_1 - \cos^2 \alpha_2)}.$$

Consequently, substitution gives

$$\Delta t = \frac{2v_0 \cos^2 \alpha_2 \cos^2 \alpha_1 (\tan \alpha_2 - \tan \alpha_1)}{g(\cos^2 \alpha_1 - \cos^2 \alpha_2)}\left[\frac{\cos \alpha_2 - \cos \alpha_1}{\cos \alpha_1 \cos \alpha_2}\right]$$

$$= \frac{2v_0 \cos \alpha_2 \cos \alpha_1 (\tan \alpha_1 - \tan \alpha_2)}{g(\cos \alpha_1 + \cos \alpha_2)}.$$

13. A marksman located at point A in Fig. P3.2 (13) wishes to hit point B on a target rotating around the X-axis with the angular velocity ω. If he fires his rifle when point B is in the position shown, in what direction must he aim in order to hit the point after the target has rotated $90°$?

Solution

If we neglect air resistance and proceed as in the text, the equations of motion are:

$$\ddot{x} = 0$$
$$\ddot{y} = 0$$
$$\ddot{z} = -g$$

with the solutions

$$x = C_1 t + C_2$$
$$y = C_3 t + C_4$$
$$z = -\tfrac{1}{2}gt^2 + C_5 t + C_6.$$

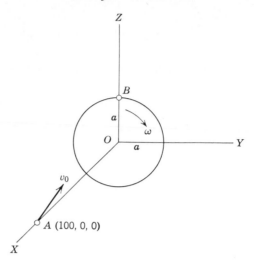

Fig. P3.2 (13)

But now we have the initial conditions:

$$x(0) = 100 \qquad \dot{x}(0) = v_0 \cos \alpha_0$$
$$y(0) = 0 \qquad \dot{y}(0) = v_0 \cos \beta_0$$
$$z(0) = 0 \qquad \dot{z}(0) = v_0 \cos \gamma_0$$

where α_0, β_0, and γ_0 are the direction cosines of the initial velocity $\mathbf{v_0}$. Hence,

$$C_2 = 100$$
$$C_1 = v_0 \cos \alpha_0.$$
$$x = v_0 t \cos \alpha_0 + 100;$$
$$C_4 = 0$$
$$C_3 = v_0 \cos \beta_0,$$
$$y = v_0 t \cos \beta_0;$$
$$C_6 = 0$$
$$C_5 = v_0 \cos \gamma_0,$$
$$z = -\tfrac{1}{2} g t^2 + v_0 t \cos \gamma_0.$$

The time necessary for the bullet to reach the target can be found by placing $x = 0$:

$$t_1 = -\frac{100}{v_0 \cos \alpha_0}$$

During this time interval the target will have rotated through an angle ωt, giving B the coordinates $(0, a \sin \omega t_1, a \cos \omega t_1)$. It follows that at $t = t_1$

$$y = v_0 t_1 \cos \beta_0 = a \sin \omega t_1$$

and

$$z = -\tfrac{1}{2}gt_1^2 + v_0 t_1 \cos \gamma_0 = a \cos \omega t_1.$$

But from the conditions of the problem, we know that

$$\omega t_1 = \frac{\pi}{2}, \qquad t_1 = \frac{\pi}{2\omega},$$

and also that

$$\cos \alpha_0 = -\frac{100}{v_0 t_1}.$$

Therefore,

$$\cos \alpha_0 = -\frac{200\,\omega}{\pi v_0},$$

while the above relations give

$$\frac{v_0 \pi}{2\omega} \cos \beta_0 = a \sin \frac{\pi}{2} = a,$$

$$\cos \beta_0 = \frac{2a\omega}{\pi v_0}$$

and

$$\frac{v_0 \pi}{2\omega} \cos \gamma_0 = \tfrac{1}{2}g \frac{\pi^2}{4\omega^2},$$

$$\cos \gamma_0 = \frac{\pi g}{4 v_0 \omega}.$$

These direction cosines determine the required direction of aim; the initial velocity must be

$$\mathbf{v_0} = \left(-\frac{200\,\omega}{\pi}\right)\hat{\mathbf{i}} + \left(\frac{2a\omega}{\pi}\right)\hat{\mathbf{j}} + \left(\frac{\pi g}{4\omega}\right)\hat{\mathbf{k}}.$$

14. A projectile of point mass m, fired from the origin, encounters air resistance proportional to its velocity but remains in the XY-plane. Solve the equations of motion and determine y_{max}.

Solution

If we assume that $C_x = C_y = C$, the equations of motion developed in the text become:

$$m\ddot{x} + C\dot{x} = 0$$

$$m\ddot{y} + C\dot{y} = -mg$$

The general solution of the first is

$$x = C_1 + C_2 e^{-\frac{C}{m}t};$$

however, with the initial conditions

$$x(0) = 0 \quad \text{and} \quad \dot{x}(0) = v_0 \cos \alpha_0,$$

$$C_1 = -C_2$$

and

$$v_0 \cos \alpha_0 = -C_2 \frac{C}{m},$$

$$C_2 = -\frac{mv_0}{C} \cos \alpha_0.$$

Therefore,

$$x = \frac{mv_0}{C} \cos \alpha_0 - \frac{mv_0}{C} \cos \alpha_0 \, e^{-\frac{C}{m} t} = \frac{mv_0}{C} \cos \alpha_0 \left(1 - e^{-\frac{C}{m} t} \right).$$

The general solution of the second equation is

$$y = C_3 + C_4 e^{-\frac{C}{m} t} - \frac{mgt}{C}.$$

The first initial condition,

$$y(0) = 0,$$

gives

$$C_3 = -C_4;$$

whereas the other condition,

$$\dot{y}(0) = v_0 \sin \alpha_0,$$

gives

$$v_0 \sin \alpha_0 = -\frac{C}{m} C_4 - \frac{mg}{C}$$

or

$$C_4 = -\frac{m}{C} \left(v_0 \sin \alpha_0 + \frac{mg}{C} \right).$$

Thus,

$$y = \frac{m}{C} \left(v_0 \sin \alpha_0 + \frac{mg}{C} \right) - \frac{m}{C} \left(v_0 \sin \alpha_0 + \frac{mg}{C} \right) e^{-\frac{C}{m} t} - \frac{mgt}{C}$$

$$= \frac{m}{C} \left(v_0 \sin \alpha_0 + \frac{mg}{C} \right) \left(1 - e^{-\frac{C}{m} t} \right) - \frac{mgt}{C}.$$

To find $y_{\max}$, we first must calculate

$$\frac{dy}{dt} = \left(v_0 \sin \alpha_0 + \frac{mg}{C} \right) e^{-\frac{C}{m} t} - \frac{mg}{C},$$

because we know that when

$$\frac{dy}{dt} = 0, \quad y = y_{\max}.$$

Therefore,

$$\left(v_0 \sin \alpha_0 + \frac{mg}{C} \right) e^{-\frac{C}{m} t} - \frac{mg}{C} = 0$$

or

$$e^{\frac{C}{m} t} = \frac{v_0 C \sin \alpha_0}{mg} + 1$$

defines the value of t when y is y_{max}:

$$t = \frac{m}{C} \ln \left[\frac{v_0 C \sin a_0}{mg} + 1 \right]$$

It follows that

$$y_{max} = \frac{m}{C^2} \left[v_0 C \sin \alpha_0 - mg \ln \left(\frac{v_0 C \sin \alpha_0}{mg} + 1 \right) \right].$$

15. Consider the two-dimensional oscillator shown in Fig. P3.2 (15).

   a. The point mass is displaced from its equilibrium position to $x = x_0$, $y = y_0$ and released at time $t = 0$. Find expressions for x and y at any time, assuming that x_0 and y_0 are very small compared to the lengths of the springs.
   b. Determine whether the path of the mass in space will be closed if $K_1 = 2K_2$ and if $K_1 = 4K_2$.

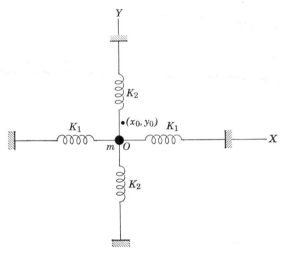

Fig. P3.2 (15)

Solution

(a) We know the equations of motion in the x- and y-directions have solutions of the form

$$x = A_1 \cos (\omega_1 t + \theta_1)$$
$$y = A_2 \cos (\omega_2 t + \theta_2);$$

by differentiation, we have

$$\dot{x} = -A_1 \omega_1 \sin (\omega_1 t + \theta_1)$$
$$\dot{y} = -A_2 \omega_2 \sin (\omega_2 t + \theta_2).$$

The initial conditions are:

$$x(0) = x_0 \qquad \dot{x}(0) = 0$$
$$y(0) = y_0 \qquad \dot{y}(0) = 0$$

Hence

$$A_1 = \frac{x_0}{\cos \theta_1} = x_0, \qquad \theta_1 = n_1 \pi$$

$$A_2 = \frac{y_0}{\cos \theta_2} = y_0, \qquad \theta_2 = n_2 \pi$$

where n_1 and n_2 are integers.

Therefore, since $\omega_1 = \sqrt{2K_1/m}$, and $\omega_2 = \sqrt{2K_2/m}$,

$$x = x_0 \cos \left(\sqrt{\frac{2K_1}{m}} t + n_1 \pi \right)$$

$$y = y_0 \cos \left(\sqrt{\frac{2K_2}{m}} t + n_2 \pi \right).$$

(b) If some set of integers (α_x, α_y) exists for which

$$\frac{\omega_{0x}}{\alpha_x} = \frac{\omega_{0y}}{\alpha_y},$$

the path of the mass in space will be closed. In the present problem

$$\frac{\omega_{0x}}{\alpha_x} = \frac{\omega_{0y}}{\alpha_y}$$

becomes

$$\frac{\sqrt{\frac{2K_1}{m}}}{a_x} = \frac{\sqrt{\frac{2K_2}{m}}}{a_y}$$

or

$$\frac{\sqrt{K_1}}{\alpha_x} = \frac{\sqrt{K_2}}{\alpha_y}$$

Therefore, if $K_1 = 2K_2$,

$$\frac{\sqrt{2}}{\alpha_x} = \frac{1}{\alpha_y},$$

$$\frac{\alpha_x}{\alpha_y} = \sqrt{2}$$

and the path will not be closed; whereas if $K_1 = 4K_2$,

$$\frac{\alpha_x}{\alpha_y} = 2$$

and the path will be closed, as illustrated previously.

16. For two simple harmonic motions at right angles, described by the equations

$$x = A_1 \sin (\omega_0 t + \delta_1)$$

and

$$y = A_2 \sin (\omega_0 t + \delta_2),$$

show that the equation of the resultant motion is

$$\sin^2 (\delta_2 - \delta_1) = \frac{x^2}{A_1^2} + \frac{y^2}{A_2^2} - \frac{2xy}{A_1 A_2} \cos (\delta_2 - \delta_1);$$

also, plot this for the two cases

$$(\delta_2 - \delta_1) = 0$$

and

$$(\delta_2 - \delta_1) = \pi/2.$$

Solution

By trigonometric identity we can rewrite the given equations in the form

$$\frac{x}{A_1} = \sin \omega t \cos \delta_1 + \cos \omega t \sin \delta_1$$

$$\frac{y}{A_2} = \sin \omega t \cos \delta_2 + \cos \omega t \sin \delta_2.$$

Multiplying the first by $\sin \delta_2$, the second by $\sin \delta_1$, and subtracting the second from the first gives

$$\frac{x}{A_1} \sin \delta_2 - \frac{y}{A_2} \sin \delta_1 = \sin \omega t \, (\cos \delta_1 \sin \delta_2 - \cos \delta_2 \sin \delta_1)$$

$$= \sin \omega t \sin (\delta_2 - \delta_1).$$

Similarly, multiplying the second by $\cos \delta_2$, the first by $\cos \delta_1$, and subtracting the first from the second gives

$$\frac{y}{A_2} \cos \delta_1 - \frac{x}{A_1} \cos \delta_2 = \cos \omega t \, (\cos \delta_1 \sin \delta_2 - \cos \delta_2 \sin \delta_1)$$

$$= \cos \omega t \sin (\delta_2 - \delta_1).$$

Squaring and adding these equations eliminates t, as required:

$$\sin^2 (\delta_2 - \delta_1) = \frac{x^2}{A_1^2} + \frac{y^2}{A_2^2} - \frac{2xy}{A_1 A_2} \cos (\delta_2 - \delta_1).$$

If $(\delta_2 - \delta_1) = 0$, this becomes

$$0 = \frac{x^2}{A_1^2} + \frac{y^2}{A_2^2} - \frac{2xy}{A_1 A_2}$$

or

$$\left(\frac{x}{A_1} - \frac{y}{A_2} \right) \left(\frac{x}{A_1} - \frac{y}{A_2} \right) = 0,$$

showing that the equation to be plotted is [Fig. P3.2 (16a)]:

$$\frac{x}{A_1} = \frac{y}{A_2}.$$

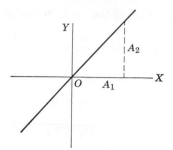

Fig. P3.2 (16*a*)

On the other hand, if $(\delta_2 - \delta_1) = \pi/2$, the equation becomes

$$1 = \frac{x^2}{A_1{}^2} + \frac{y^2}{A_2{}^2},$$

which is the equation of an ellipse [see Figs. P3.2 (16*b*) to P3.2 (16*d*)].

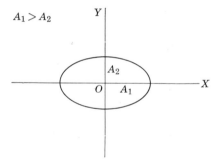

Fig. P3.2 (16*b*)

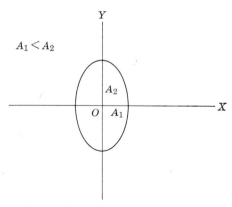

Fig. P3.2 (16*c*)

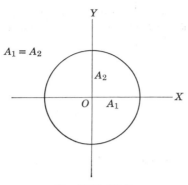

Fig. P3.2 (16d)

Exercises 3.2

1. The potential energy of a point mass m has the form
$$V = -mgx + \tfrac{1}{2}Kx^2.$$
  a. If $x = 0$ and $\dot{x} = 0$ at time $t = 0$, find x as a function of t.
  b. What is the equilibrium position of the point mass?
  c. What are the oscillation frequency and period of the motion?
  d. Describe a physical situation that could give rise to a potential of the form given.

Answer.

(a) $x = \dfrac{mg}{K}(1 - \cos \omega_0 t)$.

(b) $x_{\text{equil}} = \dfrac{mg}{K}$.

2. What is the constant of the equivalent spring for the system shown in Fig. E3.2 (2) and what is the natural frequency of the system?

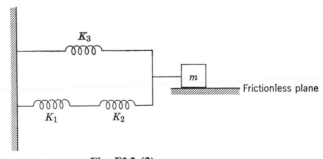

Fig. E3.2 (2)

Answer. $K = \dfrac{K_1 K_2 + K_2 K_3 + K_3 K_1}{K_1 + K_2}$.

3. The inverted simple pendulum shown in Fig. E3.2 (3) is activated by a spiral spring which supplies a torque T proportional to the deflection angle θ, $T = K\theta$.

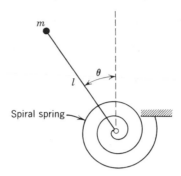

Fig. E3.2 (3)

a. Write the equation of motion for the pendulum bob, using the relationship

$$\mathbf{M} = \frac{d}{dt}(\mathbf{r} \times m\mathbf{v}).$$

b. Obtain the same equation using the Lagrangian method, noting that the derivative of the generalized potential has units of work.

c. Solve the equation for the case when θ is very small and the initial conditions are $\theta(0) = \theta_0$ and $\dot{\theta}(0) = 0$.

d. Describe the motion of the mass if $K = mgl$.

Answer. (c) $\theta = \theta_0 \cos \left(\dfrac{K - mgl}{ml^2} \right)^{\frac{1}{2}} t.$

4. A 100-lb force is applied while the system shown in Fig. E3.2 (4) is in equilibrium and the cord is tightly stretched; both blocks may be treated as point masses.

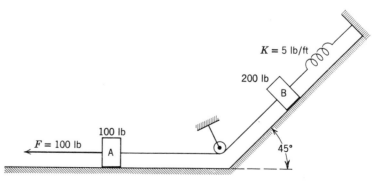

Fig. E3.2 (4)

a. Neglecting friction, calculate the acceleration of block A at the instant the force is applied.

b. If the damping coefficient for each block is 10 lb/ft/sec, find the displacement of A after 1 sec.

Answer. $\quad (b)\; x = -10e^{-g/30}\left[\left(1 + \dfrac{1}{\alpha}\right)e^{\beta} + \left(1 - \dfrac{1}{\alpha}\right)e^{-\beta}\right],$

$$\alpha = \sqrt{\frac{1-15}{g}}, \quad \beta = \sqrt{\frac{g}{60}\left(\frac{g}{15} - 1\right)}.$$

5. Solve the differential equation of motion for a unit point mass acted on by a spring force $-Kx$ and a damping force $-C\dot{x}$ if $K = (C^2/4)$, assuming that $x(0) = 0$ and $\dot{x}(0) = v_0$. Plot x versus t.

Answer. $\quad x = v_0 t e^{-\frac{C}{2}t}.$

6. A driving force $F = F_0 \cos \omega t$ acts on a point mass m, which is attached to a spring with the constant K.

a. Find the position of m as a function of time if $x = 0$ and $\dot{x} = 0$ initially.

b. What happens if $\omega = \sqrt{K/m}$; explain the result in physical terms.

7. Find an expression for the displacement of the system shown in Fig. E3.2 (7), using the initial conditions $x(0) = 0$ and $\dot{x}(0) = \dot{x}_0$.

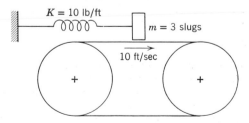

Fig. E3.2 (7)

Answer. $\quad x = \left[\dfrac{m}{C}\left(\dfrac{12m}{C} + \dot{x}_0\right) + \dfrac{3C}{\alpha}\right] - \left[\dfrac{m}{C}\left(\dfrac{12m}{\alpha} + \dot{x}_0\right)\right]e^{-\frac{C}{2}t}$

$\qquad\qquad -\dfrac{3C}{\alpha}\cos 2t - \dfrac{6m}{\alpha}\sin 2t, \quad \alpha = 2(4m^2 + C^2).$

8. A point mass rests on a conveyor moving with a speed of 10 ft/sec [Fig. E3.2 (8)]. If the damping constant is 1 lb/ft/sec, determine the equilibrium

$K = 10$ lb/ft

$m = 3$ slugs

10 ft/sec

Fig. E3.2 (8)

force in the spring. If the mass is displaced 4 in. to the right from the above equilibrium position, form an equation defining the time required for it to pass through the equilibrium position again.

Answer. $e^{-\frac{1}{8}t_1}\left[\frac{1}{3}\cos\sqrt{\frac{19.8}{6}}\,t_1 + \frac{1}{18}\sqrt{\frac{6}{19.8}}\sin\sqrt{\frac{19.8}{6}}\,t_1\right] = 0$

9. Obtain the following:

   a. Physically corresponding electrical and mechanical quantities for the case of mechanical rotation.
   b. The circuit analog for a simple pendulum.

10. Draw the analogous electrical circuit for the system shown in Fig. E3.2 (10). A unit vector in the direction of the forcing function is given by

$$\hat{F} = \frac{1}{\sqrt{6}}\hat{i} + \frac{2}{\sqrt{6}}\hat{j} - \frac{1}{\sqrt{6}}\hat{k}.$$

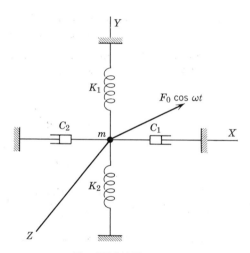

Fig. E3.2 (10)

11. A bullet is fired from a hill 500 ft above a plane, at an angle of 15° above the horizontal. The muzzle velocity is 3000 ft/sec. Neglecting air friction, at what horizontal distance will the bullet strike the plane?

   Answer. 1.45×10^5 ft.

12. A shell is to be fired at a 45°-tilted target 2000 ft away in such a manner that it will strike perpendicular to the target [Fig. E3.2 (12)]. If a maximum trajectory height has been fixed at 300 ft, what must the initial velocity v_0 and the initial angle α_0 be, neglecting air friction and the curvature and rotation of the earth? Also, approximately what will the difference in elevation be between the point of impact on the target and the gun?

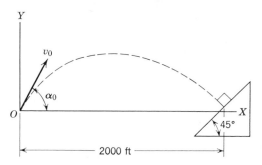

Fig. E3.2 (12)

Answer. $\alpha_0 = 35.7°$, $v_0 = 237.4$ ft/sec.

13. A point mass m is thrown from the origin with an initial velocity $\mathbf{v}_0 = 3\hat{\mathbf{i}} + 2\hat{\mathbf{j}} + \hat{\mathbf{k}}$ ft/sec [Fig. E3.2 (13)]. If gravity is represented by $\mathbf{g} = (g_0/\sqrt{6})(2\hat{\mathbf{i}} + \hat{\mathbf{j}} + \hat{\mathbf{k}})$ and air resistance is neglected, determine the coordinates of the point of impact in the XY-plane, as well as the time of flight to that point.

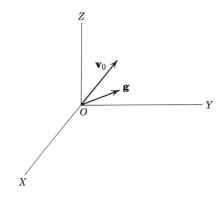

Fig. E3.2 (13)

Answer. $\left(\dfrac{2\sqrt{6}}{g_0}, \dfrac{2\sqrt{6}}{g_0}, 0\right)$.

14. A ball of mass m is dropped from a plane flying with a constant horizontal velocity v_0 when it is in the position shown in Fig. E3.2 (14). Neglecting air friction, calculate the following:

   a. The equation of the ball's trajectory.
   b. The time it will take for the ball to hit the ground after it has been released.
   c. R as a function of h and v_0.

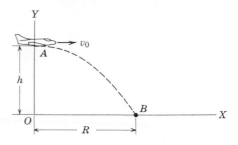

Fig. E3.2 (14)

Answer.

(a) $y = -\frac{1}{2}g\dfrac{x^2}{v_0^2} + h.$

(b) $t = \sqrt{2h/g}.$

(c) $R = v_0\sqrt{2h/g}.$

15. A small symmetrical mass m is held by four springs as shown in Fig. E3.2 (15). The XY-plane, which is the plane of motion, is horizontal and the mass slides on it without friction. Find $x(t)$ and $y(t)$ in the given coordinate system if the initial conditions are:

$$x(0) = 0, \qquad y(0) = -d$$
$$\dot{x}(0) = 0, \qquad \dot{y}(0) = 0.$$

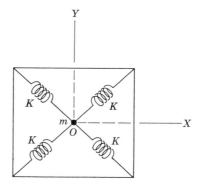

Fig. E3.2 (15)

16. If the four springs in the preceding problem are to be replaced by the two equivalent springs shown in Fig. E3.2 (16), determine the value of K_E such that the motion of m will be the same as before.

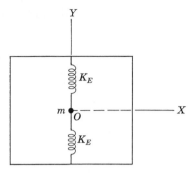

Fig. E3.2 (16)

17. Neglecting gravitational effects, find the position of the point mass m as a function of time t in Fig. 3.2 (17) if the initial conditions are the following:

a. $x(0) = y(0) = \dot{x}(0) = \dot{y}(0) = \dot{z}(0) = 0$ and $z(0) = z_0$.
b. $x(0) = \dot{y}(0) = \dot{z}(0) = 0$ and $\dot{x}(0) = \dot{x}_0$, $y(0) = y_0$, $z(0) = z_0$.

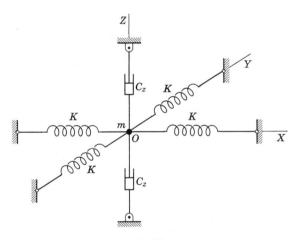

Fig. E3.2 (17)

3.3 Central and Noncentral Forces

Motions of a point object which occur under a force of the form

$$\mathbf{F} = F(r)\hat{\mathbf{h}}, \qquad (3.1)$$

where $\hat{\mathbf{h}}$ represents a unit vector in the direction of the spherical coordinate position vector $\mathbf{r}$ (Fig. 3.22), are called central force motions. Actually, if the object is in motion and this is the only force acting, we can conclude that the moment of force with respect to the origin will vanish,

$$\mathbf{M} = \mathbf{r} \times \mathbf{F} = (\mathbf{r} \times \hat{\mathbf{h}})F(r) = 0, \tag{3.2}$$

and that the angular momentum will therefore remain constant,

$$M = \frac{d}{dt}\mathbf{l} = 0, \tag{3.3}$$

$$\mathbf{l} = \mathbf{r} \times m\mathbf{v} = \text{constant}. \tag{3.4}$$

This means that the motion will be confined to the plane perpendicular to $\mathbf{l}$, in which $\mathbf{F}$ acts, so that we can work in polar coordinates with no loss in generality (Fig. 3.23):

$$\mathbf{F} = F(\rho)\hat{\mathbf{l}} \tag{3.5}$$

Even in this case, as will soon appear, the equations of motion are generally coupled, which means that the situation is basically different from that

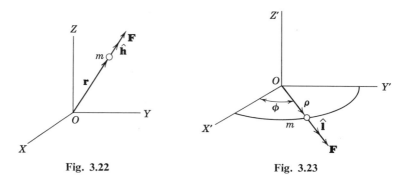

Fig. 3.22   Fig. 3.23

considered in the preceding section. On the other hand, they are not coupled very strongly, in the sense that they may easily be solved simultaneously. For this reason, central-force motion constitutes a logical transition from the uncoupled to the strongly coupled case.

The motion of the earth in the gravitational field of the sun, and the motion of the moon about the earth are often quoted as examples; this may suggest that central-force motion represents a special case of a more general situation in which the masses of both bodies are approximately the same. The latter, wherein neither body can be considered fixed, is called the two-body problem. We shall discuss it, and its logical extension known as the many-body problem, briefly toward the end of the section. In all of its forms it is a problem of great importance and widespread application in mathematical mechanics.

Since it appears that in most circumstances of interest we will know the form of the potential energy associated with (3.5), as in the gravitational case, let us use the Lagrangian method to solve the present problem. The location of the mass can be specified uniquely by ρ and ϕ, and no additional constraints exist, so we can evidently consider them independent generalized coordinates. Furthermore, we know from (3.5) that the potential V will be a function of ρ only.

$$V = V(\rho). \tag{3.6}$$

It remains to write the kinetic energy in polar coordinates. But from our earlier work [(1.45) of Chapter 1] we know that under the usual assumptions this is merely

$$T = \frac{m\mathbf{v}^2}{2} = \frac{m}{2}\mathbf{v}\cdot\mathbf{v} = \frac{m}{2}(\dot{\rho}\hat{\mathbf{l}} + \rho\dot{\phi}\hat{\mathbf{m}})\cdot(\dot{\rho}\hat{\mathbf{l}} + \rho\dot{\phi}\hat{\mathbf{m}}) = \frac{m}{2}(\dot{\rho}^2 + \rho^2\dot{\phi}^2). \tag{3.7}$$

Thus we see that

$$L = T - V = \frac{m}{2}(\dot{\rho}^2 + \rho^2\dot{\phi}^2) - V(\rho), \tag{3.8}$$

which establishes that the system is conservative.

Applying the appropriate Lagrangian equations [(2.43) of Chapter 2],

$$\frac{d}{dt}\frac{\partial L}{\partial \dot{q}_j} - \frac{\partial L}{\partial q_j} = 0 \quad \{q_j = \rho, \phi, \tag{3.9}$$

to the ρ-coordinate first, we obtain

$$\frac{d}{dt}m\dot{\rho} - m\rho\dot{\phi}^2 + \frac{\partial V}{\partial \rho} = 0, \tag{3.10}$$

or making the substitution

$$\frac{\partial V}{\partial \rho} = -F(\rho), \tag{3.11}$$

$$F(\rho) + m\rho\dot{\phi}^2 = m\ddot{\rho} ; \tag{3.12}$$

whereas applying them to the ϕ-coordinate yields

$$\frac{d}{dt}m\rho^2\dot{\phi} = 0, \tag{3.13}$$

confirming that the magnitude l of the angular momentum remains constant:

$$l = |\boldsymbol{\rho} \times m\mathbf{v}| = |\rho\hat{\mathbf{l}} \times m(\dot{\rho}\hat{\mathbf{l}} + \rho\dot{\phi}\hat{\mathbf{m}})| = m\rho^2\dot{\phi} = \text{constant} \tag{3.14}$$

Equations (3.12) and (3.14) are the scalar equations of motion; and, although each contains both of the independent generalized coordinates, it is easy to solve (3.14) for $\dot{\phi}$ and eliminate all angular dependence by substituting this in (3.12):

$$\dot{\phi} = \frac{l}{m\rho^2}, \tag{3.15}$$

$$F(\rho) + \frac{l^2}{m\rho^3} = m\ddot{\rho}. \tag{3.16}$$

In fact, we can if we wish write (3.16) in the Newtonian form

$$F'(\rho) = m\ddot{\rho}, \tag{3.17}$$

where

$$F'(\rho) = F(\rho) + \frac{l^2}{m\rho^3}, \tag{3.18}$$

and replace the real planar motion of the point mass with a fictitious one-dimensional motion in the ρ-direction under the influence of the two parts of F', the force $F(\rho)$ arising from $V(\rho)$ and the "centrifugal" force $l^2/m\rho^3$. The latter is merely the price we pay for one-dimensionalizing the problem. Of course, (3.18) implies a potential of the form

$$V'(\rho) = V(\rho) + \frac{l^2}{2m\rho^2}, \tag{3.19}$$

because

$$-\frac{\partial V'}{\partial \rho} = -\frac{\partial V}{\partial \rho} + \frac{l^2}{m\rho^3} = F(\rho) + \frac{l^2}{m\rho^3} = F'(\rho); \tag{3.20}$$

therefore, in these circumstances conservation of mechanical energy can be expressed in the form

$$T_\rho + V_\rho' = \frac{m\dot{\rho}^2}{2} + V'(\rho) = E_\rho. \tag{3.21}$$

Let us suppose specifically that (3.5) is an "inverse square" attractive force of the gravitational or electrostatic type:

$$F(\rho) = -\frac{B}{\rho^2}, \qquad B = \text{constant.} \tag{3.22}$$

This means that

$$V(\rho) = -\frac{B}{\rho}; \tag{3.23}$$

so (3.19) becomes

$$V'(\rho) = -\frac{B}{\rho} + \frac{l^2}{2m\rho^2}, \tag{3.24}$$

which may conveniently be represented as shown in Fig. 3.24. $F'(\rho)$ is also shown on the diagram to illustrate its relation to $V'(\rho)$.

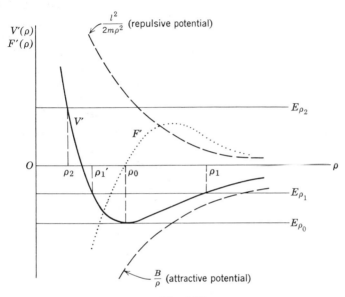

Fig. 3.24

According to (3.21), as before,

$$V'(\rho) \leqq E_\rho. \tag{3.25}$$

Thus a point object with the energy E_{ρ_0} would be forced to remain at the distance ρ_0 from the center of force O. The real planar motion would be rotation in a circular orbit around O (Fig. 3.25) and in this case, because $F'(\rho) = 0$,

$$-F(\rho) = \frac{l^2}{m\rho^3} \tag{3.26}$$

from (3.18). That is, an attractive force toward the center is at all times equaled by a centrifugal force in the opposite direction.

On the other hand, a point object with the energy E_{ρ_1} could oscillate between the distances ρ_1 and ρ_1' while yet conserving this energy. Consequently, the planar motion would be confined to the region between two circles of radius ρ_1 and ρ_1' (Fig. 3.26). The conditions under which the trajectory will become an ellipse (shown dotted in the figure) will be developed below; they should not be confused with the requirements for the three-dimensional harmonic oscillator, which is subject to a different attractive force.

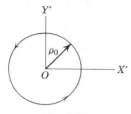

Fig. 3.25

If the object had the energy E_{ρ_2}, it could approach the center of force no closer than the distance ρ_2. This means that if it were approaching O from one direction, it would have to reverse at ρ_2 and move off in an opposed direction. Two-dimensionally, the trajectory would be a hyperbola with O as the focus (Fig. 3.27). We shall study this case in some detail later, since it is the "near-miss" type of trajectory quite common in collision processes between mutually attractive objects with central-force fields.

To solve the equations of motion (3.12) and (3.14) directly, we can proceed by replacing $V'(\rho)$ in (3.21) and isolating $\dot{\rho}$:

$$\dot{\rho} = \pm\left[\frac{2}{m}\left(E_\rho - V(\rho) - \frac{l^2}{2m\rho^2}\right)\right]^{\frac{1}{2}} \tag{3.27}$$

or

$$\int \frac{d\rho}{\sqrt{E_\rho - V(\rho) - \dfrac{l^2}{2m\rho^2}}} = \sqrt{\frac{2}{m}} \int dt. \tag{3.28}$$

Provided the integration can be carried out, this will yield $\rho = \rho(t)$; $\phi = \phi(t)$ can then be obtained from (3.15):

$$\dot{\phi} = \frac{l}{m\rho^2}$$

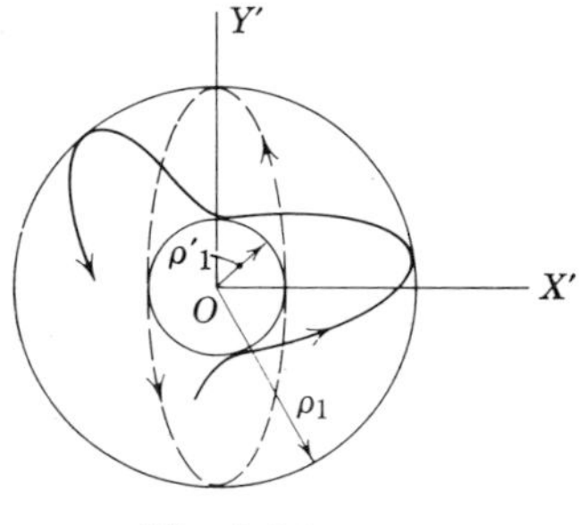

Fig. 3.26

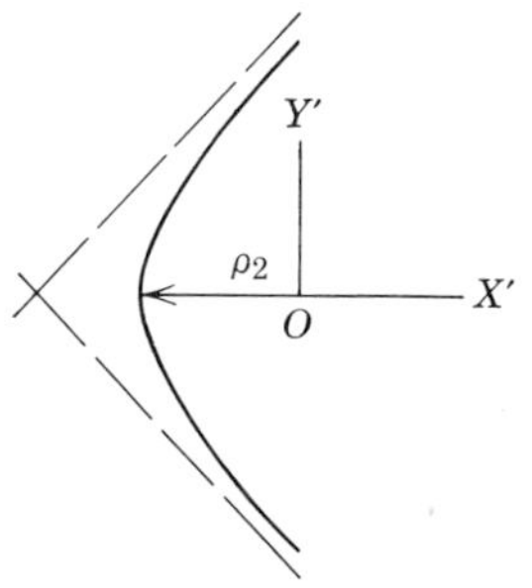

Fig. 3.27

or

$$\int d\phi = \int \frac{l}{m\rho^2} \, dt. \tag{3.29}$$

However, the integration is often difficult; and it is more instructive to develop the discussion in terms of the possible trajectories of the object, as suggested above.

We can eliminate time as a variable by repeated use of the relation (3.15), for by means of it we can write

$$\dot{\rho} = \frac{d\rho}{dt} = \frac{d\rho}{d\phi} \frac{d\phi}{dt} = \frac{l}{m\rho^2} \frac{d\rho}{d\phi} \tag{3.30}$$

and

$$\ddot{\rho} = \frac{d\dot{\rho}}{dt} = \frac{d}{d\phi}\left(\frac{l}{m} \frac{d\rho}{\rho^2 d\phi}\right)\frac{d\phi}{dt} = \frac{d}{d\phi}\left[\frac{l}{m}\left(-\frac{d\rho^{-1}}{d\phi}\right)\right]\frac{l}{m\rho^2} = -\frac{l^2}{m^2\rho^2} \frac{d^2\rho^{-1}}{d\phi^2} \, ; \tag{3.31}$$

so substitution in (3.16) gives

$$F(\rho) + \frac{l^2}{m\rho^3} = m\left(-\frac{l^2}{m^2\rho^2} \frac{d^2\rho^{-1}}{d\phi^2}\right)$$

or

$$\frac{d^2\rho^{-1}}{d\phi^2} + \rho^{-1} = -\frac{m\rho^2}{l^2} F(\rho). \tag{3.32}$$

With the right-hand side equal to zero, this equation has the same form as (2.12), though with ϕ instead of t as the independent variable, ρ^{-1} instead of x as the dependent variable, and the constant K_x/m replaced by unity. Hence the general solution of the homogeneous equation must be

$$\rho_G^{-1} = A \cos(\phi + \theta). \tag{3.33}$$

However, if the right-hand side does not vanish, we must also find a particular solution. The apparent danger of l approaching zero and causing this term to increase without limit is not real; (3.15) shows that ϕ will remain constant if $l = 0$, expressing motion along a straight line through the origin.

To simplify the problem of finding a particular solution, let us assume that $F(\rho)$ is attractive and inversely proportional to the distance from the origin, as in the case of electrostatic and gravitational forces:

$$F(\rho) = -B\rho^{-2}, \qquad B = \text{constant}. \tag{3.34}$$

Substituting in (3.32) we then obtain

$$\frac{d^2\rho^{-1}}{d\phi^2} + \rho^{-1} = \frac{m}{l^2} B, \tag{3.35}$$

and it is evident that the right-hand side must itself be a particular solution:

$$\rho_P^{-1} = \frac{m}{l^2} B. \tag{3.36}$$

Accordingly, the complete solution must be

$$\frac{1}{\rho} = A \cos{(\phi + \theta)} + \frac{m}{l^2} B. \tag{3.37}$$

As it turns out, this is a general conic curve for a set of coordinate axes

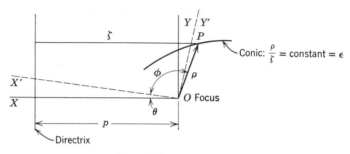

Fig. 3.28

rotated by an angle θ with respect to the axes of definition[13] (Fig. 3.28):

$$\frac{1}{\rho} = \frac{1}{p} \cos{(\phi + \theta)} + \frac{1}{\varepsilon p} \tag{3.38}$$

where

$$\frac{1}{p} = A \tag{3.39}$$

and

$$\frac{1}{\varepsilon p} = \frac{m}{l^2} B$$

or

$$\varepsilon = \frac{Al^2}{Bm}. \tag{3.40}$$

The quantity ε is called the eccentricity, and from its value alone the specific type of conic curve that the point object is describing about O can be determined. This is not surprising because it obviously contains all the critical parameters of the motion. It is easy to prove that the following

[13] Shames, I. H., *Engineering Mechanics*, pp. 393–396, Prentice-Hall, Englewood Cliffs, N.J., 1960.

types of curves will be associated with the given values of ε:

ε	Conic curve
1	parabola
<1	ellipse
>1	hyperbola
0	circle

Solution techniques will be demonstrated in the illustrative problems; however, it should be plain that, insofar as establishing the trajectory goes, the solution will usually depend on determining the value of the constant A, probably by applying certain initial conditions to (3.37). B will ordinarily be known, for example, in the case of gravitational force,

$$B = k_g mM \qquad (3.41)$$

where M is the mass of the body assumed fixed at the origin and k_g is the Newtonian constant; whereas for electrostatic force,

$$B = k_e qQ \qquad (3.42)$$

where Q is the charge of the fixed body and k_e is the Coulombic constant.[14] Moreover, because l will remain constant, it too is often given or can easily be calculated, perhaps from (3.14).

In general, if time-dependent values are required they must be obtained by integrating the equations of motion; however, the period of elliptical (and circular) orbits follows from another consideration. Noting that, in the limit, the area swept out by the position vector ρ as the angle ϕ increases by $d\phi$ will be

$$da = \tfrac{1}{2}\rho(\rho\,d\phi) = \frac{\rho^2\,d\phi}{2}, \qquad (3.43)$$

we see that the rate of area increase, or "areal" velocity, will be

$$\frac{da}{dt} = \frac{\rho^2}{2}\dot{\phi}. \qquad (3.44)$$

By the use of (3.15) this becomes

$$\frac{da}{dt} = \frac{\rho^2}{2}\frac{l}{m\rho^2} = \frac{l}{2m} = \text{constant}; \qquad (3.45)$$

[14] Halliday, H., and R. Resnick, *Physics for Students of Science and Engineering*, pp. 317–349, 555–567, Wiley, New York, 1961.

and it follows that the area swept out in one cycle is

$$a = \frac{l}{2m} \int_0^\tau dt = \frac{l\tau}{2m},$$
(3.46)

so that the period

$$\tau = \frac{2ma}{l}.$$
(3.47)

The relation (3.45) is called Kepler's second law, because it was discovered empirically by him long before it was recognized to be a natural consequence of the conservation of angular momentum.

Because of its physical importance the potential (3.23),

$$V(\rho) = -B\rho^{-1},$$

associated with an inverse square attractive force, has been featured in the preceding discussion. It should be evident, however, that the principal effect of increasing the absolute value of n in an expression of the type

$$V(\rho) = -B\rho^{-|n|}$$
(3.48)

will be merely to modify the detailed shape of the $V'(\rho)$ and $F'(\rho)$ curves in Fig. 3.24 without changing their overall form. In fact, the exponent of ρ in the repulsive component can also take on various positive values without changing this form, so that practically all central-force interactions between mutually attractive point objects are of the same general form, with counterparts of the phenomena presented above. For example, one of the most commonly used potentials for interactions between atoms is the so-called Lennard-Jones "6-12 potential"[15]:

$$V'(\rho) = 4E_{\rho_0}\left[-\left(\frac{\rho_0}{\rho}\right)^6 + \left(\frac{\rho_0}{\rho}\right)^{12}\right]$$
(3.49)

On the other hand, the form of $V'(\rho)$ does change if the sign of $|n|$ is changed in (3.48). The cases of $n = 0$ and $n = 1$, representing zero and constant forces $F(\rho)$, are perhaps of less interest than the case of $n = 2$:

$$V(\rho) = B\rho^{|n|} = B\rho^2$$
(3.50)

Notice that the change in the sign of the constant B is required to keep the force attractive, according to our sign convention:

$$F(\rho) = -\frac{\partial V}{\partial \rho} = -\frac{\partial}{\partial \rho} B\rho^2 = -2B\rho$$
(3.51)

[15] Hirschfelder, J. O., C. F. Curtiss, and R. B. Bird, *Molecular Theory of Gases and Liquids*, pp. 30–34, Wiley, New York, 1964.

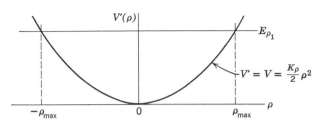

Fig. 3.29

Then, using (3.19) and (3.18),

$$V'(\rho) = B\rho^2 + \frac{l^2}{2m\rho^2} \tag{3.52}$$

and

$$F'(\rho) = -2B\rho + \frac{l^2}{m\rho^3}. \tag{3.53}$$

With

$$B = \frac{K_\rho}{2} \tag{3.54}$$

we can, therefore, write the one-dimensionalized equation of motion as

$$F'(\rho) = -K_\rho\rho + \frac{l^2}{m\rho^3} = m\ddot{\rho}. \tag{3.55}$$

Now, when $l = 0$, it is obvious that the point mass will perform a free harmonic oscillation along a line coinciding with ρ through the origin and equilibrium position O [see Figs. 3.5 and 3.29]. When $l \neq 0$, the motion will still be oscillatory (Fig. 3.30), but the object will no longer pass through the origin. It will, in fact, describe an ellipse centered on the origin. For from (3.51) and (3.54) we have

$$\mathbf{F} = F(\rho)\hat{\mathbf{l}} = -K_\rho\rho\hat{\mathbf{l}} = -K_\rho(x\hat{\mathbf{i}} + y\hat{\mathbf{j}}); \tag{3.56}$$

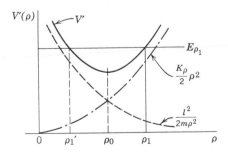

Fig. 3.30

therefore,

$$F_x = -K_\rho x \tag{3.57}$$
$$F_y = -K_\rho y, \tag{3.58}$$

and we see that the system may be regarded as an isotropic oscillator of the type discussed in connection with the condition (2.153), because here ω_{0_x} must also equal ω_{0_y}. The actual orbit will resemble the first Lissajous figure (Fig. 3.21) in this case; and larger values of n in the potential (3.50) will evidently lead to similar motions, but not to elliptical orbits.

Regarding the inverse square type of force, the hyperbolic trajectories that result for $\varepsilon > 1$ are of special interest. An attractive force is required to produce the path shown in Fig. 3.27, but it is evident that a repulsive force of the same kind would also cause an approaching object to follow a hyperbolic trajectory. Once this is realized, it is easy to understand that the related discussion can be adapted to describe collisions between all atomic nuclei whose force fields are Coulombic. We shall see later that, curiously enough, this description remains valid even when the wave properties of the particles are taken into account.[16]

If we assume the charge on one nucleus to be $Z_1 e$ and that on the other to be $Z_2 e$, where Z indicates their atomic numbers and $Z_1 \gg Z_2$, they will exert the central repulsive force

$$F(\rho) = \frac{Z_1 Z_2 e^2}{\rho^2} = B\rho^{-2}, \qquad B = Z_1 Z_2 e^2 \tag{3.59}$$

on each other as they approach. If we further assume that, because of its much greater mass, the motion of the first will be negligible during the collision, we may fix the origin of coordinates in it and apply (3.35) with the sign changed on the right-hand side:

$$\frac{d^2 \rho^{-1}}{d\phi^2} + \rho^{-1} = -\frac{m}{l^2} B = -\frac{m}{l^2} Z_1 Z_2 e^2, \tag{3.60}$$

where m represents the mass of the moving nucleus. The solution of this equation, corresponding to (3.37), will be

$$\frac{1}{\rho} = A \cos(\phi + \theta) - \frac{m}{l^2} Z_1 Z_2 e^2; \tag{3.61}$$

so that, parallel to (3.40),

$$\varepsilon = -\frac{A l^2}{Z_1 Z_2 e^2 m}. \tag{3.62}$$

[16] Symon, K. R., *Mechanics*, 2nd edition, pp. 135–139, Addison-Wesley, Reading, Mass., 1960.

However, if the incident nucleus has the energy E and the coordinate axes are unrotated so that $\theta = 0$, it can be shown[17] that the constant A must have the value

$$A = \left[\left(-\frac{m}{l^2} Z_1 Z_2 e^2\right)^2 + \frac{2mE}{l^2}\right]^{1/2}$$

(3.63)

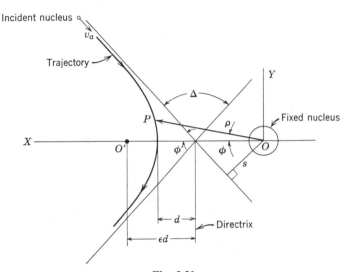

Fig. 3.31

in this conservative situation. Hence, from (3.62),

$$\varepsilon^2 = \left[\left(-\frac{m}{l^2} Z_1 Z_2 e^2\right)^2 + \frac{2mE}{l^2}\right]\left(-\frac{l^2}{Z_1 Z_2 e^2 m}\right)^2$$

$$= \left[(1)^2 + \frac{2El^2}{Z_1{}^2 Z_2{}^2 e^4 m}\right];$$

(3.64)

therefore,

$$\varepsilon = \left[1 + \frac{2El^2}{(Z_1 Z_2 e^2)^2 m}\right]^{1/2},$$

(3.65)

which will be greater than unity for nonzero values of l and E positive—as we would expect for a hyperbolic trajectory (Fig. 3.31). The length s is called the impact parameter; it is the closest distance by which the incident nucleus would approach the fixed nucleus if there were no interaction forces between them. The angle ϕ' represents the value ϕ will take when

[17] Goldstein, H., *Classical Mechanics*, pp. 76–85, Addison-Wesley, Reading, Mass., 1959.

ρ becomes infinite, and the angle Δ is the deflection that would actually be observed. Of course, the same figure could be made to describe a collision under attractive forces merely by locating the fixed nucleus and origin of coordinates at O' instead of O.

To obtain a theoretical expression for the deflection angle Δ, it is only necessary to make use of the geometry of the hyperbola.[18] This tells us that in Fig. 3.31

$$\cos \phi' = \frac{1}{\varepsilon} \tag{3.66}$$

and

$$\cot \phi' = \tan \frac{\Delta}{2} ; \tag{3.67}$$

hence

$$\tan \frac{\Delta}{2} = \frac{\cos \phi'}{(1 - \cos^2 \phi')^{\frac{1}{2}}} = \frac{1/\varepsilon}{(1 - 1/\varepsilon^2)^{\frac{1}{2}}} = (\varepsilon^2 - 1)^{-\frac{1}{2}}. \tag{3.68}$$

When we substitute for ε from (3.65), the result is

$$\tan \frac{\Delta}{2} = \left[\frac{2El^2}{(Z_1 Z_2 e^2)^2 m} \right]^{-\frac{1}{2}} = \sqrt{\frac{m}{2E}} \frac{Z_1 Z_2 e^2}{l} ; \tag{3.69}$$

with v_a representing the approach speed at large separation, so that

$$E = T = \frac{m v_a^2}{2} \tag{3.70}$$

and

$$l = s m v_a, \tag{3.71}$$

this may be rewritten as

$$\Delta = 2 \tan^{-1} \frac{Z_1 Z_2}{s m v_a^2} . \tag{3.72}$$

From (3.72) we can predict what the deflection or scattering angle will be in any central repulsive force collision involving only two point objects, provided that we know the mass of the smaller object, its approach speed, the charges of both objects, and the impact parameter. Evidently, a similar relationship (with $k_g mM$ replacing $Z_1 Z_2 e^2$) will hold for collisions of planetary bodies under attractive gravitational forces.

In the case of atomic nuclei, a single collision of this type cannot be observed in the same way as for large objects: it is customary, therefore, to make use of a quantity $\sigma = \sigma(\Delta)$, called the scattering cross section and

[18] Fadell, A. G., *Calculus with Analytic Geometry*, Vol. 1, pp. 611–656, Van Nostrand, Princeton, N. J., 1964.

defined differentially as the area of a ring lying between the radii s and $s + ds$ around O in Fig. 3.31:

$$d\sigma = 2\pi s \, ds. \tag{3.73}$$

Determining s and ds from (3.72) and substituting in this relation, we obtain

$$d\sigma = 2\pi \left(\frac{Z_1 Z_2 e^2}{2mv_a^2}\right)^2 \frac{\sin \Delta}{\sin^4 \dfrac{\Delta}{2}} \, d\Delta. \tag{3.74}$$

This is called the Rutherford scattering formula. Integrating it obviously will give $\sigma = \sigma(\Delta)$, so that it may be used to make theoretical predictions of this quantity in the same way that (3.72) can be used to make predictions of $\Delta = \Delta(s)$. It is well known that $\sigma = \sigma(\Delta)$ can also be measured experimentally. The procedure is to bombard a thin foil of the atoms whose scattering cross section is desired with a beam of much lighter particles having identical known masses, charges, and (if possible) velocities. It is then assumed that each nucleus in the foil is surrounded by a ring of area $d\sigma(\Delta)$, lying between the radii s and $s + ds$ as above, which will scatter any particle passing through it into an angle between Δ and $\Delta + d\Delta$. If N particles strike a unit area of the foil in unit time, and there are n nuclei present in this area, then it is reasonable to suppose that the number of particles scattered into the angle between Δ and $\Delta + d\Delta$ in unit time, $dN(\Delta)$, will stand in the same ratio to the total number of particles, N, as the total scattering area, $n \, d\sigma(\Delta)$, to the unit area:

$$\frac{dN(\Delta)}{N} = \frac{n \, d\sigma(\Delta)}{1}$$

or

$$d\sigma(\Delta) = \frac{dN(\Delta)}{nN}. \tag{3.75}$$

Both n and N may be predetermined and $dN(\Delta)$ can be estimated simply by placing a particle counter at various Δ's.

So far, in line with our earlier restrictions, we have confined ourselves to collision processes in which one of the two objects is much more massive than the other, so that in effect it does not move. It is immediately apparent that the deflection angle Δ in Fig. 3.31 would not have the same value if the "fixed" nucleus were allowed to move during the collision, as indicated by the dotted lines in Fig. 3.32. The motion then approaches that of the general two-body problem, which we shall discuss shortly.

First, however, it is important to recognize that the linear momentum and energy conservation techniques, applied earlier for one-dimensional motions, can be extended to this two-dimensional situation and a limited

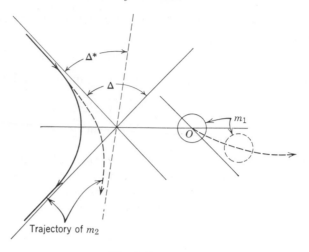

Trajectory of m_2

Fig. 3.32

amount of information obtained. That is, if no external forces act during the collision (or if they can be neglected in comparison with large internal forces), the two following relationships must be satisfied:

$$\mathbf{p}_{1a} + \mathbf{p}_{2a} = \mathbf{p}_{1e} + \mathbf{p}_{2e} \tag{3.76}$$

and

$$T_{1a} + T_{2a} = T_{1e} + T_{2e},$$

or

$$\frac{p_{1a}^2}{2m_1} + \frac{p_{2a}^2}{2m_2} = \frac{p_{1e}^2}{2m_1} + \frac{p_{2e}^2}{2m_2}, \tag{3.77}$$

where the subscripts 1 and 2 refer to the two point objects and the subscripts a and e identify the approach and escape values of the variables.

With m_1 initially at rest the motion will be confined to a plane, so that two scalar equations will be available from (3.76) and one from (3.77); however, these three equations will involve ten unknowns, the eight momentum components and the two masses (provided that the latter are not changed by the collision). If any seven are given, the remaining three can be calculated. Consider the common case illustrated in Fig. 3.33.

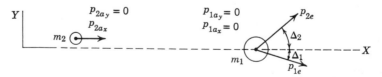

Fig. 3.33

The two equations from (3.76) will be

$$p_{2a_x} = p_{2e} \cos \Delta_2 + p_{1e} \cos \Delta_1 \qquad (3.78)$$

and

$$0 = p_{2e} \sin \Delta_2 - p_{1e} \sin \Delta_1, \qquad (3.79)$$

while (3.77) will reduce to

$$\frac{p_{2a_x}^2}{2m_2} = \frac{p_{1e}^2}{2m_1} + \frac{p_{2e}^2}{2m_2}. \qquad (3.80)$$

Three of the ten quantities have, in effect, been specified ($p_{2a_y} = p_{1a_x} = p_{1a_y} = 0$). Thus seven remain unknown: p_{2a_x}, p_{2e_x} and p_{2e_y} (or p_{2e} and Δ_2); p_{1e_x} and p_{1e_y} (or p_{1e} and Δ_1); m_1 and m_2. Four must, therefore, be obtained

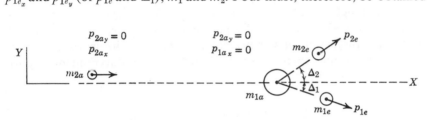

Fig. 3.34

by measurement before the other three can be determined. If, for example, m_1 and m_2 are known from past measurements, and if p_{2a_x} and Δ_2 are measured in the course of an experiment, p_{2e}, p_{1e} and Δ_1 can then be computed. It can easily be proved[19] that in general $0 \leq \Delta_2 \leq \pi$ when $m_2 < m_1$ and $0 \leq \Delta_2 \leq \pi/2$ when $m_2 > m_1$. However, it should be noted that in these circumstances only the ratio of the two masses can be calculated, not their separate values. This is so because the three equations (3.78) to (3.80) are not fully independent, in the sense that a mass conservation relation must also be satisfied; if the motion is nonrelativistic,

$$m_{1a} + m_{2a} = m_{1e} + m_{2e}. \qquad (3.81)$$

Even when m_1 and m_2 do change during the collision, the preceding method can be adapted. Suppose that all particulars are the same as in Fig. 3.33, except that m_{2a} is absorbed by m_{1a}, with two different masses, m_{2e} and m_{1e}, eventually coming off at angles Δ_1 and Δ_2 (Fig. 3.34). Then,

[19] Symon, K. R., *Mechanics*, 2nd edition, pp. 171–178, Addison-Wesley, Reading, Mass., 1960.

as long as the collision remains conservative, we can follow (3.78) to (3.81) and write:

$$m_{2a}v_{2a_x} = m_{2e}v_{2e}\cos\Delta_2 + m_{1e}v_{1e}\cos\Delta_1 \tag{3.82}$$

$$0 = m_{2e}v_{2e}\sin\Delta_2 - m_{1e}v_{1e}\sin\Delta_1 \tag{3.83}$$

$$\frac{m_{2a}}{2}v_{2a}{}^2 = \frac{m_{2e}}{2}v_{2e}{}^2 + \frac{m_{1e}}{2}v_{1e}{}^2 \tag{3.84}$$

There are now nine unknowns instead of seven (in effect, two more masses have been added); consequently, five must be specified to obtain the other four (since the mass conservation equations can now be used). For example, experiments have been conducted in which m_{2a}, v_{2a_x}, m_{1a}, Δ_1, and Δ_2 were measured, allowing m_{1e}, v_{1e}, m_{2e}, and v_{2e} to be computed.

This approach can also be modified to give some insight into nonconservative two-body collisions. If kinetic energy were absorbed or released during the interaction of the preceding example, as in neutron-induced fission of an atomic nucleus, we could take this into account merely by adding a term Q to (3.84):

$$\frac{m_{2a}v_{2a}{}^2}{2} = \frac{m_2v_{2e}{}^2}{2} + \frac{m_1v_{1e}{}^2}{2} + Q. \tag{3.85}$$

Clearly, Q is greater than zero if kinetic energy is absorbed, less than zero if it is released, and equal to zero if energy is conserved, as in the elastic case discussed above. One more unknown has been added, so one more must be specified; but this is not impossible. For example, m_{2a}, v_{2a_x}, m_{1a}, m_{1e}, Δ_1, and Δ_2 might be measured in order to determine m_{2e}, v_{2e}, v_{1e}, and Q. Evidently, this method allows for the possibility of converting mass into energy, or vice versa; it should also be noted that the preceding equations can readily be converted to relativistic form by substituting the appropriate expressions from Section 2.1 for the momentum components and kinetic energies.

There is no upper limit on the size of the bodies to which the preceding relations apply, provided they can be considered point objects, but it should be realized that this excludes the possibility of either body rotating. Rotation can be included and the principle of angular momentum conservation applied, but then each body must be treated as a system of particles. At best, only a small amount of information can be obtained from (3.85) for collision processes of this type, by interpreting Q as pure rotational kinetic energy arising from the initial translational kinetic energy.

Additionally, for nonelastic one-dimensional collisions of large bodies, the preceding equations are often supplemented by the following empirical relationship:

$$-\frac{\text{Relative escape velocity}}{\text{Relative approach velocity}} = -\frac{(v_{1e_x} - v_{2e_x})}{(v_{1a_x} - v_{2a_x})} \simeq \varepsilon, \text{ a constant} \quad (3.86)$$

assuming all motion to be restricted to the X-axis and taking its positive direction as the direction of positive velocities. Evidently, ε, called the coefficient of restitution, will be zero for a perfectly plastic collision ($v_{1e_x} = v_{2e_x}$). It can be demonstrated[20] that this quantity also represents the ratio of the total impulse delivered during recovery of the bodies from deformation to the total impulse delivered while they are originally being deformed, and will therefore approach unity for a perfectly elastic collision (in which these impulses must be equal and opposite). It should be noted, however, that the equation is not entirely independent of the momentum conservation equations. If, for example, one of the bodies has an effectively infinite mass and does not move, in an elastic collision both types of equation give the same result along the approach direction, when proper signs are attached to the velocities. Each of these points is illustrated in the accompanying problems.

It is also possible to attack such problems by converting to a coordinate system that moves with the center of mass of the two colliding point objects; for the angle Δ will remain constant in this system, and a relation connecting this $\Delta = \Delta_m$ with the angle $\Delta = \Delta_l$ actually observable in a laboratory can be developed in the following way. In the center of mass system, the two objects must have equal and opposite momenta at all points on their trajectories, because the center of mass must always carry the entire linear momentum; therefore, in this system the motion shown dotted in Fig. 3.32 ($\Delta^* = \Delta_l$) would appear as shown in Fig. 3.35.

Relative to some origin O fixed in the laboratory system, the velocity of m_2 would be given by $\dot{\mathbf{r}}_2$, whereas relative to an origin C coinciding and moving with the center of mass, its velocity could be described by $\dot{\mathbf{r}}_2'$, if $\mathbf{r}_2$ and $\mathbf{r}_2'$ represent the position vectors of m_2 with respect to O and C. Calling the position vector of the center of mass in the laboratory system $\mathbf{R}$, in the usual way, at any time it must be true that

$$\mathbf{R} + \mathbf{r}_2' = \mathbf{r}_2; \quad (3.87)$$

so, differentiating with respect to time, it follows that quite generally

$$\dot{\mathbf{R}} + \dot{\mathbf{r}}_2' = \dot{\mathbf{r}}_2. \quad (3.88)$$

[20] Becker, R. A., *Introduction to Theoretical Mechanics*, pp. 175–179, McGraw-Hill, New York, 1954.

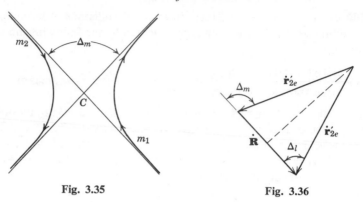

Fig. 3.35   Fig. 3.36

We know that the escape velocity $\dot{\mathbf{r}}_{2e}$ will make the angle Δ_l with the approach velocity $\dot{\mathbf{r}}_{2a}$ (Fig. 3.32); thus, placing $\dot{\mathbf{R}}$ along the direction of $\dot{\mathbf{r}}_{2a}$, (3.88) determines the angle Δ_m that $\dot{\mathbf{r}}_{2e}'$ will make with it (Fig. 3.36):

$$\tan \Delta_l = \frac{|\dot{\mathbf{r}}_{2e}'| \sin (\pi - \Delta_m)}{|\dot{\mathbf{R}}| - |\dot{\mathbf{r}}_{2e}'| \cos (\pi - \Delta_m)} = \frac{|\dot{\mathbf{r}}_{2e}'| \sin \Delta_m}{|\dot{\mathbf{R}}| + |\dot{\mathbf{r}}_{2e}'| \cos \Delta_m} \quad (3.89)$$

This transcendental equation relates Δ_l and Δ_m. It can be further simplified by noting that $\dot{\mathbf{r}}_2'$ can be expressed in terms of the relative velocity vector $\dot{\mathbf{r}}$ (Fig. 2.4) and applying conservation of linear momentum (see Fig. 3.37):

$$-\mathbf{r}_2'(m_1 + m_2) = -\mathbf{r}m_1, \quad (3.90)$$

so that

$$\dot{\mathbf{r}}_2' = \frac{m_1}{(m_1 + m_2)} \dot{\mathbf{r}}, \quad (3.91)$$

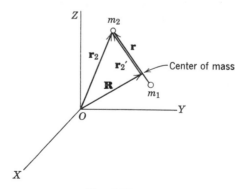

Fig. 3.37

and in particular

$$|\dot{\mathbf{r}}_{2e}'| = \frac{m_1}{(m_1 + m_2)} |\dot{\mathbf{r}}_e| . \tag{3.92}$$

But in accordance with conservation ideas

$$|\dot{\mathbf{r}}_e| = |\dot{\mathbf{r}}_a|, \tag{3.93}$$

giving

$$|\dot{\mathbf{r}}_{2e}'| = \frac{m_1}{(m_1 + m_2)} |\dot{\mathbf{r}}_a| . \tag{3.94}$$

Also, since the total linear momentum is to be conserved,

$$(m_1 + m_2)\dot{\mathbf{R}} = m_2\dot{\mathbf{r}}_a, \tag{3.95}$$

giving

$$|\dot{\mathbf{R}}| = \frac{m_2}{(m_1 + m_2)} |\dot{\mathbf{r}}_a| ; \tag{3.96}$$

therefore, substituting (3.94) and (3.96) in (3.89), we obtain

$$\tan \Delta_l = \frac{m_1 \sin \Delta_m}{m_2 + m_1 \cos \Delta_m} = \frac{\sin \Delta_m}{\dfrac{m_2}{m_1} + \cos \Delta_m} . \tag{3.97}$$

Thus, problems of this kind can be solved in a center of mass system and the angle Δ_m interpreted in terms of the observable angle Δ_l by means of (3.97). This is often easier than solving the problem in the laboratory system because, as will be demonstrated in the illustrative problems, the center of mass moves with constant velocity, kinetic energy, and angular momentum in the center of mass system. It is evident from (3.97) that Δ_m and Δ_l will have approximately the same value when $m_1 \gg m_2$. Conveniently too, the scattering cross section $\sigma(\Delta)$ can easily be expressed in both systems and related by noting that particle numbers must also be conserved.[21]

As regards the general problem of two bodies of like mass interacting with central forces, it turns out that the preceding solution for one of the bodies fixed provides the key. From our earlier discussion of Fig. 2.4 we know that it is possible to use the components of $\mathbf{R}$, the position vector of the center of mass relative to an arbitrary but fixed origin of coordinates, and $\mathbf{r}$, the position vector of m_2 relative to m_1, as independent generalized

[21] Goldstein, H., *Classical Mechanics*, pp. 85–89, Addison-Wesley, Reading, Mass., 1959.

coordinates—though in general there can be six instead of five, since the magnitude of **r** need not remain constant (see Fig. 3.38). We may therefore write the time-independent Lagrangian as

$$L = T(\dot{\mathbf{R}}, \dot{\mathbf{r}}) - V(\mathbf{R}, \mathbf{r}). \tag{3.98}$$

The position vectors of m_1 and m_2 relative to the center of mass, $\mathbf{r}_1'$ and $\mathbf{r}_2'$, are shown because it seems reasonable to assume that the total kinetic energy will be the kinetic energy of the center of mass (with both masses

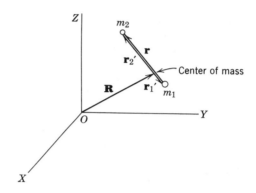

Fig. 3.38

imagined to be concentrated there) plus the sum of the kinetic energies of each mass separately with respect to the center of mass:

$$T = \tfrac{1}{2}(m_1 + m_2)\dot{\mathbf{R}}^2 + \tfrac{1}{2}m_1\dot{\mathbf{r}}_1'^2 + \tfrac{1}{2}m_2\dot{\mathbf{r}}_2'^2 \tag{3.99}$$

But $\mathbf{r}_1'$ and $\mathbf{r}_2'$ can easily be expressed in terms of **r** by means of the two relations like (3.90):

$$-\mathbf{r}_2'(m_1 + m_2) = -\mathbf{r}m_1 \tag{3.100}$$

$$-\mathbf{r}_1'(m_1 + m_2) = \mathbf{r}m_2. \tag{3.101}$$

It follows that

$$\dot{\mathbf{r}}_2'^2 = \left(\frac{m_1}{m_1 + m_2}\right)^2 \dot{\mathbf{r}}^2 \tag{3.102}$$

and

$$\dot{\mathbf{r}}_1'^2 = \left(\frac{m_2}{m_1 + m_2}\right)^2 \dot{\mathbf{r}}^2; \tag{3.103}$$

therefore, (3.99) becomes:

$$T = \frac{1}{2}(m_1 + m_2)\dot{\mathbf{R}}^2 + \frac{1}{2}m_1\left(\frac{m_1}{m_1 + m_2}\right)^2\dot{\mathbf{r}}^2 + \frac{1}{2}m_2\left(\frac{m_1}{m_1 + m_2}\right)^2\dot{\mathbf{r}}^2$$

$$= \frac{1}{2}(m_1 + m_2)\dot{\mathbf{R}}^2 + \frac{1}{2}\left[\frac{m_1 m_2(m_1 + m_2)}{(m_1 + m_2)^2}\right]\dot{\mathbf{r}}^2$$

$$= \frac{1}{2}(m_1 + m_2)\dot{\mathbf{R}}^2 + \frac{1}{2}\left(\frac{m_1 m_2}{m_1 + m_2}\right)\dot{\mathbf{r}}^2 \qquad (3.104)$$

If, in addition, we recognize that the concept of a conservative system is relative and assume the potential to be separable in the sense that

$$V = V(\mathbf{R}) + V(\mathbf{r}), \qquad (3.105)$$

where $V(\mathbf{r}) = V(x, y, z)$ represents the potential associated with the "internal" forces between the point objects and $V(\mathbf{R}) = V(X, Y, Z)$ the potential associated with any "external" forces applied to them, then (3.98) may be written as

$$L = \frac{1}{2}(m_1 + m_2)\dot{\mathbf{R}}^2 + \frac{1}{2}\left(\frac{m_1 m_2}{m_1 + m_2}\right)\dot{\mathbf{r}}^2 - V(\mathbf{R}) - V(\mathbf{r}), \quad (3.106)$$

or more properly as

$$L = \frac{1}{2}(m_1 + m_2)(\dot{X}^2 + \dot{Y}^2 + \dot{Z}^2) + \frac{1}{2}\left(\frac{m_1 m_2}{m_1 + m_2}\right)(\dot{x}^2 + \dot{y}^2 + \dot{z}^2)$$

$$- V(X, Y, Z) - V(x, y, z). \quad (3.107)$$

Now if we apply the Lagrangian equations (2.43) of Chapter 2,

$$\frac{d}{dt}\frac{\partial L}{\partial \dot{q}_j} - \frac{\partial L}{\partial q_j} = 0 \qquad \{q_j = X, Y, Z, x, y, z , \qquad (3.108)$$

we obtain

$$\mathbf{F}(\dot{\mathbf{R}}) = (m_1 + m_2)\ddot{\mathbf{R}} \qquad (3.109)$$

and

$$\mathbf{F}(\mathbf{r}) = \left(\frac{m_1 m_2}{m_1 + m_2}\right)\ddot{\mathbf{r}}. \qquad (3.110)$$

The first represents three scalar equations describing the motion of a point object of mass $(m_1 + m_2)$ relative to the origin O, under the influence of an external force applied directly to it; the second represents three scalar equations which describe the motion of a point object of mass $(m_1 m_1)/(m_1 + m_2)$ relative to m_1, under the influence of the force that m_1 exerts on m_2. Neither of these is the real object, but their motions in time uniquely determine the locations of the real objects.

Furthermore, all of our previous considerations apply to these two sets of equations; specifically, each set may be more or less strongly coupled depending on the form of **F**. But if $m_2 \ll m_1$, (3.110) becomes

$$\mathbf{F(r)} = m_2\ddot{\mathbf{r}}, \tag{3.111}$$

which certainly can include the two scalar equations (3.12) and (3.14) discussed at the beginning of this section under central-force conditions. It must be possible to reduce (3.109) in the same way and handle the two resulting equations in about the same manner as (3.12) and (3.14) under similar conditions. This justifies the statement that the earlier solution is the key to the present problem. It should be recognized, however, that when three or more point objects interact, any "exact" solution becomes much more difficult to obtain. Nevertheless, there are various ways of achieving approximate solutions of the many-body problem, and we shall make use of some of these later.

Of course, as (3.109) and (3.110) emphasize, bodies may also interact with noncentral forces; we have already encountered the magnetic force of (3.29) in Chapter 2, and various other forces of this type are possible. As an additional illustration of motions which are not yet strongly coupled, let us consider the movements of a point object with charge q and mass m in a static electromagnetic field emanating from a fixed center. In this case the electric field will be central and, if the magnetic field were not present, we could expect the motion to be of the type studied at the beginning of the section. Even with the magnetic field acting we know that, as long as neither it nor the electric field varies with time, the system may be classed as at least pseudoconservative [(3.30) of Chapter 2].

Generally, the circulating charge would experience the time-independent form of the Lorentz force described in (3.39) of Chapter 2,

$$\mathbf{F} = q\mathbf{E}(x, y, z) + q\mathbf{v}(\dot{x}, \dot{y}, \dot{z}) \times \mathbf{B}(x, y, z); \tag{3.112}$$

however, for purposes of illustration we shall further simplify the problem by assuming that (see Fig. 3.39)

$$\mathbf{E} = \text{constant} = E_y\hat{\mathbf{j}} + E_z\hat{\mathbf{k}} \tag{3.113}$$

$$\mathbf{B} = \text{constant} = B_z\hat{\mathbf{k}}. \tag{3.114}$$

Hence the vector equation of motion will be

$$\begin{aligned}
m(\ddot{x}\hat{\mathbf{i}} + \ddot{y}\hat{\mathbf{j}} + \ddot{z}\hat{\mathbf{k}}) &= q(E_y\hat{\mathbf{j}} + E_z\hat{\mathbf{k}}) + q(\dot{x}\hat{\mathbf{i}} + \dot{y}\hat{\mathbf{j}} + \dot{z}\hat{\mathbf{k}}) \times B_z\hat{\mathbf{k}} \\
&= q(E_y\hat{\mathbf{j}} + E_z\hat{\mathbf{k}}) + q(-\dot{x}B_z\hat{\mathbf{j}} + \dot{y}B_z\hat{\mathbf{i}}), \tag{3.115}
\end{aligned}$$

which yields the three scalar equations:

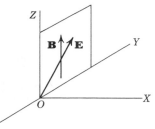

Fig. 3.39

$$\ddot{x} = \frac{qB_z}{m}\dot{y} \qquad (3.116)$$

$$\ddot{y} = \frac{qE_y}{m} - \frac{qB_z}{m}\dot{x} \qquad (3.117)$$

$$\ddot{z} = \frac{qE_z}{m} \qquad (3.118)$$

The last equation is not coupled to the others. It indicates that a uniform acceleration in the Z-direction will be present, and because it has the same form as (2.2), we see that

$$z = \frac{qE_z}{2m}t^2 + \dot{z}_0 t + z_0, \qquad (3.119)$$

where z_0 and $\dot{z}_0$ represent the initial displacement and speed in the Z-direction.

The two remaining equations are coupled, although not very strongly, because either may easily be differentiated (or integrated) and substituted in the other. If we rewrite them in the form

$$\dot{v}_x = \frac{qB_z}{m}v_y \qquad (3.120)$$

$$\dot{v}_y = \frac{qE_y}{m} - \frac{qB_z}{m}v_x, \qquad (3.121)$$

differentiate both once again,

$$\ddot{v}_x = \frac{qB_z}{m}\dot{v}_y \qquad (3.122)$$

$$\ddot{v}_y = -\frac{qB_z}{m}\dot{v}_x \qquad (3.123)$$

and cross-substitute, we obtain:

$$\ddot{v}_x + \left(\frac{qB_z}{m}\right)^2 v_x = \left(\frac{q}{m}\right)^2 B_z E_y \qquad (3.124)$$

$$\ddot{v}_y + \left(\frac{qB_z}{m}\right)^2 v_y = 0 \qquad (3.125)$$

From our earlier work it is evident that the solutions of these equations will be

$$v_x = \dot{x} = A_x \cos\left(\frac{qB_z}{m}t + \theta_x\right) + \frac{E_y}{B_z} \qquad (3.126)$$

and

$$v_y = \dot{y} = A_y \cos\left(\frac{qB_z}{m}t + \theta_y\right);\qquad(3.127)$$

therefore, integration gives:

$$x = C_x \sin\left(\frac{qB_z}{m}t + \theta_x\right) + \frac{E_y}{B_z}t + D_x\qquad(3.128)$$

$$y = C_y \sin\left(\frac{qB_z}{m}t + \theta_y\right) + D_y\qquad(3.129)$$

At most, only four initial conditions will be available for the X- and Y-directions (x_0, $\dot{x}_0$, y_0, $\dot{y}_0$), while these solutions contain six arbitrary constants—a situation arising from the additional differentiations represented by (3.122) and (3.123). However, two can be eliminated in favor of two algebraic restrictions. If we substitute the relations (3.126) and (3.127) back in the original equations (3.116) and (3.117), it is easy to prove that the result will be:

$$C_x = C_y\qquad(3.130)$$

$$\theta_y = \theta_x + \frac{\pi}{2}\qquad(3.131)$$

In other words, (3.128) and (3.129) will be solutions only if these restrictions are satisfied.

If we place

$$C_x = C\qquad(3.132)$$

and

$$\theta_x = \theta,\qquad(3.133)$$

then (3.128) to (3.131) will reduce to

$$x = C \sin\left(\frac{qB_z}{m}t + \theta\right) + \frac{E_y}{B_z}t + D_x\qquad(3.134)$$

and

$$y = C \cos\left(\frac{qB_z}{m}t + \theta\right) + D_y.\qquad(3.135)$$

Now only four arbitrary constants remain.

It is not difficult to visualize the motion described by these two relations and (3.119). If E_y were zero, the point object would move in such a way as to project a circle in the XY-plane [(3.134) and (3.135)] while accelerating uniformly in the Z-direction (3.119). The circle would be centered on the point (D_x, D_y), and the angular frequency of the motion about this point would be

$$\omega_0 = \frac{qB_z}{m}.\qquad(3.136)$$

Clearly, the actual path would be a spiral around one of the lines of force in the magnetic field; it is well established that this is indeed the type of motion that results under such circumstances. For example, it is known that the charged particles which make up the Van Allen radiation belts perform a motion generally of this type in the magnetic field of the earth, even though the associated electric field is more complex than that suggested above.[22]

When E_y is not zero, a uniform translation in the X-direction will be superimposed on the motion described above through the term involving

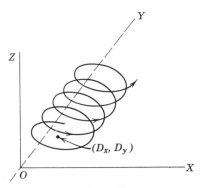

Fig. 3.40

this quantity in (3.134). The resulting skewed spiral (see Fig. 3.40) can take various specialized forms depending on the six initial conditions $(x_0, \dot{x}_0, y_0, \dot{y}_0, z_0, \dot{z}_0)$. It will be evident that the motion will always have a very different character from that possible in a central field of force.

If the Lorentz force (3.112) depends on time, the system will be non-conservative and more difficult to analyze. But it is worthwhile to observe that the problem can often be simplified through use of the vector potential **A** and scalar potential ϕ defined in Section 2.3. In (3.39) of Chapter 2, with q replacing e, the Lorentz force is given by

$$\mathbf{F} = -q\nabla\phi - q\frac{\partial \mathbf{A}}{\partial t} + q\mathbf{v} \times (\nabla \times \mathbf{A}) \qquad (3.137)$$

Since according to (3.28) and (3.35) of Chapter 2

$$-\nabla\phi = \mathbf{E}$$

and

$$\nabla \times \mathbf{A} = \mathbf{B},$$

---

[22] Chapman, S., "Sun Storms and the Earth," *American Scientist*, Vol. 49, No. 3, pp. 249–284, September 1961.

this will reduce to the form (3.112) when $\mathbf{A}$ and ϕ are independent of t; specifically, when $\mathbf{E}$ and $\mathbf{B}$ are defined as in (3.113) and (3.114), the motion described above will result.

More generally, the force on a point charge moving in a time-varying electromagnetic field will be that given by (3.137); it will be recalled, however, that the potential associated with this force was defined in (3.40) of Chapter 2, leading to the Lagrangian function

$$\mathcal{L} = \frac{m\mathbf{v}^2}{2} - q\phi + q\mathbf{A} \cdot \mathbf{v}. \tag{3.138}$$

Thus, Lagrangian and Hamiltonian methods can be applied directly, which is often helpful.[23] For example, because it follows from (2.51) of Chapter 2 and the sequel in Section 2.3 that

$$\mathbf{p} = \frac{\partial \mathcal{L}}{\partial \mathbf{v}}, \tag{3.139}$$

we may immediately conclude that the linear momentum of a point charge in an electromagnetic field characterized by the functions $\mathbf{A}$ and ϕ will be

$$\mathbf{p} = m\mathbf{v} + q\mathbf{A}, \tag{3.140}$$

not merely $m\mathbf{v}$.

Of course, depending on the magnitude of $\mathbf{v}$, it may also be necessary to make relativistic corrections in the foregoing relationships. In this connection it is interesting to note that $\mathbf{A}$ and ϕ satisfy transformation relations of the Lorentz form [(2.150), (2.151), (2.164), and (2.165) of Chapter 1] with respect to a primed coordinate system moving with the constant velocity V_y. If we regard $(A_x, A_y, A_z, ic\phi)$ as the components of the four-vector $\mathbf{U}$ in Fig. 1.43, instead of (x, y, z, ict), it is clear that we shall obtain

$$A_x = A_x' \tag{3.141}$$

$$A_z = A_z' \tag{3.142}$$

$$A_y = \frac{A_y' + \phi' V_y}{\mathcal{S}} \tag{3.143}$$

and

$$\phi = \frac{\dfrac{A_y'}{c^2} V_y + \phi'}{\mathcal{S}}, \tag{3.144}$$

instead of the equations referred to above. Thus the methods of Section 2.1 can easily be extended to cover this case of motion.

[23] Feynman, R. P., R. B. Leighton, and M. Sands, *Lectures on Physics*, Vol. 2, pp. 25.1–26.13, Addison-Wesley, Reading, Mass., 1964.

Problems 3.3

1. Calculate the orbit of a particle moving in a plane under the influence of a central force that varies directly as the first power of the distance from the center of force, $F_\rho = k\rho$.

Solution

The orbital differential equation is

$$\frac{d^2}{d\phi^2}\left(\frac{1}{\rho}\right) + \left(\frac{1}{\rho}\right) = -\frac{m\rho^2}{l^2}F(\rho),$$

or with

$$u = \frac{1}{\rho},$$

$$\frac{d^2u}{d\phi^2} + u = -\frac{m}{l^2u^2}F\left(\frac{1}{u}\right).$$

When we insert

$$F = k\rho = \frac{k}{u},$$

this becomes

$$\frac{d^2u}{d\phi^2} + u = -\frac{mk}{l^2}\cdot\frac{1}{u^3}.$$

Now, if we let

$$\frac{du}{d\phi} = p,$$

$$\frac{d^2u}{d\phi^2} = \frac{dp}{d\phi} = \frac{dp}{du}\frac{du}{d\phi} = p\frac{dp}{du};$$

substituting back in the differential equation, we obtain

$$p\frac{dp}{du} = -\left[u + \frac{mk}{l^2}\cdot\frac{1}{u^3}\right].$$

Integration then gives

$$\int p\,dp = -\int\left[u + \frac{mk}{l^2}\cdot\frac{1}{u^3}\right]du,$$

$$\tfrac{1}{2}p^2 = -\left(\frac{1}{2}u^2 - \frac{mk}{2l^2}\cdot\frac{1}{u^2}\right) + C_1,$$

$$p^2 = \frac{mk}{l^2}\cdot\frac{1}{u^2} - u^2 + C_2, \qquad C_2 = 2C_1;$$

therefore,

$$\frac{du}{d\phi} = \sqrt{\frac{mk}{l^2}\cdot\frac{1}{u^2} - u^2 + C_2}$$

or

$$\int d\phi = \int \frac{du}{\sqrt{\dfrac{mk}{l^2} \cdot \dfrac{1}{u^2} - u^2 + C_2}} = \int \frac{u\,du}{\sqrt{C_2 u^2 - u^4 + \dfrac{mk}{l^2}}}.$$

Placing

$$u^2 = s,$$

$$2u\,du = ds,$$

the above relation becomes

$$\int d\phi = \tfrac{1}{2} \int \frac{ds}{\sqrt{\dfrac{mk}{l^2} + C_2 s - s^2}}.$$

The integral of the form

$$\frac{dx}{\sqrt{ax^2 + bx + c}}$$

with $a = -1 < 0$ is

$$\frac{1}{\sqrt{-a}} \sin^{-1}\left(\frac{-2ax - b}{\sqrt{b^2 - 4ac}} \right);$$

therefore,

$$\phi = \tfrac{1}{2} \sin^{-1} \frac{2s - C_2}{\sqrt{C_2{}^2 - 4\dfrac{mk}{l^2}}} + C_3.$$

But since

$$s = u^2 = \frac{1}{\rho^2},$$

this is the same thing as

$$\phi = \tfrac{1}{2} \sin^{-1} \frac{\dfrac{2}{\rho^2} - C_2}{\sqrt{C_2{}^2 - 4\dfrac{mk}{l^2}}} + C_3;$$

therefore,

$$\frac{\dfrac{2}{\rho^2} - C_2}{\sqrt{C_2{}^2 - 4\dfrac{mk}{l^2}}} = \sin 2(\phi + C_3),$$

$$\frac{2}{\rho^2} = \sqrt{C_2{}^2 - 4\frac{mk}{l^2}} \cdot \sin 2(\phi + C_3) + C_2,$$

$$\frac{1}{\rho} = \left[\sqrt{\frac{C_2{}^2}{4} - \frac{mk}{l^2}} \cdot \sin 2(\phi + C_3) + C_1 \right]^{\!\frac{1}{2}}.$$

2. Determine the motion of an electron in the field of an atomic nucleus, considering both particles to be point objects and assuming that (*a*) the nucleus will not move, (*b*) the electron may move in a circular orbit without radiating, and (*c*) the angular momentum of the electron must have one of the discrete values $l = nh/2\pi$, $n = 1, 2, 3, \ldots$, where h is Planck's constant.

Solution

Because the force of interaction will be Coulombic and of the attractive inverse square type, the potential energy of the electron will be [Fig. P3.3 (2)]

$$V(\rho) = -\frac{Ze^2}{\rho},$$

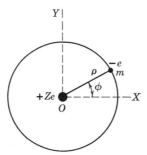

Fig. P3.3 (2)

where Z is the atomic number of the nucleus, and its kinetic energy will be

$$T = \frac{m}{2}(\dot{\rho}^2 + \rho^2\dot{\phi}^2).$$

Thus the Lagrangian function is

$$L = T - V = \frac{m}{2}(\dot{\rho}^2 + \rho^2\dot{\phi}^2) + \frac{Ze^2}{\rho}.$$

As we have seen, this implies that

$$m\rho^2\dot{\phi} = l = \text{constant}$$

and

$$m\dot{\phi}^2\rho - \frac{Ze^2}{\rho^2} - \frac{d}{dt}m\dot{\rho} = 0$$

or, combining both, that

$$\frac{d}{dt}m\dot{\rho} + \frac{Ze^2}{\rho^2} - \frac{l^2}{m\rho^3} = 0.$$

For a circular orbit it must be true that

$$\frac{d}{dt}m\dot{\rho} = 0;$$

therefore,

$$\frac{Ze^2}{\rho^2} = \frac{l^2}{m\rho^3}$$

or

$$\rho = \frac{l^2}{mZe^2}.$$

And with

$$l = n\hbar, \qquad \text{where } \hbar = \frac{h}{2\pi},$$

it follows that

$$\rho_n = \frac{n^2\hbar^2}{mZe^2} \qquad \{n = 1, 2, 3, \ldots,$$

are the only possible radii for circular orbits. These are called the Bohr radii after Niels Bohr, who first posed this problem and solved it. The first is often given the special designation

$$a_0 = \frac{\hbar^2}{mZe^2}$$

and used as a reference unit for such calculations.

It should be noticed that this theory also leads to the conclusion that the electron can only possess certain discrete energies under these conditions. Since

$$\dot{\rho} = 0,$$

its kinetic energy must be

$$\frac{m}{2}\,\rho_n{}^2\dot{\phi}^2 = \frac{m}{2}\,\rho_n{}^2\frac{l_n{}^2}{m^2\rho_n{}^4} = \frac{l_n{}^2}{2m\rho_n{}^2};$$

and its total energy will be given by

$$E = \frac{l_n{}^2}{2m\rho_n{}^2} - \frac{Ze^2}{\rho_n}$$

$$= \frac{l_n{}^2 - 2mZe^2\rho_n}{2m\rho_n{}^2}$$

$$= \frac{n^2\hbar^2 - 2mZe^2\dfrac{n^2\hbar^2}{mZe^2}}{2m\left(\dfrac{n^2\hbar^2}{mZe^2}\right)^2},$$

that is,

$$E = E_n = -\frac{mZ^2e^4}{2n^2\hbar^2} = -\frac{Ze^2}{2n^2a_0} \qquad \{n = 1, 2, 3, \ldots.$$

3. Determine the allowed orbits and energies for an electron under the same assumptions as those of the preceding problem, except that the two components of its linear momentum must satisfy the requirements that

$$\oint p_\phi \, d\phi = n_1 h$$

and

$$\oint p_\rho \, d\rho = n_2 h$$

where n_1 and n_2 are integers, and it is recognized that the orbits may not be circular.

Solution

By definition

$$l = m\rho^2 \dot\phi = p_\phi;$$

substituting in the first condition, we have

$$\int_0^{2\pi} l d\phi = n_1 h,$$

which, since l must remain constant, gives

$$2\pi l = n_1 h,$$
$$l = n_1 \hbar.$$

This was the entire requirement for the preceding problem, in which no radial motion was allowed.

In the present case, however, ρ may vary; therefore, to determine it we must solve the orbital differential equation developed for the case of central-force motion:

$$\frac{d^2}{d\phi^2}\left(\frac{1}{\rho}\right) + \left(\frac{1}{\rho}\right) = -\frac{m\rho^2}{l^2} F(\rho).$$

Because the forces will be attractive and Coulombic,

$$F(\rho) = -\frac{Ze^2}{\rho^2},$$

the equation becomes

$$\frac{d^2}{d\phi^2}\left(\frac{1}{\rho}\right) + \left(\frac{1}{\rho}\right) = \frac{Ze^2 m}{l^2},$$

which has the solutions

$$\frac{1}{\rho} = A \cos \phi + \frac{Ze^2 m}{l^2},$$

assuming that $\theta = 0$. Hence,

$$\rho = \frac{1}{A \cos \phi + \dfrac{Ze^2 m}{l^2}} = \frac{\dfrac{l^2}{Ze^2 m}}{1 + \dfrac{A l^2}{Ze^2 m} \cos \phi}.$$

Multiplying both numerator and denominator on the right-hand side by A, we see that with

$$\varepsilon = \frac{A l^2}{Ze^2 m}$$

and

$$p = \frac{1}{A},$$

as before, this will become

$$\rho = \frac{\varepsilon p}{1 + \varepsilon \cos \phi},$$

which is an alternate form for the equation of a conic curve with the angle ϕ measured as shown in Fig. 3.28 and $\theta = 0$.

Because we are investigating the motion of a bound electron, our interest is in the elliptical case. Evidently for $\phi = \pi$ and $\phi = 0$, respectively,

$$\rho_{\max} = \frac{\varepsilon p}{1 - \varepsilon}, \qquad \rho_{\min} = \frac{\varepsilon p}{1 + \varepsilon};$$

if a is the semimajor axis,

$$2a = \rho_{\max} + \rho_{\min} = p\varepsilon \left(\frac{1}{1 - \varepsilon} + \frac{1}{1 + \varepsilon} \right) = p\varepsilon \left(\frac{2}{1 - \varepsilon^2} \right)$$

or

$$\varepsilon p = a(1 - \varepsilon)^2.$$

Thus, the equation for an elliptical conic provides the following expression for ρ:

$$\rho = \frac{a(1 - \varepsilon^2)}{1 + \varepsilon \cos \phi}.$$

The second requirement was that

$$\oint p_\rho \, dp = \oint m\dot{\rho} \, d\rho = n_2 h;$$

but since

$$d\rho = \frac{d\rho}{d\phi} \, d\phi$$

and

$$\dot{\rho} = \frac{d\rho}{d\phi} \frac{d\phi}{dt},$$

this may be written as

$$\int_0^{2\pi} m\dot{\phi} \left(\frac{d\rho}{d\phi} \right) \left(\frac{d\rho}{d\phi} \right) d\phi = n_2 h.$$

Substituting

$$\dot{\phi} = \frac{l}{m\rho^2},$$

we obtain

$$\int_0^{2\pi} \frac{l}{\rho^2} \left(\frac{d\rho}{d\phi} \right)^2 d\phi = n_2 h.$$

Now, using the above expression for ρ,

$$\frac{d\rho}{d\phi} = \frac{a\varepsilon(1 - \varepsilon^2) \sin \phi}{(1 + \varepsilon \cos \phi)^2};$$

so,

$$\left(\frac{1}{\rho}\frac{d\rho}{d\phi}\right)^2 = \left[\frac{(1 + \varepsilon \cos \phi)}{a(1 - \varepsilon^2)} \cdot \frac{a\varepsilon(1 - \varepsilon^2) \sin \phi}{(1 + \varepsilon \cos \phi)^2}\right]^2 = \frac{\varepsilon^2 \sin^2 \phi}{(1 + \varepsilon \cos \phi)^2},$$

and the integral can be put in a simpler form,

$$l\varepsilon^2 \int_0^{2\pi} \frac{\sin^2 \phi \, d\phi}{(1 + \varepsilon \cos \phi)^2} = n_2 h.$$

To integrate by parts, we identify

$$\int u \, dv = uv - \int v \, du,$$

$$\int_0^{2\pi} \underbrace{\sin \phi}_{u} \underbrace{\frac{\sin \phi \, d\phi}{(1 + \varepsilon \cos \phi)^2}}_{dv}$$

$$v = \int \frac{\sin \phi \, d\phi}{(1 + \varepsilon \cos \phi)^2} = \frac{1}{\varepsilon}\left(\frac{1}{1 + \varepsilon \cos \phi}\right)$$

$$du = \cos \phi \, d\phi.$$

Hence,

$$l\varepsilon^2\left(\frac{1}{\varepsilon}\left[\frac{\sin \phi}{1 + \varepsilon \cos \phi}\right]_0^{2\pi} - \frac{1}{\varepsilon}\int_0^{2\pi} \frac{\cos \phi \, d\phi}{1 + \varepsilon \cos \phi}\right) = n_2 h$$

or

$$-l\varepsilon \int_0^{2\pi} \frac{\cos \phi \, d\phi}{1 + \varepsilon \cos \phi} = l\int_0^{2\pi}\left(\frac{1}{1 + \varepsilon \cos \phi} - 1\right) d\phi = n_2 h.$$

Integration then yields

$$l\left[\frac{2\pi}{\sqrt{1 - \varepsilon^2}} - 2\pi\right] = n_2 h$$

or

$$\frac{1}{\sqrt{1 - \varepsilon^2}} - 1 = \frac{n_2}{l}\hbar.$$

We already know, however, that

$$l = n_1\hbar;$$

so this reduces to

$$\frac{1}{\sqrt{1 - \varepsilon^2}} - 1 = \frac{n_2}{n_1},$$

which may easily be solved for ε^2:

$$\varepsilon^2 = 1 - \frac{n_1^2}{(n_1 + n_2)^2}$$

We also know the semimajor axis to be defined by

$$a = \frac{\varepsilon p}{(1 - \varepsilon^2)}$$

and, from the basic expressions for p and ε in terms of A, that

$$\varepsilon p = \frac{l^2}{Ze^2 m}.$$

Thus,

$$a = \frac{\dfrac{n_1^2 \hbar^2}{Ze^2 m}}{\dfrac{n_1^2}{(n_1 + n_2)^2}} = \frac{(n_1 + n_2)^2 \hbar^2}{Ze^2 m}.$$

Because the eccentricity and major axis of the possible orbits are determined, their geometry is now completely known. For example, with

$$n_1 + n_2 = 3$$

we obtain the results shown in Fig. P3.3 (3).

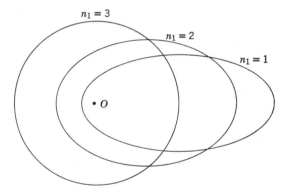

Fig. P3.3 (3)

The total energy will be given by

$$E = \frac{m}{2}(\dot{\rho}^2 + \rho^2\dot{\phi}^2) - \frac{Ze^2}{\rho};$$

further, when $\rho = \rho_{\max}$, $\dot{\rho} = 0$, while we also know that

$$\rho_{\max} = a(1 + \varepsilon).$$

Hence,

$$E = \frac{ma^2}{2}(1 + \varepsilon)^2\dot{\phi}^2 - \frac{Ze^2}{a(1 + \varepsilon)};$$

but

$$\phi^2 = \frac{n_1{}^2\hbar^2}{m^2\,\rho_{\max}^4},$$

so it follows that

$$E = \frac{n_1{}^2\hbar^2}{2ma^2(1 + \varepsilon)^2} - \frac{Ze^2}{a(1 + \varepsilon)}.$$

Since, however, combining the preceding relations for a and εp,

$$a = \frac{\dfrac{n_1{}^2\hbar^2}{Ze^2 m}}{1 - \varepsilon^2},$$

or

$$n_1{}^2\hbar^2 = a(1 - \varepsilon^2)Ze^2 m,$$

we may substitute this to obtain

$$E = \frac{a(1 - \varepsilon)(1 + \varepsilon)Ze^2 m}{2ma^2(1 + \varepsilon)^2} - \frac{Ze^2}{a(1 + \varepsilon)}$$

which reduces to

$$E = -\frac{Ze^2}{2a}.$$

Evidently the energy depends only on the major axis of the ellipse.   Also, we can rewrite the foregoing expression as

$$E = -\frac{\dfrac{Ze^2}{2(n_1 + n_2)^2\hbar^2}}{Ze^2 m} = -\frac{mZ^2e^4}{2(n_1 + n_2)^2\hbar^2}$$

which, for $n_2 = 0$, is the same result as that of the preceding problem. This modification of the original Bohr theory was first proposed by Arnold Sommerfeld.

4. A satellite is boosted to a point 150 mi above the surface of the earth and given a velocity parallel to the surface of 20,000 mi/hr relative to the earth's center. Describe the satellite's trajectory; if this is a closed orbit, determine the maximum distance from the earth's surface it will reach, the time it will take to go from this point to its point of closest approach to the surface, and the minimum escape velocity for these launching conditions.

Solution

The orbital equation for inverse square attraction is

$$\frac{1}{\rho} = A\cos(\phi + \theta) + \frac{m}{l^2}B$$

and the general conic equation is

$$\frac{1}{\rho} = \frac{1}{p}\cos(\phi + \theta) + \frac{1}{\varepsilon p};$$

thus we know that

$$\frac{1}{p} = A \quad \text{and} \quad \varepsilon = \frac{Al^2}{Bm}.$$

But since the initial velocity is normal to the radius vector ρ and the initial point must be a turning point, θ must be zero regardless of the particular conic. Also, initially

$$\phi = 0 \quad \text{and} \quad \frac{1}{p} = \frac{1}{p_0},$$

p_0 being known; so the orbital equation becomes

$$\frac{1}{p_0} = A + \frac{m}{l^2} B.$$

For this problem involving gravitational attraction

$$B = KMm,$$

where M is the mass of the earth, m the mass of the satellite, and K the universal gravitational constant. Hence

$$\frac{1}{p_0} = \frac{KMm^2}{l^2} + A,$$

and we can now solve for A:

$$A = \frac{1}{p_0} - \frac{KMm^2}{l^2} = \frac{l^2 - KMm^2 p_0}{p_0 l^2}.$$

This also determines ε:

$$\varepsilon = \frac{Al^2}{Bm} = \frac{l^2 - KMm^2 p_0}{p_0 KMm^2}$$

or, because

$$l = m p_0 v_0,$$

$$\varepsilon = \frac{p_0 v_0^2 - KM}{KM}.$$

The numerical values given are

$$p_0 = 150 + \text{radius of earth}$$
$$= 4150 \text{ mi} = 2.19 \times 10^7 \text{ ft}$$
$$v_0 = 20{,}000 \text{ mi/hr} = 2.93 \times 10^4 \text{ ft/sec}$$
$$KM = 1.43 \times 10^{16} \text{ ft}^3/\text{sec}^2.$$

Hence,

$$\varepsilon = \frac{2.19(2.93)^2 \times 10^{15} - 1.43 \times 10^{16}}{1.43 \times 10^{16}}$$

$$= \frac{1.88 - 1.43}{1.43} = \frac{0.45}{1.43} = 0.314 < 1,$$

which proves that the satellite will move in an elliptical orbit.

Clearly, ρ will be a maximum when $1/\rho$ is a minimum, and we can see from the equation

$$\frac{1}{\rho} = \frac{KMm^2}{l^2} + A \cos \phi$$

that this will be the case when $\phi = \pi$; therefore,

$$\frac{1}{\rho_{max}} = \frac{KMm^2}{l^2} - A.$$

But also from above

$$A = \frac{1}{\rho_0} - \frac{KMm^2}{l^2};$$

it follows that

$$\frac{1}{\rho_{max}} = \frac{KMm^2}{l^2} - \frac{1}{\rho_0} + \frac{KMm^2}{l^2}$$

$$= \frac{2KMm^2}{l^2} - \frac{1}{\rho_0}$$

or, with $l = m\rho_0 v_0$,

$$\frac{1}{\rho_{max}} = \frac{2KM}{\rho_0^2 v_0^2} - \frac{1}{\rho_0} = \frac{2KM - \rho_0 v_0^2}{\rho_0^2 v_0^2},$$

giving

$$\rho_{max} = \frac{\rho_0^2 v_0^2}{2KM - \rho_0 v_0^2} = \frac{(2.19 \times 2.93)^2 \times 10^{22}}{(2.86 - 1.88)10^{16}} \text{ ft}$$

$$= 4.21 \times 10^7 \text{ ft} = 7970 \text{ mi.}$$

Accordingly, the maximum distance from earth's surface will be

$$d_{max} = 7970 - 4000 = 3970 \text{ mi.}$$

Furthermore, we know that the areal velocity will be constant and given by

$$\frac{da}{dt} = \frac{\rho^2 \dot\phi}{2};$$

therefore, using the fact that

$$\dot\phi_0 = \frac{v_0}{\rho_0},$$

$$a = \int_0^\tau \frac{\rho_0 v_0}{2} \, dt = \frac{\rho_0 v_0}{2} \tau, \qquad \tau = \frac{2a}{\rho_0 v_0},$$

where τ is the period [Fig. P3.3 (4)].

We are interested in the time required for travel from point I to point II, which by symmetry will be

$$\frac{\tau}{2} = \frac{a}{\rho_0 v_0}.$$

The area of the ellipse is

$$a = \pi \alpha \beta,$$

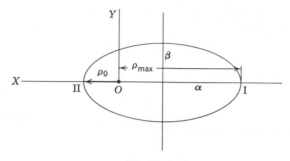

Fig. P3.3 (4)

α being the semimajor axis and β the semiminor axis. From geometry, however, we know that

$$\beta = \alpha(1 - \varepsilon^2)^{1/2},$$

and the preceding relation becomes

$$\frac{\tau}{2} = \frac{\pi\alpha^2(1 - \varepsilon^2)^{1/2}}{\rho_0 v_0}.$$

But

$$2\alpha = \rho_0 + \rho_{max},$$

so we obtain

$$\frac{\tau}{2} = \frac{\pi}{4\rho_0 v_0}(\rho_0 + \rho_{max})^2(1 - \varepsilon^2)^{1/2}.$$

Now

$$(1 - \varepsilon^2)^{1/2} = (0.9014)^{1/2} = 0.949,$$

$$(\rho_0 + \rho_{max})^2 = (2.19 \times 10^7 + 4.21 \times 10^7)^2 = 4.096 \times 10^{15} \text{ ft}^2,$$

and

$$4\rho_0 v_0 = 4(2.19)(2.93) \times 10^{11} = 2.57 \times 10^{12} \text{ ft}^2/\text{sec}^2.$$

Hence

$$\frac{\tau}{2} = 3.14 \frac{(4.1)(0.95)}{(2.57)} \times 10^3$$

$$= 4.25 \times 10^3 \text{ sec} = 1 \text{ hr } 10 \text{ min } 50 \text{ sec}.$$

The minimum escape velocity v_{0e} is that for which the trajectory becomes a parabola, that is, ε becomes equal to 1. Using the relation obtained earlier for ε, we have

$$\frac{\rho_0 v_{0e}^2 - KM}{KM} = 1.$$

$$\rho_0 v_{0e}^2 = 2KM$$

$$v_{0e} = \left(\frac{2KM}{\rho_0}\right)^{1/2} = \left(\frac{2.86 \times 10^{16}}{2.19 \times 10^7}\right)^{1/2} = (1.31 \times 10^9)^{1/2} = 3.62 \times 10^4 \text{ ft/sec}$$

$$= 24,650 \text{ mi/hr}.$$

5. Determine the form of an attractive central force that will cause a mass m to describe a circular orbit which passes through (or very near) the center of force.

Solution

If in

$$\frac{d^2\rho^{-1}}{d\phi^2} + \rho^{-1} = -\frac{m\rho^2}{l^2}F(\rho)$$

we place $\rho^{-1} = u$ and solve for $F(\rho)$, the result is

$$F(\rho) = -\frac{l^2}{m}u^2\left(\frac{d^2u}{d\phi^2} + u\right).$$

The equation of a circle of radius a whose circumference passes through the origin is given in polar coordinates by

$$\rho = 2a\cos\phi$$

or

$$u = \frac{1}{2a\cos\phi};$$

so it follows that

$$\frac{du}{d\phi} = \frac{2a\sin\phi}{4a^2\cos^2\phi} = \frac{\sin\phi}{2a\cos^2\phi}$$

and

$$\frac{d^2u}{d\phi^2} = \frac{2a\cos^3\phi + 4a\cos\phi\sin^2\phi}{4a^2\cos^4\phi}$$

$$= \frac{1}{2a\cos\phi} + \frac{\sin^2\phi}{a\cos^3\phi}.$$

Thus,

$$\frac{d^2u}{d\phi^2} + u = \frac{1}{a\cos\phi} + \frac{\sin^2\phi}{a\cos^3\phi}$$

or

$$\frac{d^2u}{d\phi^2} + u = \frac{1}{a\cos^3\phi}.$$

By substitution we then have

$$F(\rho) = -\frac{l^2}{m}\left(\frac{1}{2a\cos\phi}\right)^2\left(\frac{1}{a\cos^3\phi}\right)$$

$$= -\frac{l^2}{4a^3m}\cdot\frac{1}{\cos^5\phi}.$$

But since $\rho = 2a\cos\phi$,

$$\frac{1}{\cos^5\phi} = \frac{32a^5}{\rho^5}.$$

Therefore,

$$F(\rho) = -\frac{l^2}{4a^3m} \cdot \frac{32a^5}{\rho^5}$$

$$= -\frac{8l^2a^2}{m\rho^5}.$$

6. Determine the form of an attractive central force for which all circular orbits have the same areal velocity. Assume that the center of force coincides with the center of curvature.

Solution

The governing equation of motion is

$$F(\rho) + m\rho\dot{\phi}^2 = m\ddot{\rho}.$$

But $\ddot{\rho} = 0$ for any circular orbit; this means that

$$F(\rho) = -m\rho\dot{\phi}^2.$$

However,

$$\frac{da}{dt} = \frac{\rho^2\dot{\phi}}{2} = \text{constant} = C_1;$$

hence:

$$F(\rho) = -\frac{4m\rho^4\dot{\phi}^2}{4\rho^3} = -\frac{4mC_1^2}{\rho^3} = -\frac{C_2}{\rho^3}$$

7. Establish the criterion of circular orbit stability for the case of attractive central-force motion.

Solution

The equation of motion is

$$F(\rho) + \frac{l^2}{m\rho^3} = m\ddot{\rho},$$

which can also be written as

$$m\left(\ddot{\rho} - \frac{l^2}{m^2\rho^3}\right) = -mf(\rho)$$

where $F(\rho) = -mf(\rho)$. We shall assume that the mass m is initially traveling in a circular orbit of radius a and is perturbed slightly in the direction of ρ; that is, $\rho = a$ changes to

$$\rho = a + \delta$$

where δ is small, while

$$\dot{\rho} = \dot{\delta}$$

and

$$\ddot{\rho} = \ddot{\delta}.$$

Substituting into the equation of motion, we obtain

$$\ddot{\delta} - \frac{l^2}{m^2(a + \delta)^3} = -f(\rho)$$

or

$$\ddot{\delta} - \frac{l^2}{m^2a^3[1 + (\delta/a)]^3} = -f(\rho).$$

However, the second term on the left can be expanded by the binomial theorem,

$$(\alpha + \beta)^n = \alpha^n + n\alpha^{n-1}\beta + \frac{n(n-1)}{2!}\alpha^{n-2}\beta^2 + \cdots,$$

while the right-hand side can be expanded in a Taylor series about the point $\rho = a$:

$$f(\rho) = f(a) + f'(a)(\rho - a) + \frac{f''(a)}{2!}(\rho - a)^2 + \cdots$$

The equation then becomes:

$$\ddot{\delta} - \frac{l^2}{m^2 a^3}\left(1 - \frac{3\delta}{a} + \cdots\right) = -f(a) - \delta f'(a) + \cdots$$

Neglecting higher powers of δ/a (which will be relatively small quantities) and derivatives of $f(a)$ of order higher than one, we obtain the approximate equation

$$\ddot{\delta} - \frac{l^2}{m^2 a^3}\left(1 - \frac{3\delta}{a}\right) = -f(a) - \delta f'(a).$$

From the definition $F(\rho) = -mf(\rho)$ and the fact that

$$F(\rho) = -m\rho\dot{\phi}^2$$

for a circular orbit, we have

$$f(a) = a\dot{\phi}^2 = \frac{l^2}{m^2 a^3}.$$

Thus the above equation becomes

$$\ddot{\delta} + \left[\frac{3f(a)}{a} + f'(a)\right]\delta = 0.$$

Now we can see that as long as the quantity within the brackets is positive, the motion of m will be oscillatory in δ (which has the direction of ρ but is a small quantity). Hence the criterion of circular orbit stability can be written as

$$\frac{3}{a}f(a) + f'(a) > 0.$$

If this holds true, m will oscillate about its initial path $\rho = a$ according to the relation

$$\delta = \delta_0 \sin \omega_0 t,$$

where

$$\omega_0 = \sqrt{\frac{3 f(a)}{a} + f'(a)}.$$

In general, if the law of force is

$$-f(\rho) = -\frac{B}{\rho^n}, \qquad B = \text{constant},$$

then

$$f'(a) = -\frac{nB}{a^{n+1}} = -\frac{n}{a}f(a)$$

and

$$\omega_0 = \sqrt{\frac{f(a)}{a}(3 - n)},$$

which must be positive for orbit stability. Consequently, n must be less than 3 if the law of force is of the preceding form and circular orbital stability is required.

8. When a photon with the energy $h\nu$ collides with an electron, it will transfer kinetic energy to the electron, thereby reducing its own energy. Because h is a constant, the scattered photon must have energy $h\nu'$, where $\nu' < \nu$. The observed change in the frequency, or wavelength, of the scattered radiation is known as the Compton effect after A. H. Compton, who first treated the phenomenon as an elastic collision between two point objects. Assuming that the electron is stationary before the collision, use the diagram shown in Fig. P3.3 (8) together with the principles of conservation of energy and momentum to obtain the following:

   a. $\nu' = \nu'(\nu, \theta)$.
   b. The difference in wavelength, $(\lambda' - \lambda)$.
   c. An expression for the kinetic energy of the recoiling electron,

$$T = T(\nu, \phi) = h\nu - h\nu'.$$

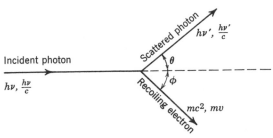

Fig. P3.3 (8)

Solution

The linear momentum of the electron is mv, whereas that of the photon is $h\nu/c$, since $mc = E/c = h\nu/c$. The electron is initially at rest, with the energy m_0c^2 and zero momentum. But after the collision its velocity will become v and its mass $m = m_0/\mathscr{S}$; therefore, its energy will be given by $mc^2 = m_0c^2/\mathscr{S}$ and its momentum by $mv = m_0v/\mathscr{S}$.

(a) From conservation of energy we obtain

$$h\nu + m_0c^2 = h\nu' + mc^2,$$

and from conservation of momentum:

$$\frac{h\nu}{c} = \frac{h\nu'}{c}\cos\theta + mv\cos\phi$$

$$0 = \frac{h\nu'}{c}\sin\theta - mv\sin\phi$$

To determine the change in frequency of the photon, ϕ can be eliminated from the last two equations. Multiplying through by c and isolating the term involving ϕ,

$$mvc \cos \phi = h(v - v' \cos \theta),$$

$$mvc \sin \phi = hv' \sin \theta.$$

Squaring and adding these then gives

$$m^2 c^2 v^2 = h^2(v^2 - 2vv' \cos \theta + v'^2 \cos^2 \theta + v'^2 \sin^2 \theta)$$

$$= h^2(v^2 - 2vv' \cos \theta + v'^2).$$

But the first equation tells us that

$$mc^2 = h(v - v') + m_0 c^2,$$

and thus that

$$m^2 c^4 = h^2(v^2 - 2vv' + v'^2) + 2h(v - v')m_0 c^2 + m_0^2 c^4.$$

Subtracting this from the above equation with $m^2 c^2 v^2$ on the left-hand side yields

$$m^2 c^2 (c^2 - v^2) = -2h^2 vv'(1 - \cos \theta) + 2h(v - v')m_0 c^2 + m_0^2 c^4,$$

which can also be written as

$$\left(\frac{m_0}{\mathscr{S}}\right)^2 c^2(c^2 - v^2) = \frac{m_0^2 c^2}{(1 - v^2/c^2)}(c^2 - v^2) = m_0^2 c^4$$

$$= -2h^2 vv'(1 - \cos \theta) + 2h(v - v')m_0 c^2 + m_0^2 c^4.$$

Thus, we find that

$$2h(v - v')m_0 c^2 = 2h^2 vv'(1 - \cos \theta)$$

or

$$\frac{(v - v')}{vv'} = \frac{1}{v'} - \frac{1}{v} = \frac{h}{m_0 c^2}(1 - \cos \theta).$$

Now we can solve for v':

$$\frac{1}{v'} = \frac{1}{v} + \frac{h}{m_0 c^2}(1 - \cos \theta) = \frac{m_0 c^2 + hv(1 - \cos \theta)}{m_0 c^2 v}$$

$$v' = \frac{m_0 c^2 v}{m_0 c^2 + hv(1 - \cos \theta)} = \frac{v}{1 + \left(\dfrac{hv}{m_0 c^2}\right)(1 - \cos \theta)}$$

Placing

$$\frac{hv}{m_0 c^2} = \alpha$$

and using the trigonometric identity

$$(1 - \cos \theta) = 2 \sin^2 \frac{\theta}{2},$$

we obtain

$$\nu' = \frac{\nu}{1 + 2\alpha \sin^2 \dfrac{\theta}{2}},$$

showing clearly that $\nu' < \nu$.

(b) The change in wavelength can also be determined from the relations defining ν':

$$\frac{1}{\nu'} - \frac{1}{\nu} = \frac{h}{m_0 c^2}(1 - \cos\theta)$$

$$c\left(\frac{1}{\nu'} - \frac{1}{\nu}\right) = \frac{h}{m_0 c}(1 - \cos\theta)$$

$$(\lambda' - \lambda) = \frac{2h}{m_0 c}\sin^2\frac{\theta}{2}$$

Evidently $\lambda' > \lambda$, as expected.

(c) Isolating the term involving ϕ in the two momentum conservation equations, then dividing the last by the first gives

$$\tan\phi = \frac{h\nu' \sin\theta}{h\nu - h\nu' \cos\theta} = \frac{\nu' \sin\theta}{\nu - \nu' \cos\theta};$$

however,

$$\nu' = \frac{\nu}{1 + 2\alpha \sin^2 \dfrac{\theta}{2}},$$

and therefore

$$\tan\phi = \frac{\nu \sin\theta}{1 + 2\alpha \sin^2 \dfrac{\theta}{2}}\left/\left(\nu - \frac{\nu \cos\theta}{1 + 2\alpha \sin^2 \dfrac{\theta}{2}}\right)\right. = \frac{\sin\theta}{1 + 2\alpha \sin^2 \dfrac{\theta}{2} - \cos\theta}.$$

By the use of trigonometric identities this can be reduced to

$$\tan\phi = \frac{2\sin\dfrac{\theta}{2}\cos\dfrac{\theta}{2}}{1 + 2\alpha \sin^2 \dfrac{\theta}{2} - \left(1 - 2\sin^2 \dfrac{\theta}{2}\right)} = \frac{1}{(1 + \alpha)\tan\dfrac{\theta}{2}},$$

which establishes that ϕ varies from $\pi/2$ to 0 as θ varies from 0 to π.
The kinetic energy of the recoiling electron will be given by

$$T = h\nu - h\nu' = h\nu\left(1 - \frac{1}{1 + 2\alpha \sin^2 \dfrac{\theta}{2}}\right) = h\nu \frac{2\alpha \sin^2 \dfrac{\theta}{2}}{1 + 2\alpha \sin^2 \dfrac{\theta}{2}}.$$

But using the relation for tan ϕ,

$$\tan\frac{\theta}{2} = \frac{1}{(1+\alpha)\tan\phi} = \frac{\sin\frac{\theta}{2}}{\cos\frac{\theta}{2}};$$

hence

$$\frac{\cos^2\frac{\theta}{2}}{\sin^2\frac{\theta}{2}} + 1 = (1+\alpha)^2\tan^2\phi + 1$$

or

$$\frac{1}{\sin^2\frac{\theta}{2}} = (1+\alpha)^2\tan^2\phi + 1,$$

so that

$$\sin^2\frac{\theta}{2} = \frac{1}{(1+\alpha)^2\tan^2\phi + 1}.$$

It follows that

$$T = hv\,\frac{2\alpha}{[(1+\alpha)^2\tan^2\phi + 1]}\left(\frac{1}{1 + \dfrac{2\alpha}{[(1+\alpha)^2\tan^2\phi + 1]}}\right)$$

$$= \frac{2\alpha hv}{(1+\alpha)^2\tan^2\phi + 2\alpha + 1}.$$

The energy of the recoiling electron varies directly as the energy of the incident photon and inversely as determined by $\tan^2\phi$.

9. A tennis ball is given a horizontal speed u from a height h above ground level. Find the total horizontal distance x that the ball will travel, as a function of u, h and the coefficient of restitution ε, before it stops bouncing [Fig. P3.3 (9)].

Fig. P3.3 (9)

Solution

Because the expression for ε involves only the components of velocity perpendicular to the plane of collision, the ball will maintain a constant

horizontal speed u. And since it falls from a height h, we can easily prove
that it will first hit the ground after a time $\sqrt{2h/g}$, with the vertical speed
$\sqrt{2gh}$, and rebound with the speed $\varepsilon\sqrt{2gh}$. The total time for all bounces
becomes

$$t = \sqrt{\frac{2h}{g}} + 2\varepsilon\sqrt{\frac{2h}{g}} + 2\varepsilon^2\sqrt{\frac{2h}{g}} + \cdots$$

$$= 2\sqrt{\frac{2h}{g}}\,[1 + \varepsilon + \varepsilon^2 \cdots - \tfrac{1}{2}]$$

or, by means of the binomial theorem,

$$t = 2\sqrt{\frac{2h}{g}}\left[\frac{1}{1-\varepsilon} - \frac{1}{2}\right]$$

$$= \left[\frac{2h}{g}\right]^{\frac{1}{2}}\left[\frac{1+\varepsilon}{1-\varepsilon}\right].$$

Thus, the total horizontal distance traveled must be

$$x = ut = u\left[\frac{2h}{g}\right]^{\frac{1}{2}}\left[\frac{1+\varepsilon}{1-\varepsilon}\right].$$

10. A point mass m_1 is at rest in the center of a hollow tube of length L and mass
m_2, which is closed at both ends and rests on a smooth, horizontal plane.
If ε is the coefficient of restitution between m_1 and m_2, and m_1 is given an
initial velocity of v_0 along the tube, find the following:

a. The velocities of m_1 and m_2 after the first impact.
b. The energy loss during the first impact.
c. The time required for m_1 to arrive back at its starting position, traveling
in its original direction.

Solution

The available equations are:

$$v_{1e} - v_{2e} = -\varepsilon(v_{1a} - v_{2a})$$

$$m_1 v_{1e} + m_2 v_{2e} = m_1 v_{1a} + m_2 v_{2a}$$

Solving these simultaneously for v_{1e} and v_{2e}, we obtain:

$$v_{1e} = \frac{m_1 v_{1a} + m_2 v_{2a} - \varepsilon m_2(v_{1a} - v_{2a})}{m_1 + m_2}$$

$$v_{2e} = \frac{m_1 v_{1a} + m_2 v_{2a} + \varepsilon m_1(v_{1a} - v_{2a})}{m_1 + m_2}$$

(a) If v_{1e} and v_{2e} denote the velocities of m_1 and m_2 after the first collision, the
above equations yield:

$$v_{1e} = \frac{m_1 - \varepsilon m_2}{m_1 + m_2}\, v_0$$

$$v_{2e} = \frac{m_1 + \varepsilon m_1}{m_1 + m_2}\, v_0$$

(b) Initially the total kinetic energy is the kinetic energy of m_1,

$$T = \tfrac{1}{2}m_1 v_0{}^2,$$

but after the first collision the total kinetic energy will be given by

$$T' = \tfrac{1}{2}m_2 v_{2e}{}^2 + \tfrac{1}{2}m_1 v_{1e}{}^2$$

$$= \tfrac{1}{2}m_2 m_1{}^2 \frac{(1 + \varepsilon)^2}{(m_1 + m_2)^2} v_0{}^2 + \tfrac{1}{2}m_1 \frac{(m_1 - \varepsilon m_2)^2}{(m_1 + m_2)^2} v_0{}^2$$

$$= \frac{m_1 v_0{}^2}{2(m_1 + m_2)^2} [m_1{}^2 + m_1 m_2(1 + \varepsilon^2) + \varepsilon^2 m_2{}^2].$$

Therefore, the change in kinetic energy is:

$$\Delta T = T' - T = \frac{m_1 v_0{}^2}{2}\left[\frac{m_1{}^2 + m_1 m_2(1 + \varepsilon^2) + \varepsilon^2 m_2{}^2}{(m_1 + m_2)^2} - 1\right]$$

$$= -\frac{1}{2}\frac{m_1 m_2}{(m_1 + m_2)}(1 - \varepsilon^2)v_0{}^2$$

(c) From $v_{1e} - v_{2e} = -\varepsilon(v_{1a} - v_{2a})$ we can see that the relative velocities between m_1 and m_2 before and after the first collision will be v_0 and $-\varepsilon v_0$, respectively. After the second collision the relative velocity will be $\varepsilon^2 v_0$. Hence, the time that will elapse until m_1 is again at its original position and traveling in its original direction must be

$$t = \frac{L}{2v_0} + \frac{L}{\varepsilon v_0} + \frac{L}{2\varepsilon^2 v_0} = \frac{L}{2v_0}\left(1 + \frac{1}{\varepsilon}\right)^2.$$

11. For the system described in the preceding problem:

a. Determine the velocities relative to the center of mass before and after the first collision.

b. Find the total loss in energy during the first impact, using a center-of-mass coordinate system.

Solution

(a) Since the total linear momentum must be conserved,

$$(m_1 + m_2)\dot{\mathbf{R}} = m_1 \dot{\mathbf{r}}_a;$$

consequently,

$$\dot{\mathbf{R}} = \left(\frac{m_1}{m_1 + m_2}\right)\dot{\mathbf{r}}_a = \frac{m_1}{m_1 + m_2}\mathbf{v}_0,$$

establishing that the velocity of the center of mass remains constant. The precollision velocity of m_1 relative to the center of mass is

$$\dot{\mathbf{r}}_{1_0}{}' = \mathbf{v}_0 - \dot{\mathbf{R}} = \mathbf{v}_0 - \frac{m_1}{m_1 + m_2}\mathbf{v}_0 = \frac{m_2}{m_1 + m_2}\mathbf{v}_0,$$

whereas the precollision velocity of m_2 relative to the center of mass must be

$$\dot{r}_{2_0}{}' = 0 - \dot{R} = -\frac{m_1}{m_1 + m_2} v_0.$$

The relationship involving the coefficient of restitution ε holds good in the center-of-mass system, provided the velocities are taken with respect to the center of mass:

$$\frac{\dot{r}_{1e}{}' - \dot{r}_{2e}{}'}{\dot{r}_{2a}{}' - \dot{r}_{1a}{}'} = \varepsilon.$$

Furthermore, relative to the center of mass it must be true that

$$m_1 \dot{r}_{1a}{}' + m_2 \dot{r}_{2a}{}' = 0$$

and

$$m_1 \dot{r}_{1e}{}' + m_2 \dot{r}_{2e}{}' = 0.$$

Solving the last two equations for $\dot{r}_{2a}{}'$ and $\dot{r}_{2e}{}'$, and replacing these in the first equation, we find that

$$\dot{r}_{1e}{}' = -\varepsilon \dot{r}_{1a}{}',$$

and in a similar manner that

$$\dot{r}_{2e}{}' = -\varepsilon \dot{r}_{2a}{}'.$$

Therefore, the postcollision velocity of m_1 with respect to the center of mass must be

$$\dot{r}_1{}' = -\frac{\varepsilon m_2}{m_1 + m_2} v_0,$$

and that of mass m_2 must be

$$\dot{r}_2{}' = +\frac{\varepsilon m_1}{m_1 + m_2} v_0.$$

(b) We have seen that in general the kinetic energy of such a system relative to the center of mass can be written as

$$T_{m_a} = \frac{1}{2} \frac{m_1 m_2}{(m_1 + m_2)} \dot{r}^2.$$

Hence, before the collision the required kinetic energy will be

$$T_{m_a} = \frac{1}{2} \frac{m_1 m_2}{(m_1 + m_2)} v_0{}^2,$$

whereas after the collision it will be

$$T_{m_e} = \frac{1}{2} \frac{m_1 m_2}{(m_1 + m_2)} \varepsilon^2 v_0{}^2.$$

Evidently the change in kinetic energy during the first impact is

$$T_{m_e} - T_{m_a} = -\frac{1}{2}\frac{m_1 m_2}{(m_1 + m_2)}(1 - \varepsilon^2)v_0^2,$$

and this must be the total energy loss during the process.

The kinetic energy of the mass center itself is

$$T_c = \tfrac{1}{2}(m_1 + m_2)\dot{\mathbf{R}}^2,$$

that is,

$$T_c = \tfrac{1}{2}(m_1 + m_2)\frac{m_1^2}{(m_1 + m_2)^2}v_0^2$$

$$= \frac{1}{2}\frac{m_1^2}{(m_1 + m_2)}v_0^2,$$

which shows that the kinetic energy of the center of mass remains constant, as required.

Exercises 3.3

1. The potential energy of an isotropic harmonic oscillator is $V = \tfrac{1}{2}kr^2$.

   a. Plot the effective potential energy for the r-motion when a particle of mass m moves with angular momentum l about the origin.
   b. Determine the energy for which the particle will move in a circular orbit.
   c. Discuss the types of motion that are possible.

   Answer. (b) $E_0 = l\sqrt{\dfrac{k}{m}}$.

2. A particle of mass m moves in space under the influence of a potential:

   $$V(r) = k \quad \text{for} \quad r < R$$
   $$V(r) = 0 \quad \text{for} \quad r > R$$

   If

   $$F'(r) = F(r) + \frac{l^2}{mr^3},$$

   sketch V versus r curves for $k > 0$ and $k < 0$. Is motion in a stable circular orbit possible in either case? If so, what is the radius of this orbit?

3. A point mass of $m = 10$ slugs moves under the influence of a constant gravitational force that is directed toward the origin of an inertial coordinate system. At a given time t the mass is located by the position vector $\mathbf{r} = 1000\hat{\mathbf{i}} + 2000\hat{\mathbf{j}} + 3000\hat{\mathbf{k}}$ ft and has a velocity of $\mathbf{v} = 4000\hat{\mathbf{i}} + 5000\hat{\mathbf{j}} + 6000\hat{\mathbf{k}}$ ft/sec. What is the direction of the normal to the plane of the trajectory?

   Answer. $\dfrac{1}{\sqrt{6}}[-\hat{\mathbf{i}} + 2\hat{\mathbf{j}} - \hat{\mathbf{k}}]$.

4. If, at some later time, the mass of the preceding problem has the position vector
$$\mathbf{r} = 6000\hat{\mathbf{i}} + 7000\hat{\mathbf{j}} + 8000\hat{\mathbf{k}} \text{ ft},$$
what will its transverse velocity v_ϕ be at that time?

Answer. $v_\phi = 600$ ft/sec.

5. In appropriate units, a satellite with $m = 3$, located at a distance of 55×10^6 from the center of the earth, has a tangential velocity $v_\phi = 2.5 \times 10^4$ at a known time. Assume a reference axis of symmetry to pass through the satellite at this time and calculate the following:

a. Its angular momentum.
b. The eccentricity of its orbit.

Answer

(a) $l = 4.12 \times 10^{12}$.
(b) $\varepsilon = 1.49$.

6. A capsule was accelerated to a velocity of 5 mi/sec relative to the center of the earth but parallel to its surface, at a distance of 4400 mi from the center. Compute the maximum and minimum distances that the capsule reached.

Answer. $\rho_{min} = 4400$ mi, $\rho_{max} = 5780$ mi.

7. An α-particle of mass 6.64×10^{-24} gm and charge 9.3×10^{-10} esu was scattered by a silver nucleus with $Z = 47$, $e = 4.7 \times 10^{-10}$ esu. The α-particle had an initial velocity of $v = 2 \times 10^9$ cm/sec and the impact parameter s was 7.85×10^{-11} cm. Calculate the scattering angle Δ. Comment on what would have happened if the impact parameter had been zero.

Answer. $\Delta = 1°8'$.

8. Prove that the general conic equation
$$\frac{1}{\rho} = \frac{1}{p}\cos(\phi + \theta) + \frac{1}{\varepsilon p}$$
yields the following curves for the given values of ε:

Curve	ε
Parabola	1
Ellipse	<1
Hyperbola	>1
Circle	0

9. Two point masses of 1 and 2 slugs are sliding over a frictionless horizontal surface with respective velocities of 5 and 10 ft/sec in such a way that their lines of approach make an angle of 60° with each other. If they remain together once they collide, determine the velocity after impact.

Answer. $\mathbf{v} = 5.0\hat{\mathbf{i}} + 5.766\hat{\mathbf{j}}$.

10. A nonrotating pingpong ball strikes a stationary basketball slightly off-center with a velocity of 10 ft/sec. If the former moves off parallel to the floor with a velocity 5 ft/sec at an angle of 60° to its original direction:

    a. Find the ratio of the masses of the balls, assuming that no rotation occurs.

    b. Show how this method would have to be modified if the collision caused both balls to rotate.

11. A point mass m_1 moves in a straight line with a velocity v and collides with a point mass m_2 that was at rest; after the collision their directions of motion are at right angles. Show that $m_1 = m_2$ for a completely elastic collision, using the laboratory coordinate system.

12. Two simple pendulums with masses m_1 and m_2 are connected to a common point [see Fig. E3.3 (12)]. If m_1 is released in the configuration shown, and the coefficient of restitution is ε, calculate the maximum angles from the vertical that the two pendulums will reach after the first collision.

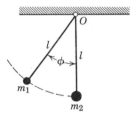

Fig. E3.3 (12)

Answer. $\quad \theta_1 = \cos^{-1}\left[1 - \dfrac{(m_1 - m_2\varepsilon)^2(1 - \cos\phi)}{(m_1 + m_2)^2}\right]$

$\qquad\quad \theta_2 = \cos^{-1}\left[1 - \dfrac{m_1^2(1 + \varepsilon)^2(1 - \cos\phi)}{(m_1 + m_2)^2}\right]$

13. A billiard ball has a velocity of $\mathbf{v} = 10\hat{\mathbf{i}} + 15\hat{\mathbf{j}}$ ft/sec as it strikes the first cushion shown in Fig. E3.3 (13). Calculate its velocity $\mathbf{v'}$ after it bounces off two more cushions, if the coefficient of restitution is always 0.8 and no friction losses occur.

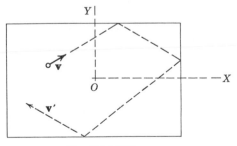

Fig. E3.3 (13)

Answer. $\quad 8.0\hat{\mathbf{i}} + 9.6\hat{\mathbf{j}}$ ft/sec.

14. The device shown in Fig. E3.3 (14) is used to test tennis balls. The balls are given an initial horizontal velocity at a height h above a smooth plane and allowed to bounce through a slot whose width is twice the diameter of the balls. Acceptable balls must pass through the slot with no vertical component of velocity. Show that

$$(\varepsilon_1^2 - \varepsilon_2^2) = \frac{d}{h},$$

where ε_1 and ε_2 are the limiting values of the coefficient of restitution.

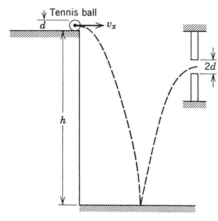

Fig. E3.3 (14)

15. Sketch the collision of Problem 11 in a center of mass system, providing proper values for the velocities involved in terms of v, and showing that your answer is in agreement with the results obtained before.

16. Let $\mathbf{r}_1$ and $\mathbf{r}_2$ be the respective laboratory position vectors of masses m_1 and m_2. If initially m_2 was located at the origin and

$$\mathbf{r}_1 = (c_1 + v_x t)\hat{\mathbf{i}} + c_2\hat{\mathbf{j}} + c_3\hat{\mathbf{k}},$$

what is the velocity of the center of mass?

Answer. $\dfrac{m_1}{m_1 + m_2} v_x\hat{\mathbf{i}}.$

17. Derive an expression for the relative kinetic energy of the two masses in the preceding problem.

Answer. $T_{\text{rel}} = \dfrac{1}{2}\dfrac{m_1 m_2}{(m_1 + m_2)} v_x^2.$

18. Prove that the solutions

$$x = C_x \sin\left(\frac{qB_z}{m} t + \theta_x\right) + \frac{E_y t}{B_z} + D_x,$$

$$y = C_y \sin\left(\frac{qB_z}{m} t + \theta_y\right) + D_y$$

of the equations of motion

$$\ddot{x} = \frac{qB_z}{m}\,\dot{y},$$

$$\ddot{y} = \frac{qE_y}{m} + \frac{qB_z}{m}\,\dot{x}$$

imply the additional conditions

$$C_x = C_y$$

and

$$\theta_y = \theta_x + \frac{\pi}{2}.$$

4

Strongly Coupled Motions

4.1 Systems of Oscillators

One of the best examples of point object motions which give rise to a strongly coupled set of equations is that of a group of masses coupled together by some combination of springs and dashpots. The existence of electrical and other analogs for such a system make it quite general, while simultaneous solutions can almost never be achieved by simple substitution without considerable labor. Since, as we have seen in Chapter 2, the Lagrangian method can generate strongly coupled sets of scalar equations of motion just as easily as weakly coupled or uncoupled sets, it is logical to set about formulating the general coupled-oscillator problem in this way. We also know that the matrix methods of Section 1.3 can be used to solve systems of simultaneous linear differential equations, so it will be desirable to cast the results in matrix form as soon as possible.

We shall begin by omitting dashpots and limiting our considerations to small, conservative, harmonic oscillations about some equilibrium configuration, characterized by the fact that it minimizes the potential energy, like the static equilibrium position of Fig. 3.2 or the circular orbit of Fig. 3.25. Under these circumstances, it is well established that most systems involving a fixed number of masses n moving in three-dimensional space will be holonomic; therefore, we may conclude that if k constraint equations of the form (2.6) of Chapter 2 can be written, $3n - k$ independent generalized coordinates q_j will exist, and the potential energy of the system can be expressed as

$$V = V(q_1, q_2, \ldots, q_{3n-k}). \tag{1.1}$$

More particularly, for the same reasons we can conclude[1] that

$$V = \tfrac{1}{2}\kappa_{lm} q_l q_m \qquad \{l, m = 1, 2, \ldots, 3n - k, \tag{1.2}$$

where the κ_{lm} are real constants obtained from evaluating

$$\kappa_{lm} = \frac{\partial^2 V}{\partial q_l\, \partial q_m} = \frac{\partial^2 V}{\partial q_m\, \partial q_l} = \kappa_{ml} \tag{1.3}$$

at the equilibrium values of the coordinates q_l and q_m. As an illustration, with $l, m = 1, 2$ the relation (1.2) will yield

$$V = \tfrac{1}{2}(\kappa_{1m} q_1 q_m + \kappa_{2m} q_2 q_m) \qquad \{m = 1, 2$$
$$= \tfrac{1}{2}(\kappa_{11} q_1 q_1 + \kappa_{12} q_1 q_2 + \kappa_{21} q_2 q_1 + \kappa_{22} q_2 q_2); \tag{1.4}$$

if

$$q_1 = x \tag{1.5}$$
$$q_2 = 0, \tag{1.6}$$

with the constant κ_{11} identified as K_x, (1.4) will reduce to the spring potential used before [(2.26) of Chapter 3]

$$V_x = \frac{K_x x^2}{2}. \tag{1.7}$$

As stated above, this amounts to restricting ourselves to the free vibrations of a system composed entirely of masses and linearly elastic springs (or their equivalents). If dissipative or time-varying forces are applied, the system will become nonconservative, and even though in special cases the equations of motion may remain linear, the preceding form for the total potential cannot be assumed. Neither can it be assumed if the displacements become too large, when the equations of motion will almost certainly become nonlinear. Later we will comment briefly on the nonconservative case, but the nonlinear case will not be treated at present.

In the same way, following the ideas developed in (2.26) to (2.31) of Chapter 2, if we define the total kinetic energy by the general quadratic form

$$T = \tfrac{1}{2}\mu_{lm} \dot{q}_l \dot{q}_m \qquad \{l, m = 1, 2, \ldots, 3n - k, \tag{1.8}$$

where the $\mu_{lm} = \mu_{ml}$ are real constants, then for $l, m = 1, 2$ we will obtain

$$T = \tfrac{1}{2}(\mu_{11} \dot{q}_1 \dot{q}_1 + \mu_{12} \dot{q}_1 \dot{q}_2 + \mu_{21} \dot{q}_1 \dot{q}_2 + \mu_{22} \dot{q}_2 \dot{q}_2); \tag{1.9}$$

---

[1] Corben, H. C., and P. Stehle, *Classical Mechanics*, 2nd edition, pp. 113–117, Wiley, New York, 1960.

and under conditions analogous to (1.5) and (1.6),

$$\dot{q}_1 = \dot{x} \tag{1.10}$$

$$\dot{q}_2 = 0, \tag{1.11}$$

this will reduce to the usual expression for the kinetic energy, when μ_{11} is identified with the appropriate mass [(2.25) of Chapter 3].

Combining (1.8) and (1.2), we obtain the Lagrangian for the system:

$$L = \tfrac{1}{2}\mu_{lm}\dot{q}_l\dot{q}_m - \tfrac{1}{2}\kappa_{lm}q_lq_m, \tag{1.12}$$

where both $[\mu_{lm}]$ and $[\kappa_{lm}]$ are symmetric matrices with real and constant elements. By making use of these properties of the coefficient matrices, application of the Lagrange equations (2.43) of Chapter 2,

$$\frac{d}{dt}\frac{\partial L}{\partial \dot{q}_j} - \frac{\partial L}{\partial q_j} = 0 \qquad \{j = 1, 2, \ldots, 3n - k,$$

will then yield the following $3n - k$ equations of motion:

$$\mu_{lm}\ddot{q}_m + \kappa_{lm}q_m = 0 \qquad \{l, m = 1, 2, \ldots, 3n - k. \tag{1.13}$$

For example, if j is limited to 1 and 2, l and m will be restricted to the same values; so that, using (1.4) and (1.9), the Lagrangian (1.12) will become

$$L = \tfrac{1}{2}(\mu_{11}\dot{q}_1\dot{q}_1 + \mu_{12}\dot{q}_1\dot{q}_2 + \mu_{21}\dot{q}_2\dot{q}_1 + \mu_{22}\dot{q}_2\dot{q}_2)$$
$$- \tfrac{1}{2}(\kappa_{11}q_1q_1 + \kappa_{12}q_1q_2 + \kappa_{21}q_2q_1 + \kappa_{22}q_2q_2). \tag{1.14}$$

Now, for $j = 1$ we obtain:

$$\frac{d}{dt}\frac{\partial L}{\partial \dot{q}_1} = \mu_{11}\ddot{q}_1 + \frac{\mu_{12}}{2}\ddot{q}_2 + \frac{\mu_{21}}{2}\ddot{q}_2 \tag{1.15}$$

$$-\frac{\partial L}{\partial q_1} = \kappa_{11}q_1 + \frac{\kappa_{12}}{2}q_2 + \frac{\kappa_{21}}{2}q_2 \tag{1.16}$$

Therefore, if the constants $\mu_{12} = \mu_{21}$ and $\kappa_{12} = \kappa_{21}$, Lagrange's equation for this case will be

$$\mu_{11}\ddot{q}_1 + \mu_{12}\ddot{q}_2 + \kappa_{11}q_1 + \kappa_{12}q_2 = 0. \tag{1.17}$$

For $j = 2$ it follows in the same way that

$$\mu_{21}\ddot{q}_1 + \mu_{22}\ddot{q}_2 + \kappa_{21}q_1 + \kappa_{22}q_2 = 0. \tag{1.18}$$

These two equations clearly will be the direct result of expanding (1.13) for $l, m = 1, 2$.

From Section 1.3 we know that the matrix equation

$$\mathcal{M}\ddot{\mathcal{Q}} + \mathcal{K}\mathcal{Q} = 0 \tag{1.19}$$

will be equivalent to the indicial equation (1.13), provided its matrices are defined by the corresponding indicial forms, and the second index of the q's is understood to be one as before. Therefore, assuming that the inverse of $\mathscr{M}$ exists, we can premultiply by it and obtain

$$\ddot{\mathscr{Q}} + (\mathscr{M}^{-1}\mathscr{K})\mathscr{Q} = 0. \tag{1.20}$$

From this we can see that if the following operator equation holds,

$$(\mathscr{M}^{-1}\mathscr{K})\mathscr{Q} = \mathscr{N}\mathscr{Q} = \Omega_0^2\mathscr{Q}, \tag{1.21}$$

where Ω_0 is a real scalar quantity and Ω_0^2 necessarily a positive constant, the resulting vector equation will resemble that for a simple harmonic oscillator:

$$\ddot{\mathscr{Q}} + \Omega_0^2\mathscr{Q} = 0. \tag{1.22}$$

Of course, in general the vector $\mathscr{Q}$ would have $3n - k$ components, but if it happened to have only one, q_1, and this was identified with the x-direction, (1.22) would in fact reduce to (2.12) of Chapter 3,

$$\ddot{x} + \omega_0^2 x = 0, \qquad \omega_0^2 = K_x/m = \Omega_0^2,$$

whose solution we have studied in detail. Evidently the vectors satisfying (1.21), and thus (1.22), will constitute a smaller subset of the set satisfying (1.19) and (1.20).

The implication is that the motion of the entire system of masses can be described by the oscillations, in both length and direction, of the vector $\mathscr{Q}$ in an imaginary space of $3n - k$ dimensions. Solving the set of simultaneous equations (1.19), or (1.13), must amount to determining the variation of each of the components of this vector as a function of time. However, when (1.21) holds only the length of $\mathscr{Q}$ will change, and these oscillations will be harmonic with the angular frequency Ω_0. This follows immediately from observing that (1.22) can also be written in the form

$$\left(\frac{d^2}{dt^2}\right)\mathscr{Q} = -\Omega_0^2\mathscr{Q}, \tag{1.23}$$

but more generally from the fact that $(\mathscr{M}^{-1}\mathscr{K}) = \mathscr{N}$ is a linear vector operator. It is known[2] that for each such operator certain vectors exist which will preserve their orientation when operated on, even though the operation may change their length.

Vectors that satisfy an operator equation of the form (1.21),

$$\mathcal{O}\mathbf{v} = \lambda\mathbf{v} \tag{1.24}$$

[2] Friedman, B., *Principles and Techniques of Applied Mathematics*, pp. 57–130, Wiley, New York, 1957.

where $\mathcal{O}$ indicates an appropriate operator and λ some scalar quantity, are called the characteristic vectors, or eigenvectors, of that operator; and the scalar quantity λ multiplying the vector is known as its eigenvalue. In the present case, of course, the eigenvalue of any eigenvector $\mathcal{Q}$ is the square of the angular frequency characteristic of that vector's harmonic oscillations in length. Because the directions of eigenvectors are fixed, new coordinates n_j in their directions, called normal coordinates, can always be introduced as linear combinations of the $3n - k$ generalized coordinates q_j. In such coordinates the matrix of $\mathcal{O}$ will be diagonal.[3]

This point needs special emphasis. Carrying out the operations suggested in the transition from (1.19) to (1.20) for the special case of $l, m = 1$, 2 establishes the proper indicial form of the latter:

$$\mathcal{M}^{-1}[\mathcal{M}\ddot{\mathcal{Q}} + \mathcal{K}\mathcal{Q}] = \begin{bmatrix} \ddot{q}_1 \\ \ddot{q}_2 \end{bmatrix} + \begin{vmatrix} \mu_{11} & \mu_{12} \\ \mu_{21} & \mu_{22} \end{vmatrix}^{-1} \begin{bmatrix} \mu_{22} & -\mu_{12} \\ -\mu_{21} & \mu_{11} \end{bmatrix} \begin{bmatrix} \kappa_{11} & \kappa_{12} \\ \kappa_{21} & \kappa_{22} \end{bmatrix} \begin{bmatrix} q_1 \\ q_2 \end{bmatrix}$$

$$= \begin{bmatrix} \ddot{q}_1 \\ \ddot{q}_2 \end{bmatrix} + \frac{1}{(\mu_{11}\mu_{22} - \mu_{21}\mu_{22})}$$

$$\times \begin{bmatrix} (\mu_{22}\kappa_{11} - \mu_{12}\kappa_{21}) & (\mu_{22}\kappa_{12} - \mu_{12}\kappa_{22}) \\ (-\mu_{21}\kappa_{11} + \mu_{11}\kappa_{21}) & (-\mu_{21}\kappa_{12} + \mu_{11}\kappa_{22}) \end{bmatrix} \begin{bmatrix} q_1 \\ q_2 \end{bmatrix}$$

$$= \begin{bmatrix} \ddot{q}_1 \\ \ddot{q}_2 \end{bmatrix} + \begin{bmatrix} \nu_{11} & \nu_{12} \\ \nu_{21} & \nu_{22} \end{bmatrix} \begin{bmatrix} q_1 \\ q_2 \end{bmatrix} = 0, \tag{1.25}$$

$$\ddot{q}_m + \nu_{mp}q_p = \ddot{\mathcal{Q}} + \mathcal{N}\mathcal{Q} = 0. \tag{1.26}$$

In general, the matrix $[\nu_{mp}] = \mathcal{N}$ will not be diagonal, and the equation in each of the components of q_m will contain terms involving other of its components and the off-diagonal terms of $[\nu_{mp}]$:

$$\ddot{q}_1 + \nu_{11}q_1 + \nu_{12}q_2 = 0 \tag{1.27}$$

$$\ddot{q}_2 + \nu_{21}q_1 + \nu_{22}q_2 = 0 \tag{1.28}$$

In other words, the equations will be strongly coupled, reflecting the multiple physical interconnections of the masses. But if the eigenvectors of the operator $\mathcal{N}$ can be determined, then normal coordinates in these directions,

$$n_j = n_j(q_1, q_2, \ldots), \tag{1.29}$$

[3] Corben, H. C., and P. Stehle, *Classical Mechanics*, 2nd edition, pp. 345–363, Wiley, New York, 1960.

can be built up from linear combinations of the generalized coordinates in such a way that the set of scalar equations like (1.25) may be replaced by the scalar set:

$$
\begin{bmatrix} \ddot{n}_1 \\ \ddot{n}_2 \\ \cdot \\ \cdot \\ \cdot \end{bmatrix} + \begin{bmatrix} \omega_{0_1}^{\;2} & 0 & \cdots \\ 0 & \omega_{0_2}^{\;2} & \\ \cdot & & \cdot \\ \cdot & & \cdot \\ \cdot & & & \cdot \end{bmatrix} \begin{bmatrix} n_1 \\ n_2 \\ \cdot \\ \cdot \\ \cdot \end{bmatrix} = 0 \qquad (1.30)
$$

Equations (1.30) are entirely uncoupled and, thus, describe an independent collection of simple harmonic motions, as indicated by the selection of $\omega_{0_j}^{\;2}$ for the diagonal elements of $[\nu_{mp}]$. Clearly, no transfer of energy will occur between such motions.

It follows from the preceding discussion that the problem of determining the eigenvectors of a linear operator is closely related to the problem of describing the small vibrations of a strongly coupled system, and a standard procedure for accomplishing the former exists. It is based on the fact that such vectors must satisfy an equation of the form (1.24), or specifically (1.21),

$$
\mathcal{N}\mathcal{Q} = \Omega_0^2 \mathcal{Q}.
$$

In indicial notation this becomes

$$
\nu_{mp} q_p = \omega_0^2 q_m; \qquad (1.31)
$$

but expanding,

$$
\nu_{11} q_1 + \nu_{12} q_2 + \nu_{13} q_3 + \cdots = \omega_0^2 q_1
$$
$$
\nu_{21} q_1 + \nu_{22} q_2 + \nu_{23} q_3 + \cdots = \omega_0^2 q_2 \qquad (1.32)
$$
$$
\cdots \cdots \cdots \cdots \cdots \cdots \cdots \cdots \cdots \cdots ,
$$

regrouping,

$$
(\nu_{11} - \omega_0^2) q_1 + \nu_{12} q_2 + \nu_{13} q_3 + \cdots = 0
$$
$$
\nu_{21} q_1 + (\nu_{22} - \omega_0^2) q_2 + \nu_{23} q_3 + \cdots = 0 \qquad (1.33)
$$
$$
\cdots \cdots \cdots \cdots \cdots \cdots \cdots \cdots \cdots \cdots ,
$$

and inserting appropriate components of Kronecker's delta,

$$
(\nu_{11} - \omega_0^2\,\delta_{11}) q_1 + (\nu_{12} - \omega_0^2\,\delta_{12}) q_2 + (\nu_{13} - \omega_0^2\,\delta_{13}) q_3 + \cdots = 0
$$
$$
(\nu_{21} - \omega_0^2\,\delta_{21}) q_1 + (\nu_{22} - \omega_0^2\,\delta_{22}) q_2 + (\nu_{23} - \omega_0^2\,\delta_{23}) q_3 + \cdots = 0
$$
$$
\cdots \cdots \cdots \cdots \cdots \cdots \cdots \cdots \cdots \cdots \cdots \cdots \cdots \cdots ,
$$

$$
(1.34)
$$

we see that (1.31) can also be written as

$$(\nu_{mp} - \omega_0^2\,\delta_{mp})q_p = 0 \qquad \{m, p = 1, 2, \ldots, 3n - k. \qquad (1.35)$$

Such a set of linear homogeneous algebraic equations will possess a nontrivial solution only if the determinant of the coefficients vanishes [(3.61) of Chapter 1]; therefore, we conclude that

$$|\nu_{mp} - \omega_0^2\,\delta_{mp}| = 0. \qquad (1.36)$$

Expanding (1.36), with the $3n - k$ degrees of freedom indicated by f, we obtain

$$\begin{vmatrix} (\nu_{11} - \omega_0^2) & \nu_{12} & \nu_{13} & \cdots & \nu_{1f} \\ \nu_{21} & (\nu_{22} - \omega_0^2) & \nu_{23} & \cdots & \nu_{2f} \\ \cdot & & & & \cdot \\ \cdot & & & & \cdot \\ \cdot & & & & \cdot \\ \nu_{f1} & \cdots\cdots\cdots\cdots\cdots\cdots\cdots & & & (\nu_{ff} - \omega_0^2) \end{vmatrix} = 0, \qquad (1.37)$$

which is an algebraic equation of degree f in ω_0^2. The roots of this so-called secular equation $(\omega_{0_1}^2, \omega_{0_2}^2, \ldots, \omega_{0_f}^2)$ will be the eigenvalues of all the eigenvectors that satisfy (1.31) or (1.21). It is shown in the last reference that all the eigenvalues will be real, though they may be degenerate [since (1.37) may have repeated roots], and also that the eigenvectors associated with nondegenerate eigenvalues will be orthogonal. This last property is the one which makes it possible to assert that the matrix of the operator $\mathcal{N} = [\nu_{mp}]$ will become diagonal in normal coordinates.

With the eigenvalues known, the eigenvectors can be determined by a procedure we shall discuss later. For the present, however, we will work only with the "eigenfrequencies" and their associated amplitude relations because these will suffice to characterize the behavior of one-dimensional multidegree of freedom systems, such as the two-degree of freedom system shown in Fig. 4.1. It is assumed that the displacements of the masses will

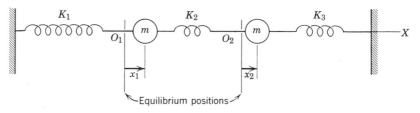

Fig. 4.1

remain small and conservative. No separate constraint equations can be written; so we see that two independent generalized coordinates will suffice to describe the motion $(1 \cdot n - k = 1 \cdot 2 - 0 = 2)$; and it is evident that the displacement functions x_1 and x_2 will serve for the purpose.

Replacing q by x, (1.26) yields:

$$\ddot{x}_1 + \nu_{11}x_1 + \nu_{12}x_2 = 0 \qquad (1.38)$$

$$\ddot{x}_2 + \nu_{21}x_1 + \nu_{22}x_2 = 0 \qquad (1.39)$$

The problem now is to interpret ν_{11}, ν_{12}, ν_{21}, and ν_{22} in terms of the spring constants K_1, K_2 and the mass m. In the present case this can easily be done by constructing the equations of motion on physical grounds and comparing the result with (1.38) and (1.39); but in more complex cases, relating the coupling constants to the system parameters is often the most difficult part of the problem.

Assuming both masses to be displaced in the positive direction to the positions shown in Fig. 4.1, the left-hand spring will elongate an amount x_1, the right-hand spring will compress an amount x_2, and, if $x_1 > x_2$, the center spring will compress an amount $(x_1 - x_2)$. Hence, remembering that the force exerted by each spring will be proportional to its change in length, we may immediately write Newton's equation for the mass on the left,

$$m\ddot{x}_1 = -K_1 x_1 - K_2(x_1 - x_2), \qquad (1.40)$$

then for the mass on the right,

$$m\ddot{x}_2 = K_2(x_1 - x_2) - K_1 x_2. \qquad (1.41)$$

Putting these in the same form as (1.38) and (1.39),

$$\ddot{x}_1 + \frac{(K_1 + K_2)}{m} x_1 - \frac{K_2}{m} x_2 = 0 \qquad (1.42)$$

$$\ddot{x}_2 - \frac{K_2}{m} x_1 + \frac{(K_1 + K_2)}{m} x_2 = 0, \qquad (1.43)$$

we can compare the two sets of equations and see that

$$\nu_{11} = \frac{K_1 + K_2}{m} = \nu_{22} \qquad (1.44)$$

$$\nu_{12} = -\frac{K_2}{m} = \nu_{21}. \qquad (1.45)$$

It follows that (1.37) will take the specific form:

$$\begin{vmatrix} \left(\dfrac{K_1 + K_2}{m} - \omega_0{}^2\right) & -\dfrac{K_2}{m} \\[2ex] -\dfrac{K_2}{m} & \left(\dfrac{K_1 + K_2}{m} - \omega_0{}^2\right) \end{vmatrix} = 0 \qquad (1.46)$$

or

$$\left(\frac{K_1 + K_2}{m}\right)^2 - \frac{2(K_1 + K_2)}{m}\,\omega_0{}^2 + \omega_0{}^4\left(\frac{K_2}{m}\right)^2 = 0,$$

$$\omega_0{}^4 - \frac{2(K_1 + K_2)}{m}\,\omega_0{}^2 + \frac{K_1{}^2 + 2K_1 K_2}{m^2} = 0. \qquad (1.47)$$

Therefore,

$$\omega_0{}^2 = \frac{2(K_1 + K_2)}{2m} \pm \frac{1}{2}\left[4\left(\frac{K_1 + K_2}{m}\right)^2 - 4\left(\frac{K_1{}^2 + 2K_1 K_2}{m^2}\right)\right]^{\frac{1}{2}}$$

$$= \frac{K_1}{m} + \frac{K_2}{m} \pm \frac{K_2}{m}, \qquad (1.48)$$

giving

$$\omega_{0_1}{}^2 = \frac{K_1}{m} + \frac{2K_2}{m}, \qquad \omega_{0_1} = \pm\left(\frac{K_1 + 2K_2}{m}\right)^{\frac{1}{2}} \qquad (1.49)$$

and

$$\omega_{0_2}{}^2 = \frac{K_1}{m}, \qquad \omega_{0_2} = \pm\left(\frac{K_1}{m}\right)^{\frac{1}{2}}. \qquad (1.50)$$

These are the eigenvalues, arranged in order of decreasing magnitude, with their associated eigenfrequencies. Let us see what amplitude relationships they imply. Because we know that the motion will be harmonic, we know that a solution of (1.42) and (1.43) of the form,

$$x_1 = A_1 e^{i\omega_{0_1}t} \qquad (1.51)$$

$$x_2 = A_2 e^{i\omega_{0_1}t}, \qquad (1.52)$$

must exist. Thus, we can simply substitute these back into either of the equations to determine one of the necessary relations between amplitudes. For example, substituting in (1.42), we obtain

$$-A_1\left(\frac{K_1 + 2K_2}{m}\right) + A_1\left(\frac{K_1 + K_2}{m}\right) - A_2\frac{K_2}{m} = 0,$$

$$A_1 = -A_2. \qquad (1.53)$$

The same result follows from substituting (1.51) and (1.52) in (1.43); and in a similar manner

$$x_1 = B_1 e^{i\omega_{0_2}t} \tag{1.54}$$

$$x_2 = B_2 e^{i\omega_{0_2}t} \tag{1.55}$$

leads to

$$B_1 = B_2. \tag{1.56}$$

Furthermore, the same relations between amplitudes hold if the solutions involving the negative eigenfrequencies are used.

We conclude that there are two basic modes of vibration for this system: one in which the masses move in opposite directions with equal amplitudes at all times and the angular frequency $|\omega_{0_1}|$ of (1.49), and one in which the masses move in the same direction with equal amplitudes and the frequency $|\omega_{0_2}|$ of (1.50). These are called the normal modes. It will be noted that in both cases the absolute ratio of the amplitudes in the different degrees of freedom remains constant; this is typical of "eigenvibrations." It is also typical that each degree of freedom implies one absolute eigenfrequency; therefore, the number of normal modes will become very large as the number of degrees of freedom multiply. But it is the very fact that such orderly modes continue to exist for all periodic motions that underlies our ability to represent the wave motions of the following section by linear combinations of harmonic functions.

The general solution of the equations of motion (1.42) and (1.43) can be formed by superimposing the solutions reflected by (1.49) and (1.50), (1.53) and (1.56):

$$x_1 = A_1 e^{i\omega_{0_1}t} + A_1' e^{-i\omega_{0_1}t} + B_1 e^{i\omega_{0_2}t} + B_1' e^{-i\omega_{0_2}t} \tag{1.57}$$

$$x_2 = -A_1 e^{i\omega_{0_1}t} - A_1' e^{-i\omega_{0_1}t} + B_1 e^{i\omega_{0_2}t} + B_1' e^{-i\omega_{0_2}t} \tag{1.58}$$

Hence, if $A_1 = A_1' = 0$ or $B_1 = B_1' = 0$ the system will vibrate in one of its normal modes, whereas if neither case is true it will vibrate in some combination of these. For example, with $A_1' = B_1' = 0$ and

$$A_1 = B_1 = \frac{A}{2}, \tag{1.59}$$

corresponding to initial conditions of $x_2(0) = 0$ and $x_1(0) = A$, by taking real parts we obtain

$$x_1 = \frac{A}{2}(\cos \omega_{0_1}t + \cos \omega_{0_2}t) \tag{1.60}$$

and

$$x_2 = \frac{A}{2}(\cos \omega_{0_2}t - \cos \omega_{0_1}t), \tag{1.61}$$

or by trigonometric identity:

$$x_1 = \left\{ A \cos\left[\frac{(\omega_{0_1} - \omega_{0_2})t}{2}\right] \right\} \cos\left[\frac{(\omega_{0_1} + \omega_{0_2})t}{2}\right] \tag{1.62}$$

$$x_2 = \left\{ A \sin\left[\frac{(\omega_{0_1} - \omega_{0_2})t}{2}\right] \right\} \sin\left[\frac{(\omega_{0_1} + \omega_{0_2})t}{2}\right] \tag{1.63}$$

This is the phenomenon known as "beats" (see Fig. 4.2). The dependence of x_1 and x_2 on t takes the form of harmonic waves whose amplitudes are also harmonically modulated and 90° out of phase.

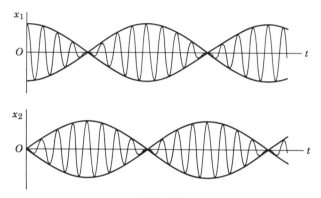

Fig. 4.2

Because the eigenvectors will always be directed along the X-axis in this case, we can try to construct the normal coordinates as the simplest linear combinations of x_1 and x_2, that is, as:

$$n_1 = x_1 - x_2 = 2A_1 e^{i\omega_{0_1}t} + 2A_1' e^{-i\omega_{0_1}t}$$

$$= C_1 e^{i\left(\frac{K_1 + 2K_2}{m}\right)^{1/2}t} + C_1' e^{-i\left(\frac{K_1 + 2K_2}{m}\right)^{1/2}t} \tag{1.64}$$

$$n_2 = x_1 + x_2 = 2B_1 e^{i\omega_{0_2}t} + 2B_1' e^{-i\omega_{0_2}t}$$

$$= D_1 e^{i\left(\frac{K_1}{m}\right)^{1/2}t} + D_1' e^{-i\left(\frac{K_1}{m}\right)^{1/2}t} \tag{1.65}$$

These are evidently satisfactory, since each contains only one of the eigenfrequencies and will therefore satisfy the equations of motion in the required form (1.30):

$$\ddot{n}_1 + \omega_{0_1}^2 n_1 = 0 \tag{1.66}$$

$$\ddot{n}_2 + \omega_{0_2}^2 n_2 = 0 \tag{1.67}$$

Equations (1.66) and (1.67) clearly are uncoupled, but it should now be plain that finding the normal coordinates that accomplish this amounts to solving the original problem. Usually, however, we do not actually have to find them; it is the very fact that they exist which is most useful. Eigenfrequencies are often called normal frequencies, because both the normal modes of vibration and the normal coordinates are characterized by them.

Also, it is instructive to observe that the normal coordinates depend on particular combinations of the physical constants of the system. In effect, this means that the mathematical problem could be much simplified in the beginning if only we knew what combined constants to use. Similar situations often arise in mathematical mechanics, and one standard procedure is to introduce so-called "constitutive equations," modeled on experimental results, to represent the large-scale effects of such constants. This is the basic method of the mechanics of "continua," as we shall come to understand, whereas the mechanics of "discontinua" is concerned with discovering the constants themselves.

The preceding example could be generalized, if we so wished, by assigning different values to the two masses and a different constant to each of the three springs,[4] and various other illustrations of strongly coupled conservative systems could be given. On about the same level of difficulty, the double-pendulum [Problems 2.3(9) and (12) of Chapter 2] could be analyzed for its eigenfrequencies; and, as a more advanced case, the eigenvibrations of a diatomic, dumbell-shaped molecule could be determined.[5,6] Since it demonstrates most of the important aspects of such problems, we shall limit ourselves to the one example presented; but for the sake of completeness we should recognize that, even in this case, the same results could have been obtained in a slightly different way.

We could have started with the equations of motion in the form (1.13),

$$\mu_{lm}\ddot{x}_m + \kappa_{lm}x_m = 0 \qquad \{m, l = 1, 2 \tag{1.68}$$

$$\mu_{l1}\ddot{x}_1 + \mu_{l2}\ddot{x}_2 + \kappa_{l1}x_1 + \kappa_{l2}x_2 = 0 \qquad \{l = 1, 2$$

$$\mu_{11}\ddot{x}_1 + \mu_{12}\ddot{x}_2 + \kappa_{11}x_1 + \kappa_{12}x_2 = 0 \tag{1.69}$$

$$\mu_{21}\ddot{x}_1 + \mu_{22}\ddot{x}_2 + \kappa_{21}x_1 + \kappa_{22}x_2 = 0, \tag{1.70}$$

instead of the form (1.26). Then, by arbitrarily trying the harmonic solutions

$$x_1 = A_1 e^{i\omega_0 t} \tag{1.71}$$

$$x_2 = A_2 e^{i\omega_0 t} \tag{1.72}$$

[4] Symon, K. R., *Mechanics*, 2nd edition, pp. 188–198, Addison-Wesley, Reading, Mass., 1960.

[5] Haar, D. ter, *Elements of Hamiltonian Mechanics*, 2nd edition, pp. 57–69, North-Holland, Amsterdam, 1964.

[6] Becker, R. A., *Introduction to Theoretical Mechanics*, pp. 348–361, McGraw-Hill, New York, 1954.

in these equations of motion, we would have obtained the conditions:

$$(\kappa_{11} - \mu_{11}\omega_0^2)A_1 + (\kappa_{12} - \mu_{12}\omega_0^2)A_2 = 0 \tag{1.73}$$

$$(\kappa_{21} - \mu_{21}\omega_0^2)A_1 + (\kappa_{22} - \mu_{22}\omega_0^2)A_2 = 0 \tag{1.74}$$

Thus, to find nonzero solutions for A_1 and A_2 we would have had to place the determinant of the coefficients equal to zero:

$$\begin{vmatrix} (\kappa_{11} - \mu_{11}\omega_0^2) & (\kappa_{12} - \mu_{12}\omega_0^2) \\ (\kappa_{21} - \mu_{21}\omega_0^2) & (\kappa_{22} - \mu_{22}\omega_0^2) \end{vmatrix} = 0 \tag{1.75}$$

This yields a quadratic equation in ω_0^2 as before.

Specifically, if by comparing (1.40) and (1.41) with (1.69) and (1.70) we conclude that for Fig. 4.1

$$\mu_{12} = 0 = \mu_{21} \tag{1.76}$$

$$\mu_{11} = m = \mu_{22} \tag{1.77}$$

$$\kappa_{11} = K_1 + K_2 = \kappa_{22} \tag{1.78}$$

$$\kappa_{12} = -K_2 = \kappa_{21}, \tag{1.79}$$

(1.75) becomes

$$\begin{vmatrix} (K_1 + K_2 - m\omega_0^2) & -K_2 \\ -K_2 & (K_1 + K_2 - m\omega_0^2) \end{vmatrix} = 0, \tag{1.80}$$

which is the same as (1.46) and therefore gives the same two eigenfrequencies, $|\omega_{0_1}|$ and $|\omega_{0_2}|$ of (1.49) and (1.50). Substituting the first of these, together with the values of the constants established in (1.76) to (1.79) back into (1.73) and (1.74) then results in the requirement that the amplitudes be equal and of opposite sign, while substitution of the second leads to the requirement that they be equal and of the same sign. Thus the results of both methods are formally identical; but whereas the former more clearly demonstrates the nature and meaning of eigenfrequencies and is convenient when each equation of motion contains only one acceleration term, the latter should be used whenever each equation contains more than one acceleration term (as in the case of the double-pendulum).

As regards nonconservative systems, it will be recalled that our earlier treatment of the isolated one-dimensional oscillator featured an analysis of a general equation of motion having the form (2.81) of Chapter 3,

$$m\ddot{x} + C\dot{x} + Kx = f(t), \tag{1.81}$$

of which (2.12) of that chapter, utilized above in conjunction with (1.22), is a special case. We infer that if an uncoupled system of $1, 2, \ldots, n$ oscillators of the type shown in Fig. 3.13 (or Fig. 3.14) were present, their equations of motion would obviously be:

$$m_1 \ddot{x}_1 + C_1 \dot{x}_1 + K_1 x_1 = f_1(t)$$
$$m_2 \ddot{x}_2 + C_2 \dot{x}_2 + K_2 x_2 = f_2(t)$$

$$\cdot \qquad\qquad \cdot$$
$$\cdot \qquad\qquad \cdot \qquad\qquad (1.82)$$
$$\cdot \qquad\qquad \cdot$$

$$m_n \ddot{x}_n + C_n \dot{x}_n + K_n x_n = f_n(t)$$

On the left-hand side, each consists of terms proportional to the acceleration, velocity, and displacement of the mass being considered.

In the most general case of coupling for such a system, where each subsystem (like Fig. 3.14) is connected to the next and the last to ground, the left-hand side of the equation of motion for any mass, m_i, will have to contain terms proportional to its own acceleration, velocity, and displacement as well as to that of every other mass ($m_{i+1}, m_{i+2}, \ldots, m_n$ and m_{i-1}, $m_{i-2}, \ldots, m_1$), because each will ultimately exert these three types of forces on m_i as it moves.

For example, if only three masses were present, so that $m_{i-1} = m_1$, $m_i = m_2$, and $m_{i+1} = m_3 = m_n$, the equations of motion for the system would be:

$$m_{11} \ddot{x}_1 + C_{11} \dot{x}_1 + K_{11} x_1 + m_{12} \ddot{x}_2 + C_{12} \dot{x}_2 + K_{12} x_2$$
$$+ m_{13} \ddot{x}_3 + C_{13} \dot{x}_3 + K_{13} x_3 = f_1(t)$$
$$m_{22} \ddot{x}_2 + C_{22} \dot{x}_2 + K_{22} x_2 + m_{21} \ddot{x}_1 + C_{21} \dot{x}_1 + K_{21} x_1$$
$$+ m_{23} \ddot{x}_3 + C_{23} \dot{x}_3 + K_{23} x_3 = f_2(t) \quad (1.83)$$
$$m_{33} \ddot{x}_3 + C_{33} \dot{x}_3 + K_{33} x_3 + m_{31} \ddot{x}_1 + C_{31} \dot{x}_1 + K_{31} x_1$$
$$+ m_{32} \ddot{x}_2 + C_{32} \dot{x}_2 + K_{32} x_2 = f_3(t)$$

where the m's, C's, and K's represent the required proportionality constants, with the first index indicating the mass acted upon and the second the mass acting on it. It is easy to see that these may be written more concisely as:

$$m_{ij} \ddot{x}_j + C_{ij} \dot{x}_j + K_{ij} x_j = f_i(t) \qquad \{i, j = 1, 2, 3 \qquad (1.84)$$

Equation (1.84) can readily be extended to cover the case of n masses and, with

$$x_j = q_m \qquad\qquad (1.85)$$
$$m_{ij} = \mu_{lm} \qquad\qquad (1.86)$$
$$K_{ij} = \kappa_{lm} \qquad\qquad (1.87)$$
$$C_{ij} = 0 = f_i(t), \qquad\qquad (1.88)$$

transformed to the one-dimensional version of the case discussed above, equation (1.13).

Of course, (1.84) is considerably more difficult to deal with than (1.13), but once again matrix methods may be applied, and with the aid of high-speed electronic computers satisfactory solutions can often be achieved. It can be shown[7] that, as long as $C_{ij} = 0$, normal coordinates may be found and the resulting set of equations,

$$m_{ij}\ddot{x}_j + K_{ij}x_j = f_i(t) \qquad \{i, j = 1, 2, \ldots, n, \tag{1.89}$$

uncoupled, as in (1.30), by writing

$$\ddot{n}_j + \omega^2_{0_{(j)}} n_j = Q_j(t) \qquad \{j = 1, 2, \ldots, n, \tag{1.90}$$

where the $Q_j(t)$ are generalized forces depending on the $f_i(t)$ as the original coordinates depend on the normal coordinates. Thus methods similar to those discussed above for the case of $f_i(t) = 0$ can still be used. However, when $C_{ij} \neq 0$, even if $f_i(t) = 0$, the three matrices $[m_{ij}]$, $[C_{ij}]$, and $[K_{ij}]$ cannot in general be diagonalized simultaneously and normal coordinates cannot be found. Only the generalized form of (1.36) is available then, and a satisfactory solution is more difficult to attain.

The situation can best be clarified by an application of Laplace transform theory.[8] For our purposes it will be sufficient to remark that the Laplace transform of a single-valued function $g(t)$ is defined for $t \geq 0$ as

$$\mathscr{L}g(t) = G(s) = \int_0^\infty g(t)e^{-st}\, dt, \tag{1.91}$$

where s is a complex variable with its real part Re (s) greater than some positive number b, such that the integral converges absolutely and the inverse transform yields $g(t)$ when the parameter c appearing in it is greater than b:

$$\mathscr{L}^{-1}\mathscr{L}g(t) = g(t) = \mathscr{L}^{-1}G(s) = \frac{1}{2\pi i}\int_{c-i\infty}^{c+i\infty} G(s)e^{st}\, ds \tag{1.92}$$

Using (1.91) it is easy to show that, with $g(0)$ indicating the value of $g(t)$ at $t = 0$, or its limiting value as t positive approaches zero,

$$\mathscr{L}\left[\frac{d}{dt}g(t)\right] = sG(s) - g(0), \tag{1.93}$$

$$\mathscr{L}\left[\frac{d^2}{dt^2}g(t)\right] = s^2G(s) - sg(0) - \frac{d}{dt}g(0), \tag{1.94}$$

and so on.

[7] Symon, K. R., *Mechanics*, 2nd edition, pp. 481–497; Addison-Wesley, Reading, Mass., 1960.

[8] Hochstadt, H., *Differential Equations*, pp. 58–81, Holt, Rinehart and Winston, New York, 1964.

Thus, with $x_j(t)$ in the role of $g(t)$,

$$\mathcal{L}x_j(t) = X_j(s), \qquad \mathcal{L}\dot{x}_j(t) = sX_j(s) - x_j(0),$$
$$\mathcal{L}\ddot{x}_j(t) = s^2 X_j(s) - sx_j(0) - \dot{x}_j(0), \tag{1.95}$$

whereas with $f_i(t)$ as $g(t)$,

$$\mathcal{L}f_i(t) = F_i(s). \tag{1.96}$$

It follows that (1.84) can be transformed to

$$m_{ij}[s^2 X_j(s) - sx_j(0) - \dot{x}_j(0)] + C_{ij}[sX_j(s) - x_j(0)] + K_{ij}X_j(s) = F_i(s) \tag{1.97}$$

or

$$[s^2 m_{ij} + sC_{ij} + K_{ij}]X_j(s) = F_i(s) + [sm_{ij} + C_{ij}]x_j(0) + m_{ij}\dot{x}_j(0). \tag{1.98}$$

Defining the square matrix

$$\mathcal{A} = s^2 m_{ij} + sC_{ij} + K_{ij} = [a_{ij}] \tag{1.99}$$

along with the column matrices

$$\mathcal{X} = [X_j(s)] \tag{1.100}$$

and

$$\mathcal{Y} = F_i(s) + [sm_{ij} + C_{ij}]x_j(0) + m_{ij}\dot{x}_j(0) = [y_i], \tag{1.101}$$

we see that this has the same form as (3.50) of Chapter 1,

$$\mathcal{A}\mathcal{X} = \mathcal{Y}.$$

Therefore, the solution of the system of equations (1.84) must be given by

$$\mathcal{X} = \mathcal{A}^{-1}\mathcal{Y}, \tag{1.102}$$

while according to (1.100) and the first of equations (1.95), taking the inverse transform of this will yield the $x_j(t)$:

$$\mathcal{L}^{-1}\mathcal{A}^{-1}\mathcal{Y} = \mathcal{L}^{-1}\mathcal{X} = \mathcal{L}^{-1}X_j(s) = \mathcal{L}^{-1}\mathcal{L}x_j(t) = x_j(t). \tag{1.103}$$

But we know from (3.44) of Chapter 1 that

$$A^{-1} = \frac{[A_{ji}]}{|A|}; \tag{1.104}$$

so, it becomes apparent that a solution will actually exist only if $|\mathcal{A}| \neq 0$. When $\mathcal{A}$ is singular, we are left with the condition

$$|\mathcal{A}| = |s^2 m_{ij} + sC_{ij} + K_{ij}| = 0, \tag{1.105}$$

which represents the generalization of (1.36) mentioned above. Under such circumstances, it is probably preferable to recast (1.84) into first-order integrodifferential form, as in (2.99) and (2.105) of Chapter 3, and proceed by the highly developed methods of systems analysis.[9,10]

Problems 4.1

1. Two masses, m_1 and m_2, resting on a smooth surface are joined together by a spring of negligible mass with the constant K and relaxed length l. Assuming that the motion remains one-dimensional, calculate the following:

   a. The Lagrangian and the equations of motion for the system.
   b. The normal coordinates.

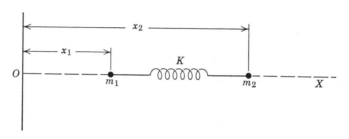

Fig. P4.1 (1)

Solution

   Because the motion must occur along a single line, we may select x_1 and x_2 as independent generalized coordinates, as shown in Fig. P4.1 (1), where O represents an arbitrary but fixed origin. The kinetic and potential energies of the system will then be

$$T = \tfrac{1}{2}[m_1\dot{x}_1{}^2 + m_2\dot{x}_2{}^2]$$

and

$$V = \tfrac{1}{2}K[(x_2 - x_1) - l]^2,$$

the order of the quantities $(x_2 - x_1)$ and l being determined so that a positive sign will be associated with tension in the spring. When we place

$$x_2 - l = X_2,$$

these become

$$T = \tfrac{1}{2}[m_1\dot{x}_1{}^2 + m_2\dot{X}_2{}^2]$$

and

$$V = \tfrac{1}{2}K[X_2 - x_1]^2.$$

Hence,

$$L = T - V = \tfrac{1}{2}[m_1\dot{x}_1{}^2 + m_2\dot{X}_2{}^2] - \tfrac{1}{2}K[X_2{}^2 - 2X_2x_1 + x_1{}^2];$$

[9] Pipes, L. A., *Applied Mathematics for Engineers and Physicists*, pp. 158–162, McGraw-Hill, New York, 1946.
[10] Koenig, H. E., and W. A. Blackwell, *Electrochemical System Theory*, pp. 109–188, McGraw-Hill, New York, 1961.

and Lagrange's equations,

$$\frac{d}{dt}\frac{\partial L}{\partial \dot{x}_1} - \frac{\partial L}{\partial x_1} = 0$$

$$\frac{d}{dt}\frac{\partial L}{\partial \dot{X}_2} - \frac{\partial L}{\partial X_2} = 0,$$

yield

$$m_1\ddot{x}_1 + Kx_1 - KX_2 = 0$$

$$m_2\ddot{X}_2 + KX_2 - Kx_1 = 0$$

or

$$\ddot{x}_1 + \frac{K}{m_1}x_1 - \frac{K}{m_1}X_2 = 0$$

$$\ddot{X}_2 - \frac{K}{m_2}x_1 + \frac{K}{m_2}X_2 = 0.$$

Therefore,

$$v_{11} = \frac{K}{m_1}, \qquad v_{12} = -\frac{K}{m_1},$$

$$v_{21} = -\frac{K}{m_2}, \qquad v_{22} = \frac{K}{m_2},$$

and the secular equation becomes:

$$\begin{vmatrix} \dfrac{K}{m_1} - \omega_0{}^2 & -\dfrac{K}{m_1} \\[2ex] -\dfrac{K}{m_2} & \dfrac{K}{m_2} - \omega_0{}^2 \end{vmatrix} = 0$$

$$\left[\frac{K}{m_1} - \omega_0{}^2\right]\left[\frac{K}{m_2} - \omega_0{}^2\right] - \frac{K^2}{m_1m_2} = 0$$

$$\frac{K^2}{m_1m_2} - \frac{K}{m_1}\omega_0{}^2 - \frac{K}{m_2}\omega_0{}^2 + \omega_0{}^4 - \frac{K^2}{m_1m_2} = 0$$

$$\omega_0{}^2\left[\omega_0{}^2 - \frac{K}{m_1} - \frac{K}{m_2}\right] = 0$$

Its roots must be

$$\omega_{0_1}{}^2 = \frac{K}{m_1} + \frac{K}{m_2} = \frac{K(m_1 + m_2)}{m_1m_2}$$

and

$$\omega_{0_2}{}^2 = 0.$$

Solutions for the equations of motion will exist such that

$$x_1 = A_1e^{i\omega_{01}t} + A_1{}'e^{-i\omega_{01}t}$$

$$X_2 = A_2e^{i\omega_{01}t} + A_2{}'e^{-i\omega_{01}t}$$

and, because $\omega_{0_2}^{2} = 0$ indicates a repeated root of the characteristic equation for the normal coordinate form of one of the equations of motion,

$$x_1 = B_1 + B_1't$$

$$X_2 = B_2 + B_2't.$$

Substituting the latter with $B_1' = B_2' = 0$ into the first equation of motion, we obtain

$$B_1 = B_2,$$

whereas with $B_1 = B_2 = 0$ the result is

$$B_1' = B_2'.$$

In the same way, substitution of the former with $A_1' = A_2' = 0$ gives

$$-A_1\omega_{0_1}^{2}e^{i\omega_{0_1}t} + \frac{K}{m_1} A_1 e^{i\omega_{0_1}t} - \frac{K}{m_1} A_2 e^{i\omega_{0_1}t} = 0,$$

$$-A_1\omega_{0_1}^{2} + \frac{K}{m_1} A_1 = \frac{K}{m_1} A_2 ;$$

and inserting the value of $\omega_{0_1}^{2}$, we obtain

$$A_1\left[-\frac{K(m_1 + m_2)}{m_1 m_2} + \frac{K}{m_1}\right] = \frac{K}{m_1} A_2$$

or

$$A_1 = -\frac{m_2}{m_1} A_2.$$

Similarly, substitution with $A_1 = A_2 = 0$ leads to

$$A_1' = -\frac{m_2}{m_1} A_2'.$$

Therefore, the general solutions of the equations of motion will be

$$x_1 = A_1 e^{i\omega_{0_1}t} + A_1' e^{-i\omega_{0_1}t} + B_1 + B_1't$$

$$X_2 = -\frac{m_1}{m_2} A_1 e^{i\omega_{0_1}t} - \frac{m_1}{m_2} A_1' e^{-i\omega_{0_1}t} + B_1 + B_1't;$$

and the normal coordinates can be written as

$$n_1 = x_1 - X_2 = A_1\left(\frac{m_2 + m_1}{m_2}\right)e^{i\omega_{0_1}t} + A_1'\left(\frac{m_2 + m_1}{m_2}\right)e^{-i\omega_{0_1}t}$$

$$n_2 = \frac{m_1}{m_2} x_1 + X_2 = \left(\frac{m_1 + m_2}{m_2}\right)B_1 + \left(\frac{m_1 + m_2}{m_2}\right)B_1't.$$

The latter represents a uniform translation of the center of mass with the spring relaxed, and the former an oscillation relative to the center of mass with the angular frequency $|\omega_{0_1}|$.

2. Consider the coupled simple-pendulums shown in Fig. P4.1 (2a). Assuming that the spring is without tension when the bars of the pendulums are vertical, and that both spring and bars are massless with the latter restricted to small angular motions in one plane only, find the eigenfrequencies of the system.

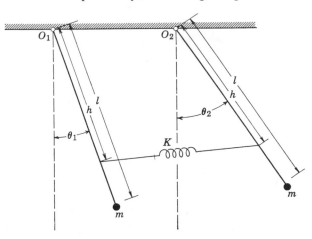

Fig. P4.1 (2a)

Solution

The net extension of the spring for any allowed configuration will be approximately $h(\theta_1 - \theta_2)$; thus, because the force exerted by the spring on either mass will be h/l times the force exerted at the point where the spring joins the bar, the total spring force can be written as

$$\pm \frac{h}{l} Kh(\theta_2 - \theta_1),$$

and this may be considered to act in a nearly horizontal direction. Assuming the force exerted by a bar alone on a mass to be roughly equal to mg, the horizontal component of this force will be

$$-mg \sin \theta_1 \simeq -mg \frac{l\theta_1}{l} \simeq -mg\theta_1$$

for one mass and $-mg\theta_2$ for the other. Thus, with the spring in tension, the equations of motion will take the form:

$$m(l\ddot{\theta}_1) = -mg\theta_1 + K \frac{h^2}{l} (\theta_2 - \theta_1)$$

$$m(l\ddot{\theta}_2) = -mg\theta_2 - K \frac{h^2}{l} (\theta_2 - \theta_1).$$

When we rewrite these as

$$\ddot{\theta}_1 + \left(\frac{g}{l} + \frac{Kh^2}{ml^2} \right) \theta_1 - \frac{Kh^2}{ml^2} \theta_2 = 0$$

$$\ddot{\theta}_2 + \left(\frac{g}{l} + \frac{Kh^2}{ml^2} \right) \theta_2 - \frac{Kh^2}{ml^2} \theta_1 = 0$$

and make the substitutions

$$\alpha = \frac{g}{l} + \frac{Kh^2}{ml^2}$$

$$\beta = \frac{Kh^2}{ml^2},$$

they become

$$\ddot{\theta}_1 + \alpha\theta_1 - \beta\theta_2 = 0$$
$$\ddot{\theta}_2 + \alpha\theta_2 - \beta\theta_1 = 0.$$

This time, let us try harmonic solutions of the form:

$$\theta_1 = A \sin(\omega_0 t + \delta)$$
$$\theta_2 = B \sin(\omega_0 t + \delta)$$

Substituting these into the equations of motion gives the simultaneous equations

$$(\alpha - \omega_0^2)A - \beta B = 0$$

and

$$-\beta A + (\alpha - \omega_0^2)B = 0;$$

so that, equating the determinant of the coefficients of A and B to zero, we obtain the secular equation

$$\omega_0^4 - 2\alpha\omega_0^2 + (\alpha^2 - \beta^2) = 0.$$

Its roots are

$$\omega_{0_1}^2 = \alpha + \beta = \frac{g}{l} + \frac{2Kh^2}{ml^2}$$

$$\omega_{0_2}^2 = \alpha - \beta = \frac{g}{l};$$

from these and the first of the simultaneous equations we see that the ratio of amplitudes is either

$$\frac{A_1}{B_1} = \frac{\beta}{\alpha - \omega_{0_1}^2} = \frac{\dfrac{Kh^2}{ml^2}}{\dfrac{g}{l} + \dfrac{Kh^2}{ml^2} - \dfrac{g}{l} - \dfrac{2Kh^2}{ml^2}} = -1$$

or

$$\frac{A_2}{B_2} = \frac{\beta}{\alpha - \omega_{0_2}^2} = \frac{\dfrac{Kh^2}{ml^2}}{\dfrac{g}{l} + \dfrac{Kh^2}{ml^2} - \dfrac{g}{l}} = 1.$$

Substitution in the second simultaneous equation will give the same results.

The two normal modes of vibration are illustrated in Fig. P4.1 (2b). In the first mode there will be a phase difference of 180° in the oscillations of the two pendulums, and the spring will exert a force leading to a higher frequency. In the second mode the vibrations of the pendulums will have the same amplitude and be in phase; there will be no force in the spring, so that the frequency of vibration will be the same as that for a simple pendulum.

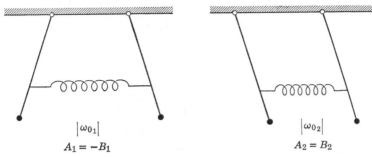

Fig. P4.1 (2b)

The general solution can now be written by superimposing these two vibrations, observing the required relationships between amplitudes:

$$\theta_1 = A_1 \sin (\omega_{0_1} t + \delta_1) + A_2 \sin (\omega_{0_2} t + \delta_2)$$
$$\theta_2 = -A_1 \sin (\omega_{0_1} t + \delta_1) + A_2 \sin (\omega_{0_2} t + \delta_2)$$

This leaves the constants A_1, A_2, δ_1, and δ_2 to be determined from initial conditions.

3. Determine the expressions for the eigenfrequencies of the system shown in Fig. P4.1 (3).

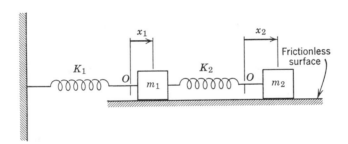

Fig. P4.1 (3)

Solution

Assuming that $x_2 > x_1$, the following forces will act on the masses:

Hence the equations of motion are

$$m_1 \ddot{x}_1 = -K_1 x_1 + K_2 (x_2 - x_1)$$

and

$$m_2 \ddot{x}_2 = -K_2 (x_2 - x_1);$$

or if we let

$$\frac{K_1 + K_2}{m_1} = a, \qquad \frac{K_2}{m_1} = b, \qquad \frac{K_2}{m_2} = c,$$

then they become

$$\ddot{x}_1 + ax_1 - bx_2 = 0$$
$$\ddot{x}_2 - cx_1 + cx_2 = 0.$$

Again assuming solutions of the form

$$x_1 = A \sin(\omega_0 t + \delta)$$
$$x_2 = B \sin(\omega_0 t + \delta)$$

and substituting in the equations of motion, we obtain the simultaneous equations

$$(a - \omega_0^2)A - bB = 0$$

and

$$- cA + (c - \omega_0^2)B = 0.$$

To obtain the eigenfrequencies we must find the roots of the secular equation:

$$(a - \omega_0^2)(c - \omega_0^2) - bc = 0,$$

$$\omega_0^4 - (a + c)\omega_0^2 + c(a - b) = 0;$$

$$\omega_0^2 = \frac{a + c}{2} \pm \sqrt{\left(\frac{a + c}{2}\right)^2 - c(a - b)}$$

$$= \frac{a + c}{2} \pm \sqrt{\left(\frac{a - c}{2}\right)^2 + bc}$$

$$= \frac{K_1 + K_2}{2m_1} + \frac{K_2}{2m_2} \pm \sqrt{\left(\frac{K_1 + K_2}{2m_1} + \frac{K_2}{2m_2}\right)^2 - \frac{K_2 K_1}{m_1 m_2}}.$$

This expression determines $|\omega_{0_1}|$ and $|\omega_{0_2}|$.

4. A forcing function $F(t)$ is acting on mass m_1 of the coupled oscillator shown in Fig. P4.1 (4).

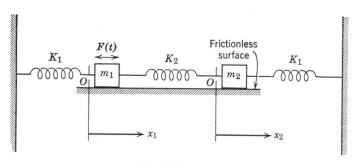

Fig. P4.1 (4)

a. Write the equations of motion with x_1 and x_2 as generalized coordinates.
b. Show that these equations give rise to uncoupled equations of motion when expressed in terms of the normal coordinates n_1 and n_2, where $n_1 = x_1 - x_2$ and $n_2 = x_1 + x_2$.

Solution

(a) Forming the equations of motion in the same way as before, we obtain:

$$m\ddot{x}_1 + (K_1 + K_2)x_1 - K_2 x_2 = F(t)$$
$$m\ddot{x}_2 - K_2 x_1 + (K_1 + K_2)x_2 = 0$$

(b) Because

$$n_1 = x_1 - x_2$$

and

$$n_2 = x_1 + x_2,$$

it follows that

$$x_1 = \frac{n_1 + n_2}{2}$$

and

$$x_2 = \frac{n_1 - n_2}{2}.$$

Substituting in the equations of motion, they become:

$$\frac{m}{2}[\ddot{n}_1 + \ddot{n}_2] + \left(\frac{K_1 + K_2}{2}\right)(n_1 + n_2) - \frac{K_2}{2}(n_1 - n_2) = F(t)$$

$$\frac{m}{2}[\ddot{n}_1 - \ddot{n}_2] + \left(\frac{K_1 + K_2}{2}\right)(n_1 - n_2) - \frac{K_2}{2}(n_1 + n_2) = 0$$

Adding these, we obtain one of the uncoupled equations of motion:

$$m\ddot{n}_1 + [K_1 + K_2]n_1 - K_2 n_1 = F(t),$$
$$m\ddot{n}_1 + K_1 n_1 = F(t);$$

subtracting them gives the other:

$$m\ddot{n}_2 + (K_1 + K_2)n_2 + K_2 n_2 = F(t),$$
$$m\ddot{n}_2 + (K_1 + 2K_2)n_2 = F(t).$$

5. Using the independent generalized coordinates shown for the spring-mass system of Fig. P4.1 (5), apply Lagrange's method to obtain the equations of motion; also determine the eigenfrequencies.

Solution

To form the Lagrangian, we must express the kinetic and potential energy in terms of x_1 and x_2:

$$T = \tfrac{1}{2}m_1\dot{x}_1{}^2 + \tfrac{1}{2}m_2\dot{x}_2{}^2$$
$$V = \tfrac{1}{2}K_1 x_1{}^2 + \tfrac{1}{2}K_2(x_2 - x_1)^2$$

No gravitational term enters the latter because x_2 is measured from the equilibrium position. Hence,

$$L = T - V = \tfrac{1}{2}m_1\dot{x}_1{}^2 + \tfrac{1}{2}m_2\dot{x}_2{}^2 - \tfrac{1}{2}K_1 x_1{}^2 - \tfrac{1}{2}K_2(x_2 - x_1)^2.$$

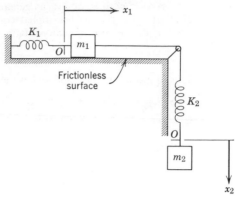

Fig. P4.1 (5)

Now we may apply the Lagrange equations

$$\frac{d}{dt}\frac{\partial L}{\partial \dot{x}_1} - \frac{\partial L}{\partial x_1} = 0$$

and

$$\frac{d}{dt}\frac{\partial L}{\partial \dot{x}_2} - \frac{\partial L}{\partial x_2} = 0.$$

The result is

$$m_1\ddot{x}_1 + K_1 x_1 - K_2(x_2 - x_1) = 0$$

and

$$m_2\ddot{x}_2 + K_2(x_2 - x_1) = 0.$$

These are the same equations of motion obtained in Problem 3, so the eigenfrequencies will also be the same.

Exercises 4.1

1. Find the eigenfrequencies for the system shown in Fig. E4.1 (1), assuming that θ remains small and the motion occurs in a single plane.

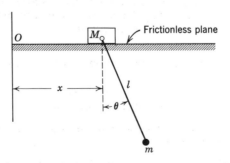

Fig. E4.1 (1)

2. For the one-dimensional system illustrated in Fig. E4.1 (2), determine the following:

    a. The equations of motion for small vibrations.
    b. The combined constants ν_{lm}.
    c. The eigenfrequencies.
    d. The solutions $x_1(t)$ and $x_2(t)$.

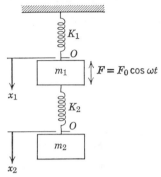

Fig. E4.1 (2)

3. If $m_1 = m_2 = 10$ lb sec²/in. and $K_1 = K_2 = K_3 = 1000$ lb/in., find the eigenfrequencies of the system shown in Fig. E.4.1 (3), assuming small displacements.

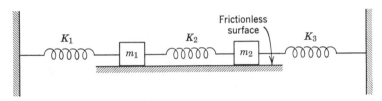

Fig. E4.1 (3)

4. Assuming that as long as θ_1 and θ_2 remain small the equations of motion for the double-pendulum shown in Fig. E4.1 (4) can be written as

$$(m_1 + m_2)l_1^2\ddot{\theta}_1 + m_2 l_1 l_2 \ddot{\theta}_2 - (m_1 + m_2)gl_1\theta_1 = 0$$

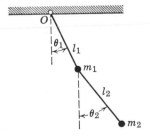

Fig. E4.1 (4)

and

$$m_2 l_1 l_2 \ddot{\theta}_1 + m_2 l_2^2 \ddot{\theta}_2 - m_2 g l_2 \theta_2 = 0,$$

find the normal frequencies of the system. Also, what amplitude relations are required?

5. Consider the dynamic vibration absorber represented by the mass m_2 and the spring K_2 in Fig. E4.1 (5). A machine, indicated by m_1, is subjected to an

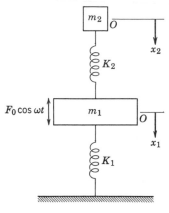

Fig. E4.1 (5)

oscillating force $F_0 \cos \omega t$ because of imperfect balancing, and is mounted on an elastic foundation with a spring constant of K_1. By selecting m_2 and K_2 in such a way that ω will be the natural frequency ω_0 of the entire system, show that the condition for the machine to remain stationary is

$$K_2 = m_2 \omega_0^2.$$

4.2 The Wave Equation and Its Solutions

Of the many types of motions possible in a strongly coupled, multi-mass system of the kind described at the start of the previous section, there is one type of special importance—those disturbances of a periodic nature which are commonly called waves. To see how these arise, let us again restrict ourselves to a conservative system, containing no dashpots or time-varying applied forces, in which all displacements remain small. More specifically, let us consider a long linear array, similar to the one illustrated in Fig. 4.1 and analyzed in detail in the text, but incorporating some large number of masses, n (see Fig. 4.3). For simplicity, we shall consider all springs to have the same constant, K.

When stated in this way it is apparent that the problem, once again, is to determine the elements v_{ij} in a secular equation like (1.36),

$$|v_{ij} - \omega_0^2 \delta_{ij}| = 0, \tag{2.1}$$

so that the eigenfrequencies of the system and all associated information can be calculated. This requires that the specific form of the equations of motion (1.26), expressed in terms of the particular generalized coordinates x_i,

$$\ddot{x}_i + v_{ij}x_j = 0 \qquad \{i, j = 1, 2, 3, \ldots, n, \tag{2.2}$$

be established.

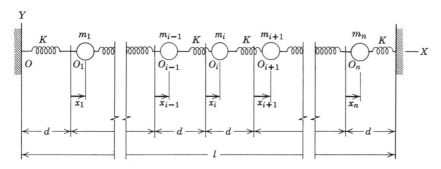

Fig. 4.3

To do so, it is perhaps most convenient to construct the Lagrangian function by writing down the total kinetic and potential energy for the system. We know that these must be functions of the type described by (1.8) and (1.2); therefore, referring to Fig. 4.3, we conclude that

$$T = \tfrac{1}{2} \sum_{i=1}^{n} m_{(i)} \dot{x}_i^2 \tag{2.3}$$

and

$$V = \tfrac{1}{2} \sum_{i=1}^{n+1} K(x_i - x_{i-1})^2. \tag{2.4}$$

Thus,

$$L = T - V = \tfrac{1}{2} \sum_{i=1}^{n} m_{(i)} \dot{x}_i^2 - \tfrac{1}{2} \sum_{i=1}^{n+1} K(x_i - x_{i-1})^2; \tag{2.5}$$

and applying Lagrange's equations,

$$\frac{d}{dt}\frac{\partial L}{\partial \dot{x}_i} - \frac{\partial L}{\partial x_i} = 0 \qquad \{i = 1, 2, 3, \ldots, n, \tag{2.6}$$

we obtain the set of simultaneous equations

$$\ddot{x}_i + \frac{2K}{m_{(i)}} x_i - \frac{K}{m_{(i)}} (x_{i+1} + x_{i-1}) = 0 \qquad \{i = 1, 2, 3, \ldots, n. \quad (2.7)$$

This becomes apparent if, for example, we place $n = 4$; for then

$$L = \tfrac{1}{2} m_1 \dot{x}_1^2 + \tfrac{1}{2} m_2 \dot{x}_2^2 + \tfrac{1}{2} m_3 \dot{x}_3^2 + \tfrac{1}{2} m_4 \dot{x}_4^2$$
$$- \tfrac{1}{2} K(x_1 - x_0)^2 - \tfrac{1}{2} K(x_2 - x_1)^2 - \tfrac{1}{2} K(x_3 - x_2)^2$$
$$- \tfrac{1}{2} K(x_4 - x_3)^2 - \tfrac{1}{2} K(x_5 - x_4)^2; \qquad (2.8)$$

and since $x_0 = x_5 = 0$, (2.6) yields:

$$m_1 \ddot{x}_1 + K x_1 - K x_2 + K x_1 = 0 \qquad (2.9)$$
$$m_2 \ddot{x}_2 + K x_2 - K x_1 - K x_3 + K x_2 = 0 \qquad (2.10)$$
$$m_3 \ddot{x}_3 + K x_3 - K x_2 - K x_4 + K x_3 = 0 \qquad (2.11)$$
$$m_4 \ddot{x}_4 + K x_4 - K x_3 + K x_4 = 0 \qquad (2.12)$$

or

$$\ddot{x}_1 + \frac{2K}{m_1} x_1 - \frac{K}{m_1} x_2 = 0 \qquad (2.13)$$

$$\ddot{x}_2 + \frac{2K}{m_2} x_2 - \frac{K}{m_2} (x_3 + x_1) = 0 \qquad (2.14)$$

$$\ddot{x}_3 + \frac{2K}{m_3} x_3 - \frac{K}{m_3} (x_4 + x_2) = 0 \qquad (2.15)$$

$$\ddot{x}_4 + \frac{2K}{m_4} x_4 - \frac{K}{m_4} x_3 = 0. \qquad (2.16)$$

Notice that (2.7) will provide equations of motion for any part of the system, whether the fixed ends are included or not.

Comparing equations (2.13) to (2.16) with those which are generated by (2.2) with $i, j = 1, 2, 3, 4$,

$$\ddot{x}_i + \nu_{i1} x_1 + \nu_{i2} x_2 + \nu_{i3} x_3 + \nu_{i4} x_4 = 0$$

$$\ddot{x}_1 + \nu_{11} x_1 + \nu_{12} x_2 + \nu_{13} x_3 + \nu_{14} x_4 = 0 \qquad (2.17)$$
$$\ddot{x}_2 + \nu_{21} x_1 + \nu_{22} x_2 + \nu_{23} x_3 + \nu_{24} x_4 = 0 \qquad (2.18)$$
$$\ddot{x}_3 + \nu_{31} x_1 + \nu_{32} x_2 + \nu_{33} x_3 + \nu_{34} x_4 = 0 \qquad (2.19)$$
$$\ddot{x}_4 + \nu_{41} x_1 + \nu_{42} x_2 + \nu_{43} x_3 + \nu_{44} x_4 = 0, \qquad (2.20)$$

to establish the pattern in which the elements will appear, it follows that in general (2.1) will become:

$$\begin{vmatrix} \left(\dfrac{2K}{m_1} - \omega_0{}^2\right) & -\dfrac{K}{m_1} & 0 & 0 & \cdots\cdots \\[2ex] -\dfrac{K}{m_2} & \left(\dfrac{2K}{m_2} - \omega_0{}^2\right) & -\dfrac{K}{m_2} & 0 & \cdots\cdots \\[2ex] 0 & -\dfrac{K}{m_3} & \left(\dfrac{2K}{m_3} - \omega_0{}^2\right) & -\dfrac{K}{m_3} & \cdots\cdots \\[2ex] \cdots\cdots & \cdots\cdots & \cdots\cdots & \cdots\cdots & \cdots \\[1ex] \cdots\cdots\cdots\cdots\cdots\cdots\cdots & & & -\dfrac{K}{m_n} & \left(\dfrac{2K}{m_n} - \omega_0{}^2\right) \end{vmatrix} = 0$$

$$(2.21)$$

This is an algebraic equation, whose specific form does depend on the fact that the ends of the array are fixed, and whose n roots are the squares of the eigenfrequencies of the system. It is apparent that these will be difficult to determine when n is large.

Fortunately, an easier way to obtain the eigenfrequencies of such a system exists—provided there really are a great many masses, closely spaced, nearly equal, and coupled together in about the same way. When conditions like these prevail, as they must on the average in a thin metallic bar, for example, we can define a mass per unit length,

$$m = \frac{m_i}{d}, \tag{2.22}$$

as well as a new quantity

$$E_y = Kd, \tag{2.23}$$

called Young's modulus of elasticity, and rewrite the equations of motion (2.7) as

$$\ddot{x}_i = \frac{E_y}{m}\left[\frac{x_{i+1} - 2x_i + x_{i-1}}{d^2}\right]. \tag{2.24}$$

The quantity in the brackets is exactly the finite difference expression for the second partial derivative of the displacement function x_i (which depends both on the position coordinate x measured from the fixed origin O and on the time t) with respect to x, evaluated at the point i.[11]

---

[11] Jeffreys, H., and B. S. Jeffreys, *Methods of Mathematical Physics*, pp. 261–312, Cambridge, 1962.

To avoid confusing notation it is customary, therefore, to use the symbol ϕ for the generalized coordinate representing the displacement function,

$$\phi_i(x, t) = x_i(x, t) \tag{2.25}$$

in this case, and rewrite (2.24) in the form

$$\ddot{\phi}_i = \frac{E_y}{m} \left[\frac{\phi_{i+1} - 2\phi_i + \phi_{i-1}}{d^2} \right] \tag{2.26}$$

before making the transition to the second partial derivatives in x and also t:

$$\left[\frac{\partial^2 \phi}{\partial t^2} \right]_i = \frac{E_y}{m} \left[\frac{\partial^2 \phi}{\partial x^2} \right]_i \tag{2.27}$$

Now if ϕ is a continuous function of x and t, which can also be differentiated at least twice with respect to these variables at each point, we can drop the subscript i and write (2.27) simply as

$$\frac{\partial^2}{\partial t^2} \phi(x, t) = \frac{E_y}{m} \frac{\partial^2}{\partial x^2} \phi(x, t). \tag{2.28}$$

This will be the equation of motion for any segment of the continuous system, regardless of its end conditions.

The last step completes a transition from the system of discrete masses and springs shown in Fig. 4.3 to a "continuous" system. Such systems are, of course, especially amenable to mathematical analysis; and from this point onward, whenever it is possible to do so without violating the material properties involved, we shall make a similar transition to facilitate the analysis of many-particle systems.

Using the equation of motion (2.28), the fixed-end boundary conditions

$$\phi(0, t) = 0 \tag{2.29}$$

$$\phi(l, t) = 0, \tag{2.30}$$

and some simple initial condition such as a zero initial velocity,

$$\dot{\phi}(x, 0) = 0, \tag{2.31}$$

it is not difficult to obtain the eigenfrequencies. Expecting acceptable motions to have an harmonic character from the preceding discussion, we observe that assuming $\phi(x, t)$ to have the special form

$$\phi = X(x)T(t) \tag{2.32}$$

where $X(x)$ represents some function of x only and $T(t)$ a function only of

t, will cause the partial differential equation (2.28) to separate into two ordinary differential equations, each of which describes an harmonic oscillation.

Carrying out the substitution of (2.32), (2.28) becomes

$$X \frac{d^2 T}{dt^2} = T \frac{E_y}{m} \frac{d^2 X}{dx^2} \qquad (2.33)$$

or, completing the separation of variables,

$$\frac{1}{T} \frac{d^2 T}{dt^2} = \frac{E_y}{m} \frac{1}{X} \frac{d^2 X}{dx^2} . \qquad (2.34)$$

Because the left-hand side of this relation is independent of x and the right-hand side is independent of t, and because the two sides are equal, both must be independent of x and t. This means that both sides can only be equal to the same constant. If, for the moment, we arbitrarily select $-\omega_0^2$, (2.34) yields

$$\frac{d^2 X}{dx^2} + \left(\omega_0^2 \frac{m}{E_y} \right) X = 0 \qquad (2.35)$$

and

$$\frac{d^2 T}{dt^2} + \omega_0^2 T = 0, \qquad (2.36)$$

which we know to have the solutions

$$X = A_1 \cos \omega_0 \sqrt{\frac{m}{E_y}} x + A_2 \sin \omega_0 \sqrt{\frac{m}{E_y}} x \qquad (2.37)$$

and

$$T = A_3 \cos \omega_0 t + A_4 \sin \omega_0 t, \qquad (2.38)$$

neglecting the trivial case when $\omega_0 = 0$.

This makes it clear that one form of (2.32) can be

$$\phi = \left(A_1 \cos \omega_0 \sqrt{\frac{m}{E_y}} x + A_2 \sin \omega_0 \sqrt{\frac{m}{E_y}} x \right) (A_3 \cos \omega_0 t + A_4 \sin \omega_0 t), \qquad (2.39)$$

while

$$\dot{\phi} = \left(A_1 \cos \omega_0 \sqrt{\frac{m}{E_y}} x + A_2 \sin \omega_0 \sqrt{\frac{m}{E_y}} x \right)$$
$$\times (-\omega_0 A_3 \sin \omega_0 t + \omega_0 A_4 \cos \omega_0 t). \qquad (2.40)$$

But, applying the initial condition (2.31), we obtain the relation

$$\omega_0 A_4 \left(A_1 \cos \omega_0 \sqrt{\frac{m}{E_y}} x + A_2 \sin \omega_0 \sqrt{\frac{m}{E_y}} x \right) = 0, \qquad (2.41)$$

which shows that

$$A_4 = 0; \tag{2.42}$$

whereas the first boundary condition, (2.29), gives

$$A_1(A_3 \cos \omega_0 t + A_4 \sin \omega_0 t) = 0 \tag{2.43}$$

and establishes that

$$A_1 = 0. \tag{2.44}$$

Thus if we place

$$A_2 A_3 = A, \tag{2.45}$$

what remains of (2.39) is

$$\phi = A \sin \omega_0 \sqrt{\frac{m}{E_y}} \, x \cos \omega_0 t. \tag{2.46}$$

Use of the last boundary condition, (2.30), therefore shows that the relation

$$A \sin \omega_0 \sqrt{\frac{m}{E_y}} \, l \cos \omega_0 t = 0 \tag{2.47}$$

must be satisfied. But even if we decide to leave the amplitude A and the time t arbitrary, it will be satisfied whenever

$$\sin \omega_0 \sqrt{\frac{m}{E_y}} \, l = 0, \tag{2.48}$$

which is to say, whenever

$$\omega_0 \sqrt{\frac{m}{E_y}} \, l = \alpha\pi \qquad \{\alpha = 0, 1, 2, \ldots \tag{2.49}$$

The last equation defines the eigenfrequencies,

$$\omega_0 = \frac{\alpha\pi}{l} \sqrt{\frac{E_y}{m}} \qquad \{\alpha = 1, 2, \ldots, \tag{2.50}$$

again neglecting the case when $\omega_0 = 0$.

Substituting this expression for ω_0 in (2.46), which describes how the x-direction displacement ϕ of any point in the system from its equilibrium position will depend on the distance x of that point from the fixed origin O and on the time t measured from zero time, we obtain

$$\phi = A \sin \frac{\alpha\pi}{l} x \cos \frac{\alpha\pi}{l} \sqrt{\frac{E_y}{m}} \, t. \tag{2.51}$$

This shows that at all times ϕ will be zero, not only at $x = 0$ and $x = l$ as required by the boundary conditions, but also at certain other values of x whenever $\alpha > 1$. For example, when $\alpha = 2$, ϕ will also vanish at

$x = l/2$; when $\alpha = 3$, it will vanish at the additional points $x = l/3$ and $x = 2l/3$; and so on. Between such fixed points the displacement of any given point will vary periodically with time and its distance from the origin. The physical configurations that result from assigning α different values are called standing longitudinal waves; of course, each will have a distinct eigenfrequency $|\omega_0|$.

Actually, system motions of this general type are easier to visualize for transverse waves, in which displacements are perpendicular rather than parallel to the reference direction. The method of analysis for such waves remains much the same. If we imagine the system of Fig. 4.3 to be

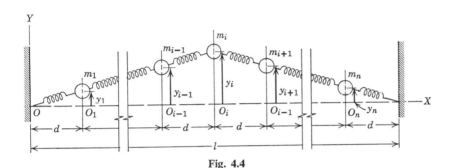

Fig. 4.4

restricted to displacements in the y-direction (or z-direction) as in Fig. 4.4, instead of in the x-direction, the total kinetic energy will be

$$T = \tfrac{1}{2} \sum_{i=1}^{n} m_{(i)} \dot{y}_i{}^2. \tag{2.52}$$

And if we further assume that, because displacements must remain small, the tensile force F in each spring will remain constant (so that $V = F\delta$ where δ represents the change in length of the spring), the total potential energy can be written as

$$V = \sum_{i=1}^{n+1} F[\sqrt{d^2 + (y_i - y_{i-1})^2} - d]$$

$$= \sum_{i=1}^{n+1} Fd\left[\sqrt{1 + \frac{1}{d^2}(y_i - y_{i-1})^2} - 1\right] \tag{2.53}$$

or, expanding the square root by the binomial theorem, as

$$V = \sum_{i=1}^{n+1} Fd\left[1 + \frac{1}{2d^2}(y_i - y_{i-1})^2 - 1\right] = \frac{1}{2} \sum_{i=1}^{n+1} \frac{F}{d}(y_i - y_{i-1})^2. \tag{2.54}$$

Therefore, except for replacing x_i with y_i and K with F/d, the Lagrangian function (2.5), and thus the simultaneous equations of motion (2.7), will be the same as before. This means that, with mass per unit length defined in the same way as (2.22), the equations of motion in a form parallel to (2.24) will be

$$\ddot{y}_i = \frac{F}{m}\left[\frac{y_{i+1} - 2y_i + y_{i-1}}{d^2}\right]. \tag{2.55}$$

Making the transition to the second partial derivatives and the displacement function notation used before,

$$\phi_i(x, t) = y_i(x, t), \tag{2.56}$$

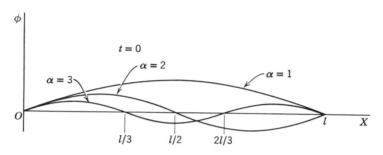

Fig. 4.5

we obtain the equation of motion for a corresponding continuous system, such as an elastic string under constant tension, as

$$\frac{\partial^2}{\partial t^2}\phi(x, t) = \frac{F}{m}\frac{\partial^2}{\partial x^2}\phi(x, t). \tag{2.57}$$

Hence, when we use the same boundary and initial conditions, (2.29) to (2.31), and assume the same product form for the solutions, (2.32), the eigenfrequencies will turn out to be

$$\omega_0 = \frac{\alpha\pi}{l}\sqrt{\frac{F}{m}} \qquad \{\alpha = 1, 2, 3, \ldots, \tag{2.58}$$

with the associated standing wave configurations:

$$\phi = A\sin\frac{\alpha\pi}{l}x\cos\frac{\alpha\pi}{l}\sqrt{\frac{F}{m}}\,t \tag{2.59}$$

Several of these are illustrated at $t = 0$ in Fig. 4.5.

Not counting the permanent ones at the ends, we see that exactly $(\alpha - 1)$ zeros of ϕ, called nodes, will be associated with each possible stable or normal mode of vibration determined by assigning some integer value to α.

In principle an infinite number of such modes will exist, since the system
has been treated as if it were continuous. But, just as in the simple two
mass–three spring example of the preceding section, it can vibrate in any
one of these alone if all the others happen to vanish. More likely, it will
be vibrating in a combination of the normal modes, because of starting
from some irregular configuration.

However, if we assume as before that the general solution may be constructed by superimposing normal mode solutions, we can still determine
$\phi(x, t)$ in such a case by using (2.58) and (2.59) to write

$$\phi = \sum_{\alpha=1}^{\infty} A_\alpha \sin \frac{\alpha \pi}{l} x \cos \frac{\alpha \pi}{l} \sqrt{\frac{F}{m}}\, t \tag{2.60}$$

and applying the given initial configuration to evaluate the coefficients

Fig. 4.6

A_α. Suppose, for example, that a string of the type shown in Fig. 4.5 is
known to have the shape shown in Fig. 4.6 at zero time:

$$\phi(x, 0) = \begin{cases} \dfrac{\phi_0}{l_0} x & \text{for} \quad 0 \leq x \leq l_0 \\[2ex] \dfrac{\phi_0}{(l - l_0)} (l - x) & \text{for} \quad l_0 \leq x \leq l \end{cases} \tag{2.61}$$

If it is released with no initial velocity, the y-direction displacement at any
position x at any time t will be given by (2.60), provided the relations
given in (2.61) are used to eliminate the remaining arbitrary constants A_α.

From elementary integration theory we know that in general

$$\int_0^l \sin \frac{\alpha \pi}{l} x \sin \frac{\beta \pi}{l} x\, dx = \begin{cases} 0 & \text{if} \quad \alpha \neq \beta \\[1ex] \dfrac{l}{2} & \text{if} \quad \alpha = \beta; \end{cases} \tag{2.62}$$

so it follows that multiplying both sides of (2.60) by $\sin \beta \pi x/l$ at $t = 0$

and integrating from 0 to l will isolate the A_α:

$$\int_0^l \phi(x, 0) \sin \frac{\beta\pi}{l} x \, dx = \int_0^l \sum_{\alpha=1}^\infty A_\alpha \sin \frac{\alpha\pi}{l} x \sin \frac{\beta\pi}{l} x \, dx, \quad (2.63)$$

$$\int_0^l \phi(x, 0) \sin \frac{\alpha\pi}{l} x \, dx = A_\alpha \frac{l}{2}. \quad (2.64)$$

Substituting from (2.61) we obtain

$$A_\alpha = \frac{2}{l} \int_0^{l_0} \frac{\phi_0}{l_0} x \sin \frac{\alpha\pi}{l} x \, dx + \frac{2}{l} \int_{l_0}^l \frac{\phi_0}{(l - l_0)} (l - x) \sin \frac{\alpha\pi}{l} x \, dx, \quad (2.65)$$

which yields

$$A_\alpha = \frac{2\phi_0 l^2}{l_0(l - l_0)\pi^2 \alpha^2} \frac{1}{} \sin \frac{\alpha\pi}{l} l_0, \quad (2.66)$$

and therefore conclude that the particular form (2.60) will take is

$$\phi = \frac{2\phi_0 l^2}{l_0(l - l_0)\pi^2} \sum_{\alpha=1}^\infty \frac{1}{\alpha^2} \sin \frac{\alpha\pi}{l} l_0 \sin \frac{\alpha\pi}{l} x \cos \frac{\alpha\pi}{l} \sqrt{\frac{F}{m}} t. \quad (2.67)$$

This defines the shape that the plucked string of Fig. 4.6 will have at any subsequent time, to whatever accuracy desired. Ordinarily the series will converge on the actual shape at a given time within the first few terms (e.g., $\alpha = 1, 2, 3, 4$) and describe it quite closely, as demonstrated in Problem 4.2(1). Actually, (2.67) represents a special case of the well-known Fourier sine series.[12] The general form corresponding to (2.60) is

$$\phi = \sum_{\alpha=1}^\infty \left[A_\alpha \sin \frac{\alpha\pi}{l} x \cos \frac{\alpha\pi}{l} \sqrt{\frac{F}{m}} t + B_\alpha \sin \frac{\alpha\pi}{l} x \sin \frac{\alpha\pi}{l} \sqrt{\frac{F}{m}} t \right], \quad (2.68)$$

so that

$$\phi(x, 0) = \sum_{\alpha=1}^\infty A_\alpha \sin \frac{\alpha\pi}{l} x \quad (2.69)$$

and

$$\dot{\phi}(x, 0) = \sum_{\alpha=1}^\infty B_\alpha \frac{\alpha\pi}{l} \sqrt{\frac{F}{m}} \sin \frac{\alpha\pi}{l} x, \quad (2.70)$$

while the coefficients may be determined from the general formulae

$$A_\alpha = \frac{2}{l} \int_0^l \phi(x, 0) \sin \frac{\alpha\pi}{l} x \, dx \quad (2.71)$$

[12] Courant, R., *Differential and Integral Calculus*, 2nd edition, Vol. 1, pp. 425–456, Interscience, New York, 1957.

and

$$B_\alpha = \frac{2}{\alpha\pi\sqrt{F/m}} \int_0^l \dot\phi(x, 0) \sin\frac{\alpha\pi}{l} x\, dx, \tag{2.72}$$

the first of which corresponds to (2.64).

A Fourier cosine series,

$$\phi = \sum_{\alpha=1}^\infty \left[C_\alpha \cos\frac{\alpha\pi}{l} x \cos\frac{\alpha\pi}{l}\sqrt{\frac{F}{m}}\, t + D_\alpha \cos\frac{\alpha\pi}{l} x \sin\frac{\alpha\pi}{l}\sqrt{\frac{F}{m}}\, t \right] \tag{2.73}$$

$$C_\alpha = \frac{2}{l} \int_0^l \phi(x, 0) \cos\frac{\alpha\pi}{l} x\, dx \tag{2.74}$$

$$D_\alpha = \frac{2}{\alpha\pi\sqrt{F/m}} \int_0^l \dot\phi(x, 0) \cos\frac{\alpha\pi}{l} x, \tag{2.75}$$

also exists, of course, following from the cosine relationship parallel to (2.62). This is often needed for a different type of boundary conditions, in which the slope $d\phi/dx$ vanishes at the ends rather than ϕ.

It will have been noted that the longitudinal wave equation (2.28) and the transverse wave equation (2.57) are very similar in form. In fact, if we simply agree to interpret $\phi(x, t)$ as x-direction displacements in the first case and y-direction displacements in the second, and if we further agree to accept

$$c^2 = \frac{E_y}{m} \tag{2.76}$$

for longitudinal waves along with

$$c^2 = \frac{F}{m} \tag{2.77}$$

for transverse waves, then independently of what the end conditions may be, we can write

$$\frac{\partial^2}{\partial t^2} \phi(x, t) - c^2 \frac{\partial^2}{\partial x^2} \phi(x, t) = 0 \tag{2.78}$$

to describe either type of one-dimensional wave motion.

So far we have studied only one of the many possible solutions of this partial differential equation—the one which results from assuming that $\phi(x, t)$ has the form $X(x)T(t)$ and that the separation constant is $-\omega_0^2$. However, it is not difficult to obtain the general solution. Temporarily adopting the operator notation

$$\frac{\partial}{\partial x} = D_x, \qquad \frac{\partial^2}{\partial x^2} = D_x^2, \tag{2.79}$$

we can rewrite (2.78) as

$$\frac{\partial^2}{\partial t^2}\phi - (cD_x)^2\phi = 0. \tag{2.80}$$

Comparing this with the ordinary differential equation (2.35) of Chapter 3,

$$\frac{d^2x}{dt} - \beta^2 x = 0, \tag{2.81}$$

whose general solution we know to be (2.37) of that chapter,

$$x = B_1 e^{\beta t} + B_2 e^{-\beta t}, \tag{2.82}$$

we can guess that the desired solution will be of the form

$$\phi = g(x)e^{cD_x t} + h(x)e^{-cD_x t}, \tag{2.83}$$

because the general solutions of partial differential equations must involve arbitrary functions like $g(x)$ and $h(x)$ where those of ordinary differential equations involve arbitrary constants.[13]

The meaning of (2.83), as it stands, is not very clear. But if we note that Taylor's expansion of an arbitrary continuous, and continuously differentiable, function of x, $f(x)$, can be written in the following way,

$$f(x + \Delta x) = f(x) + \frac{\Delta x}{1!}D_x f(x) + \frac{\Delta x^2}{2!}D_x^2 f(x) + \cdots$$

$$= f(x)\left[1 + \frac{\Delta x}{1!}D_x + \frac{\Delta x^2}{2!}D_x^2 + \cdots\right] \tag{2.84}$$

or

$$f(x + \Delta x) = f(x)e^{\Delta x D_x}, \tag{2.85}$$

then it becomes obvious that by placing

$$\Delta x = \pm ct \tag{2.86}$$

we can obtain terms like those on the right-hand side of (2.83):

$$g(x + ct) = g(x)e^{cD_x t} \tag{2.87}$$
$$h(x - ct) = h(x)e^{-cD_x t} \tag{2.88}$$

The conclusion is that

$$\phi = g(x + ct) + h(x - ct) \tag{2.89}$$

should represent the general solution of (2.78); indeed, it is easy to prove that this is so by direct substitution. Observe that the minus sign appearing

[13] Sneddon, I. N., *Elements of Partial Differential Equations*, pp. 88–105, McGraw-Hill, New York, 1957.

in (2.78) leads to the selection of real exponentials in (2.83) and, finally, to the real functions of (2.89). This is characteristic of so-called hyperbolic partial differential equations. Elliptic partial differential equations differ only in having a plus sign, but their general solution necessarily involves complex functions of the independent variables.[14]

As to the physical meaning of (2.89), consider one of its terms alone,

$$h(x - ct). \tag{2.90}$$

Presumably this function could be plotted at zero time relative to an origin O and some definite curve could be obtained,

$$[h(x - ct)]_{t=0} = h(x); \tag{2.91}$$

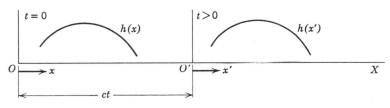

Fig. 4.7

however, at any later time exactly the same curve would be obtained by plotting the function relative to an origin O' displaced an amount ct in a positive direction from the original origin (Fig. 4.7), because then

$$h[(x - ct)]_{t>0} = h[(x' + ct) - ct]_{t>0} = h(x'). \tag{2.92}$$

It appears that $h(x - ct)$ may be interpreted as a curve of fixed shape $h(x)$ moving in the positive x-direction with a constant speed c; this interpretation of c is consistent with its use in (2.76) and (2.77), which implies that it possesses the units of speed (e.g., $1b/1b\text{-sec}^2/\text{in.}/\text{in.} = \text{in.}^2/\text{sec}^2$ for c^2).

In the same way, of course,

$$g(x + ct) \tag{2.93}$$

can be understood to mean a curve of fixed shape $g(x)$ moving in the negative x-direction with the speed c. Thus the general solution (2.89) is seen to be the sum of two "waveforms" propagating in opposite directions, called progressive waves. In principle, even highly irregular curves could qualify as such waveforms, but on the basis of the preceding discussion of eigenfrequencies and normal modes, it is reasonable to think that we will be

[14] Hildebrand, F. B., *Advanced Calculus for Applications*, pp. 389–394, Prentice-Hall, Englewood Cliffs, N.J., 1962.

especially interested in those which are harmonic functions of time, that is, those which have the form:

$$\phi = f(x)e^{-i\omega_0 t}. \tag{2.94}$$

Here $f(x)$ is not an entirely arbitrary function of x, for if we substitute (2.94) in equation (2.78),

$$\frac{\partial^2 \phi}{\partial t^2} - c^2 \frac{\partial^2 \phi}{\partial x^2} = 0,$$

we obtain the ordinary differential equation

$$\frac{d^2}{dx^2} f(x) + \left(\frac{\omega_0}{c}\right)^2 f(x) = 0, \tag{2.95}$$

whose general solution we know to be

$$f(x) = A_1 e^{i\frac{\omega_0}{c}x} + A_2 e^{-i\frac{\omega_0}{c}x}. \tag{2.96}$$

The implication is that (2.94) will satisfy the equation of motion only if $f(x)$ has the form (2.96); in other words, we must have

$$\phi = \left(A_1 e^{i\frac{\omega_0}{c}x} + A_2 e^{-i\frac{\omega_0}{c}x}\right)e^{-i\omega_0 t} = A_1 e^{i\frac{\omega_0}{c}(x-ct)} + A_2 e^{-i\frac{\omega_0}{c}(x+ct)} \tag{2.97}$$

or, applying Euler's formulae [(2.40) and (2.41) of Chapter 3],

$$\phi = A_1 \cos\frac{\omega_0}{c}(x-ct) + iA_1 \sin\frac{\omega_0}{c}(x-ct)$$

$$+ A_2 \cos\frac{\omega_0}{c}(x+ct) - iA_2 \sin\frac{\omega_0}{c}(x+ct). \tag{2.98}$$

These solutions are sums of functions of $(x + ct)$ and $(x - ct)$, as required, and in addition consist entirely of harmonic forms. We can construct various periodic "plane" waves moving in the positive x-direction by superpositions of the real and imaginary parts of the terms involving $(x - ct)$ in (2.98), just as superpositions of these parts of the terms involving $(x + ct)$ will yield the same type of waves moving in the negative x-direction. On the other hand, we may also represent the former by the first term on the far right in (2.97) and the latter by the last term. All will remain solutions of the equation of motion (2.78). Similar conclusions follow from use of the positive exponential in (2.94), since (2.95) results in either case, and this fact is reflected by the appearance of ω_0 as a scalar quantity.

As before, ω_0 is the natural angular frequency of the oscillating system (originally of each mass, now of each point of the linear continuum) in radians per unit time. But because there is no further need for ω_0 to carry two signs, and little danger of confusing it with the angular frequency of an applied force, it is customary merely to write

$$\omega = |\omega_0| = 2\pi\nu, \qquad (2.99)$$

where $\nu = \nu_0$ is the oscillation frequency in cycles per unit time. The period is then defined by

$$\tau = \frac{1}{\nu} = \frac{2\pi}{\omega}. \qquad (2.100)$$

Such a definition tends to focus attention on the motion of a single point in the system as the wave moves by it, but we may also imagine ourselves to be moving in the same direction as the wave with the same speed c, so that we may observe the waveform as a whole. The length associated with one complete cycle, called the wavelength, evidently will be

$$\lambda = \frac{c}{\nu}; \qquad (2.101)$$

therefore it follows that the period may alternately be interpreted as the time required for one wavelength to pass a given point:

$$\tau = \frac{\lambda}{c} \qquad (2.102)$$

Similarly, the number of wavelengths that will pass the given point in unit time must be

$$\frac{c}{\lambda} = \frac{1}{\tau} = \nu, \qquad (2.103)$$

which provides the corresponding interpretation of oscillation frequency.

These relations and the solution form (2.97) suggest the definition of another useful scalar quantity called the angular wave number:

$$k = \frac{\omega}{c} = \frac{2\pi\nu}{c} = \frac{2\pi}{\lambda} \qquad (2.104)$$

$+$ for waves traveling in the $+\,x$-direction

$-$ for waves traveling in the $-\,x$-direction

For then we can describe a plane wave that may be propagating in either direction by writing

$$\phi = Ae^{i(\pm kx - \omega t)}, \qquad (2.105)$$

one moving in the negative x-direction by choosing the negative sign for k to obtain

$$\phi = Ae^{-i(kx+\omega t)} = Ae^{-i\frac{\omega}{c}(x+ct)}, \tag{2.106}$$

as in the last term of (2.97), and one moving in the positive x-direction by choosing the positive sign for k to obtain

$$\phi = Ae^{i(kx-\omega t)} = Ae^{i\frac{\omega}{c}(x-ct)}, \tag{2.107}$$

as in the preceding term of (2.97).

At this point it is easy to see how the standing waves studied earlier arise from progressive waves propagating through one another, perhaps as a result of their reflection from fixed ends. Suppose that from (2.98) we compose a solution consisting of two sine waves with the same amplitude A_1 and angular frequency ω, but moving in opposite directions:

$$\phi = A_1 \sin (kx - \omega t) + A_1 \sin (kx + \omega t) \tag{2.108}$$

By trigonometric reduction it follows that, with $2A_1 = A$, this can also be written as

$$\phi = A \sin kx \cos \omega t = A \sin \frac{\omega}{c} x \cos \omega t, \tag{2.109}$$

which is the same as (2.46) if we identify c as $\sqrt{E_y/m}$. This should make it clear that assuming $\phi(x, t)$ to have the special form $X(x)T(t)$, as we did in (2.32) to cause the partial differential equation of motion to separate into two ordinary differential equations, is equivalent to assuming that the solutions of interest will be standing waves.

Although more generally the solutions of (2.78) will be progressive waves with one of the forms displayed above, standing waves, because of their dynamic stability, seem to occupy a privileged position in nature and, therefore, deserve our special attention. We have considered only one type so far—the one given in (2.39), that resulted from assuming the separation constant to be $-\omega_0^2$ with $\omega_0 > 0$. However, it is not difficult to exhaust all of the possibilities.

First, merely by recognizing that when $\omega_0 = 0$ the solutions of (2.35) and (2.36), with $E_y/m = c^2$ and $\omega_0 = \omega$,

$$\frac{d^2X}{dx^2} + \left(\frac{\omega}{c}\right)^2 X = 0 \tag{2.110}$$

$$\frac{d^2T}{dt^2} + \omega^2 T = 0, \tag{2.111}$$

will be

$$X = B_1 x + B_2 \tag{2.112}$$

$$T = B_3 t + B_4, \tag{2.113}$$

we can add the product of these to (2.39) and write:

$$\phi = \left(A_1 \cos \frac{\omega}{c} x + A_2 \sin \frac{\omega}{c} x\right)(A_3 \cos \omega t + A_4 \sin \omega t)$$
$$+ (B_1 x + B_2)(B_3 t + B_4) \tag{2.114}$$

A convenient notation for expressing the same thing is

$$\phi = \left.\begin{matrix}\cos \\ \sin\end{matrix}\frac{\omega}{c} x\right\}\left.\begin{matrix}\cos \\ \sin\end{matrix} \omega t\right\} + \left.\begin{matrix}x \\ 1\end{matrix}\right\}\left.\begin{matrix}t \\ 1\end{matrix}\right\}, \tag{2.115}$$

where the braces indicate a linear combination of the terms included. Of course, it is also possible to write these solutions in terms of imaginary exponentials:

$$\phi = \left.e^{\pm i \frac{\omega}{c} x}\right\}\left. e^{\pm i \omega t}\right\} + \left.\begin{matrix}x \\ 1\end{matrix}\right\}\left.\begin{matrix}t \\ 1\end{matrix}\right\} \tag{2.116}$$

Next, when $+\omega^2$ is used for the separation constant instead of $-\omega^2$, rather than (2.110) and (2.111) we obtain

$$\frac{d^2 X}{dx^2} - \left(\frac{\omega}{c}\right)^2 X = 0 \tag{2.117}$$

and

$$\frac{d^2 T}{dt^2} - \omega^2 T = 0, \tag{2.118}$$

whose solutions for $\omega = 0$ will be the same as those given above, and whose other solutions will take the form of real exponentials, or hyperbolic functions:

$$\phi = \left.e^{\pm \frac{\omega}{c} x}\right\}\left. e^{\pm \omega t}\right\} + \left.\begin{matrix}x \\ 1\end{matrix}\right\}\left.\begin{matrix}t \\ 1\end{matrix}\right\} \tag{2.119}$$

$$\phi = \left.\begin{matrix}\cosh \\ \sinh\end{matrix}\frac{\omega}{c} x\right\}\left.\begin{matrix}\cosh \\ \sinh\end{matrix} \omega t\right\} + \left.\begin{matrix}x \\ 1\end{matrix}\right\}\left.\begin{matrix}t \\ 1\end{matrix}\right\} \tag{2.120}$$

It can be proved[15] that (2.116) and (2.119), with their alternate forms (2.115) and (2.120), constitute all of the standing wave solutions of the

[15] Irving, J., and N. Mullineux, *Mathematics in Physics and Engineering*, pp. 6–8, 12–15, Academic, New York, 1959.

one-dimensional wave equation (2.78),

$$\frac{\partial^2 \phi}{\partial t^2} - c^2 \frac{\partial^2 \phi}{\partial x^2} = 0,$$

or

$$\phi_{xx} = c^{-2}\phi_{tt} \qquad (2.121)$$

using the subscript notation for partial derivatives mentioned earlier.[16] Furthermore, these solutions can easily be generalized to two and three-dimensions. If we allow our waves to propagate in some arbitrary direction in the XY-plane, rather than requiring them to propagate along the X-axis, the displacement function will depend on both x and y as well as t,

$$\phi = \phi(x, y, t), \qquad (2.122)$$

and the equation of motion will become

$$\phi_{xx} + \phi_{yy} = c^{-2}\phi_{tt}. \qquad (2.123)$$

As before, points may only displace in the direction of propagation (a longitudinal wave) or in either one of two normal directions perpendicular to this (transverse waves), but these displacements can always be expressed in terms of their projections on the coordinate axes.

   Accordingly, to obtain the standing wave solutions we can again assume a product form like (2.32):

$$\phi = X(x)\,Y(y)T(t) \qquad (2.124)$$

Substitution in (2.123) will then yield

$$\frac{c^2}{X}\frac{d^2 X}{dx^2} = \frac{1}{T}\frac{d^2 T}{dt^2} - \frac{c^2}{Y}\frac{d^2 Y}{dy^2}; \qquad (2.125)$$

and equating both sides to the constant $-\omega_1^2$ gives:

$$\frac{d^2 X}{dx^2} + \left(\frac{\omega_1}{c}\right)^2 X = 0 \qquad (2.126)$$

$$\frac{c^2}{Y}\frac{d^2 Y}{dy^2} = \frac{1}{T}\frac{d^2 T}{dt^2} + \omega_1^2 \qquad (2.127)$$

But the last equation can be separated again; equating both sides to a second constant $-\omega_2^2$, we find that

$$\frac{d^2 Y}{dy^2} + \left(\frac{\omega_2}{c}\right)^2 Y = 0 \qquad (2.128)$$

---

[16] Jeffrey, A., "Non-Linear Waves," *International Science and Technology*, No. 31, pp. 37–44, July 1964.

and

$$\frac{d^2T}{dt^2} + (\omega_1{}^2 + \omega_2{}^2)T = 0, \qquad (2.129)$$

or with

$$\omega_1{}^2 + \omega_2{}^2 = \omega^2, \qquad (2.130)$$

$$\frac{d^2T}{dt^2} + \omega^2 T = 0. \qquad (2.131)$$

Since (2.126), (2.128), and (2.131) all have the same form as before, it becomes evident that the standing wave solutions of the two-dimensional wave equation (2.123) will be either

$$\phi = \begin{matrix}\cos \\ \sin\end{matrix}\frac{\omega_1}{c}\,x\Big\} \begin{matrix}\cos \\ \sin\end{matrix}\frac{\omega_2}{c}\,y\Big\} \begin{matrix}\cos \\ \sin\end{matrix}\,\omega t\Big\} + \begin{matrix}x \\ 1\end{matrix}\Big\} \begin{matrix}y \\ 1\end{matrix}\Big\} \begin{matrix}t \\ 1\end{matrix}\Big\} \qquad (2.132)$$

or, using positive separation constants,

$$\phi = \begin{matrix}\cosh \\ \sinh\end{matrix}\frac{\omega_1}{c}\,x\Big\} \begin{matrix}\cosh \\ \sinh\end{matrix}\frac{\omega_2}{c}\,y\Big\} \begin{matrix}\cosh \\ \sinh\end{matrix}\,\omega t\Big\} + \begin{matrix}x \\ 1\end{matrix}\Big\} \begin{matrix}y \\ 1\end{matrix}\Big\} \begin{matrix}t \\ 1\end{matrix}\Big\}, \qquad (2.133)$$

at least in one of their forms.

Similarly, if we allow the waves to propagate in some arbitrary direction in three-dimensional space, the displacement function will depend on all three position coordinates and time,

$$\phi = \phi(x, y, z, t), \qquad (2.134)$$

and the wave equation becomes

$$\phi_{xx} + \phi_{yy} + \phi_{zz} = c^{-2}\phi_{tt}. \qquad (2.135)$$

By assuming that

$$\phi = X(x)\,Y(y)Z(z)T(t) \qquad (2.136)$$

and defining three constants ω_1, ω_2, and ω_3 such that

$$\omega_1{}^2 + \omega_2{}^2 + \omega_3{}^2 = \omega^2 \qquad (2.137)$$

in the same way as before, it is easy to show that one form of the standing wave solutions will be

$$\phi = \begin{matrix}\cos \\ \sin\end{matrix}\frac{\omega_1}{c}\,x\Big\} \begin{matrix}\cos \\ \sin\end{matrix}\frac{\omega_2}{c}\,y\Big\} \begin{matrix}\cos \\ \sin\end{matrix}\frac{\omega_3}{c}\,z\Big\} \begin{matrix}\cos \\ \sin\end{matrix}\,\omega t\Big\} + \begin{matrix}x \\ 1\end{matrix}\Big\} \begin{matrix}y \\ 1\end{matrix}\Big\} \begin{matrix}z \\ 1\end{matrix}\Big\} \begin{matrix}t \\ 1\end{matrix}\Big\} \qquad (2.138)$$

or

$$\phi = \begin{matrix}\cosh \\ \sinh\end{matrix}\frac{\omega_1}{c}\,x\Big\} \begin{matrix}\cosh \\ \sinh\end{matrix}\frac{\omega_2}{c}\,y\Big\} \begin{matrix}\cosh \\ \sinh\end{matrix}\frac{\omega_3}{c}\,z\Big\} \begin{matrix}\cosh \\ \sinh\end{matrix}\,\omega t\Big\} + \begin{matrix}x \\ 1\end{matrix}\Big\} \begin{matrix}y \\ 1\end{matrix}\Big\} \begin{matrix}z \\ 1\end{matrix}\Big\} \begin{matrix}t \\ 1\end{matrix}\Big\}. \qquad (2.139)$$

Just as in the one-dimensional case, these will arise from the interference of progressive waves, but the form that harmonic progressive wave solutions will take in three dimensions may be inferred from (2.105),

$$\phi = Ae^{i(\pm kx - \omega t)}.$$

The wave number k can be generalized to a vector quantity, capable of describing propagation in any direction, merely by recognizing that a wavelength in an arbitrary direction can be described by its three coordinate projections λ_x, λ_y, λ_z, and following the definition (2.104) to form

$$\mathbf{k} \approx \left(\frac{2\pi}{\lambda_x}, \frac{2\pi}{\lambda_y}, \frac{2\pi}{\lambda_z} \right). \tag{2.140}$$

Thus to describe an harmonic plane wave propagating in any direction defined by a vector $\mathbf{r}$, we may write

$$\phi = Ae^{i(\mathbf{k} \cdot \mathbf{r} - \omega t)}. \tag{2.141}$$

In rectangular Cartesian coordinates we know that

$$\phi_{xx} + \phi_{yy} + \phi_{zz} = \nabla^2 \phi; \tag{2.142}$$

therefore, it follows that the one, two- and three-dimensional wave equations can all be expressed as

$$\nabla^2 \phi = c^{-2} \phi_{tt}. \tag{2.143}$$

Furthermore, it is known[17] that the operator ∇^2 takes the forms indicated below in various other coordinate systems:

Coordinates	Transformation	∇^2
Polar ρ, ϕ	$x = \rho \cos \phi$ $y = \rho \sin \phi$	$\dfrac{\partial^2}{\partial \rho^2} + \dfrac{1}{\rho} \dfrac{\partial}{\partial \rho} + \dfrac{1}{\rho^2} \dfrac{\partial^2}{\partial \phi^2}$
Cylindrical ρ, ϕ, z	$x = \rho \cos \phi$ $y = \rho \sin \phi$ $z = z$	$\dfrac{\partial^2}{\partial \rho^2} + \dfrac{1}{\rho} \dfrac{\partial}{\partial \rho} + \dfrac{1}{\rho^2} \dfrac{\partial^2}{\partial \phi^2} + \dfrac{\partial^2}{\partial z^2}$
Spherical r, ϕ, θ	$x^2 + y^2 + z^2 = r^2$ $y/z = \tan \phi$ $z = r \cos \theta$	$\dfrac{1}{r^2} \dfrac{\partial}{\partial r}\left(r^2 \dfrac{\partial}{\partial r} \right) + \dfrac{1}{r^2 \sin \theta} \dfrac{\partial}{\partial \theta}\left(\sin \theta \dfrac{\partial}{\partial \theta} \right)$ $+ \dfrac{1}{r^2 \sin^2 \theta} \dfrac{\partial^2}{\partial \phi^2}$

[17] Irving, J., and N. Mullineux, *Mathematics in Physics and Engineering*, pp. 827–830, Academic, New York, 1959.

The progressive waves described by (2.141) will remain solutions of (2.143) in any of these coordinate systems; but, more significantly, the equation remains separable in all of them, allowing the standing wave solutions to be determined in the same way as before. For example, if we wished to obtain the latter for three-dimensional motion in spherical coordinates, we could write the displacement function as

$$\zeta = \zeta(r, \phi, \theta, t), \tag{2.144}$$

assume it to have the form

$$\zeta = R(r)\Phi(\phi)\Theta(\theta)T(t), \tag{2.145}$$

and substitute in (2.143),

$$\nabla^2\zeta = \frac{1}{r^2}\frac{\partial}{\partial r}\left(r^2\frac{\partial\zeta}{\partial r}\right) + \frac{1}{r^2\sin\theta}\frac{\partial}{\partial\theta}\left(\sin\theta\frac{\partial\zeta}{\partial\theta}\right) + \frac{1}{r^2\sin^2\theta}\frac{\partial^2\zeta}{\partial\phi^2} = \frac{1}{c^2}\frac{\partial^2\zeta}{\partial t^2}, \tag{2.146}$$

to obtain separated ordinary differential equations in r, ϕ, and θ. We shall return to this problem later and see how the resulting equations can be solved in terms of certain special functions which are widely used in mathematical mechanics.

Because no squares or higher powers of ϕ or its derivatives appear in (2.143), the equation may be classified as linear; and like the ordinary differential equation case studied in Sections 3.1 and 3.2, it is this property which underlies our ability to superimpose solutions, as we did to obtain (2.60). Thus, for completeness it is desirable to note that the right-hand side of the equation can also be expanded, in somewhat the same way that (1.13) of Chapter 3 was created, without destroying its linearity. The most general of such forms is

$$\nabla^2\phi = C_1\phi_{tt} + C_2\phi_t + C_3\phi - \theta(x, y, z, t), \tag{2.147}$$

where the C's indicate constants and θ some other general function of the independent variables.

Various well-known equations follow from (2.147) by placing one or several of the coefficients C, and possibly the function θ, equal to zero. For example, in addition to the case studied in detail above $(C_2 = C_3 = \theta = 0)$, when $C_1 = C_3 = \theta = 0$, the heat or diffusion equation results:

$$\nabla^2\phi = C_2\phi_t; \tag{2.148}$$

and when $C_1 = C_2 = \theta = 0$, the result is an eigenequation resembling (1.21), called the Helmholtz equation:

$$\nabla^2\phi = C_3\phi \tag{2.149}$$

Further, when $C_1 = C_2 = C_3 = 0$ and $\theta = \theta(x\ y, z)$, Poisson's equation, important in field theory, is obtained:

$$\nabla^2\phi = -\theta(x, y, z) \qquad (2.150)$$

This includes the case when $\theta = C_4$, another constant:

$$\nabla^2\phi = -C_4; \qquad (2.151)$$

however, when the constant is zero the form that follows is called Laplace's equation:

$$\nabla^2\phi = 0 \qquad (2.152)$$

All of these equations will be encountered time and again in the work that follows—though the C's may have certain special values, such as $C_1 = c^{-2}$ in (2.143), and various symbols may be used instead of ϕ, such as ζ in (2.146). In addition to those of (2.143), solutions of (2.148) and (2.152) are illustrated in the problems at the end of this section; (2.149) will be found to play a fundamental role also in the following chapter. Equations (2.150) to (2.152), together with (2.143) itself and the fully expanded form (2.147), are the central relations of electrodynamics. In fact (2.147), sometimes called the transmission equation, can be regarded as only one of the component equations of the vector form

$$\nabla^2\mathbf{A} = \alpha_1\mathbf{A}_{tt} + \alpha_2\mathbf{A}_t + \alpha_3\mathbf{A} - \mathbf{f}(x, y, z, t) \qquad (2.153)$$

which is studied in advanced electromagnetic field theory.

Since no derivatives of ϕ with respect to x, y, and z other than those represented by ∇^2 appear in (2.147), all of the equations which follow from it may be considered specialized wave equations; and although their solutions may differ considerably from those developed for (2.143), they will nevertheless continue to resemble them in certain important ways. The appearance of a Fourier series in the solution of Problem 4.2(5), which features equation (2.152), and the form of the Bessel functions, which arise as solutions of (2.148) in Problem 4.2(6), will demonstrate this point.

It may also be helpful to observe that (2.147) can be written in the Newtonian form

$$C_1\frac{\partial^2\phi}{\partial t^2} = \nabla^2\phi - C_2\phi_t - C_3\phi + \theta(x, y, z, t) = F(x, y, z, \dot{x}, \dot{y}, \dot{z}, t).$$

$$(2.154)$$

Each of the terms on the right-hand side can be interpreted as a force of some type, as in (1.12) and (2.80) of Chapter 3, provided C_1 is taken to define the effective mass of the vibrating system in appropriate units.

Problems 4.2

1. Solve the one-dimensional wave equation

$$\phi_{xx} = c^{-2}\phi_{tt}$$

for a stretched string of unit length with the initial configuration:

$$\phi(x, 0) = \begin{cases} \dfrac{x}{5} & \text{for } 0 \leqq x \leqq \tfrac{1}{2} \\[2mm] \dfrac{1-x}{5} & \text{for } \tfrac{1}{2} \leqq x \leqq 1 \end{cases}$$

Solution

We know that the waves will be transverse, with the displacement in the y-direction given by

$$\phi = \sum_{\alpha=1}^{\infty} A_\alpha \sin \alpha\pi x \cos \alpha\pi c t,$$

since $l = 1$ and $c = \sqrt{F/m}$. When $t = 0$,

$$\phi = \sum_{\alpha=1}^{\infty} A_\alpha \sin \alpha\pi x;$$

so,

$$\frac{A_\alpha}{2} = \int_0^1 \phi(x) \sin \alpha\pi x \, dx,$$

and

$$A_\alpha = \tfrac{2}{5}\int_0^{\frac{1}{2}} x \sin \alpha\pi x \, dx + \tfrac{2}{5}\int_{\frac{1}{2}}^1 (1-x)\sin \alpha\pi x \, dx.$$

To carry out the integration, it is convenient to make the substitutions

$$\alpha\pi x = \zeta, \qquad x = \frac{\zeta}{\alpha\pi}, \qquad dx = \frac{d\zeta}{\alpha\pi},$$

noting that this requires the unit length to be replaced by $\alpha\pi$ in the limits. Thus

$$A_\alpha = \tfrac{2}{5}\int_0^{\frac{\alpha\pi}{2}} \frac{\zeta}{\alpha\pi} \sin \zeta \, \frac{d\zeta}{\alpha\pi} + \tfrac{2}{5}\int_{\frac{\alpha\pi}{2}}^{\alpha\pi} \left(1 - \frac{\zeta}{\alpha\pi}\right) \sin \zeta \, \frac{d\zeta}{\alpha\pi},$$

which can be rewritten as

$$A_\alpha = \frac{2}{5(\alpha\pi)^2}\left[\int_0^{\frac{\alpha\pi}{2}} \zeta \sin \zeta \, d\zeta + \alpha\pi \int_{\frac{\alpha\pi}{2}}^{\alpha\pi} \sin \zeta \, d\zeta - \int_{\frac{\alpha\pi}{2}}^{\alpha\pi} \zeta \sin \zeta \, d\zeta\right].$$

But

$$\int \zeta \sin \zeta \, d\zeta = \sin \zeta - \zeta \cos \zeta$$

and

$$\int \sin \zeta \, d\zeta = -\cos \zeta;$$

therefore,

$$A_\alpha = \frac{2}{5(\alpha\pi)^2}\left(\left[\sin\zeta - \zeta\cos\zeta\right]_0^{\frac{\alpha\pi}{2}} - \alpha\pi\left[\cos\zeta\right]_{\frac{\alpha\pi}{2}}^{\alpha\pi} - \left[\sin\zeta - \zeta\cos\zeta\right]_{\frac{\alpha\pi}{2}}^{\alpha\pi}\right)$$

$$= \frac{2}{5(\alpha\pi)^2}\left(\sin\frac{\alpha\pi}{2} - 0 - 0 + 0 - \alpha\pi\cos\alpha\pi + 0 - 0 + \alpha\pi\cos\alpha\pi\right.$$

$$\left. + \sin\frac{\alpha\pi}{2} - 0\right)$$

$$= \frac{4}{5\alpha^2\pi^2}\sin\frac{\alpha\pi}{2}.$$

The complete solution must be:

$$\phi = \sum_{\alpha=1}^{\infty} \frac{4}{5\alpha^2\pi^2}\sin\frac{\alpha\pi}{2}\sin\alpha\pi x \cos\alpha\pi ct$$

Let us study the behavior of the first few terms. The first five coefficients may easily be calculated from the above formula for A_α:

α	A_α
1	+0.081
2	0
3	−0.009
4	0
5	+0.003

It appears that the sequence is converging rapidly, so that

$$\phi = 0.081 \sin \pi x \cos \pi ct - 0.009 \sin 3\pi x \cos 3\pi ct + 0.003 \sin 5\pi x \cos 5\pi ct$$

should be a reasonably accurate solution. The first two of these terms are illustrated in Fig. P4.2 (1) for $t = 0$.

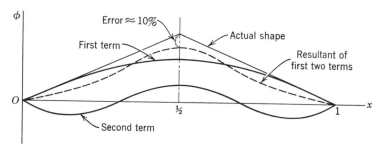

Fig. P4.2 (1)

2. Solve the vibrating string problem [Fig. P4.2 (2)] for the boundary conditions

$$\phi(0, t) = \phi(L, t) = 0$$

and the initial conditions

$$\phi(x, 0) = f(x)$$
$$\phi_t(x, 0) = g(x).$$

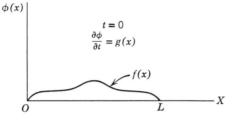

Fig. P4.2 (2)

Solution

Because the equation of motion

$$\phi_{xx} = c^{-2}\phi_{tt}$$

is linear, the problem can be solved by superimposing the solutions of two separate simpler problems: one with some initial velocity $g(x)$ but no initial displacement, and one with an initial displacement $f(x)$ but no initial velocity.

If we place

$$\phi = \eta + \zeta$$

and choose ζ such that

$$\zeta_{xx} = c^{-2}\zeta_{tt},$$

along with

$$\zeta(0, t) = \zeta(L, t) = 0$$

and

$$\zeta(x, 0) = 0$$
$$\zeta_t(x, 0) = g(x),$$

it follows from the equation of motion and the conditions given,

$$\eta_{xx} + \zeta_{xx} = c^{-2}\eta_{tt} + c^{-2}\zeta_{tt}$$
$$\eta(0, t) + \zeta(0, t) = 0, \qquad \eta(x, 0) + \zeta(x, 0) = f(x)$$
$$\eta(L, t) + \zeta(L, t) = 0, \qquad \eta_t(x, 0) + \zeta_t(x, 0) = g(x),$$

that

$$\eta_{xx} = c^{-2}\eta_{tt}$$
$$\eta(0, t) = \eta(L, t) = 0$$
$$\eta(x, 0) = f(x)$$
$$\eta_t(x, 0) = 0.$$

Now, if we assume

$$\eta = XT$$

and substitute in the last equation of motion, we obtain

$$\frac{c^2}{X} X_{xx} = \frac{1}{T} T_{tt} = -\omega^2,$$

selecting $-\omega^2$ as the separation constant. Hence the solution of the equation in x will be

$$X = C_1 \sin \frac{\omega}{c} x + C_2 \cos \frac{\omega}{c} x;$$

however, applying the boundary conditions

$$X(0) = 0 \to C_2 = 0$$

and

$$X(L) = 0 \to \sin \frac{\omega}{c} L = 0,$$

$$\omega_\alpha = \frac{\alpha \pi c}{L} \qquad \{\alpha = 1, 2, \dots;$$

thus

$$X = C_1 \sin \frac{\alpha \pi}{L} x.$$

In the same way

$$T = C_3 \sin \omega_\alpha t + C_4 \cos \omega_\alpha t;$$

but

$$T_t(0) = 0 \to C_3 = 0,$$

so

$$T = C_4 \cos \frac{\alpha \pi c}{L} t.$$

It follows that

$$\eta = C_5 \sin \frac{\alpha \pi}{L} x \cos \frac{\alpha \pi c}{L} t,$$

and we can write the general solution as

$$\eta = \sum_{\alpha=1}^{\infty} A_\alpha \sin \frac{\alpha \pi}{L} x \cos \frac{\alpha \pi c}{L} t.$$

If we like, this may be rewritten as a sum of a function of $(x - ct)$ and a function of $(x + ct)$ by applying the proper trigonometric identity:

$$\eta = \sum_{\alpha=1}^{\infty} \frac{A_\alpha}{2} \left[\sin \frac{\alpha \pi}{L}(x - ct) + \sin \frac{\alpha \pi}{L} (x + ct) \right]$$

Furthermore, since at zero time

$$\eta(x, 0) = f(x),$$

we know that

$$f(x) = \sum_{\alpha=1}^{\infty} A_\alpha \sin \frac{\alpha \pi}{L} x,$$

from which the A_α's can be determined by the Fourier method.

Similarly, by solving the ζ part of the original equation together with its boundary and initial conditions, we can obtain

$$\zeta = \sum_{\alpha=1}^{\infty} B_\alpha \sin \frac{\alpha\pi}{L} x \sin \frac{\alpha\pi c}{L} t$$

and

$$g(x) = \sum_{\alpha=1}^{\infty} B_\alpha \frac{\alpha\pi c}{L} \sin \frac{\alpha\pi}{L} x.$$

Of course, the total solution will be given by

$$\phi = \eta + \zeta.$$

3. Find the wave that results from superimposing two waves with the same amplitude A, but with slightly different wavelengths and velocities:

$$\phi_1 = A \sin \frac{2\pi}{\lambda_1} (x - c_1 t)$$

$$\phi_2 = A \sin \frac{2\pi}{\lambda_2} (x - c_2 t).$$

Solution

Since $k = 2\pi/\lambda$ and $\omega = 2\pi\nu = 2\pi c/\lambda$, the component waves can be written as:

$$\phi_1 = A \sin (k_1 x - \omega_1 t)$$
$$\phi_2 = A \sin (k_2 x - \omega_2 t)$$

Superimposing and applying the appropriate trigonometric identity, we obtain

$$\phi = \phi_1 + \phi_2 = 2A \sin \{\tfrac{1}{2}(k_1 x - \omega_1 t + k_2 x - \omega_2 t)\}$$
$$\times \cos \{\tfrac{1}{2}(k_1 x - \omega_1 t - k_2 x + \omega_2 t)\}$$

$$= 2A \sin \left(\frac{k_1 + k_2}{2} x - \frac{\omega_1 + \omega_2}{2} t \right) \cos \left(\frac{k_1 - k_2}{2} x - \frac{\omega_1 - \omega_2}{2} t \right).$$

But if we assume that the differences in wavelength and velocity are very small, so that

$$k_1 = k + dk, \qquad k_2 = k - dk$$

and

$$\omega_1 = \omega + d\omega, \qquad \omega_2 = \omega - d\omega,$$

then

$$\phi = \{2A \cos [(dk)x - (d\omega)t]\} \sin (kx - \omega t).$$

The term

$$\{2A \cos [(dk)x - (d\omega)t]\}$$

represents a modulation of the progressive plane wave

$$\sin (kx - \omega t),$$

which is the average of the two components. Thus we have a moving sine wave whose amplitude is modulated by a moving cosine wave [see Fig. P4.2 (3)].

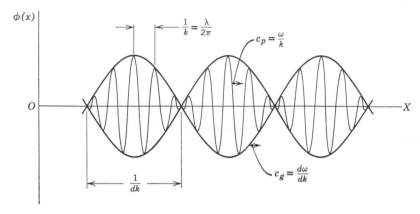

Fig. P4.2 (3)

Because the latter can also be written as

$$\sin \frac{2\pi}{\lambda}\left(x - \frac{\omega}{k}\,t\right),$$

we see that the velocity of the wave itself, called the phase velocity, must be

$$c_p = \frac{\omega}{k}\,;$$

in the same way the velocity of the amplitude-modulating wave, called the group velocity, must be

$$c_g = \frac{d\omega}{dk}\,.$$

It is evident that

$$c_g = \frac{d(c_p k)}{dk} = c_p + k\frac{dc_p}{dk}\,;$$

but since

$$k\frac{dc_p}{dk} = \frac{2\pi}{\lambda}\left(\frac{dc_p}{d\lambda}\frac{d\lambda}{dk}\right) = \frac{2\pi}{\lambda}\left(-\frac{2\pi}{k^2}\right)\frac{dc_p}{d\lambda} = -\frac{4\pi^2}{\lambda}\left(\frac{\lambda^2}{4\pi^2}\right)\frac{dc_p}{d\lambda} = -\lambda\frac{dc_p}{d\lambda}\,,$$

this also takes the form

$$c_g = c_p - \lambda\frac{dc_p}{d\lambda}\,,$$

relating the two velocities. The quantity $dc_p/d\lambda$ measures the dispersion caused by the medium; if there is no dispersion, energy will be transported with the phase velocity. The group velocity phenomenon can be observed in water waves, where $dc_p/d\lambda > 0$ so that $c_g < c_p$. Individual waves will appear to die out at the front of one group and reappear at the back of the next.

4. Reduce the nonhomogeneous wave equation

$$\phi_{xx} = c^{-2}\phi_{tt} + \theta(x)$$

to three ordinary differential equations.

Solution

Clearly, if we try the form $\phi = X(x)T(t)$ the equation is not separable, because in

$$T\frac{d^2X}{dx^2} = \frac{X}{c^2}\frac{d^2T}{dt^2} + \theta(x)$$

the variables cannot be separated; we can, however, try

$$\phi = X(x)T(t) + \gamma(x).$$

Then,

$$\phi_x = T\frac{dX}{dx} + \frac{d\gamma}{dx}$$

$$\phi_{xx} = T\frac{d^2X}{dx^2} + \frac{d^2\gamma}{dx^2}$$

and

$$\phi_{tt} = X\frac{d^2T}{dt^2} \; ;$$

so substitution gives

$$T\frac{d^2X}{dx^2} + \frac{d^2\gamma}{dx^2} = \frac{X}{c^2}\frac{d^2T}{dt^2} + \theta(x).$$

If $d^2\gamma/dx^2 = \theta(x)$, we are left with

$$T\frac{d^2X}{dx^2} = \frac{X}{c^2}\frac{d^2T}{dt^2},$$

which separates as before. Hence the equations to be satisfied are

$$\frac{d^2\gamma}{dx^2} = \theta(x)$$

$$\frac{d^2X}{dx^2} + \left(\frac{\omega}{c}\right)^2 X = 0$$

$$\frac{d^2T}{dt^2} + \omega^2 T = 0$$

where $-\omega^2$ is the separation constant.

5. If in the two-dimensional rectangular region illustrated in Fig. P4.2 (5) the temperature function τ (analogous to the displacement function ϕ) is independent of time, and satisfies the equation

$$\tau_{xx} + \tau_{yy} = 0$$

together with the boundary conditions

$$\tau_x(0, y) = 0 \quad \text{for} \quad 0 < y < h$$
$$\tau_x(l, y) = 0 \quad \text{for} \quad 0 < y < h$$
$$\tau_y(x, h) = 0 \quad \text{for} \quad 0 < x < l$$

and

$$\tau_y(x, 0) = f(x) \quad \text{for} \quad 0 < x < l,$$

what particular form will it have?

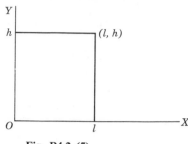

Fig. P4.2 (5)

Solution

The requirement is to solve the two-dimensional Laplace equation for the steady-state temperature distribution $\tau(x, y)$ subject to the given boundary conditions. Since it is reasonable to think of this as arising from standing heat waves, let us try for a solution of the form

$$\tau = X(x)\,Y(y).$$

Indicating ordinary derivatives of these functions by primes and substituting in the equation of motion, we obtain:

$$X''Y + XY'' = 0$$

$$\frac{X''}{X} = -\frac{Y''}{Y} = -k^2, \qquad \text{a constant}$$

$$X'' + k^2 X = 0$$
$$Y'' - k^2 Y = 0$$

But applying the first two boundary conditions we see that

$$\tau_x(0, y) = X'(0)\,Y(y) = 0 \rightarrow X'(0) = 0$$

and

$$\tau_x(l, y) = X'(l)\,Y(y) = 0 \rightarrow X'(l) = 0.$$

Consequently it follows from writing the solution of the equation $X'' + k^2 X = 0$ as

$$X = C_1 \cos kx + C_2 \sin kx,$$

and differentiating with respect to x,

$$X'(x) = -kC_1 \sin kx + C_2 k \cos kx,$$

that

$$X'(0) = C_2 k = 0 \rightarrow C_2 = 0$$

and

$$X'(l) = -kC_1 \sin kl = 0 \rightarrow k = \frac{n\pi}{l} \qquad \{n = 0, 1, 2, \ldots$$

Therefore,

$$X = C_1 \cos \frac{n\pi}{l}\, x\,.$$

Considering the other equation,

$$Y'' - \left(\frac{n\pi}{l}\right)^2 Y = 0,$$

we can write the solution as

$$Y = B_1 \cosh \frac{n\pi}{l} y + B_2 \sinh \frac{n\pi}{l} y,$$

and differentiate it with respect to y,

$$Y'(y) = \frac{n\pi}{l} B_1 \sinh \frac{n\pi}{l} y + B_2 \frac{n\pi}{l} \cosh \frac{n\pi}{l} y;$$

so that when we apply the third boundary condition the result is

$$\tau_y(x, h) = X(x) Y'(h) = 0 \rightarrow Y'(h) = 0 = \frac{n\pi}{l} B_1 \sinh \frac{n\pi}{l} h + \frac{n\pi}{l} B_2 \cosh \frac{n\pi}{l} h$$

or

$$B_2 = - \frac{B_1 \sinh \dfrac{n\pi}{l} h}{\cosh \dfrac{n\pi}{l} h} = -B_1 \tanh \frac{n\pi}{l} h.$$

Thus,

$$Y = B_1 \left[\cosh \frac{n\pi}{l} y - \tanh \frac{n\pi}{l} h \sinh \frac{n\pi}{l} y \right]$$

$$= \frac{B_1}{\cosh \dfrac{n\pi}{l} h} \left[\cosh \frac{n\pi}{l} y \cosh \frac{n\pi}{l} h - \sinh \frac{n\pi}{l} y \sinh \frac{n\pi}{l} h \right]$$

$$= B_3 \cosh \frac{n\pi}{l} (y - h).$$

We have determined everything but the coefficients C_n in the expression

$$\tau(x, y) = \sum_{n=0}^{\infty} C_n \cosh \frac{n\pi}{l} (y - h) \cos \frac{n\pi}{l} x;$$

but the final boundary condition yields

$$\tau_y(x, 0) = \sum_{n=0}^{\infty} C_n \frac{n\pi}{l} \sinh \frac{n\pi}{l} (-h) \cos \frac{n\pi}{l} x = f(x).$$

If we let

$$C_n \frac{n\pi}{l} \sinh \left(-\frac{n\pi h}{l} \right) = A_n,$$

this may be written in the usual Fourier form,

$$\sum_{n=0}^{\infty} A_n \cos \frac{n\pi}{l} x = f(x),$$

and we immediately know that:

$$A_n = \frac{2}{l} \int_0^l f(x) \cos \frac{n\pi}{l} x \, dx \qquad \{n \neq 0$$

$$A_0 = \frac{1}{l} \int_0^l f(x) \, dx$$

6. In the long, symmetrical solid cylinder shown in Fig. P4.2 (6a) the temperature function τ is independent of z and ϕ and satisfies the heat equation

$$\nabla^2 \tau = \frac{1}{\alpha^2} \tau_t,$$

α^2 being the thermal diffusivity, as well as the boundary and initial conditions:

$$\tau(a, t) = 0$$
$$\tau(\rho, 0) = g(\rho)$$

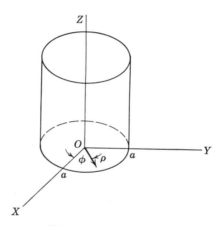

Fig. P4.2 (6a)

Obtain an appropriate algebraic expression for $\tau(\rho, t)$.

Solution

If we replace ∇^2 by its expanded cylindrical coordinate form, the heat equation becomes

$$\tau_{\rho\rho} + \frac{1}{\rho} \tau_\rho + \frac{1}{\rho^2} \tau_{\phi\phi} + \tau_{zz} = \alpha^{-2}\tau_t;$$

but since in this case τ is known to be independent of ϕ and z, the equation reduces to

$$\tau_{\rho\rho} + \frac{1}{\rho} \tau_\rho = \alpha^{-2}\tau_t.$$

Again we may consider a product form of solution,

$$\tau(\rho, t) = P(\rho)T(t),$$

and substitute to obtain

$$TP'' + \frac{T}{\rho} P' = \frac{P}{\alpha^2} T'$$

or

$$\frac{P''}{P} + \frac{P'}{\rho P} = \frac{T'}{\alpha^2 T} = -k^2, \qquad \text{a constant.}$$

The sign of the constant follows from noting that an exponential increase of temperature with time is impossible.

Clearly, the solution of the equation

$$T' + (\alpha k)^2 T = 0$$

will be

$$T = C_1 e^{-(\alpha k)^2 t}.$$

Let us consider the other equation,

$$\frac{d^2 P(\rho)}{d\rho^2} + \frac{1}{\rho} \frac{dP(\rho)}{d\rho} + k^2 P(\rho) = 0.$$

Although we have not encountered an equation of this type before, it is not difficult to recognize it as a Bessel form, the solutions of which are well known. To put it in the standard form for a Bessel equation of order p,

$$x^2 \frac{d^2 y}{dx^2} + x \frac{dy}{dx} + (x^2 - p^2)y = 0,$$

we can utilize the change of variable

$$x = k\rho \qquad \{k > 0,$$

x being understood as the independent Bessel variable, not a position co-ordinate. Then we may write

$$\frac{dP}{d\rho} = \frac{dP}{dx} \frac{dx}{d\rho} = k \frac{dP}{dx}$$

and

$$\frac{d^2 P}{d\rho^2} = \frac{d}{d\rho} \left(\frac{dP}{d\rho} \right) = \frac{d}{dx} \left(k \frac{dP}{dx} \right) \frac{dx}{d\rho}$$

$$= k^2 \frac{d^2 P}{dx^2}.$$

Now if we place $P(\rho)$ equal to the dependent Bessel variable,

$$y(x) = P(\rho),$$

and substitute, the result is

$$k^2 \frac{d^2 y}{dx^2} + \frac{k^2}{x} \frac{dy}{dx} + k^2 y = 0$$

or, dividing by k^2 and multiplying by x^2,

$$x^2 \frac{d^2 y}{dx^2} + x \frac{dy}{dx} + x^2 y = 0,$$

which must be a Bessel equation of order zero.

Reference to standard tables[18] will show the solutions of the Bessel equation of order zero to be

$$y = J_0(x) = \sum_{n=0}^{\infty} \frac{(-1)^n \left(\frac{x}{2}\right)^{2n}}{(n!)^2}$$

and

$$y = J_0(x) \log x + \sum_{n=0}^{\infty} \frac{(-1)^{n+1}\beta(n)x^{2n}}{2^{2n}(n!)^2} \qquad \{\beta = 1 + \tfrac{1}{2} + \tfrac{1}{3} + \cdots + \frac{1}{n};$$

however, the second solution has singularities at the origin, where $x = k\rho = 0$, and thus is not permissible. The first solution is illustrated in Fig. P4.2 (6*b*).

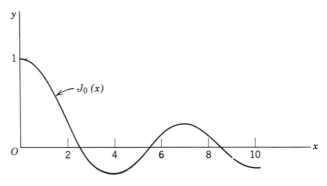

Fig. P4.2 (6*b*)

We conclude that $\tau(\rho, t)$ must be given by

$$\tau = AJ_0(x)e^{-(\alpha k)^2 t} = AJ_0(k\rho)e^{-(\alpha k)^2 t}.$$

Applying the boundary condition

$$\tau(a, t) = 0,$$

we see that it will be satisfied if

$$J_0(k, a) = 0.$$

This can be accomplished by writing $\tau(\rho, t)$ in the form

$$\tau = \sum_{i=1}^{\infty} A_i J_0(k_i \rho)e^{-k_i^2 \alpha^2 t}$$

and selecting the k_i such that

$$J_0(k_i a) = 0 \qquad \{i = 1, 2, 3, \ldots.$$

[18] Abramowitz, M., and I. A. Stegun (eds.), *Handbook of Mathematical Functions*, pp. 358, 359, Dover, New York, 1965.

If we use the initial condition

$$\tau(\rho, 0) = g(\rho),$$

it follows that

$$\sum_{i=1}^{\infty} A_i J_0(k_i \rho) = g(\rho),$$

and from this relation the A_i's can be calculated in about the same way as before by taking advantage of the orthogonality of the Bessel functions. The formula which results is:

$$A_i = \frac{\displaystyle\int_0^a \rho g(\rho) J_0(k_i \rho)\, d\rho}{\dfrac{a^2}{2}\, [J_1(k_i a)]^2}.$$

7. The equation that describes the vibrations of a circular membrane in polar coordinates [Fig. P4.2 (7)] is

$$w_{\rho\rho} + \frac{1}{\rho} w_\rho + \frac{1}{\rho^2} w_{\phi\phi} = c^{-2} w_{tt},$$

w being the preferred symbol for the displacement function in this case. If the boundary and initial conditions are

$$w(a, \phi, t) = 0$$

$$w(\rho, \phi, 0) = f(\rho, \phi)$$

and

$$w_t(\rho, \phi, 0) = 0,$$

solve for $w(\rho, \phi, t)$.

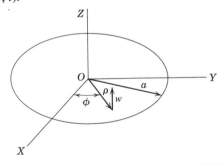

Fig. P4.2 (7)

Solution

Assuming that

$$w = P(\rho)\Phi(\phi)T(t),$$

substitution and further separation gives

$$\frac{1}{c^2 T} T_{tt} = \frac{1}{P}\left(P_{\rho\rho} + \frac{1}{\rho} w_\rho\right) + \frac{1}{\Phi \rho^2} \Phi_{\phi\phi} = -\lambda^2, \qquad \text{a constant.}$$

For the solution of the equation in t,

$$T'' + (c\lambda)^2 T = 0,$$

we may write

$$T = D \cos c\lambda t + D' \sin c\lambda t.$$

But the last initial condition tells us that D' must be zero; thus

$$T = D \cos c\lambda t.$$

Separating again,

$$\frac{1}{P}(\rho^2 P_{\rho\rho} + \rho P_\rho) + \lambda^2 \rho^2 = -\frac{1}{\Phi}\Phi_{\phi\phi} = \mu^2, \qquad \text{a constant,}$$

we can immediately write the solution of the equation in ϕ,

$$\Phi'' + \mu^2\Phi = 0,$$

as

$$\Phi = C \sin \mu\phi + C' \cos \mu\phi.$$

The remaining equation is

$$\rho^2 P'' + \rho P' + (\lambda^2\rho^2 - \mu^2)P = 0,$$

which is of the Bessel form. If we require μ to be some integer n, we may represent the solutions as

$$P = J_n(\lambda\rho)$$

where λ is any of the roots λ_{nj} of the equation

$$J_n(\lambda a) = 0,$$

which follows from the boundary condition.

We conclude that

$$w = P\Phi T = J_n(\lambda_{nj}\rho)(A_{nj} \cos n\phi + B_{nj} \sin n\phi) \cos c\lambda_{nj}t,$$

while the most general solution should be

$$w = \sum_{n=0}^{\infty} \sum_{j=1}^{\infty} J_n(\lambda_{nj}\rho)(A_{nj} \cos n\phi + B_{nj} \sin n\phi) \cos c\lambda_{nj}t.$$

However, making use of the initial configuration,

$$w(\rho, \phi, 0) = f(\rho, \phi),$$

we see that

$$f(\rho, \phi) = \sum_{n=0}^{\infty}\left\{\left[\sum_{j=1}^{\infty} A_{nj}J_n(\lambda_{nj}\rho)\right]\cos n\phi + \left[\sum_{j=1}^{\infty} B_{nj}J_n(\lambda_{nj}\rho)\right]\sin n\phi\right\},$$

and the formulae for the Fourier coefficients yield the relations

$$\sum_{j=1}^{\infty} A_{nj}J_n(\lambda_{nj}\rho) = \begin{cases} \dfrac{1}{\pi}\displaystyle\int_{-\pi}^{\pi} f(\rho, \phi) \cos n\phi \, d\phi & \{n = 1, 2, 3, \ldots \\[2ex] \dfrac{1}{2\pi}\displaystyle\int_{-\pi}^{\pi} f(\rho, \phi) \, d\phi & \{n = 0 \end{cases}$$

and

$$\sum_{j=1}^{\infty} B_{nj} J_n(\lambda_{nj}\rho) = \frac{1}{\pi} \int_{-\pi}^{\pi} f(\rho, \phi) \sin n\phi \, d\phi.$$

These determine the A_{nj} and B_{nj}.[19]

Exercises 4.2

1. Prove that a solution of the form

$$\phi = g(x + ct) + h(x - ct)$$

will always satisfy the one-dimensional wave equation

$$\phi_{xx} = c^{-2}\phi_{tt}.$$

2. Put the solution

$$\phi = A \sin \frac{\alpha \pi}{l} x \cos \frac{\alpha \pi c}{l} t + B \sin \frac{\alpha \pi}{l} x \sin \frac{\alpha \pi c}{l} t$$

of the one-dimensional wave equation in the form

$$\phi = g(x + ct) + h(x - ct).$$

3. Show that a solution of the form

$$\phi = \frac{g(r + ct) + h(r - ct)}{r}$$

will satisfy the three-dimensional wave equation.

4. Determine the displacement function $\phi(x, t)$ for a vibrating string of length l if the boundary and initial conditions are:

$$\phi(0, t) = \phi(l, t) = 0$$
$$\phi(x, 0) = 0$$
$$\phi_t(x, 0) = v(x).$$

5. An elastic cord of length $l = 4$ ft is fixed at both ends. If a point at $x = 1$ ft is displaced laterally a distance of $\frac{1}{10}$ ft and released from rest [see Fig. E4.2 (5)], find the motion of the cord by the Fourier method, starting with

$$\phi = \sum_{\alpha=1}^{\infty} A_\alpha \sin \frac{\alpha \pi}{l} x \cos \frac{\alpha \pi c}{l} t.$$

Fig. E4.2 (5)

[19] Hildebrand, F. B., *Advanced Calculus for Applications*, pp. 226–231, Prentice-Hall, Englewood Cliffs, N.J., 1962.

6. An elastic bar with fixed ends is acted upon by a constant axial force P applied at the middle, as shown in Fig. E4.2 (6). Accordingly, the initial configuration of the system is

$$\phi(x, 0) = \varepsilon x \quad \text{for} \quad 0 < x < l/2$$

$$\phi(x, 0) = \varepsilon(l - x) \quad \text{for} \quad l/2 < x < l$$

where ε, the unit elongation in the left-hand part of the bar, is equal to the unit compression in the right-hand part. Derive the general expression for the displacement of bar cross-sections as a function of position and time, $\phi(x, t)$, and show how the Fourier coefficients can be evaluated without actually carrying out the integration.

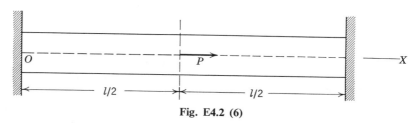

Fig. E4.2 (6)

7. Consider two sine waves having the same frequency but different amplitudes and phase angles. If the displacements associated with these waves are in the same direction, they can be represented by the expressions

$$\phi_1 = A_1 \sin (\omega t + \alpha_1)$$

and

$$\phi_2 = A_2 \sin (\omega t + \alpha_2).$$

Show that their resultant will be a sine wave of amplitude

$$A_3 = [A_1^2 + A_2^2 + 2A_1 A_2 \cos (\alpha_1 - \alpha_2)]^{1/2}$$

and phase angle

$$\alpha_3 = \tan^{-1} \left[\frac{A_1 \sin \alpha_1 + A_2 \sin \alpha_2}{A_1 \cos \alpha_1 + A_2 \cos \alpha_2} \right].$$

8. Two waves of the form

$$\phi_1 = 18 \sin (3\pi t - 6\beta)$$

$$\phi_2 = 18 \sin (3\pi t + 6\beta)$$

are superimposed. Describe the resulting wave and calculate its amplitude at the following points:

a. $\beta = \pi$

b. $\beta = \dfrac{5\pi}{2}$

What is the special significance of these points?

9. How many boundary conditions are required for a solution of the equation

$$\nabla^2 \phi = c^{-2} \phi_{tt}$$

in three dimensions? Formulate the conditions that should be used when the equation is applied to the vibrations of a fluid filling a rectangular box, and explain how they will enter into the solution.

10. Expressing the equation governing one-dimensional heat flow in the form

$$\tau_{xx} = \alpha^{-2} \tau_t,$$

where α^2 is a constant and τ is the temperature function, solve for $\tau(x, t)$ in the cylinder shown in Fig. E4.2 (10) if the boundary and initial conditions are

$$\tau(0, t) = 0$$

$$\tau(L, t) = T_0, \text{ a constant}$$

$$\tau(x, 0) = 0.$$

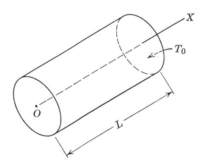

Fig. E4.2 (10)

4.3   Electromagnetic Waves

While an oscillating point mass will produce a material wave only if it is strongly coupled to others, electromagnetic waves are generated by oscillating point charges and require no material medium for their propagation. If, for example, a static charge starts to vibrate periodically along a short line segment at time $t = 0$, periodically oscillating electric and magnetic fields $\mathbf{E}(\mathbf{r}, t)$ and $\mathbf{H}(\mathbf{r}, t)$ will be generated. At every point on a radial line through the center of the segment, $\mathbf{E}$ will remain perpendicular to $\mathbf{H}$ at all times; and these combined fields will propagate outward along the line with the speed c by the process of mutual induction. Being in phase, they may have the plane wave configuration shown in Fig. 4.8 along the positive X-axis at some later time t.

These well-known physical facts, and much of the rest of classical electrodynamics as well, are contained in Maxwell's equations [(3.31) to (3.34) of Chapter 2]:

$$\nabla \times \mathbf{E} + \mathbf{B}_t = 0$$

$$\nabla \cdot \mathbf{B} = 0$$

$$\nabla \times \mathbf{H} - \mathbf{D}_t = \mathbf{J} = \mathbf{j} + \rho\mathbf{v}$$

$$\nabla \cdot \mathbf{D} = \rho$$

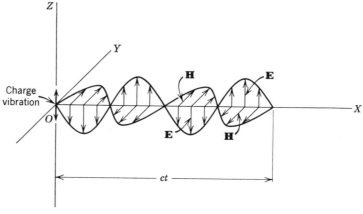

Fig. 4.8

To understand why this is so, let us begin by eliminating the electric and magnetic flux densities $\mathbf{D}(\mathbf{r}, t)$ and $\mathbf{B}(\mathbf{r}, t)$ from the equations. Because

$$\mathbf{D} = \varepsilon\mathbf{E}, \tag{3.1}$$

$$\mathbf{B} = \mu\mathbf{H} \tag{3.2}$$

and

$$\mathbf{j} = \sigma\mathbf{E} \tag{3.3}$$

where ε is the permittivity, μ the permeability, and σ the conductivity of the medium containing the fields,[20] they can immediately be rewritten in the form

$$\nabla \times \mathbf{E} = -\mu\mathbf{H}_t \tag{3.4}$$

$$\nabla \cdot \mathbf{H} = 0 \tag{3.5}$$

$$\nabla \times \mathbf{H} = \varepsilon\mathbf{E}_t + \sigma\mathbf{E} + \rho\mathbf{v} \tag{3.6}$$

$$\nabla \cdot \mathbf{E} = \frac{\rho}{\varepsilon}, \tag{3.7}$$

[20] Holt, C. A., *Introduction to Electromagnetic Fields and Waves*, pp. 113–136, Wiley, New York, 1963.

provided the medium is homogeneous and isotropic so that ε and μ can be considered constants. In a vacuum both may be placed equal to unity.

However, if we are willing to restrict ourselves to a region far from the source of the field, in which there are no charges other than those in possible drift currents, $\rho = 0$ and (3.4) to (3.7) become:

$$\nabla \times \mathbf{E} = -\mu \mathbf{H}_t \tag{3.8}$$

$$\nabla \cdot \mathbf{H} = 0 \tag{3.9}$$

$$\nabla \times \mathbf{H} = \varepsilon \mathbf{E}_t + \sigma \mathbf{E} \tag{3.10}$$

$$\nabla \cdot \mathbf{E} = 0 \tag{3.11}$$

With the equations in this form it is easy to see why they describe electromagnetic waves of the type illustrated in Fig. 4.8.

The development features the well-known relationship for any vector $\mathbf{w}$ [see Problem 1.2(14)]:

$$\nabla \times \nabla \times \mathbf{w} = -\nabla^2 \mathbf{w} \quad \text{if} \quad \nabla \cdot \mathbf{w} = 0 \tag{3.12}$$

Using this, if we form the cross product of both sides of (3.8) with ∇,

$$\nabla \times \nabla \times \mathbf{E} = -\mu (\nabla \times \mathbf{H})_t, \tag{3.13}$$

then substitute for $\nabla \times \mathbf{H}$ from (3.10),

$$\begin{aligned} \nabla \times \nabla \times \mathbf{E} &= -\mu \left(\varepsilon \mathbf{E}_t + \sigma \mathbf{E} \right)_t \\ &= -\mu \varepsilon \mathbf{E}_{tt} - \mu \sigma \mathbf{E}_t, \end{aligned} \tag{3.14}$$

and recognize the existence of (3.11), the result is

$$\nabla^2 \mathbf{E} = \alpha_1 \mathbf{E}_{tt} + \alpha_2 \mathbf{E}_t, \tag{3.15}$$

where

$$\alpha_1 = \varepsilon \mu \tag{3.16}$$

and

$$\alpha_2 = \sigma \mu. \tag{3.17}$$

Similarly, starting with (3.10), substituting for $\nabla \times \mathbf{E}$ from (3.8) and recognizing (3.9), we obtain:

$$\begin{aligned} \nabla \times \nabla \times \mathbf{H} &= \varepsilon (\nabla \times \mathbf{F})_t + \sigma (\nabla \times \mathbf{E}) \\ &= -\varepsilon \mu \mathbf{H}_{tt} - \sigma \mu \mathbf{H}_t \end{aligned} \tag{3.18}$$

or

$$\nabla^2 \mathbf{H} = \alpha_1 \mathbf{H}_{tt} + \alpha_2 \mathbf{H}_t. \tag{3.19}$$

It is now evident that both (3.15), describing the way $\mathbf{E}$ varies with $\mathbf{r}$ and t, and (3.19), describing the corresponding variation of $\mathbf{H}$, are wave equations of the general form (2.153).

When the medium is nonconducting, σ will be zero and

$$\alpha_2 = 0. \tag{3.20}$$

In this case the energy-dissipating terms associated with drift currents will vanish, and the equations of motion of the resulting conservative system will be:

$$\nabla^2 \mathbf{E} = \alpha_1 \mathbf{E}_{tt} \tag{3.21}$$

$$\nabla^2 \mathbf{H} = \alpha_1 \mathbf{H}_{tt} \tag{3.22}$$

Since, for a plane wave of the kind shown in Fig. 4.8, both $\mathbf{E}$ and $\mathbf{H}$ depend only on x and t, the first of these clearly represents the three scalar equations,

$$\frac{\partial^2}{\partial t^2} E_x(x, t) - \frac{1}{\alpha_1} \frac{\partial^2}{\partial x^2} E_x(x, t) = 0 \tag{3.23}$$

$$\frac{\partial^2}{\partial t^2} E_y(x, t) - \frac{1}{\alpha_1} \frac{\partial^2}{\partial x^2} E_y(x, t) = 0 \tag{3.24}$$

$$\frac{\partial^2}{\partial t^2} E_z(x, t) - \frac{1}{\alpha_1} \frac{\partial^2}{\partial x^2} E_z(x, t) = 0, \tag{3.25}$$

while the second represents the three equations:

$$\frac{\partial^2}{\partial t^2} H_x(x, t) - \frac{1}{\alpha_1} \frac{\partial^2}{\partial x^2} H_x(x, t) = 0 \tag{3.26}$$

$$\frac{\partial^2}{\partial t^2} H_y(x, t) - \frac{1}{\alpha_1} \frac{\partial^2}{\partial x^2} H_y(x, t) = 0 \tag{3.27}$$

$$\frac{\partial^2}{\partial t^2} H_z(x, t) - \frac{1}{\alpha_1} \frac{\partial^2}{\partial x^2} H_z(x, t) = 0 \tag{3.28}$$

All are of the form (2.78),

$$\frac{\partial^2}{\partial t^2} \phi(x, t) - c^2 \frac{\partial^2}{\partial x^2} \phi(x, t) = 0;$$

therefore, it follows that the constant

$$\alpha_1 = \varepsilon\mu = \frac{1}{c^2}, \tag{3.29}$$

where c is known to be the propagation speed of the wave. An analysis of the units of ε and μ gives the same result; for example,

$$\varepsilon\mu = \frac{\text{farads}}{\text{meter}} \times \frac{\text{henrys}}{\text{meter}} = \frac{T^2 Q^2}{L^3 M} \times \frac{LM}{Q^2} = \frac{T^2}{L^2} = \frac{1}{\text{speed}^2}.$$

Under circumstances where ε and μ vary, the speed of the wave may also vary, of course. This is reflected in the relation defining the index of refraction n for any medium of propagation:

$$n = \frac{c}{c'} = \sqrt{\varepsilon\mu}, \tag{3.30}$$

where c' represents the speed of a light wave in the medium and c its speed in a vacuum. As long as the product of ε and μ equals unity, there is no distinction between c and c'; it can also be shown[21] that, as long as there is very little change in one wavelength, n can continue to be regarded as a constant and (2.78) applied. This is the reason why c was selected to represent the propagation velocity of a plane wave; electromagnetic waves are featured in this book, and these are known to propagate with the speed of light.

For similar reasons, the general Maxwell equations are often written as[22]

$$\nabla \times \mathbf{E} + \mathbf{B}_t = 0 \tag{3.31}$$

$$\nabla \cdot \mathbf{B} = 0 \tag{3.32}$$

$$c^2 \nabla \times \mathbf{B} - \mathbf{E}_t = \frac{\mathbf{J}}{\varepsilon} \tag{3.33}$$

$$\nabla \cdot \mathbf{E} = \frac{\rho}{\varepsilon} \tag{3.34}$$

These come directly from the first ones given [(3.31) to (3.34) of Chapter 2] when $\mathbf{H}$ is replaced by $\mathbf{B}/\mu$, $\mathbf{D}$ by $\varepsilon\mathbf{E}$, and $\varepsilon\mu$ by $1/c^2$ through use of the relations given above.

It also follows that the general solutions of all of the equations will be of the form (2.89),

$$\phi = g(x + ct) + h(x - ct)$$

or, because we are only interested in waves propagating outward from the source,

$$\phi = h(x - ct). \tag{3.35}$$

Hence, we may write:

$$E_x = h_1(x - ct) \tag{3.36}$$

$$E_y = h_2(x - ct) \tag{3.37}$$

$$E_z = h_3(x - ct) \tag{3.38}$$

[21] Goldstein, H., *Classical Mechanics*, pp. 310–312, Addison-Wesley, Reading, Mass., 1959.

[22] Feynman, R. P., R. B. Leighton, and M. Sands, *Lectures on Physics*, Vol. 2, pp. 20–1, Addison-Wesley, Reading, Mass., 1964.

and

$$H_x = h_4(x - ct) \tag{3.39}$$

$$H_y = h_5(x - ct) \tag{3.40}$$

$$H_z = h_6(x - ct) \tag{3.41}$$

Furthermore, in view of the fact that the divergence of both $\mathbf{E}(x, t)$ and $\mathbf{H}(x, t)$ is zero, from (3.9) and (3.11), the relations

$$\frac{\partial}{\partial x} E_x = 0 \tag{3.42}$$

and

$$\frac{\partial}{\partial x} H_x = 0 \tag{3.43}$$

also apply. Therefore E_x and H_x must be constants, for which zero may be selected, since static fields of this type actually are absent. With

$$E_x = 0 \tag{3.44}$$

and

$$H_x = 0, \tag{3.45}$$

the resulting waves obviously will be transverse.

Also, substituting the solutions for the y- and z-components [(3.37), (3.38), (3.40), and (3.41)] in the appropriate scalar equations represented by (3.8),

$$\frac{\partial}{\partial x} E_z = \mu \frac{\partial}{\partial t} H_y \tag{3.46}$$

and

$$\frac{\partial}{\partial x} E_y = -\mu \frac{\partial}{\partial t} H_z, \tag{3.47}$$

we see that

$$\frac{\partial}{\partial x} h_3(x - ct) = \mu \frac{\partial}{\partial t} h_5(x - ct) \tag{3.48}$$

so that

$$h_3(x - ct) = -\mu h_5(x - ct), \tag{3.49}$$

and

$$\frac{\partial}{\partial x} h_2(x - ct) = -\mu \frac{\partial}{\partial t} h_6(x - ct) \tag{3.50}$$

so that

$$h_2(x - ct) = \mu h_6(x - ct). \tag{3.51}$$

We conclude that in the present case, the components of **E** and **H** must be:

$$E_x = 0 \tag{3.52}$$

$$E_y = h_2(x - ct) \tag{3.53}$$

$$E_z = h_3(x - ct) \tag{3.54}$$

$$H_x = 0 \tag{3.55}$$

$$H_y = -\frac{h_3(x - ct)}{\mu} \tag{3.56}$$

$$H_z = \frac{h_2(x - ct)}{\mu} \tag{3.57}$$

With these values

$$\mathbf{E} \cdot \mathbf{H} = (h_2 \hat{\mathbf{j}} + h_3 \hat{\mathbf{k}}) \cdot \left(-\frac{h_3}{\mu} \hat{\mathbf{j}} + \frac{h_2}{\mu} \hat{\mathbf{k}} \right)$$

$$= -\frac{h_2 h_3}{\mu} + \frac{h_3 h_2}{\mu} ; \tag{3.58}$$

therefore,
$$\mathbf{E} \cdot \mathbf{H} = 0 \tag{3.59}$$

and the fields must be perpendicular at all times, as stated in the beginning and illustrated in Fig. 4.8. However, because H_z and F_y need not be zero in general, the wave configuration shown can actually rotate about the X-axis. If it does not, the electromagnetic wave is said to be plane-polarized; if it does, but the y- and z-components are related in such a way that the tips of **E** and **H** describe ellipses (or circles), the wave is said to be elliptically (or circularly) polarized. For a source of the type assumed, E_y will be zero along the X-axis and the wave will be plane-polarized. The initial claim that **E** and **H** will remain in phase is also substantiated by (3.52) to (3.57). Of course if $\mu = 1$, as for light or radio waves propagating in empty space, they will also have the same magnitude:

$$|\mathbf{E}| = \sqrt{h_2^2 + h_3^2} = |\mathbf{H}|. \tag{3.60}$$

The cross product of **E** with **H** is a vector quantity of fundamental importance in electrognematic theory. Multiplied by c^2, it can be identified[23] with the energy flow density, or flux, and is called the Poynting vector **S**:

$$\mathbf{S} = c^2 \mathbf{E} \times \mathbf{H} \tag{3.61}$$

Furthermore, by expressing the Lorentz force [(3.39) of Chapter 2] in terms of **E** and **H**,

$$\mathbf{F} = \rho \mathbf{E} + \mu \rho \mathbf{v} \times \mathbf{H}, \tag{3.62}$$

---

[23] Feynman, R. P., R. B. Leighton, and M., Sands, *Lectures on Physics*, Vol. 2, pp. 27–5, Addison-Wesley, Reading, Mass., 1964.

and making use of Maxwell's equations to eliminate ρ and $\rho\mathbf{v}$, it can be shown[24] that the electromagnetic field will exert a total force

$$\mathbf{F}_T = \frac{d}{dt} \int_V \frac{\mathbf{S}}{c^2} \, dV \tag{3.63}$$

on any matter present within the volume V, provided it occupies only a small part of the volume a long way from any of the boundaries. Since in general force is equal to the time rate of change of linear momentum, it follows that

$$\mathbf{g} = \frac{\mathbf{S}}{c^2} = \mathbf{E} \times \mathbf{H} \tag{3.64}$$

represents the linear momentum density of the field, sometimes called the electromagnetic momentum.

Being by definition in the direction of propagation, the Poynting vector for the present case establishes that the relative orientation of $\mathbf{E}$ to $\mathbf{H}$ will follow the right-hand screw rule, as suggested in Fig. 4.8:

$$\mathbf{S} = c^2 \mathbf{E} \times \mathbf{H} = c^2(E_y H_z - E_z H_y)\hat{\imath} = \frac{c^2}{\mu}(h_2^2 + h_3^2)\hat{\imath} \tag{3.65}$$

This also shows that the magnitude of the energy flux is divided equally between the contributions from the electric field and the magnetic field.

If a perfectly reflecting unit surface were to be placed in the field perpendicular to the X-axis, the momentum of the radiation striking it in unit time would be

$$|\mathbf{g}| = \frac{|\mathbf{S}|}{c^2} = \frac{1}{\mu}(h_2^2 + h_3^2); \tag{3.66}$$

and since all of this would be reflected, the change in the momentum in the same interval of time—equal to the force p exerted on the surface—would be that associated with a change of sign of the momentum vector, or just twice its magnitude:

$$p = \frac{2}{\mu}(h_2^2 + h_3^2) \tag{3.67}$$

This is what is commonly called radiation pressure.

At the moment it may seem rather strange to attribute momentum to electromagnetic waves, which possess no mass; ordinarily, however, the momentum is associated with particles called photons assumed to exist in the field. Together, the three components of this momentum and the

[24] Page, L., *Introduction to Theoretical Physics*, 3rd edition, pp. 530–537, Van Nostrand, Princeton, N.J., 1965.

energy of the photon constitute a four-vector, in accordance with relativistic requirements [(1.67) to (1.87) of Chapter 2]. In the next chapter we shall learn that we must also associate waves closely resembling the present type with particles that previously were thought to carry only mass. Actually, both of these effects are well documented by experiment and simply represent our deepened understanding of the nature of physical reality.

Returning to (3.15) and (3.19), we see that when the medium of propagation is highly conducting, $\alpha_2 = \sigma\mu$ will be large relative to $\alpha_1 = 1/c^2$; the first term, associated with the Maxwell displacement current, can then be neglected relative to the second term on the right-hand side. The result is:

$$\nabla^2 \mathbf{E} = \sigma\mu \mathbf{E}_t \qquad (3.68)$$

$$\nabla^2 \mathbf{H} = \sigma\mu \mathbf{H}_t \qquad (3.69)$$

Each of these represents three scalar equations; and if again $\mathbf{E}$ and $\mathbf{H}$ depend only on x and t, all will be of the form (2.148),

$$\frac{\partial}{\partial x^2} \phi(x, t) - C_2 \frac{\partial}{\partial t} \phi(x, t) = 0,$$

diffusion equations whose solutions are Bessel functions [see Problem 4.2(6)]. It is worth noting that with the aid of (3.3),

$$\mathbf{E} = \frac{\mathbf{j}}{\sigma},$$

(3.68) can also be expressed in terms of the drift current density:

$$\nabla^2 \mathbf{j} = \sigma\mu \mathbf{j}_t \qquad (3.70)$$

Because these equations apply to most common metallic conductors, the latter form is especially useful.

Actually, to deal with more complicated situations it is preferable to express Maxwell's equations in terms of the scalar and vector potential functions $\phi(\mathbf{r}, t)$ and $\mathbf{A}(\mathbf{r}, t)$ defined by (3.35) and (3.36) of Chapter 2,

$$\mathbf{B} = \nabla \times \mathbf{A}$$

and

$$\mathbf{E} = -\nabla\phi - \mathbf{A}_t.$$

Since these amount to alternate expressions for the first two Maxwell equations, if we decide to work with the form given in (3.31) to (3.34), we are left with the problem of reforming (3.33) and (3.34),

$$c^2 \nabla \times \mathbf{B} - E_t = \frac{\mathbf{J}}{\varepsilon}$$

and

$$\nabla \cdot \mathbf{E} = \frac{\rho}{\varepsilon}.$$

The obvious thing to do is to replace $\mathbf{B}$ and $\mathbf{E}$ in the last two equations with their equivalent expressions involving $\mathbf{A}$ and ϕ from above. Equation (3.33) becomes

$$c^2[\nabla \times (\nabla \times \mathbf{A})] + (\nabla\phi + \mathbf{A}_t)_t = \frac{\mathbf{J}}{\varepsilon} \tag{3.71}$$

or, again using the identity for the triple vector product,

$$c^2[\nabla(\nabla \cdot \mathbf{A}) - \nabla^2\mathbf{A}] + (\nabla\phi)_t + \mathbf{A}_{tt} = \frac{\mathbf{J}}{\varepsilon} ; \tag{3.72}$$

whereas (3.34) takes the form

$$\nabla \cdot (\nabla\phi + \mathbf{A}_t) = - \frac{\rho}{\varepsilon} \tag{3.73}$$

or

$$\nabla^2\phi + (\nabla \cdot \mathbf{A})_t = - \frac{\rho}{\varepsilon}. \tag{3.74}$$

Now it is evident that by choosing

$$\nabla \cdot \mathbf{A} = -c^{-2}\phi_t, \tag{3.75}$$

both (3.72) and (3.74) can be converted into the wave equation form which we know from above is required:

$$\nabla^2\mathbf{A} = c^{-2}\mathbf{A}_{tt} - \mu\mathbf{J} \tag{3.76}$$

and

$$\nabla^2\phi = c^{-2}\phi_{tt} - \varepsilon^{-1}\rho. \tag{3.77}$$

Selecting the divergence of $\mathbf{A}$ as in (3.75) can be justified[25] on the basis that the electric and magnetic fields defined by the relations (3.35) and (3.36) of Chapter 2 are invariant under a gauge transformation, in the sense that neither will be changed by the addition of an arbitrary vector function to $\mathbf{A}$ and a related scalar function to ϕ.

In an uncharged and nonconducting medium the last term in both equations can be ignored, so that (3.76) and (3.77) become

$$\nabla^2\mathbf{A} = c^{-2}\mathbf{A}_{tt} \tag{3.78}$$

and

$$\nabla^2\phi = c^{-2}\phi_{tt}. \tag{3.79}$$

[25] Lorentz, H. A., *The Theory of Electrons*, pp. 17–20, 238–240, Dover, New York, 1952.

These represent four scalar equations, as opposed to the six indicated by
(3.23) to (3.28). The number of equations to be satisfied is actually the
same in both cases, because (3.75) represents two more independent
relations; but because the last two do not enter actively in most applications, solution procedures are usually simplified. All four equations will
again be of the form (2.78); therefore, it is more or less evident that a
shortened procedure similar to that carried out in (3.35) to (3.67) can be
followed.

However, under these conditions it is also possible to make direct application of the more detailed methods developed in the preceding section.
To see this, let us select $-\nabla\zeta(\mathbf{r}, t)$ for an arbitrary vector function to be
added to some known solution $\mathbf{A}'$, and for the related scalar function to
be added to ϕ', $\zeta_t(\mathbf{r}, t)$. With

$$\mathbf{A} = \mathbf{A}' - \nabla\zeta \tag{3.80}$$

and

$$\phi = \phi' + \zeta_t \tag{3.81}$$

it may easily be proved that the definitions of $\mathbf{B}$ and $\mathbf{E}$ will not change.
Substituting in (3.75), it follows that $\zeta(\mathbf{r}, t)$ must satisfy the relation:

$$\nabla^2\zeta - c^{-2}\zeta_{tt} = \nabla \cdot \mathbf{A}' + c^{-2}\phi_t'. \tag{3.82}$$

But with $\mathbf{J}$ and ρ vanishing, we may select

$$\mathbf{A}' = 0 \tag{3.83}$$

and

$$\phi' = 0 \tag{3.84}$$

to satisfy the original equations (3.72) and (3.74); therefore, (3.80) to
(3.82) reduce to:

$$\mathbf{A} = -\nabla\zeta \tag{3.85}$$

$$\phi = \zeta_t \tag{3.86}$$

$$\nabla^2\zeta - c^{-2}\zeta_{tt} = 0 \tag{3.87}$$

The last two of these may be used to select $\zeta(\mathbf{r}, t)$ in such a way that

$$\phi(\mathbf{r}, t) = 0, \tag{3.88}$$

whereas the first defines $\mathbf{A}$ in terms of ζ. Then the basic relations (3.35) and
(3.36) of Chapter 2 reduce to

$$\mathbf{B} = \nabla \times \mathbf{A}, \tag{3.89}$$

$$\mathbf{E} = -\mathbf{A}_t, \tag{3.90}$$

while the equations of motion (3.78) and (3.79) with the gauge condition (3.75) become:

$$\nabla^2 \mathbf{A} = c^{-2}\mathbf{A}_{tt} \tag{3.91}$$

$$\nabla \cdot \mathbf{A} = 0 \tag{3.92}$$

Thus $\mathbf{A}(\mathbf{r}, t)$ is the only unknown function; we may proceed to solve (3.91) in the same way as before, satisfy (3.92) separately, and obtain the magnetic and electric fields from (3.89) and (3.90).

In general, (3.91) represents three scalar equations of the form

$$\frac{\partial^2}{\partial x^2} A_x + \frac{\partial^2}{\partial y^2} A_x + \frac{\partial^2}{\partial z^2} A_x = c^{-2} \frac{\partial^2}{\partial t^2} A_x \tag{3.93}$$

where

$$A_x = A_x(x, y, z, t). \tag{3.94}$$

Therefore, when the boundary conditions lead to standing waves, or when the progressive waves are periodic in such a way that they may be built up from standing waves, each of these may be separated into three eigen-equations in the position coordinates and an harmonic oscillator equation in the time by means of the type of assumption featured in Section 4.2,

$$A_x(x, y, z, t) = X_x(x) Y_x(y) Z_x(z) T_x(t); \tag{3.95}$$

hence the equation may be solved in the same way as (2.135). We conclude that its solutions can be written as in (2.141):

$$A_x = a_{\alpha x} e^{i(\mathbf{k}_{\alpha x} \cdot \mathbf{r} - \omega_{\alpha x} t)} \qquad \{\alpha = 1, 2, 3, \ldots \tag{3.96}$$

with $a_{\alpha x}$ representing the amplitude of each component eigenwave, $\mathbf{k}_{\alpha x}$ its characteristic vector, and $\omega_{\alpha x}$ its angular frequency.

Furthermore, all three such solutions may be combined by introducing a unit vector $\hat{\mathbf{e}}_\alpha$ in the direction of the electric polarization and writing:

$$\mathbf{A}_\alpha = \hat{\mathbf{e}}_\alpha a_\alpha e^{i(\mathbf{k}_\alpha \cdot \mathbf{r} - \omega_\alpha t)} \qquad \{\alpha = 1, 2, 3, \ldots . \tag{3.97}$$

From this it is easy to see that (3.92) will be satisfied by every $\mathbf{A}_\alpha$ if we require that

$$\hat{\mathbf{e}}_\alpha \cdot \mathbf{k}_\alpha = 0, \tag{3.98}$$

in other words, that the polarization vector $\hat{\mathbf{e}}_\alpha$ be perpendicular to the wave vector $\mathbf{k}_\alpha$. Of course, $\mathbf{A}$ may be obtained as the sum of all $\mathbf{A}_\alpha$:

$$\mathbf{A}(\mathbf{r}, t) = \sum_\alpha \mathbf{A}_\alpha(\mathbf{r}, t) \tag{3.99}$$

Interestingly enough, since according to (3.95) this last equation may also be written in the form

$$A(\mathbf{r}, t) = \sum_\alpha \mathbf{R}_\alpha(\mathbf{r}) T_\alpha(t) \qquad (3.100)$$

for any set of standing waves described by the $\mathbf{R}_\alpha$, the amplitude of A at a given point in space will depend entirely on the T_α. But we know the latter to satisfy an equation like (2.111),

$$\ddot{T}_\alpha + \omega_\alpha^2 T_\alpha = 0. \qquad (3.101)$$

This means that the electromagnetic radiation field may be represented as an infinite system of independent harmonic oscillators in the generalized coordinates T_α, and the properties of the field derived from the statistical properties of the system.[26]

When such an approach is used, the field is most conveniently described by means of a total Hamiltonian function

$$H = \sum_\alpha H_\alpha, \qquad (3.102)$$

where the sum of the kinetic and potential energy for one of the oscillators can be written as

$$H_\alpha = \tfrac{1}{2}(p_\alpha^2 + \omega_\alpha^2 T_\alpha^2) \qquad (3.103)$$

if T_α is recognized as the generalized position coordinate. Application of the Hamiltonian equations [(2.58) and (2.59) of Chapter 2],

$$\frac{\partial H_\alpha}{\partial T_\alpha} = -\dot{p}_\alpha \qquad (3.104)$$

$$\frac{\partial H_\alpha}{\partial p_\alpha} = \dot{T}_\alpha, \qquad (3.105)$$

then yields (3.101) directly. This is the main reason why the Hamiltonian function, and its corresponding operator, are featured in the quantum mechanical procedures of the following chapter.

For highly conducting media, the first term on the right-hand side of (3.76) and (3.77) can be neglected. Then parallel to (3.69) and (3.68) or (3.70), the equations become

$$\nabla^2 A = -\mu J \qquad (3.106)$$

and

$$\nabla^2 \phi = -\varepsilon^{-1} \rho. \qquad (3.107)$$

Again four scalar equations are represented, though in this case they are of a somewhat simpler form.

[26] Heitler, W., *The Quantum Theory of Radiation*, 3rd edition, pp. 38–42, Oxford, 1957.

In fact, it is immediately apparent that if the charge density does not depend on the time t,

$$\rho = \rho(\mathbf{r}), \tag{3.108}$$

(3.107) will be a Poisson equation of the form (2.150); and if in addition only steady electric currents are present,

$$\mathbf{J} = \mathbf{J}(\mathbf{r}), \tag{3.109}$$

this will also be true of the three scalar equations equivalent to (3.106). From the known form of the solution of Poisson's equation,[27] we can conclude that in such a case ϕ will be given by

$$\phi = \int_V \frac{\rho(\mathbf{r})}{4\pi\varepsilon r} \, dV \tag{3.110}$$

and $\mathbf{A}$ by

$$\mathbf{A} = \int_V \frac{\mu \mathbf{J}(\mathbf{r})}{4\pi r} \, dV, \tag{3.111}$$

where V indicates the volume under consideration.

Actually, when ρ and $\mathbf{J}$ depend on time as well as on position,

$$\rho = \rho(\mathbf{r}, t) \tag{3.112}$$

$$\mathbf{J} = \mathbf{J}(\mathbf{r}, t), \tag{3.113}$$

solutions very similar to these continue to apply. The only difference is that at any time t, ρ and $\mathbf{J}$ will depend on the retarded time $t - r/c$, an effect due to the fact that the phase of the wave generally lags the phase of the source:

$$\phi = \int_V \frac{\rho(\mathbf{r}, t - r'/c)}{4\pi\varepsilon r'} \, dV \tag{3.114}$$

$$\mathbf{A} = \int_V \frac{\mu \mathbf{J}(\mathbf{r}, t - r'/c)}{4\pi r'} \, dV \tag{3.115}$$

where r' indicates the distance between the volume element at $\mathbf{r}$, containing sources, and the point in the field at which the values of ϕ and $\mathbf{A}$ are desired. The solutions for the actual magnetic and electric fields follow directly from these and (3.35), (3.36) of Chapter 2:

$$\mathbf{H} = \frac{\mathbf{B}}{\mu} = \nabla \times \int_V \frac{\mathbf{J}(\mathbf{r}, t - r'/c)}{4\pi r'} \, dV \tag{3.116}$$

$$\mathbf{E} = -\nabla \int_V \frac{\rho(\mathbf{r}, t - r'/c)}{4\pi\varepsilon r'} \, dV - \frac{\partial}{\partial t} \int_V \frac{\mu \mathbf{J}(\mathbf{r}, t - r'/c)}{4\pi r'} \, dV \tag{3.117}$$

[27] Sneddon, I. N., *Elements of Partial Differential Equations*, pp. 254–257, McGraw-Hill, New York, 1957.

Problems 4.3

1. Calculate the components of the electric field **E** and magnetic field **H** for a plane polarized electromagnetic wave, propagating along a line bounded by perpendicular perfectly reflecting surfaces, in an uncharged and nonconducting medium.

Solution

In such a medium the governing equations are

$$\nabla^2 \mathbf{E} = c^{-2} \mathbf{E}_{tt}$$

and

$$\nabla^2 \mathbf{H} = c^{-2} \mathbf{H}_{tt},$$

together with the supplementary conditions

$$\nabla \cdot \mathbf{E} = 0$$

and

$$\nabla \cdot \mathbf{H} = 0.$$

However, if we select the X-axis for the axis of propagation, as in Fig. 4.8, and the Y-axis for the direction of polarization, **E** can only have the components E_y, E_x and **H** only the components H_z, H_x—all of them depending on x and t alone. But the last two equations can then be used to prove that E_x and H_x must remain constant; so the only equations remaining to be solved are:

$$\frac{\partial^2}{\partial t^2} E_y(x, t) - c^2 \frac{\partial^2}{\partial x^2} E_y(x, t) = 0$$

$$\frac{\partial^2}{\partial t^2} H_z(x, t) - c^2 \frac{\partial^2}{\partial x^2} H_z(x, t) = 0$$

These being of the same form, let us work with the one in $E_y(x, t)$.

The general solution of this equation we know to be of the form (2.89),

$$E_y = g(x + ct) + h(x - ct);$$

but since in this case the reflecting surfaces will give rise to standing waves, we can be more specific about the functional form of $h(x - ct)$ and $g(x + ct)$ than for the unpolarized progressive wave discussed in the text. The assumption that

$$E_y = X(x)T(t)$$

is permissible; therefore, substitution in the partial differential equation for E_y gives:

$$X \frac{d^2 T}{dt^2} = c^2 T \frac{d^2 X}{dx^2}$$

Separating variables and equating both sides of the resulting equation to $-\omega^2$, we obtain

$$\frac{d^2 T}{dt^2} + \omega^2 T = 0$$

and

$$\frac{d^2X}{dx^2} + \left(\frac{\omega}{c}\right)^2 X = 0$$

or, identifying ω/c with the wave number k,

$$\frac{d^2X}{dx^2} + k^2 X = 0.$$

Hence, neglecting the case when $\omega = 0$, the solutions can be written in the form

$$E_y = (A_1 \cos kx + A_2 \sin kx)(A_3 \cos \omega t + A_4 \sin \omega t);$$

but, just as in (2.39) to (2.60), the boundary conditions will lead to eigenfrequencies $\omega_\alpha \{\alpha = 1, 2, 3, \ldots,$ defining wave numbers k_α. Consequently, the general solution can be expressed by writing

$$E_y = \sum_{\alpha=1}^{\infty} A_\alpha \sin k_\alpha x \cos \omega_\alpha t$$

and using the Fourier method to determine the A_α from some initial condition. By the same reasoning, since in this case ω will remain unchanged, the general solution of the equation for $H_z(x, t)$ can be written as:

$$H_z = \sum_{\alpha=1}^{\infty} B_\alpha \sin k_\alpha x \cos \omega_\alpha t$$

This is a simplified case of a "resonant cavity."

2. Calculate the component in the direction of propagation of the electric field **E** for an harmonic electromagnetic wave, propagating through an uncharged medium in a long rectangular, perfectly conducting tube with sides l_1 and l_2.

Solution

The governing equations now are

$$\nabla^2 \mathbf{E} = c^{-2}\mathbf{E}_{tt} + \sigma\mu\mathbf{E}_t$$

and

$$\nabla^2 \mathbf{H} = c^{-2}\mathbf{H}_{tt} + \sigma\mu\mathbf{H}_t,$$

together with $\nabla \cdot \mathbf{E} = 0$ and $\nabla \cdot \mathbf{H} = 0$; but the latter cannot be applied in the same way as before, because $\mathbf{E} = \mathbf{E}(x, y, z, t)$ and $\mathbf{H} = \mathbf{H}(x, y, z, t)$. Our attention will be restricted to the first equation; and let us take propagation to be in the X-direction.

Because of the geometry involved and the fact that time dependence in most cases of practical interest is harmonic, it is common[28] to assume $\mathbf{E}(x, y, z, t)$ to be of the form

$$\mathbf{E} = \mathbf{E}^*(y, z)e^{-\gamma x}e^{i\omega t},$$

where $\mathbf{E}^*$ indicates a complex amplitude with a phase factor included (for example, $E_x^* = E_x e^{i\theta_x}$) and γ represents a complex propagation constant

[28] Jackson, J. D., *Classical Electrodynamics*, pp. 240–247, Wiley, New York, 1965.

incorporating both an attenuation constant α and a retardation constant β,

$$\gamma = \alpha + i\beta.$$

Of course, this means that we are restricting ourselves to standing waves which vary harmonically in x and t; but periodic progressive waves can be constructed from linear combinations of these and the form offers many mathematical advantages.

Substituting, we see **E*** to be defined by:

$$\nabla^2 \mathbf{E}^* + \gamma^2 \mathbf{E}^* = -c^{-2}\omega^2 \mathbf{E}^* + i\sigma\mu\omega \mathbf{E}^*$$

or

$$\nabla^2 \mathbf{E}^* = -(\gamma^2 + k^2 - i\sigma\mu\omega)\mathbf{E}^*$$

where ω/c has been replaced by k; and if we in addition place

$$\gamma^2 + k^2 - i\sigma\mu\omega = \kappa^2,$$

this becomes

$$\nabla^2 \mathbf{E}^* + \kappa^2 \mathbf{E}^* = 0.$$

Consequently, for the component in the X-direction the governing equation is:

$$\nabla^2 E_x^*(y, z) + \kappa^2 E_x^*(y, z) = 0$$

If we further assume that we can compose E_x^* from standing waves and write

$$E_x^*(y, z) = Y(y)Z(z),$$

substitution yields

$$Y\frac{d^2Z}{dz^2} + Z\frac{d^2Y}{dy^2} + \kappa^2 YZ = 0$$

or, dividing through by YZ,

$$\frac{1}{Z}\frac{d^2Z}{dz^2} + \frac{1}{Y}\frac{d^2Y}{dy^2} = -\kappa^2.$$

It then follows in the usual way that we may place both of the terms on the left equal to constants,

$$\frac{1}{Z}\frac{d^2Z}{dz^2} = -k_z^2$$

and

$$\frac{1}{Y}\frac{d^2Y}{dy^2} = -k_y^2,$$

provided that

$$k_y^2 + k_z^2 = \kappa^2.$$

The solution of these equations is obvious from (2.132); therefore, we may immediately write

$$E_x^* = \frac{\cos}{\sin}\left. k_y y\right\} \frac{\cos}{\sin}\left. k_z z\right\},$$

subject to the condition that

$$k_y^2 + k_z^2 = \gamma^2 + k^2 - i\sigma\mu\omega.$$

It follows that

$$E_x = {\cos \atop \sin} k_y y \Big\} {\cos \atop \sin} k_z z \Big\} e^{-(\gamma x - i\omega t)}.$$

Because the tube within which the wave travels is a perfect conductor, the boundary conditions available may be expressed in the following way [see Exercise 4.3 (1)]:

$$E_x(0, z, t) = 0$$

$$E_x(y, 0, t) = 0$$

$$E_x(l_1, z, t) = 0$$

$$E_x(y, l_2, t) = 0$$

Therefore, in the same way as in (2.39) to (2.60), the first two of these result in the elimination of the cosine terms from the linear combinations in the expression for E_x, leaving

$$E_x = A \sin k_y y \sin k_z z e^{-(\gamma x - i\omega t)},$$

and the last two lead to the eigenfrequencies

$$k_y = \frac{\alpha_1 \pi}{l_1} \qquad \{\alpha_1 = 1, 2, 3, \ldots$$

$$k_z = \frac{\alpha_2 \pi}{l_2} \qquad \{\alpha_2 = 1, 2, 3, \ldots .$$

We conclude that the general expression for E_x is

$$E_x = e^{-\alpha x} \sum_{\alpha_1, \alpha_2}^{\infty} A_{\alpha_1 \alpha_2} \sin \frac{\alpha_1 \pi}{l_1} y \sin \frac{\alpha_2 \pi}{l_2} z \cos(\omega t - \beta x),$$

where the value $\alpha + i\beta$ has been substituted for γ and the real part of the imaginary exponential has been taken. Corresponding expressions can be obtained in about the same way for the other two components of **E**, although relations for these in terms of E_x can easily be developed (as in the reference quoted above), and also for the three components of the magnetic field **H**. This is a simplified case of a "wave guide." Of course wave guides can also be resonant cavities, if reflecting surfaces exist at the ends.

3. If the medium in the preceding problem becomes nonconducting and no attenuation of the wave occurs, find its phase velocity $c_p = \omega/\beta$ and critical frequency ω_c.

Solution

With these restrictions the expression relating the parameters of the problem,

$$k_y{}^2 + k_z{}^2 = \gamma^2 + k^2 - i\sigma\mu\omega,$$

will become

$$k_y{}^2 + k_z{}^2 + \beta^2 = k^2,$$

because $\gamma = \alpha + i\beta$ and α vanishes along with σ. Hence

$$\beta = \sqrt{\left(\frac{\omega}{c}\right)^2 - \left[\left(\frac{\alpha_1 \pi}{l_1}\right)^2 + \left(\frac{\alpha_2 \pi}{l_2}\right)^2\right]},$$

replacing k with ω/c and using the known values for k_y and k_z. Evidently α_1 and α_2 can take the values $1, 2, 3, \ldots$.

Accordingly, the phase velocity will be

$$c_p = \frac{\omega}{\beta} = \frac{c}{\sqrt{1 - \left(\frac{\omega_0}{\omega}\right)^2}}$$

where

$$\omega_0 = c\sqrt{\left(\frac{\alpha_1 \pi}{l_1}\right)^2 + \left(\frac{\alpha_2 \pi}{l_2}\right)^2};$$

so it follows that transmission will occur only above some critical frequency ω_c determined by

$$\omega = \omega_c = \omega_0.$$

Actually, this is usually defined as $\omega_0/2\pi$, so that we may write:

$$\omega_c = \frac{\omega_0}{2\pi} = \frac{c}{2}\sqrt{\left(\frac{\alpha_1}{l_1}\right)^2 + \left(\frac{\alpha_2}{l_2}\right)^2}$$

4. If a wire of length l, with the cross-sectional area $a = \pi r^2$ and conductivity σ, connects a dc source to a resistive load and carries a steady current I, find the power P dissipated as heat.

Solution

The electric and magnetic fields associated with a perfect conductor must exist entirely in the dielectric surrounding it, because they cannot exist inside of it [see Exercise 4.3 (4)]. At the surface of the conductor the electric field can have only a normal component, whereas the magnetic field can have only a tangential component. In this sense the conductor can function as a wave guide and, thus, as a guide for the energy flow.

However, if the conductor is slightly imperfect, the electric field will have a small tangential component $E_\parallel$ at its surface in the direction of the current flow.[29] The Poynting vector (3.61) describes the energy flux and, assuming $\varepsilon\mu = 1$, it is given by

$$\mathbf{S} = \mathbf{E} \times \mathbf{H}.$$

Hence, this component of $\mathbf{E}$ will combine with $H_\parallel$, the tangential component of $\mathbf{H}$ perpendicular to $E_\parallel$, to give a component of $\mathbf{S}$ directed radially into the wire:

$$S_\perp = E_\parallel H_\parallel$$

It follows that P will be the product of $S_\perp$ with the surface area of the wire:

$$P = 2\pi r l S_\perp$$

---

[29] Jackson, J. D., *Classical Electrodynamics*, pp. 236–240, Wiley, New York, 1965.

We know from Ohm's law (3.3) that the drift current

$$j = \sigma E_{\parallel};$$

therefore,

$$E_{\parallel} = \frac{j}{\sigma} = \frac{I}{\sigma \pi r^2},$$

assuming the current I to be uniformly distributed over the cross section. Furthermore, because the fields are not varying in time and the density of charges with the velocity $\mathbf{v}$ is zero, (3.6) reduces to

$$\nabla \times \mathbf{H} = \sigma \mathbf{E};$$

it follows from this that

$$H_{\parallel} = \sigma \int E_{\parallel} \, dr = \sigma \int \frac{I}{\sigma \pi} r^{-2} \, dr = \frac{I}{2\pi r}.$$

Therefore,

$$P = 2\pi r l E_{\parallel} H_{\parallel} = 2\pi r l \left(\frac{I}{\sigma \pi r^2}\right)\frac{I}{2\pi r} = \frac{I^2 l}{\sigma \pi r^2}$$

in watts. Often this is written as

$$P = I^2 R,$$

with

$$R = \frac{l}{\sigma \pi r^2}$$

defined as the dc resistance of the wire.

5. Writing the Fourier series for waves restricted to a one-dimensional region of length l as

$$\phi = \frac{1}{l} \sum_{-\infty}^{\infty} f\left(\frac{\alpha \pi}{l}\right) e^{i\frac{\alpha \pi}{l} x},$$

where $f(\alpha\pi/l)$ represents the coefficients, derive the Fourier integral.

Solution

Allowing l to become very large, with f remaining a continuous function of

$$\frac{\alpha \pi}{l} = \frac{\omega}{c} = k,$$

the change in the series for each increase of α by one unit will become small. Thus we can replace the summation by an integration with

$$d\alpha = \frac{l}{\pi} \, dk$$

and write the series in the form:

$$\phi = \frac{1}{\pi} \int_{-\infty}^{\infty} f(k) e^{ikx} \, dk,$$

where the $f(k)$ may be found from the usual coefficient formulae.

This is the Fourier integral. By means of it and with appropriate $f(k)$, any piecewise-continuous and square-integrable function $\phi(x)$ can be represented in an unbounded region. We will need such a means of representation for the wave packets of the following chapter.

6. Solve the general wave equations in $\mathbf{A}$ and ϕ,

$$\nabla^2 \mathbf{A} = c^{-2}\mathbf{A}_{tt} - \mu \mathbf{J}$$
$$\nabla^2 \phi = c^{-2}\phi_{tt} - \varepsilon^{-1}\rho,$$

for a point source in empty space whose unit strength τ varies with time.

Solution
Since the source will give rise to spherical waves, spherical coordinates are called for; furthermore, because in this case both the equation in ϕ and the component equations of the one in $\mathbf{A}$ feature a function that depends only on r and t, we may represent them all by writing

$$\zeta = \zeta(r, t)$$

and [as in (2.146)] express ∇^2 in the form:

$$\nabla^2 \zeta(r, t) = \frac{1}{r^2}\frac{\partial}{\partial r}\left(r^2 \frac{\partial \zeta}{\partial r}\right)$$

$$= \frac{\partial^2 \zeta}{\partial r^2} + \frac{2}{r}\frac{\partial \zeta}{\partial r}$$

$$= \frac{1}{r}\frac{\partial^2}{\partial r^2}(r\zeta)$$

Hence, the representative equation becomes:

$$\frac{1}{r}\frac{\partial^2}{\partial r^2}(r\zeta) - \frac{1}{c^2}\frac{\partial^2}{\partial t^2}\zeta = -\tau(t),$$

where $\tau(t)$ can mean either $\mu J_{x,y,z}(t)$ or $\varepsilon^{-1}\rho(t)$.
But we know that far from the source in such an uncharged and non-conducting medium $\zeta(r, t)$ must satisfy an equation of the same type with the right-hand term missing:

$$\frac{1}{r}\frac{\partial}{\partial r^2}(r\zeta) - \frac{1}{c^2}\frac{\partial^2 \zeta}{\partial t^2} = 0$$

or, multiplying through by $-c^2 r$,

$$\frac{\partial^2}{\partial t^2}(r\zeta) - c^2 \frac{\partial^2}{\partial r^2}(r\zeta) = 0.$$

This has the same form as (2.78), so the solution must resemble that part of (2.89) which represents an outgoing wave:

$$r\zeta = h(r - ct)$$

or

$$\zeta = \frac{h(r - ct)}{r}.$$

However, any function

$$f\left(\frac{r - ct}{-c}\right) = f(t - r/c)$$

will also be a function of $(r - ct)$; therefore, we may write the solution in the form

$$\zeta = \frac{f(t - r/c)}{r}$$

if we wish. This has the advantage of suggesting that f be interpreted as a function of a retarded time.

On the other hand, because of its inverse dependence on r, we may expect this same solution to satisfy the complete representative equation near the source. For as r approaches zero, the retardation r/c may be neglected relative to any t of interest, so that

$$\zeta_{r \to 0} = \frac{f(t)}{r}.$$

And since the derivatives of this ζ with respect to r will become large as r decreases, while those with respect to t will remain unchanged, it follows that the equation will reduce to the Poisson form

$$\nabla^2 \zeta = -\tau(t).$$

As mentioned in the text, this is known to have the solution

$$\zeta = \int_V \frac{\tau(t)}{4\pi r} \, dV,$$

V indicating a volume closely surrounding the source.

Consequently, we should be able to write the general solution in the form

$$\zeta = \int_V \frac{T(t - r/c)}{4\pi r} \, dV,$$

where T represents some total function of the retarded time $(t - r/c)$ and V means a volume surrounding the source at any distance. This is the basic form of (3.114) and (3.115).

Exercises 4.3

1. Prove that the tangential component of the electric field $\mathbf{E}$ must vanish at the surface of a perfect conductor.

2. Determine the component E_y of the electric field $\mathbf{E}(x, y, z, t)$ and the component H_z of the magnetic field $\mathbf{H}(x, y, z, t)$ in Problem 4.3 (2).

3. How would the final solution for E_x given in Problem 4.3 (2) have to be modified if the tube was made very short and perfectly reflecting normal surfaces added to the ends?

4. Prove that no **E** or **H** fields can exist in a perfect conductor, and discuss qualitatively what happens in a thin layer near the surface if the conductor is good but not quite perfect.

5. Starting from (3.78) and (3.79) in **A** and ϕ, instead of (3.21) and (3.22) in **E** and **H**, obtain the solutions (3.53) to (3.58).

6. Prove that changing **A**′ and ϕ′ to

$$\mathbf{A} = \mathbf{A}' - \nabla \zeta(\mathbf{r}, t)$$

and

$$\phi = \phi' + \frac{\partial}{\partial t} \zeta(\mathbf{r}, t)$$

will not change **B** and **E**; also show that with **A**′ = 0 and ϕ′ = 0, these relations and (3.87),

$$\nabla^2 \zeta(\mathbf{r}, t) - \frac{1}{c^2} \frac{\partial^2}{\partial t^2} \zeta(\mathbf{r}, t) = 0,$$

may be used to select $\zeta(\mathbf{r}, t)$ so that $\phi(\mathbf{r}, t) = 0$ everywhere.

7. From energy considerations, establish that the amplitude of an electromagnetic wave emitted from a point source in empty space will decrease as $1/r$.

5

Physical Laws for a Particle

5.1 Particle Waves, State Functions, and the Uncertainty Principle

All of the basic units of matter and electromagnetic radiation called fundamental particles have this in common: sometimes they behave like point objects and at other times like waves. Electrons, for example, act very much like small, charged solid bodies in the beam of an oscilloscope and yet exhibit the interference pattern of waves when passed through a crystal diffraction grating; it is also well-known that light propagates like a wave but can exert pressure like a material substance.[1] The present-day view is that such particles arise from constructive and destructive interference of waves in different kinds of physical fields. Suggestive of this is the fact that negligible diffraction effects will appear on a screen when a beam of light photons or electrons impinge on it through a large opening in a solid plate. But an interference pattern will appear for the photons as the dimensions of the opening are reduced to less than the wavelength of the light and, presumably, would also appear for the electrons if the opening could be made small enough. In any event, the intensity at any point in this pattern (or one from a diffraction grating of many openings), which must be directly proportional to the rate of particle arrival, can be calculated by imagining each point on the edge of the opening to act as the source of a new wave.[2]

In other words, as long as the opening is large enough for the great majority of the photons or electrons to pass through it without being

[1] Eisberg, R. M., *Fundamentals of Modern Physics*, pp. 79–86, 139–163, Wiley, New York, 1963.
[2] Slater, J. C., and N. H. Frank, *Introduction to Theoretical Physics*, pp. 258–264, 329–342, McGraw-Hill, New York, 1933.

affected, they will behave for the most part like point objects. But whenever the opening becomes so small that most of the particles must interact with one of its edges in order to get through, the end result of all such interactions (in which particles may be deflected or possibly even destroyed and reformed) will be the type of distribution described above. Because we understand the electromagnetic nature of the waves associated with light photons, it is possible to think of them as real waves; but because we do not yet fully understand the nature of the waves associated with particles like electrons, we must regard them merely as a computational device which enables us to calculate the spatial distribution of a stream of particles after they have interacted with some material detector.

For the same reason, and also because we do not know the precise structure of the fundamental particles, we cannot determine the details of such interactions and must, therefore, interpret the results probabilistically. The procedure is to imagine that a particle with the total energy E and linear momentum p has associated with it, at all times, a descriptive wave with the frequency

$$\nu = \frac{\omega}{2\pi} = \frac{E}{h} \tag{1.1}$$

and the wavelength

$$\lambda = \frac{h}{p}, \tag{1.2}$$

where h is Planck's constant (equal to about 6.625×10^{-27} erg-sec). The probability that the particle will be found at a given point in space is then taken to be proportional to the intensity of this wave at the point. For example, if we represent the wave by the function

$$\Psi = \Psi(x, y, z, t), \tag{1.3}$$

the probability of finding the particle it represents at the point (x, y, z) at the time t would be proportional to

$$|\Psi|^2, \tag{1.4}$$

being the square of the wave amplitude, which measures the intensity. We shall see later that Ψ is an inherently complex function for a material particle, reflecting the fact that any physical significance it may have is indirect, so that (1.4) can also be written[3] as

$$\Psi^*\Psi, \tag{1.5}$$

where Ψ^* indicates the complex conjugate of Ψ; the result will always be a real, positive number.

[3] Churchill, R. V., *Introduction to Complex Variables and Applications*, pp. 5–11, McGraw-Hill, New York, 1948.

Equation (1.1) was first proposed by Albert Einstein in the course of his study of the photoelectric effect, while the unit of energy $h\nu$ or $\hbar\omega$ (where $\hbar$ means $h/2\pi$) was called a quantum in line with earlier results obtained for black-body radiation by Max Planck. On the other hand, (1.2) was originally suggested by Louis de Broglie on purely theoretical grounds, and the probabilistic interpretation of the wave function Ψ was advanced by Max Born to reconcile conflicting theoretical concepts.[4,5] All of this, however, need not concern us here. Each idea is now firmly established by experimental fact, and it only remains for us to explore their combined implications. Clearly, it is important to do so, not only in order to understand fundamental particle motions, but also to understand the physical and chemical properties of materials made up of these particles.

By its very nature the wave function Ψ, often called a state function, must characterize the dynamic state of a particle; and it follows from the ideas explained above that we can represent it as a plane harmonic wave, or a superposition of such waves.[6] Thus, in accordance with (2.107) and (2.141) of Chapter 4, we should write

$$\Psi = Ae^{i(kx - \omega t)} \tag{1.6}$$

for the simplest case of a single wave of this kind propagating in the positive X-direction, and

$$\Psi = Ae^{i(\mathbf{k}\cdot\mathbf{r} - \omega t)} \tag{1.7}$$

for one propagating in an arbitrary direction.

The requirements expressed by the relations (1.1) and (1.2) can easily be incorporated in this. We need merely to note that

$$\omega = \frac{E}{\hbar} \tag{1.8}$$

and

$$k = \frac{2\pi}{\lambda} = \frac{p}{\hbar}, \tag{1.9}$$

from which

$$\mathbf{k} = \frac{\mathbf{p}}{\hbar}; \tag{1.10}$$

thus (1.7) becomes

$$\Psi(\mathbf{r}, t) = Ae^{\frac{i}{\hbar}(\mathbf{p}\cdot\mathbf{r} - Et)}. \tag{1.11}$$

[4] Messiah, A., *Quantum Mechanics*, Vol. 1, pp. 3–44, Wiley, New York, 1961.

[5] Bohm, D., *Quantum Theory*, pp. 5–172, Prentice-Hall, Englewood Cliffs, N.J., 1958.

[6] Dicke, R. H., and J. P. Wittke, *Introduction to Quantum Mechanics*, pp. 21–34, Addison-Wesley, Reading, Mass., 1960.

However, it must be emphasized that although (1.11) represents a particle with definite momentum **p** and energy E, it does not localize the particle in space or time. According to (1.4), the probability of finding the particle with this state function at any point **r** and time t is

$$|\Psi|^2 = |A|^2 \left| e^{\frac{i}{\hbar}(\mathbf{p}\cdot\mathbf{r} - Et)} \right|^2 = |A|^2 \left| \cos\frac{1}{\hbar}(\mathbf{p}\cdot\mathbf{r} - Et) + i \sin\frac{1}{\hbar}(\mathbf{p}\cdot\mathbf{r} - Et) \right|^2$$

$$= |A|^2 \left[\cos^2\frac{1}{\hbar}(\mathbf{p}\cdot\mathbf{r} - Et) + \sin^2\frac{1}{\hbar}(\mathbf{p}\cdot\mathbf{r} - Et) \right] = |A|^2, \qquad (1.12)$$

a constant for any given amplitude. Actually, this imprecision of expression is an essential feature of the mechanics of quanta-carrying particles, called quantum mechanics.

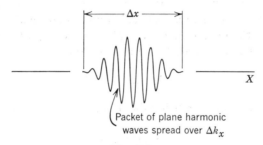

Packet of plane harmonic waves spread over Δk_x

Fig. 5.1

Returning to the example of light waves striking a plate containing one small hole, we know that photons are created in the escaping waves by the interference of wavelets of slightly different frequencies emanating from the edges of the hole. Let us confine our attention to just one plane, in which several waves like (1.6), with various amplitudes but frequencies differing by an amount $\Delta\omega$ (their wave numbers would then differ by Δk, since $k = \omega/c$), might be propagating. By Fourier methods it can be shown[7,8] that a "wave packet" of length Δx will be formed if a spread of Δk_x exists in the frequencies of the waves propagating in the X-direction (see Fig. 5.1), the two quantities being inversely related through a constant near unity whose exact value depends on the amplitudes of the component waves:

$$\Delta x \simeq \frac{1}{\Delta k_x} \qquad (1.13)$$

[7] Kemble, E. C., *The Fundamental Principles of Quantum Mechanics*, pp. 35–41, Dover, New York, 1958.
[8] Schiff, L. J., *Quantum Mechanics*, pp. 6–16, McGraw-Hill, New York, 1955.

But because from (1.9)

$$\Delta k_x = \frac{\Delta p_x}{\hbar},$$ (1.14)

we see (1.13) to imply the relation

$$\Delta p_x \, \Delta x \simeq \hbar.$$ (1.15)

If we identify the packet with a photon, and agree that it can also serve as the descriptive wave for a localized mass-carrying particle like an electron, it follows that a quantum particle necessarily must become less localized (Δx will increase) as the spread of values, or uncertainty, in the momentum, Δp_x, decreases. Hence it is consistent that a particle should become completely delocalized ($\Delta x \to \infty$) if its momentum is determined exactly ($\Delta p_x \to 0$), as in (1.11). In no case can simultaneous measurements of the position and momentum of such a particle be made with a product uncertainty less than $\hbar$, although any value greater than $\hbar$ can be obtained. Thus it is customary to write (1.15) in the form

$$\Delta p_x \, \Delta x \gtrsim \hbar.$$ (1.16)

Corresponding relations exist for the Y- and Z-directions,

$$\Delta p_y \, \Delta y \gtrsim \hbar$$ (1.17)

$$\Delta p_z \, \Delta z \gtrsim \hbar;$$ (1.18)

and without much difficulty an analogous expression involving the energy E and time t can be established,[9,10]

$$\Delta E \, \Delta t \gtrsim \hbar.$$ (1.19)

Collectively, (1.16) to (1.19) express the important uncertainty principle, first stated by Werner Heisenberg. From the foregoing discussion it should be clear that this principle is more than a mere limitation on our measurement capabilities; in a sense it also expresses a basic property of the structure of fundamental particles. They cannot be described apart from waves, which interaction with any physical object will disturb; therefore, they cannot be observed without changing their description, possibly even their structure.

If there were only two waves differing by Δk to superimpose in the manner suggested above, then selecting the imaginary part of (1.6) and

[9] Beard, D. B., *Quantum Mechanics*, pp. 15–31, Allyn and Bacon, Boston, Mass., 1963.
[10] Messiah, A., *Quantum Mechanics*, Vol. 1, pp. 129–149, Wiley, New York, 1961.

using equal amplitudes for purposes of simplicity, we could proceed as in Problem 4.2(3) and write:

$$\Psi = \Psi_1 + \Psi_2 = A \sin (kx - \omega t) + A \sin [(k + \Delta k)x - (\omega + \Delta\omega)t]$$
$$= \{2A \cos [(\Delta k)x - (\Delta\omega)t]\} \sin (kx - \omega t), \qquad (1.20)$$

which can also be written as

$$\Psi = \left\{2A \cos \frac{\Delta\omega}{c_g}\left[x - \left(\frac{\Delta\omega}{\Delta k}\right)t\right]\right\} \sin \frac{\omega}{c_p}\left(x - \frac{\omega}{k}t\right). \qquad (1.21)$$

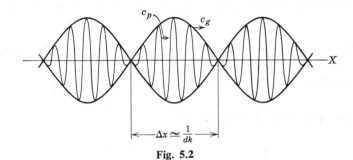

Fig. 5.2

Here c_p represents the propagation velocity of the plane harmonic wave

$$\sin \frac{\omega}{c_p}\left(x - \frac{\omega}{k}t\right)$$

and, accordingly, must be given by

$$c_p = \frac{\omega}{k}. \qquad (1.22)$$

It is called the phase velocity to distinguish it from the propagation velocity c_g of the amplitude modulated group

$$2A \cos \frac{\Delta\omega}{c_g}\left[x - \left(\frac{\Delta\omega}{\Delta k}\right)t\right],$$

which evidently will be given by

$$c_g = \frac{\Delta\omega}{\Delta k}, \qquad (1.23)$$

or in the limit

$$c_g = \frac{d\omega}{dk}. \qquad (1.24)$$

These are illustrated above in Fig. 5.2.

Clearly, the foregoing cannot be used to describe a single particle. To obtain an individual wave packet of the kind shown in Fig. 5.1, an infinite number of such waves with infinitesimally differing frequencies and wave numbers must be superimposed. Using (1.6) in its complete form and removing the restriction on amplitude, we must write:

$$\Psi = \int_{-\infty}^{\infty} A(k)e^{i[kx-\omega(k)t]}\, dk \tag{1.25}$$

where, if k_0 represents some central value,

$$A(k) \neq 0 \quad \text{only if} \quad (k_0 - \varepsilon) < k < (k_0 + \varepsilon) \quad \text{with} \quad \varepsilon \ll k_0. \tag{1.26}$$

Within this range of k-values, $\omega(k)$ may be expanded in a Taylor series:

$$\omega(k) = \omega[k_0 + (k - k_0)] = \omega(k_0) + (k - k_0)\left(\frac{d\omega}{dk}\right)_{k_0} + \cdots ; \tag{1.27}$$

substitution in (1.25) then leads to[11]

$$\Psi = f\left[x - \left(\frac{d\omega}{dk}\right)_{k_0} t\right]e^{i[k_0 x - \omega(k_0)t]}, \tag{1.28}$$

where f indicates some function of the quantity in the adjacent brackets. This has the same general form as (1.21), but represents one isolated wave packet instead of a series. From the exponential representing the resulting plane harmonic wave and the modulating function f defining the group, we see that (1.22) and (1.24) defining the phase and group velocities,

$$c_p = \frac{\omega}{k}$$

and

$$c_g = \frac{d\omega}{dk},$$

continue to hold when evaluated at k_0 (Fig. 5.3).

The preceding discussion establishes that it is the velocity of the wave group c_g that should be identified with the velocity of the particle v_x, but it is worthwhile to note that this is fully consistent with conservation principles. If we identify the particle velocity in the usual way as

$$v_x = \frac{p_x}{m}, \tag{1.29}$$

---

[11] Dicke, R. H., and J. P. Wittke, *Introduction to Quantum Mechanics*, pp. 31–33, Addison-Wesley, Reading, Mass., 1960.

then using (1.24) we must have

$$\frac{p_x}{m} = \frac{d\omega}{dk}.$$ (1.30)

From (1.9), however, we know that $p_x = \hbar k$; therefore, it follows that

$$d\omega = \frac{\hbar}{m} k \, dk.$$ (1.31)

Integrating, we obtain

$$\omega = \frac{\hbar}{2m} k^2 + \text{constant};$$ (1.32)

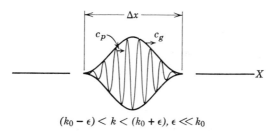

$$(k_0 - \epsilon) < k < (k_0 + \epsilon), \ \epsilon \ll k_0$$

Fig. 5.3

and if we multiply through by $\hbar$, the result is

$$\hbar\omega = \frac{(\hbar k)^2}{2m} + \hbar \, (\text{constant}),$$ (1.33)

which in view of (1.1) and (1.9) can also be written as

$$E = \frac{p_x^2}{2m} + \hbar \, (\text{constant}).$$ (1.34)

It is only necessary to interpret $\hbar$ multiplying the constant of integration as the potential energy V for this to express conservation of mechanical energy in its usual form.

Even when we give E its relativistic value, the identification remains consistent.[12] For from the conservation equation (1.96) of Chapter 2,

$$E^2 = c^2 p_x^2 + m_0^2 c^4;$$ (1.35)

[12] Eisberg, R. M., *Fundamentals of Modern Physics*, pp. 141–146, Wiley, New York, 1963.

and taking the differential of both sides, we have

$$2E \, dE = c^2 2p_x \, dp_x$$

or

$$\frac{dE}{dp_x} = c^2 \frac{p_x}{E}. \tag{1.36}$$

But because of the relations (1.1), (1.9), and (1.24), it must also be true that

$$\frac{dE}{dp_x} = \frac{d\omega}{dk} = c_g; \tag{1.37}$$

therefore, we must have

$$c_g = c^2 \frac{p_x}{E} \tag{1.38}$$

or, using (1.29) of this chapter and (1.83) of Chapter 2,

$$c_g = c^2 \frac{mv_x}{mc^2} = v_x. \tag{1.39}$$

Thus, just as (1.6) can be used to describe a nonlocalized particle, (1.28) can be used to represent a localized particle with some definite velocity. However, to assure correspondence with physical reality, both of these Ψ-functions should possess certain other properties as well as those emphasized above. First, they should remain finite at large distances from the reference origin. If they do not, the probability of finding the particle they represent at these distances, proportional to $\Psi^*\Psi$, will necessarily become very large and make it impossible to develop any local detail. In practice what this means is that, even though real wave functions may sometimes be used, those which increase toward infinity must be discarded at the outset.

Second, wave functions to be useful should be normalized. That is, their final form will have to be obtained by carrying out the operation

$$\int \Psi^*\Psi \, dv = 1, \tag{1.40}$$

where dv indicates an element of the spatial volume in which the particle is known to be confined. Application of this relation to a certain volume by inserting specific limits of integration amounts to requiring that the particle be somewhere in that volume; once this has been done, we can state that the resulting $\Psi^*\Psi$ at any point in the volume will be exactly equal to the probability of finding the particle at that point.

Problems 5.1

1. Find the de Broglie wavelength of the following:

   a. An electron with 10 eV of kinetic energy.
   b. A dust particle with a radius $r = 10^{-4}$ cm and a density of $\rho = 1$ gm/cm^3 moving with the speed $v = 1$ cm/sec.
   c. A marble with a mass of 0.1 kg moving with the speed $v = 1$ m/sec.

   Solution
   In all cases we must apply the relation

   $$\lambda = \frac{h}{p} = \frac{h}{mv},$$

   where

   $$h = 6.625 \times 10^{-27} \text{ erg sec or } \frac{\text{gm cm}^2}{\text{sec}}.$$

   (a)
   $$T = \tfrac{1}{2}mv^2$$

   and
   $$p = mv;$$

   therefore,
   $$p = \sqrt{2mT},$$

   where
   $$m = 9.1 \times 10^{-28} \text{ gm}$$

   and
   $$T = 10 \text{ eV} = 1.6 \times 10^{-11} \text{ erg}.$$

   Thus,
   $$p = \sqrt{2 \times 9.1 \times 10^{-28} \times 1.6 \times 10^{-11}}$$
   $$= 1.706 \times 10^{-19} \text{ gm cm/sec};$$

   it follows that

   $$\lambda = \frac{6.625 \times 10^{-27}}{1.706 \times 10^{-19}} = 3.869 \times 10^{-8} \text{ cm} = 3.869 \text{ Å}.$$

   (b)
   $$p = mv = \tfrac{4}{3}\pi r^3 \rho v = \tfrac{4}{3}\pi (10^{-4})^3(1)(1)$$
   $$= 0.419 \times 10^{-11} \text{ gm cm/sec}.$$

   Hence,

   $$\lambda = \frac{6.625 \times 10^{-27}}{0.419 \times 10^{-11}} = 1.575 \times 10^{-15} \text{ cm} = 1.575 \times 10^{-7} \text{ Å}.$$

   (c)
   $$\lambda = \frac{6.625 \times 10^{-27}}{(0.10 \times 10^3)100}$$
   $$= 6.625 \times 10^{-31} \text{ cm} = 6.625 \times 10^{-23} \text{ Å}.$$

Thus, to observe the wave nature of matter one must choose particles with low values of momentum. At ordinary velocities, this means that the mass must be very small.

2. Compute the wavelength of a thermal neutron at room temperature.

Solution

It is well known that average kinetic energy and absolute temperature are related in the following way:

$$\tfrac{1}{2}mv^2 = \tfrac{3}{2}kT$$

where k is Boltzmann's constant, equal to 1.380 × 10⁻¹⁶ erg/deg, and T is the temperature in °K. In this case m is the neutron mass, 1.675 × 10⁻²⁴ gm. Evidently, room temperature will be $273 + 27 = 300$ °K. Using the de Broglie relation, we have

$$\tfrac{1}{2}mv^2 = \frac{p^2}{2m} = \frac{1}{2m}\left(\frac{h}{\lambda}\right)^2 = \tfrac{3}{2}kT;$$

therefore,

$$p = \sqrt{3mkT},$$

and

$$\lambda = \frac{h}{\sqrt{3mkT}} = \frac{6.625 \times 10^{-27}}{[3(1.675 \times 10^{-24})(1.380 \times 10^{-16})300]^{\frac{1}{2}}} = 1.80 \text{ Å.}$$

3. Show that for de Broglie waves the particle velocity is equal to the group velocity.

Solution

From Problem 4.2(3), we know that the group velocity c_g for a system of waves is related to the phase velocity c_p by

$$c_g = c_p - \lambda\frac{dc_p}{d\lambda},$$

where λ is the wavelength of individual waves in the system. It follows that

$$c_g = \lambda^2\left(\frac{c_p}{\lambda^2} - \frac{1}{\lambda}\frac{dc_p}{d\lambda}\right) = -\lambda^2\frac{d}{d\lambda}\left(\frac{c_p}{\lambda}\right) = -\lambda^2\frac{dv}{d\lambda},$$

where v is the frequency of the wave; thus

$$\frac{1}{c_g} = -\frac{1}{\lambda^2}\frac{d\lambda}{dv} = \frac{d}{dv}\left(\frac{1}{\lambda}\right).$$

For the particle we know that

$$T = \tfrac{1}{2}mv^2 = E - V$$

or

$$v = \left[\frac{2(E - V)}{m}\right]^{\frac{1}{2}}.$$

Therefore, using de Broglie's relationship, we have

$$\frac{1}{\lambda} = \frac{mv}{h} = \frac{m}{h}\left[\frac{2(E - V)}{m}\right]^{\frac{1}{2}} = \frac{1}{h}[2m(E - V)]^{\frac{1}{2}}.$$

Substituting this value of $1/\lambda$ in the preceding equation for c_g,

$$\frac{1}{c_g} = \frac{d}{dv}\left[\frac{1}{h}\ \sqrt{2m(E-V)}\right];$$

and replacing E by hv, we have

$$\frac{1}{c_g} = \frac{1}{h}\frac{d}{dv}[2m(hv-V)]^{\frac{1}{2}}$$

$$= \frac{1}{h}\cdot\frac{1}{2}\ [2m(hv-V)]^{\frac{1}{2}}\cdot 2mh$$

$$= \left[\frac{m}{2(E-V)}\right]^{\frac{1}{2}} = \frac{1}{v}\,,$$

or

$$c_g = v.$$

4. Monochromatic radiation with a wavelength of 6620 Å strikes the surface of a metal with a work function ϕ of 1.5 eV. What will the maximum velocity of the emitted electrons be, and what de Broglie wavelength will be associated with the electrons having this velocity?

Solution

If E represents the energy of an incident light photon, it is known that in general

$$E - \phi = \tfrac{1}{2}mv^2,$$

where m is the mass of the emitted electron and v is its velocity. But

$$E = hv$$

and

$$c = \lambda v,$$

where λ and v are the wavelength and frequency of the photon and c is the velocity of light; so,

$$E = \frac{hc}{\lambda}.$$

Hence,

$$v = \left[\frac{2}{m}\left(\frac{hc}{\lambda}-\phi\right)\right]^{\frac{1}{2}}.$$

Using

$$h = 6.62\times 10^{-27}\ \text{erg sec}$$

$$c = 3.00\times 10^{10}\ \text{cm/sec}$$

$$\lambda = 6.62\times 10^{-5}\ \text{cm},$$

we see that

$$\frac{hc}{\lambda} = \frac{(6.62)(3.00)}{6.62}\times\frac{10^{-17}}{10^{-5}} = 3.00\times 10^{-12}\ \text{erg};$$

and since $1 \text{ eV} = 1.6 \times 10^{-12}$ erg,

$$\frac{hc}{\lambda} - \phi = (3.00 - 2.4) \times 10^{-12} = 6.00 \times 10^{-13} \text{ erg.}$$

Therefore, with $m = 9.1 \times 10^{-28}$ gm,

$$v = \left[\frac{2}{9.1} \times 6.00 \times 10^{15} \right]^{\frac{1}{2}} = [13.2 \times 10^{14}]^{\frac{1}{2}}$$

$$= 3.7 \times 10^7 \text{ cm/sec.}$$

The de Broglie wavelength of the electron with this velocity will be

$$\lambda = \frac{h}{p},$$

where

$$p = mv = (9.1 \times 10^{-28} \text{ gm})(3.7 \times 10^7 \text{ cm/sec}) = 3.37 \times 10^{-20} \text{ gm cm/sec};$$

and because

$$\text{gm cm/sec} = \text{gm} \frac{\text{cm}^2}{\text{sec}^2} \left(\frac{\text{sec}}{\text{cm}} \right) = \text{erg sec/cm},$$

$$\lambda = \frac{6.62 \times 10^{-27} \text{ erg sec}}{3.37 \times 10^{-20} \text{ erg sec/cm}} \simeq 19 \times 10^{-8} \text{ cm} = 19 \text{ Å.}$$

5. Compute the order of magnitude of $\Delta x \Delta p_x$ for the case of a particle observed under a very high resolution light microscope [Fig. P5.1 (5)].

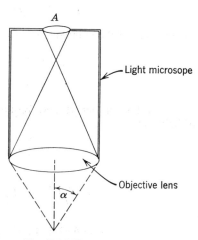

A

Light microsope

Objective lens

α

Fig. P5.1 (5)

Solution

The resolving power of a light microscope is approximately $(\lambda/\sin \alpha)$, where λ is the wavelength of the light; therefore,

$$\Delta x \simeq \frac{\lambda}{\sin \alpha}.$$

We may assume that only one photon scattered from the particle must enter the microscope in order for an observation to be made at A, and we know the momentum of the photon will be

$$p = \frac{h}{\lambda}.$$

However, because we cannot know at what point the photon passed through the objective lens, the uncertainty in the momentum must be:

$$\Delta p_x \simeq 2p \sin \alpha = \frac{2h \sin \alpha}{\lambda}.$$

It follows that

$$\Delta p_x \, \Delta x \simeq 2h = 4\pi\hbar$$

which, of course, is greater than $\hbar$ as required by the uncertainty principle.

6. An electron is known to have been emitted at some instant within an interval of 1.0×10^{-9} sec. What minimum uncertainty must exist in its energy?

Solution

The uncertainty principle says that

$$\Delta E \, \Delta t \gtrsim \hbar;$$

therefore,

$$\Delta E \gtrsim \frac{h}{2\pi \Delta t} = \frac{6.62 \times 10^{-27} \text{ erg sec}}{6.28 \times 10^{-9} \text{ sec}} \simeq 8 \times 10^{-7} \text{ eV}.$$

7. Calculate the following:
   a. The essential uncertainty in the momentum of a proton of mass 1.672×10^{-24} gm confined to the nucleus of an atom with a diameter of approximately 10^{-12} cm.
   b. The minimum kinetic energy and velocity of the proton.

Solution

(a) With

$$\Delta x \, \Delta p \simeq h,$$

it follows that

$$\Delta p \simeq \frac{6.6 \times 10^{-27}}{10^{-12}}$$

$$\simeq 6.6 \times 10^{-15} \text{ gm cm/sec}.$$

(b) Assuming that

$$p_{\min} = \Delta p = 6.6 \times 10^{-15},$$

we have

$$v_{\min} = \frac{6.6 \times 10^{-15}}{1.672 \times 10^{-24}} = 3.948 \times 10^{9} \text{ cm/sec};$$

then

$$T_{\min} = \tfrac{1}{2}mv_{\min}^2 = \frac{1.672 \times 10^{-24}}{2} (3.948 \times 10^9)^2 \text{ erg}$$

$$= \frac{1.672 \times 10^{-24}(3.948)^2 \times 10^{18}}{2(1.602 \times 10^{-12})} = 8.136 \times 10^6 \text{ eV}$$

$$= 8.14 \text{ MeV}.$$

8. Quantum particles emitted by a source pass through a slit of width d and impinge on a photographic plate.

    a. Show that the angle θ, defining the half-width of the central maximum of the particle-wave diffraction pattern, is approximately equal to λ/d.

    b. Using the uncertainty principle to estimate the transverse momentum introduced in passing through the slit, show that the deflection angle θ of the particles is also approximately equal to λ/d.

    c. Explain why both treatments lead to the same prediction.

Solution

(a) Assuming a minimum to exist at the point P [see Fig. P5.1 (8a)], this point must be one wavelength farther away from the upper edge of the slit (E) than from the lower edge (C). Thus the secondary wavelet from

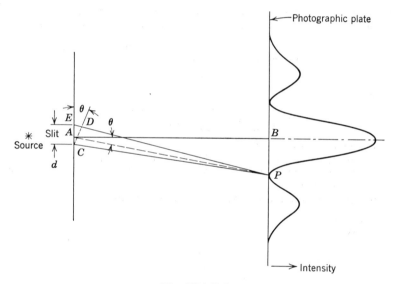

Fig. P5.1 (8a)

the point in the slit adjacent to the upper edge will travel approximately $\lambda/2$ farther than that from the point at the center, so that a phase difference of π will exist at P, and the two will cancel. Similarly, the wavelet from the next point below the upper edge will cancel that from the next point below the center, and this pairing-off can be continued to include all the points in the wavefront.

    From the figure, CE is perpendicular to AB and CD is approximately perpendicular to AP. Therefore,

$$ECD \simeq BAP = \theta$$

and

$$\sin \theta \simeq \frac{\lambda}{d},$$

or

$$\theta \simeq \frac{\lambda}{d}.$$

(b) If a particle is made to pass through a slit of width d [see Fig. P5.1 ($8b$)], its coordinate in the direction of this width becomes known with the accuracy

$$\Delta y = d.$$

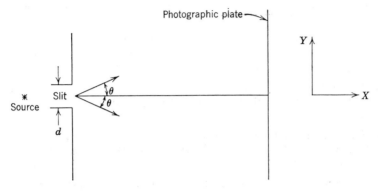

Fig. P5.1 ($8b$)

The uncertainty in the momentum of the particle parallel to the screen introduced by its passing through the slit will be

$$\Delta p_y \simeq p_x\theta = \frac{b}{\lambda}\theta;$$

thus,

$$\Delta y\,\Delta p_y \simeq \frac{h}{\lambda}\theta d.$$

But the uncertainty principle requires that

$$\Delta y\,\Delta p_y \simeq h;$$

therefore,

$$h \simeq \frac{h}{\lambda}\theta d$$

or

$$\theta \simeq \frac{\lambda}{d}.$$

(c) Both treatments lead to the same prediction because of the complementary nature of the point object and wave behavior of particles. In wave theory, the intensity is measured by the square of the amplitude and expresses the energy; whereas in particle theory, the intensity expresses the relative probability of finding a particle at a given position, particles obeying this statistically. But both theories are merely alternate ways of viewing the same physical process.

Exercises 5.1

1. What is the wavelength of an electron whose velocity is 10^8 cm/sec; and through what potential difference must an electron be accelerated to produce a wavelength of 1 Å?

2. In an experiment, a beam of helium atoms was obtained from an enclosure heated to a temperature of 127° C. What was the de Broglie wavelength of the helium atoms in the beam?

3. Show that the allowed orbits in the Bohr atomic model [Problem 3.3 (2)] are those for which the circumference of the orbit can exactly contain an integral number of de Broglie wavelengths.

4. What is the lowest possible energy for a neutron confined to a "one-dimensional box" 1.0×10^{-12} cm long (the approximate diameter of an atomic nucleus)?

5. Find the uncertainties in the velocities of an electron and a proton when they are known to be located between atoms separated by a distance of 5.0×10^{-8} cm.

6. According to Bohr's theory of atomic structure, the radius of the nth permitted orbit is

$$\rho_n = n^2 a_0,$$

where a_0 is the radius of the orbit corresponding to $n = 1$, and the orbital angular momentum l of the nth orbit is $n\hbar$. Show that this is inconsistent with the uncertainty principle.

5.2   Schrödinger's Equation and Quantum Operators

Just as Newton's equation must follow from conservation of energy for a point object [(2.64) of Chapter 2], the equation of motion that a nonrelativistic, nonlocalized quantum particle with the state function (1.11),

$$\Psi = A e^{\frac{i}{\hbar}(\mathbf{p}\cdot\mathbf{r}-Et)} = A e^{\frac{i}{\hbar}(p_x x + p_y y + p_z z - Et)}, \tag{2.1}$$

must obey, can be obtained from the three-dimensional generalization of (1.34),

$$E = \frac{p^2}{2m} + \hbar \,(\text{constant}) = T + V. \tag{2.2}$$

However, we must also agree to define conservative forces acting on the particle in the same way as before [(1.40) of Chapter 2],

$$\mathbf{F}(x, y, z) = -\nabla V(x, y, z), \tag{2.3}$$

so that the potential energy can be generalized beyond constant values and (2.2) written as

$$\frac{p^2}{2m} + V(x, y, z) = E. \tag{2.4}$$

The last form suggests that we seek appropriate substitutions for p^2 and E in terms of Ψ; and it is evident that both can be generated by differentiating (2.1)—twice with respect to the spatial coordinates, once with respect to time:

$$\nabla^2\Psi = \left(\frac{\partial^2}{\partial x^2} + \frac{\partial^2}{\partial y^2} + \frac{\partial^2}{\partial z^2}\right) Ae^{\frac{i}{\hbar}(p_x x + p_y y + p_z z - Et)}$$

$$= \frac{i}{\hbar^2}(p_x^2 + p_y^2 + p_z^2)Ae^{\frac{i}{\hbar}(p_x x + p_y y + p_z z - Et)}$$

$$= -\frac{p^2}{\hbar^2}\Psi, \tag{2.5}$$

so

$$p^2 = -\frac{\hbar^2}{\Psi}\nabla^2\Psi; \tag{2.6}$$

and

$$\frac{\partial\Psi}{\partial t} = \frac{\partial}{\partial t} Ae^{\frac{i}{\hbar}(\mathbf{p\,r} - Et)}$$

$$= -\frac{i}{\hbar} EAe^{\frac{i}{\hbar}(\mathbf{p.r} - Et)}$$

$$= -\frac{i}{\hbar} E\Psi, \tag{2.7}$$

giving

$$E = -\frac{\hbar}{i\Psi}\frac{\partial\Psi}{\partial t} = i\frac{\hbar}{\Psi}\frac{\partial\Psi}{\partial t}. \tag{2.8}$$

Hence, substituting (2.6) and (2.8) in (2.4), we obtain

$$-\frac{\hbar^2}{\Psi 2m}\nabla^2\Psi + V(x, y, z) = i\frac{\hbar}{\Psi}\frac{\partial\Psi}{\partial t} \tag{2.9}$$

or

$$\left[-\frac{\hbar^2}{2m}\nabla^2 + V(x, y, z)\right]\Psi = i\hbar\frac{\partial\Psi}{\partial t}. \tag{2.10}$$

In view of the fact that the left-hand side of (2.9) is just the Hamiltonian function $T + V$, the bracketed quantity on the left in (2.10) is called the

Hamiltonian operator H and the equation is usually written more concisely as

$$H\Psi = i\hbar\Psi_t. \tag{2.11}$$

This is the desired equation of motion, called Schrödinger's equation after its discoverer; every state function $\Psi = \Psi(x, y, z, t)$ which is a solution of a given physical problem must satisfy it[13] and, ordinarily, certain boundary conditions as well. It possesses at least two unusual features: the imaginary number i is part of the equation, and only a first time derivative of Ψ appears. Because it is satisfied by a wave function and is, in any event, a special case of the general form (2.147) of Chapter 4, we know that it is a linear, homogeneous wave equation; but since it involves i, its general solution must involve complex functions,[14] as noted before.

In the case of a photon moving in an electromagnetic field characterized by the vector potential $\mathbf{A}(x, y, z, t)$ and the scalar potential $\phi(x, y, z, t)$, as in (3.138) to (3.140) of Chapter 3, it is not difficult to show[15] that the Hamiltonian operator in (2.11) must have the form

$$H = \left[\frac{1}{2m}\left(\frac{\hbar}{i}\nabla - \frac{e}{i}\mathbf{A}\right)^2 + e\phi\right] \tag{2.12}$$

instead of that given in (2.10). And, if relativistic effects are to be included, it would appear that the generalization of (1.96) of Chapter 2,

$$p^2c^2 + m_0^2c^4 = E^2 \tag{2.13}$$

should be used[15] to express energy conservation instead of (2.4). But, differentiating (2.7) again with respect to t to define E^2 and substituting this along with p^2 from (2.6), we obtain

$$-c^2\frac{\hbar^2}{\Psi}\nabla^2\Psi + m_0^2c^4 = -\frac{\hbar^2}{\Psi}\frac{\partial^2\Psi}{\partial t^2} \tag{2.14}$$

or

$$\nabla^2\Psi - \left(\frac{m_0c}{\hbar}\right)^2\Psi = c^{-2}\Psi_{tt}, \tag{2.15}$$

which is no longer of the Schrödinger form, since it contains no i and incorporates a second instead of a first time derivative of Ψ. This is called the Klein-Gordon equation; it can be used for a relativistic quantum wave

[13] Beard, D. B., *Quantum Mechanics*, pp. 52–66, Allyn and Bacon, Boston, Mass., 1963.

[14] Eisberg, R. M., *Fundamentals of Modern Physics*, pp. 164–172, Wiley, New York, 1963.

[15] Messiah, A., *Quantum Mechanics*, Vol. 1, pp. 63–68, Wiley, New York, 1961.

equation only by reinterpreting the state function Ψ. A preferable equation of motion in the Schrödinger form has been developed by Dirac and will be presented later. For the present, considerations will be limited to mass-carrying particles moving at relatively low velocities and (2.10) will be adopted as the governing equation.

Obviously, (2.10) will be satisfied by a traveling wave of the form (2.1). But if we interest ourselves in solutions that can be written as a product of a function of the space coordinates and a function of the time,

$$\Psi = \psi(x, y, z)T(t), \tag{2.16}$$

substitution in (2.10) will yield:

$$T\left[-\frac{\hbar^2}{2m}\nabla^2 + V(x, y, z)\right]\psi = \psi i\hbar \frac{\partial T}{\partial t}$$

or

$$\frac{1}{\psi}\left[-\frac{\hbar^2}{2m}\nabla^2 + V(x, y, z)\right]\psi = \frac{i\hbar}{T}\frac{\partial T}{\partial t}. \tag{2.17}$$

Because all four variables are independent and the left side of the equation is a function only of the position coordinates, while the right side is a function of the time t alone, both sides must be equal to the same constant.[16] Recognizing in advance that this constant will prove to be the total energy, we shall call it E. Hence the right-hand side gives

$$\frac{dT}{dt} - \frac{ET}{i\hbar} = 0$$

or

$$\frac{dT}{dt} + \frac{i}{\hbar}ET = 0, \tag{2.18}$$

which has the solution

$$T = Ae^{-\frac{i}{\hbar}Et}$$

where A represents an arbitrary constant. The left-hand side becomes

$$\left[-\frac{\hbar^2}{2m}\nabla^2 + V(x, y, z)\right]\psi = E\psi \tag{2.19}$$

or simply

$$H\psi = E\psi \tag{2.20}$$

where, of course, $\psi = \psi(x, y, z)$ only.

We conclude that the $\Psi(x, y, z, t)$ of interest can be written as

$$\Psi = A\psi e^{-\frac{i}{\hbar}Et} \tag{2.21}$$

[16] Schiff, L. I., *Quantum Mechanics*, 27–28, McGraw-Hill, New York, 1955.

provided $\psi(x, y, z)$ separately satisfies (2.20), called Schrödinger's time-independent equation. Notice that it has the form of an eigenequation of the type studied earlier [(1.24) of Chapter 4]. Each eigenfunction ψ_n will necessarily have an eigenvalue E_n associated with it, so that (2.20) is sometimes written in the form

$$H\psi_n = E_n\psi_n, \tag{2.22}$$

where n can be 1, 2, 3, ... This equation no longer contains an i, so its solutions need not be complex, though complex forms usually prove to be the most convenient ones. It should also be noted that, even though the equation contains no time derivatives of t, it still qualifies as a wave equation in the sense of (2.149) of Chapter 4. Of course, we see from (2.21) that each eigenfunction ψ_n of ψ implies a corresponding eigenfunction of Ψ_n of Ψ.

These eigenfunctions of the operator H are said to describe "stationary" particle states, for the simple reason that $\psi_n{}^*\psi_n = \Psi_n{}^*\Psi_n$ will be independent of time. In fact, when we take advantage of the possibility of superposition of solutions and write the general solution of (2.11),

$$H\Psi = i\hbar\Psi_t.$$

as

$$\Psi = \sum_{n=1}^{\infty} A_n\psi_n e^{-\frac{i}{\hbar}E_n t} \tag{2.23}$$

with the complex conjugate

$$\Psi^* = \sum_{m=1}^{\infty} A_m{}^*\psi_m{}^* e^{\frac{i}{\hbar}E_m t}, \tag{2.24}$$

this conclusion still holds. For whenever there is only one eigenvalue, $m = n$ and $\Psi_n{}^*\Psi_n$ will reduce to $\psi_n{}^*\psi_n$.[17]

It follows that if

$$\int_{-\infty}^{\infty} \Psi_n{}^*(x, t)\Psi_n(x, t)\, dx = 1, \tag{2.25}$$

it must additionally be true that

$$\int_{-\infty}^{\infty} \psi_n{}^*(x)\psi_n(x)\, dx = 1. \tag{2.26}$$

Furthermore, as the last reference shows, all eigenfunctions will satisfy an orthogonality relation of the type

$$\int_{-\infty}^{\infty} \psi_n{}^*(x)\psi_m(x)\, dx = 0, \qquad m \neq n. \tag{2.27}$$

[17] Eisberg, R. M., *Fundamentals of Modern Physics*, pp. 184–192, Wiley, New York, 1963.

The orthonormality conditions

$$\int_{-\infty}^{\infty} \psi_n{}^*(x)\psi_m(x)\,dx = \delta_{nm} \tag{2.28}$$

summarize both of the last equations, and using them it is not difficult to prove that state functions in the general solution form (2.23), (2.24) can be normalized merely by requiring that

$$\sum_{n=1}^{\infty} A_n{}^* A_n = 1. \tag{2.29}$$

Of course, the A_n can be used to satisfy initial and boundary conditions in much the same way as before [(2.39) to (2.67) of Chapter 4]. Additional examples are provided in the problems.

Returning to the basic solution (2.21),

$$\Psi = A\psi e^{-\frac{i}{\hbar}Et},$$

comparison with the form (1.11),

$$\Psi = A e^{\frac{i}{\hbar}(\mathbf{p}\cdot\mathbf{r} - Et)} = A e^{\frac{i}{\hbar}\mathbf{p}\cdot\mathbf{r}} e^{-\frac{i}{\hbar}Et}, \tag{2.30}$$

in which the meaning of A, E, and $\mathbf{p}$ is established, confirms that the constant A must be the amplitude A and the constant E the energy E. Also we see that

$$\psi = e^{\frac{i}{\hbar}\mathbf{p}\cdot\mathbf{r}}. \tag{2.31}$$

This suggests that the operator concept encountered in (2.20), where H is shown to be the operator equivalent of the energy E, may be expanded to find an operator for the momentum $\mathbf{p}$.

Following the same procedure used to obtain (2.6), we see that with ψ defined by (2.31),

$$\nabla^2 \psi = \left(\frac{i}{\hbar}\right)^2 p^2 \psi \tag{2.32}$$

or

$$\left(\frac{\hbar}{i}\right)^2 \nabla^2 \psi = p^2 \psi. \tag{2.33}$$

If we select the positive square root of $(\hbar/i)^2$ to preserve the consistency of the sign convention in the classical limit, this suggests that

$$\frac{\hbar}{i}\nabla\psi = \mathbf{p}\psi; \tag{2.34}$$

in other words, that

$$\frac{\hbar}{i}\nabla \approx \left(\frac{\hbar}{i}\frac{\partial}{\partial x}, \frac{\hbar}{i}\frac{\partial}{\partial y}, \frac{\hbar}{i}\frac{\partial}{\partial z}\right) \qquad (2.35)$$

should be the operator equivalent of

$$\mathbf{p} \approx (p_x, p_y, p_z). \qquad (2.36)$$

Equation (2.34) is an eigenequation like (2.20), as may be emphasized by placing

$$\frac{\hbar}{i}\nabla = \mathbf{P} \qquad (2.37)$$

and writing it as

$$\mathbf{P}\psi = \mathbf{p}\psi, \qquad (2.38)$$

though vectors instead of scalars are involved in this case. Moreover, if we assume the solution to be a product of functions of x, y, and z separately,

$$\psi = X(x)\,Y(y)Z(z), \qquad (2.39)$$

then

$$\frac{\hbar}{i}\left(\hat{\mathbf{i}}\frac{\partial}{\partial x} + \hat{\mathbf{j}}\frac{\partial}{\partial y} + \hat{\mathbf{k}}\frac{\partial}{\partial z}\right)XYZ = (p_x\hat{\mathbf{i}} + p_y\hat{\mathbf{j}} + p_z\hat{\mathbf{k}})XYZ,$$

and we obtain three scalar equations like

$$\frac{\hbar}{i}\frac{dX}{dx} = p_x X \qquad (2.40)$$

or

$$\frac{dX}{dx} - \frac{i}{\hbar}p_x X = 0, \qquad (2.41)$$

with the solution

$$X = A_x e^{\frac{i}{\hbar}p_x x}. \qquad (2.42)$$

Hence,

$$\psi = A_x A_y A_z e^{\frac{i}{\hbar}(p_x x + p_y y + p_z z)}; \qquad (2.43)$$

placing

$$A_x A_y A_z = A, \qquad (2.44)$$

this can be written as

$$\psi = A e^{\frac{i}{\hbar}\mathbf{p}\cdot\mathbf{r}}, \qquad (2.45)$$

which is just (2.31) with the amplitude constant A of (2.30) included on the right-hand side.

We conclude that the eigenfunctions ψ_n of the energy operator H, with the eigenvalues E_n, will also be eigenfunctions of the linear momentum operator **P**, with the eigenvalues $\mathbf{p}_n$. Furthermore, because the form (2.45) can be multiplied by an arbitrary function of time and still remain a solution of (2.38), we see that

$$\psi e^{-\frac{i}{\hbar}Et} = Ae^{\frac{i}{\hbar}(\mathbf{p}\cdot\mathbf{r}-Et)} = \Psi \qquad (2.46)$$

should also be a solution of this equation, which might be expected from the known fact that to every eigenfunction ψ_n of ψ there must correspond an eigenfunction Ψ_n of Ψ.

In the same way that ∇^2 of the operator H applied to Ψ or ψ leads to the eigenequation (2.38), $V(x, y, z)$ applied to Ψ or ψ leads to the eigenequation

$$\mathbf{R}\psi = \mathbf{r}\psi, \qquad (2.47)$$

where **R** represents a position operator.[18] However, the solution of this equation clearly must be compatible with the requirement that $\psi^*\psi$ should vanish everywhere except at the point at which the particle is known to be, and yield unity there. Such a solution is called a Dirac delta-function and is represented by writing

$$\psi = \delta(\mathbf{R} - \mathbf{r}); \qquad (2.48)$$

it has the following properties by definition:

$$\delta(\mathbf{R} - \mathbf{r}) = 0, \qquad \mathbf{R} \neq \mathbf{r} \qquad (2.49)$$

$$\int_{-\infty}^{\infty} \delta(\mathbf{R} - \mathbf{r}) \, d\mathbf{R} = 1 \qquad (2.50)$$

In practice what this means is that the position coordinates x, y, z, and thus the potential $V(x, y, z)$, are all their own operators. Any of these operating on ψ or Ψ simply yields itself multiplying the state function.

Recalling that the angular momentum is given in (1.48) to (1.52) of Chapter 2 by

$$\mathbf{l} = \mathbf{r} \times \mathbf{p}$$

or

$$l_x = yp_z - zp_y$$

$$l_y = zp_x - xp_z$$

$$l_z = xp_y - yp_x,$$

[18] Dicke, R. H., and J. P. Wittke, *Introduction to Quantum Mechanics*, pp. 64–71, Addison-Wesley, Reading, Mass., 1960.

we see that the above operators imply other operators for the angular
momentum components:

$$\frac{\hbar}{i}\left(y\frac{\partial}{\partial z} - z\frac{\partial}{\partial y}\right) = L_x \qquad (2.51)$$

$$\frac{\hbar}{i}\left(z\frac{\partial}{\partial x} - x\frac{\partial}{\partial z}\right) = L_y \qquad (2.52)$$

$$\frac{\hbar}{i}\left(x\frac{\partial}{\partial y} - y\frac{\partial}{\partial x}\right) = L_z \qquad (2.53)$$

For reasons that will appear later, it is also convenient to use these to define
an operator for l^2, the square of the angular momentum:

$$L_x{}^2 + L_y{}^2 + L_z{}^2 = L^2 \qquad (2.54)$$

In the same way, various other secondary operators can be defined in
terms of the primary ones discussed above.

Problems 5.2

1. Solve the one-dimensional Schrödinger equation for a free particle. What
is the probability density $\Psi^*\Psi$ for this case?

Solution
    For the particle to remain free, the potential energy must remain constant
and may be considered zero. Because this potential is not a function of time,
the problem reduces to solving the following time-independent Schrödinger
equation:

$$-\frac{\hbar^2}{2m}\frac{d^2\psi(x)}{dx^2} = E\psi(x)$$

The solution is

$$\psi = C_1 e^{\frac{i}{\hbar}\sqrt{2mE}\,x} + C_2 e^{-\frac{i}{\hbar}\sqrt{2mE}\,x}.$$

It follows that the solution of the time-dependent equation

$$-\frac{\hbar^2}{2m}\frac{\partial^2\Psi}{\partial x^2} = i\hbar\frac{\partial\Psi}{\partial t}$$

can be written in the form

$$\Psi(x,\,t) = e^{-\frac{i}{\hbar}Et}\,\psi(x).$$

Hence, if no other conditions are given,

$$\Psi = e^{-\frac{i}{\hbar}Et}\left(C_1 e^{\frac{i}{\hbar}\sqrt{2mE}\,x} + C_2 e^{-\frac{i}{\hbar}\sqrt{2mE}\,x}\right).$$

Considering the special case when $C_2 = 0$,

$$\Psi = C_1 e^{\frac{i}{\hbar}(\sqrt{2mE}\,x - Et)} = C_1 \cos\left[\frac{i}{\hbar}(\sqrt{2mE}\,x - Et)\right]$$

$$+ iC_1 \sin\left[\frac{i}{\hbar}(\sqrt{2mE}\,x - Et)\right].$$

Of course, this is a wave with angular frequency

$$\omega = \frac{E}{\hbar}$$

and phase velocity

$$c_p = \frac{\omega}{k} = \sqrt{\frac{E}{2m}}\,.$$

The probability density is

$$\Psi^*\Psi = C_1^* e^{-\frac{i}{\hbar}(\sqrt{2mE}\,x - Et)} C_1 e^{\frac{i}{\hbar}(\sqrt{2mE}\,x - Et)} = C_1^* C_1,$$

which implies that the probability of finding the particle anywhere along the X-axis is the same. It is, however, moving in the positive x-direction with some definite momentum p. With C_1 instead of C_2 equal to zero it would be moving in the negative x-direction.

Notice that it is impossible to normalize a wave function when $\Delta x = \infty$, since then

$$\int_{-\infty}^{\infty} \Psi^*\Psi \, dx = \int_{-\infty}^{\infty} A^*A \, dx = A^*A \int_{-\infty}^{\infty} dx.$$

In reality, however, a truly free particle cannot exist and Δx remains finite.

2. The Schrödinger equation for a rigid body rotating about a fixed axis passing through it is

$$-\frac{\hbar^2}{2I}\frac{\partial^2 \Psi}{\partial \phi^2} = i\hbar \frac{\partial \Psi}{\partial t},$$

where I is the moment of inertia characterizing the distribution of mass about the axis and ϕ is the angle describing the rotation of any element. Find the eigenfunctions and energy eigenvalues.

Solution

Trying the solution form

$$\Psi(\phi, t) = \Phi(\phi)T(t),$$

we obtain

$$-\frac{\hbar^2}{2I} T\Phi'' = i\hbar\Phi T';$$

and dividing through by ΦT, the result is

$$-\frac{\hbar^2}{2I}\frac{\Phi''}{\Phi} = i\hbar \frac{T'}{T} = E,$$

where E is a separation constant representing the energy.

We then have two ordinary differential equations,

$$\Phi'' + \frac{2I}{\hbar^2} E\Phi = 0$$

and

$$T' + \frac{iE}{\hbar} T = 0,$$

the solutions of which are,

$$\Phi = Ae^{i\frac{\sqrt{2IE}}{\hbar}\phi}$$

$$T = e^{-\frac{i}{\hbar}Et}.$$

But, in order for the total solution to be single-valued, it must also be true that

$$\Phi(\phi + 2\pi) - \Phi(\phi) = 0.$$

Therefore,

$$\frac{\sqrt{2IE}}{\hbar}(\phi + 2\pi) - \frac{\sqrt{2IE}}{\hbar}\phi = 2n\pi \qquad \{n = 1, 2, 3, \ldots$$

or

$$\frac{\sqrt{2IE}}{\hbar} = n;$$

so the energy eigenvalues are

$$E_n = \frac{n^2\hbar^2}{2I}$$

and the eigenfunctions are

$$\Psi_n = Ae^{i\left(\frac{\sqrt{2IE_n}}{\hbar}\right)\phi} e^{-\frac{i}{\hbar}E_n t}$$

It is also interesting to note that the operator $(\hbar/i)(\partial/\partial\phi)$ corresponds to the angular momentum about the axis of rotation.

3. Given that for a particle in a one-dimensional "box" of length b,

$$\Psi(x, 0) = C\sin\frac{2\pi x}{b} \quad \text{for} \quad 0 < x < b/2$$

and

$$\Psi(x, 0) = 0 \quad \text{elsewhere.}$$

a. Find a_n in the general solution $\Psi(x, t) = \sum_{n=1}^{\infty} a_n\Psi_n(x, t)$.

b. Show that $\sum_n a_n{}^*a_n = 1$.

Solution

We know that

$$\int_0^{b/2} \Psi(x, 0)\Psi^*(x, 0)\, dx = 1;$$

thus

$$\int_0^{b/2} \Psi(x, 0)\Psi^*(x, 0)\, dx = \int_0^{b/2} C^2 \sin^2 \frac{2\pi x}{b}\, dx = C^2 \int_0^{b/2} \left(\frac{1}{2} - \frac{\cos \frac{4\pi x}{2}}{2} \right) dx$$

$$= C^2 \frac{b}{4} - \left[\frac{C^2 b}{8\pi} \sin \frac{4\pi x}{b} \right]_0^{b/2} = \frac{C^2 b}{4} = 1,$$

and

$$C = \frac{2}{\sqrt{b}}.$$

Therefore,

$$\Psi(x, 0) = \begin{cases} \dfrac{2}{\sqrt{b}} \sin \dfrac{2\pi x}{b} & \text{for} \quad 0 < x < b/2 \\ 0 & \text{for} \quad b/2 < x < b. \end{cases}$$

Moreover, we know that in general we can write

$$\Psi(x, t) = \psi_n(x)T(t) = A \sin \frac{n\pi x}{b} \cdot e^{-\frac{i}{\hbar}E_n t},$$

and it must be true that

$$\int_0^b \Psi(x, t)\Psi^*(x, t)\, dx = 1.$$

Thus, in the same way as above,

$$\int_0^b A^2 \sin^2 \frac{n\pi x}{b}\, dx = 1$$

and

$$A = \sqrt{\frac{2}{b}}.$$

We conclude that

$$\psi_n = \sqrt{\frac{2}{b}} \sin \frac{n\pi x}{b}.$$

(a) Since at $t = 0$

$$\Psi(x, 0) = \sum_{n=1}^{\infty} a_n \Psi_n(x, 0)$$

in the region $0 < x < b/2$, both sides of this relation may be multiplied by $\Psi_l^*(x, 0)$ and integrated over the region to define the coefficients a_n in the Fourier manner. The result is

$$a_n = \int_0^{b/2} \Psi(x, 0)\Psi_n^*(x, 0)\, dx;$$

therefore,

$$a_n = \int_0^{b/2} \frac{2}{\sqrt{b}} \sin \frac{2\pi x}{b} \cdot \sqrt{\frac{2}{b}} \sin \frac{n\pi x}{b}\, dx.$$

From a table of integrals

$$\int \sin \alpha x \sin \beta x \, dx = \frac{\sin (\alpha - \beta)x}{2(\alpha - \beta)} - \frac{\sin (\alpha + \beta)x}{2(\alpha + \beta)}$$

provided that $\alpha^2 \neq \beta^2$. Thus

$$a_1 = \frac{2\sqrt{2}}{b} \left[\frac{\sin \frac{\pi x}{b}}{\frac{2\pi}{b}} - \frac{\sin \frac{3\pi x}{b}}{\frac{6\pi}{b}} \right]_0^{b/2} = \frac{\sqrt{2}}{\pi} \left[1 + \frac{1}{3} \right] = \frac{4\sqrt{2}}{3\pi},$$

but

$$a_2 = \frac{2\sqrt{2}}{b} \int_0^{b/2} \sin^2 \frac{2\pi x}{b} \, dx = \frac{2\sqrt{2}}{b} \int_0^{b/2} \left[\frac{1}{2} - \frac{\cos \frac{4\pi x}{b}}{2} \right] dx$$

$$= \frac{2\sqrt{2}}{b} \frac{b}{4} = \frac{1}{\sqrt{2}} .$$

In general,

$$a_n = \frac{\sqrt{2}}{\pi} \left[\frac{\sin (n-2) \frac{\pi x}{b}}{(n-2)} - \frac{\sin (n+2) \frac{\pi x}{b}}{(n+2)} \right]_0^{b/2} ;$$

so

$$a_3 = \frac{\sqrt{2}}{\pi} \left[1 - \frac{1}{5} \right] = \frac{4\sqrt{2}}{5\pi}$$

$$a_4 = \frac{\sqrt{2}}{\pi} \left[\frac{\sin \frac{2\pi x}{b}}{2} - \frac{\sin \frac{6\pi x}{b}}{6} \right]_0^{b/2} = 0$$

$$a_5 = \frac{\sqrt{2}}{\pi} \left[\frac{\sin \frac{3\pi x}{b}}{3} - \frac{\sin \frac{7\pi x}{b}}{7} \right]_0^{b/2} = \frac{\sqrt{2}}{\pi} \left[-\frac{1}{3} + \frac{1}{7} \right] = -\frac{4\sqrt{2}}{21\pi}$$

$$a_6 = \frac{\sqrt{2}}{\pi} \left[\frac{\sin \frac{4\pi x}{b}}{4} - \frac{\sin \frac{8\pi x}{b}}{8} \right]_0^{b/2} = 0,$$

and so on. All of the remaining a_n will be zero when n is even, and they can be calculated from the formula given above when n is odd.

(b) Because

$$\Psi(x, t) = \sum_{n=1}^{\infty} a_n \Psi_n(x, t)$$

and

$$\int_0^b \Psi^*(x, t)\Psi(x, t) \, dx = 1,$$

if we calculate

$$\int_0^b \Psi^*(x, t)\Psi(x, t)\, dx = \sum_n a_n^* a_n \int_0^b \psi_n^*(x)\psi_n(x)\, dx$$

$$+ \sum_{\substack{l\;n \\ l \neq n}} a_l^* a_n e^{-i\frac{(E_n - E_l)}{\hbar}t} \int_0^b \psi_l^*(x)\psi_n(x)\, dx = 1,$$

then due to the orthogonal properties of eigenfunctions,

$$\int_0^b \psi_n^*(x)\psi_m(x)\, dx = 0 \quad \text{f c r} \quad m \neq n,$$

and the fact that $a_n^* = a_n$ in this case where all are real,

$$\sum_n a_n^2 \frac{2}{b} \int_0^b \sin^2\frac{n\pi x}{b}\, dx = 1.$$

Therefore, since

$$\sum_n a_n^2 \frac{2}{b} \int_0^b \sin^2\frac{n\pi x}{b}\, dx = \sum_n a_n^2 \frac{2}{b} \int_0^b \left[\frac{1}{2} - \frac{\cos\frac{2n\pi x}{b}}{2}\right] dx = \sum_n a_n^2 \left(\frac{2}{b}\right)\left(\frac{b}{2}\right),$$

$$\sum_n a_n^2 = 1.$$

4. If $V(x, t) = V(x, -t)$, find $\Psi(x, -t)$ in terms of $\Psi(x, t)$. Also, show that the probability of finding a particle at any point x and time t is equal to the probability of finding a particle at the same point at the time $-t$,

$$\Psi^*(x, t)\Psi(x, t) = \Psi^*(x, -t)\Psi(x, -t).$$

Solution

The Schrödinger equation with $V(x, t)$ will be

$$-\frac{\hbar^2}{2m}\frac{\partial^2}{\partial x^2}\Psi(x, t) + V(x, t)\Psi(x, t) = i\hbar\frac{\partial}{\partial t}\Psi(x, t),$$

whereas with $V(x, -t)$ it will be

$$-\frac{\hbar^2}{2m}\frac{\partial^2}{\partial x^2}\Psi(x, -t) + V(x, -t)\Psi(x, -t) = i\hbar\frac{\partial}{\partial t}\Psi(x, -t).$$

But because the negative sign will appear in the exponential involving t, we see that

$$\frac{\partial}{\partial t}\Psi(x, -t) = -\frac{\partial}{\partial t}\Psi(x, t)$$

and

$$\frac{\partial^2}{\partial x^2}\Psi(x, t) = \frac{\partial^2}{\partial x^2}\Psi(x, -t).$$

Making use of these results and the fact that $V(x, t) = V(x, -t)$, the two above equations may be rewritten as

$$-\frac{\hbar^2}{2m}\frac{\partial^2}{\partial x^2}\Psi(x, t) + V(x, t)\Psi(x, t) = +i\hbar\frac{\partial}{\partial t}\Psi(x, t)$$

and

$$-\frac{\hbar^2}{2m}\frac{\partial^2}{\partial x^2}\Psi(x, t) + V(x, t)\Psi(x, t) = -i\hbar\frac{\partial}{\partial t}\Psi(x, t).$$

When we compare these, it is evident that if the first involves $\Psi(x, t)$, the second will involve $\Psi^*(x, t)$; therefore,

$$\Psi(x, -t) = \Psi^*(x, t)$$

$$\Psi^*(x, -t) = \Psi(x, t)$$

and it follows that

$$\Psi^*(x, t)\Psi(x, t) = \Psi^*(x, -t)\Psi(x, -t).$$

Exercises 5.2

1. Try the following forms of Ψ in the Schrödinger equation for a particle moving under a constant potential V_0 and comment on the results:

   a. $\Psi = A \sin (kx - \omega t)$.
   b. $\Psi = A \cos (kx - \omega t)$.
   c. $\Psi = A[\cos (kx - \omega t) + i \sin (kx - \omega t)]$.

2. A particle moves along the X-axis under the influence of the force

$$F = -k \sinh \alpha x;$$

   write the time-independent Schrödinger equation for the particle and find a solution for small x.

   Answer $\psi = Ae^{i\sqrt{2m\left(E - \frac{k}{\alpha}\right)}\frac{x}{\hbar}}$ for $E > \frac{k}{\alpha}$

   $$\psi = Be^{\sqrt{2m\left(\frac{k}{\alpha} - E\right)}\frac{x}{\hbar}}$$ for $E < \frac{k}{\alpha}$.

3. Show that the Fourier integral

$$\Psi(x, t) = \int_{-\infty}^{+\infty} A(k)e^{i(kx - \omega t)}\, dk$$

   is a solution of the Schrödinger equation for $V = V_0$, a constant, and arbitrary $A(k)$, provided that

$$\hbar\omega(k) = \frac{\hbar^2 k^2}{2m} + V_0.$$

4. Prove that $\Psi_n^*(x, t)\Psi_n(x, t) = \psi_n^*(x)\psi_n(x)$ for any particular eigenstate.

5. Using the orthonormality condition

$$\int_{-\infty}^{\infty} \psi_n{}^*(x)\psi_m(x)\,dx = \delta_{nm},$$

establish that the state function in the general solution of the Schrödinger equation can be normalized to give

$$\sum_{n=1}^{\infty} a_n{}^* a_n = 1.$$

5.3   The Correspondence Principle and Expectation Values

It is immediately apparent that an eigenfunction ψ_n of the linear momentum operator **P** and the energy operator H cannot in addition be an eigenfunction of the position operator **R**. If it could be, not only could the exact momentum $\mathbf{p}_n$ and energy E_n of the particle be defined simultaneously, the position could also be precisely determined; this would then violate the uncertainty principle.

The inference is that all quantum mechanical operators should satisfy an additional relationship, which may be formulated explicitly by considering that if we have two such operators A and B with the same eigenfunction ψ_n, it must be true that:

$$A\psi_n = a_n\psi_n, \qquad B\psi_n = b_n\psi_n \tag{3.1}$$

$$AB\psi_n = Ab_n\psi_n = b_n A\psi_n = b_n a_n\psi_n \tag{3.2}$$

$$BA\psi_n = Ba_n\psi_n = a_n B\psi_n = a_n b_n\psi_n \tag{3.3}$$

$$(AB - BA)\psi_n = 0 \tag{3.4}$$

On the other hand, if ψ_n cannot be an eigenfunction of both A and B, it follows that

$$(AB - BA)\psi_n \neq 0. \tag{3.5}$$

The expression

$$(AB - BA), \tag{3.6}$$

sometimes written as

$$[A, B], \tag{3.7}$$

is called the commutator of the operators A and B. As long as it vanishes for the operators involved, eigenvalues may be identified with the corresponding observable quantities and the uncertainty principle will still be satisfied. However, it is also necessary that such operators yield the correct result in the classical limit. That is, the equations of quantum mechanics must reduce to the accepted equations of point object mechanics under conditions where the wave properties of the particles are unimportant; this is called the correspondence principle.[19]

Actually, both of these requirements may be met simultaneously by demanding that the commutators of the generalized position and linear momentum operators satisfy the following relationships:[20]

$$[q_j, q_k] = 0 \tag{3.8}$$

$$\left[\frac{\hbar}{i}\frac{\partial}{\partial q_j}, \frac{\hbar}{i}\frac{\partial}{\partial q_k}\right] = 0 \tag{3.9}$$

$$\left[q_j, \frac{\hbar}{i}\frac{\partial}{\partial q_k}\right] = i\hbar\delta_{jk} \tag{3.10}$$

It is possible, in fact, to develop all of the preceding quantum mechanical equations from a postulational basis that features these relations.[21] From them we can immediately see that pairs of operators like

$$[x, y] = 0 \tag{3.11}$$

will always commute; therefore, the ordinary rules of algebra will apply to them, and the corresponding observable quantities may be determined simultaneously with unlimited precision. The same is true of pairs like

$$\left[\frac{\hbar}{i}\frac{\partial}{\partial x}, \frac{\hbar}{i}\frac{\partial}{\partial y}\right] = 0, \tag{3.12}$$

but pairs like

$$\left[x, \frac{\hbar}{i}\frac{\partial}{\partial x}\right] = i\hbar \tag{3.13}$$

clearly do not commute. Mathematically this means that a special type of algebra must be used to work with these operators; physically it means that the two corresponding observable quantities cannot be measured simultaneously with arbitrary accuracy. However, as long as the latter fact is recognized and (3.13) observed in the algebra, the correspondence principle will be satisfied.

Of course, (3.13) could have been obtained directly by evaluating the given commutator:

$$\left[x, \frac{\hbar}{i}\frac{\partial}{\partial x}\right]\psi_n = \frac{\hbar}{i}\left(x\frac{\partial}{\partial x}\psi_n - \frac{\partial}{\partial x}x\psi_n\right) = -\frac{\hbar}{i}\psi_n = i\hbar\psi_n \tag{3.14}$$

[19] Dicke, R. H., and J. P. Wittke, *Introduction to Quantum Mechanics*, pp. 122–136, Addison-Wesley, Reading, Mass., 1960.

[20] Messiah, A., *Quantum Mechanics*, Vol. 1, pp. 199–212, Wiley, New York, 1961.

[21] Rojansky, V., *Introductory Quantum Mechanics*, pp. 2–8, 72–106, Prentice-Hall, Englewood Cliffs, N.J., 1959.

It is usually easiest to apply this direct method whenever the commutativity of operators which are functions of those appearing in (3.8) to (3.10) is to be tested. Suppose, for example, that we wanted to know whether or not the angular momentum component operators L_x and L_y will commute. Using the relations (2.51) and (2.52), we could calculate:

$$[L_x, L_y]\psi_n = -\hbar^2\left(y\frac{\partial}{\partial z} - z\frac{\partial}{\partial y}\right)\left(z\frac{\partial\psi_n}{\partial x} - x\frac{\partial\psi_n}{\partial z}\right)$$

$$+ \hbar^2\left(z\frac{\partial}{\partial x} - x\frac{\partial}{\partial z}\right)\left(y\frac{\partial\psi_n}{\partial z} - z\frac{\partial\psi_n}{\partial y}\right)$$

$$= -\hbar^2\left[yz\frac{\partial^2\psi_n}{\partial z\,\partial x} + y\frac{\partial\psi_n}{\partial x} - yx\frac{\partial^2\psi_n}{\partial z^2} - z^2\frac{\partial^2\psi_n}{\partial y\,\partial x} + zx\frac{\partial^2\psi_n}{\partial y\,\partial z}\right]$$

$$+ \hbar^2\left[zy\frac{\partial^2\psi_n}{\partial x\,\partial z} - z^2\frac{\partial^2\psi_n}{\partial x\,\partial y} - xy\frac{\partial^2\psi_n}{\partial z^2} + xz\frac{\partial^2\psi_n}{\partial z\,\partial y} + x\frac{\partial\psi_n}{\partial y}\right]$$

$$= \hbar^2\left(x\frac{\partial}{\partial y} - y\frac{\partial}{\partial x}\right)\psi_n = i\hbar L_z\psi_n \qquad (3.15)$$

In the same way it can be shown that none of the other angular momentum operators commute and, in fact, that

$$[L_x, L_y] = i\hbar L_z, \qquad [L_y, L_x] = -i\hbar L_z \qquad (3.16)$$

$$[L_y, L_z] = i\hbar L_x, \qquad [L_z, L_y] = -i\hbar L_x \qquad (3.17)$$

$$[L_z, L_x] = i\hbar L_y, \qquad [L_x, L_z] = -i\hbar L_y. \qquad (3.18)$$

On the other hand, the square of the total angular momentum operator,

$$L^2 = L_x^2 + L_y^2 + L_z^2, \qquad (3.19)$$

will commute with any one of the three components:

$$[L^2, L_x] = 0 \qquad (3.20)$$

$$[L^2, L_y] = 0 \qquad (3.21)$$

$$[L^2, L_z] = 0 \qquad (3.22)$$

One important difficulty remains. For a particle in an indefinite state, the appropriate Ψ will represent a complete set of eigenfunctions Ψ_n, each with its own eigenvalue for any given operator. This is illustrated both by the construction of the wave packet described in (1.28) and Fig. 5.3 and by the nature of the general solution summarized in (2.23) and (2.24). But every such eigenvalue represents an observable value of the dynamic variable in question, and it is not at all clear which of these will be observed on any one measurement. Statistical principles must be applied to predict the most probable value.

By definition, when the Ψ-function for a particle is normalized, $\Psi^*\Psi$ is its position probability density. Thus the average value of its x-position coordinate, for example, should be given by

$$\bar{x} = \int \Psi^*\Psi x \, dx, \tag{3.23}$$

which can also be written in the form

$$\bar{x} = \int \Psi^* x \Psi \, dx, \tag{3.24}$$

since x is its own operator. This is the value of x that would most probably be observed by a measurement, being the average predicted for a large number of simultaneous measurements on the different members of the set. It is usually called the expectation value of x.

Furthermore, $\Psi^*\Psi$ can also be interpreted as the momentum and energy probability density when Ψ is normalized[22]; therefore, the expectation value of the x-component of the particle's momentum should be given by

$$\bar{p}_x = \int \Psi^*\Psi p_x \, dx \tag{3.25}$$

or, replacing p_x by its operator equivalent,

$$\bar{p}_x = \int \Psi^* \frac{\hbar}{i} \frac{\partial}{\partial x} \Psi \, dx. \tag{3.26}$$

In the same way

$$\bar{E} = \int \Psi^* H \Psi \, d\mathbf{r}, \tag{3.27}$$

where H is the Hamiltonian operator. And, in fact, quite generally with Ψ normalized we may write

$$\bar{a} = \int \Psi^* A \Psi \, d\mathbf{r}, \tag{3.28}$$

where a represents any observable quantity with an associated operator A.

[22] Dicke, R. H., and J. P. Wittke, *Introduction to Quantum Mechanics*, pp. 71–75, Addison-Wesley, Reading, Mass., 1960.

That such a procedure is consistent with our earlier development may be seen by considering the case of one specific eigenfunction Ψ_n of Ψ, satisfying the eigenequation

$$A\Psi_n = a_n\Psi_n. \tag{3.29}$$

Applying (3.28), we obtain:

$$\bar{a} = \int \Psi_n{}^* A\Psi_n \, d\mathbf{r} = a_n \int \Psi^*\Psi \, d\mathbf{r} = a_n \tag{3.30}$$

In other words, the expectation value can be nothing but the eigenvalue of Ψ_n.

More generally, let us consider a particle known to be in a state of one-dimensional harmonic oscillation, for which the state function of lowest energy will be shown later to be

$$\psi_0 = N_0 e^{-\frac{\alpha}{2} x^2}, \tag{3.31}$$

where N_0 represents a normalization constant and

$$\alpha = \frac{\sqrt{mK}}{\hbar}. \tag{3.32}$$

It should be clear that $\psi^*\psi$ can be used for the probability density instead of $\Psi^*\Psi$ since no explicit dependence on time is involved; and because in this case ψ is real, $\psi^*\psi$ becomes simply $\psi_0{}^2$. The value of x being indefinite, we must apply (3.24) to find its expectation value:

$$\bar{x} = \int_{-\infty}^{\infty} x\psi_0{}^2 \, dx = N_0{}^2 \int_{-\infty}^{\infty} xe^{-\alpha x^2} \, dx = 0 \tag{3.33}$$

Similarly, applying (3.26):

$$\bar{p}_x = \int_{-\infty}^{\infty} \psi_0 \frac{\hbar}{i} \frac{\partial}{\partial x} \psi_0 \, dx = N_0{}^2 \int_{-\infty}^{\infty} e^{-\frac{\alpha}{2} x^2} \frac{\hbar}{i} \frac{\partial}{\partial x} e^{-\frac{\alpha}{2} x^2} \, dx$$

$$= i\hbar\alpha N_0{}^2 \int_{-\infty}^{\infty} xe^{-\alpha x^2} \, dx = 0 \tag{3.34}$$

Physically, we know that both of these results are reasonable. Of course, all such formulae should be understood to apply only to the result of the first measurement on a wave-particle system, because any measurement will necessarily disturb it.

An additional implication of the correspondence principle is that the expectation values of the dynamic variables for a wave packet representing a particle should be related according to the laws of classical mechanics.

This follows from the fact that wave packets can be constructed for large particles whose motion we know to obey these laws, as well as for small particles.

Consider the velocity of the centroid of such a packet, given as the first time derivative of the expectation value of x:

$$\dot{\bar{x}} = \frac{d}{dt} \int \Psi^* x \Psi \, dx = \int \left(\frac{\partial \Psi^*}{\partial t} x \Psi + \Psi^* x \frac{\partial \Psi}{\partial t} \right) dx \qquad (3.35)$$

where Ψ and Ψ^* represent the total wave function. From Schrödinger's equation [(2.10) of Chapter 5], we know that

$$\frac{\partial \Psi}{\partial t} = \frac{i\hbar}{2m} \nabla^2 \Psi - \frac{i}{\hbar} V \Psi \qquad (3.36)$$

and

$$\frac{\partial \Psi^*}{\partial t} = - \frac{i\hbar}{2m} \nabla^2 \Psi^* + \frac{i}{\hbar} V \Psi^*; \qquad (3.37)$$

therefore, substitution in (3.35) leads to

$$\dot{\bar{x}} = \frac{i\hbar}{2m} \int (\Psi^* x \nabla^2 \Psi - \Psi x \nabla^2 \Psi^*) \, dx, \qquad (3.38)$$

and integration by parts yields

$$\dot{\bar{x}} = - \frac{i\hbar}{m} \int \Psi^* \nabla \Psi \, dx = \frac{1}{m} \int \Psi^* \frac{\hbar}{i} \frac{\partial}{\partial x} \Psi \, dx. \qquad (3.39)$$

If we apply (3.26), it follows that

$$\dot{\bar{x}} = \frac{\bar{p}_x}{m}, \qquad (3.40)$$

which parallels the classical relation [(2.66) of Chapter 2]

$$\dot{x} = \frac{p_x}{m},$$

and provides another justification for identifying the group velocity of the wave packet with the velocity of the particle.

In the same way, calculation of $\dot{\bar{p}}_x$ for the packet from (3.26) leads to

$$\dot{\bar{p}}_x = - \frac{\partial \overline{V(x)}}{\partial x} = \bar{F}_x \qquad (3.41)$$

or

$$m\ddot{\bar{x}} = \bar{F}_x, \qquad (3.42)$$

which is just the quantum form of Newton's equation for motion in the
X-direction. Also $\dot{\bar{E}}$ turns out to be zero, so that

$$\bar{E} = \text{constant}, \tag{3.43}$$

as we would expect.

If the wave packet is very narrow, the particle must almost certainly be
at some definite location; then (3.40) to (3.43) and the corresponding
classical relations will, for all practical purposes, be identical. Unfortu-
nately, however, the uncertainty principle causes all such packets to
broaden rapidly with time[23]; and, as a consequence, the latter are of little
value in solving problems in which quantum effects are important.
Generally speaking, these will be problems involving motions of particles
smaller than molecules. For even though larger particles are composed
of smaller fundamental particles and, therefore, possess combined wave
functions which must satisfy the uncertainty principle, in most cases
measurement errors can be kept negligibly small for particles larger than
very simple molecules.

Problems 5.3

1. Show that

$$[H, x] = \frac{\hbar}{i} \frac{p_x}{m}.$$

Solution

We know that in general for a conservative system the operator

$$H = -\frac{\hbar^2}{2m}\left[\frac{\partial^2}{\partial x^2} + \frac{\partial^2}{\partial y^2} + \frac{\partial^2}{\partial z^2}\right] + V(x, y, z).$$

Therefore, the product of the operator H with the operator x must be

$$Hx = \left\{-\frac{\hbar^2}{2m}\left[\frac{\partial^2}{\partial x^2} + \frac{\partial^2}{\partial y^2} + \frac{\partial^2}{\partial z^2}\right]\right\}x + V(x, y, z)x$$

$$= -\frac{\hbar^2}{2m}\left[x\frac{\partial^2}{\partial x^2} + 2\frac{\partial}{\partial x} + x\frac{\partial^2}{\partial y^2} + x\frac{\partial^2}{\partial z^2}\right] + V(x, y, z,)x,$$

because

$$\frac{\partial^2}{\partial x^2}[xf(x)] = \frac{\partial}{\partial x}\left[x\frac{\partial f(x)}{\partial x} + f(x)\right] = x\frac{\partial^2 f(x)}{\partial x^2} + 2\frac{\partial f(x)}{\partial x};$$

[23] Powell, J. L., and B. Crasemann, *Quantum Mechanics*, pp. 79–81, Addison-Wesley, Reading, Mass., 1961.

whereas, the product of the operator x with the operator H will be

$$xH = -\frac{\hbar^2}{2m}\left[x\frac{\partial^2}{\partial x^2} + x\frac{\partial^2}{\partial y^2} + x\frac{\partial^2}{\partial z^2}\right] + xV(x, y, z).$$

It follows that

$$[H, x] = (Hx - xH)$$

$$= -\frac{\hbar^2}{2m}\left[x\frac{\partial^2}{\partial x^2} + 2\frac{\partial}{\partial x} + x\frac{\partial^2}{\partial y^2} + x\frac{\partial^2}{\partial z^2} - x\frac{\partial^2}{\partial x^2} - x\frac{\partial^2}{\partial y^2} - x\frac{\partial^2}{\partial z^2}\right]$$

$$+ V(x, y, z)x - xV(x, y, z)$$

$$= -\frac{\hbar^2}{m}\frac{\partial}{\partial x}.$$

But we also know that the operator equivalent of p_x is $(\hbar/i)(\partial/\partial x)$; if, therefore, we multiply the right-hand side of this relation by p_x and divide it by $(\hbar/i)(\partial/\partial x)$, the required result is obtained

$$[H, x] = -\frac{i\hbar}{m}p_x = \frac{\hbar}{i}\frac{p_x}{m}.$$

2. Find E_0, the expectation value of the energy of the ground state, for the simple harmonic oscillator.

Solution

The appropriate wave function is

$$\psi_0 = N_0 e^{-\frac{\alpha}{2}x^2}$$

where

$$\alpha = \frac{\sqrt{mK}}{\hbar}$$

and

$$N_0 = \left(\frac{\alpha}{\pi}\right)^{\frac{1}{4}}.$$

Furthermore, since

$$E = \frac{1}{2m}p_x^2 + \frac{K}{2}x^2,$$

we see that we must calculate $\overline{p_x^2}$ and $\overline{x^2}$ in order to find $\overline{E_0}$.
Applying the expectation value formula,

$$\overline{x^2} = \int_{-\infty}^{\infty}\psi_0 x^2\psi_0\,dx$$

or

$$\overline{x^2} = \left(\frac{\alpha}{\pi}\right)^{\frac{1}{2}}\int_{-\infty}^{+\infty}e^{-\frac{\alpha}{2}x^2}x^2 e^{-\frac{\alpha}{2}x^2}\,dx$$

$$= \left(\frac{\alpha}{\pi}\right)^{\frac{1}{2}}\int_{-\infty}^{+\infty}x^2 e^{-\alpha x^2}\,dx$$

$$= \left(\frac{\alpha}{\pi}\right)^{\frac{1}{2}}\frac{1}{2\alpha}\left(\frac{\pi}{\alpha}\right)^{\frac{1}{2}} = \frac{1}{2\alpha}.$$

Hence, substituting for α,

$$\overline{x^2} = \frac{\hbar}{2\sqrt{mK}} = \frac{\hbar\omega}{2K}.$$

In the same way,

$$\overline{p_x^2} = \left(\frac{\alpha}{\pi}\right)^{1/2} \int_{-\infty}^{+\infty} e^{-\frac{\alpha}{2}x^2} \left(\frac{\hbar}{i}\frac{\partial}{\partial x}\right)^2 e^{-\frac{\alpha}{2}x^2} \, dx$$

$$= -\hbar^2 \left(\frac{\alpha}{\pi}\right)^{1/2} \int_{-\infty}^{+\infty} e^{-\frac{\alpha}{2}x^2} \frac{\partial^2}{\partial x^2} e^{-\frac{\alpha}{2}x^2} \, dx$$

$$= -\hbar^2 \left(\frac{\alpha}{\pi}\right)^{1/2} \left[\int_{-\infty}^{+\infty} e^{-\frac{\alpha}{2}x^2} \left(\alpha^2 x^2 e^{-\frac{\alpha}{2}x^2} - \alpha e^{-\frac{\alpha}{2}x^2} \right) dx \right]$$

$$= -\hbar^2 \left(\frac{\alpha}{\pi}\right)^{1/2} \left[\alpha^2 \int_{-\infty}^{+\infty} x^2 e^{-\alpha x^2} \, dx - \alpha \int_{-\infty}^{+\infty} e^{-\alpha x^2} \, dx \right]$$

$$= -\hbar^2 \left(\frac{\alpha}{\pi}\right)^{1/2} \left[\alpha^2 \frac{1}{2\alpha}\left(\frac{\pi}{\alpha}\right)^{1/2} - \alpha\left(\frac{\pi}{\alpha}\right)^{1/2} \right]$$

$$= -\hbar^2 \left(\frac{\alpha}{2} - \alpha\right)$$

$$= \hbar^2 \frac{\alpha}{2};$$

substituting for α, we obtain:

$$\overline{p_x^2} = \frac{\hbar^2}{2} \frac{\sqrt{mK}}{\hbar} = \frac{\hbar}{2}\sqrt{mK} = \frac{\hbar m\omega}{2}.$$

Now we can compute the expectation value of the energy:

$$\overline{E_0} = \frac{1}{2m}\overline{p_x^2} + \frac{K}{2}\overline{x^2}$$

$$= \frac{1}{2m}\left(\frac{\hbar m\omega}{2}\right) + \frac{K}{2}\left(\frac{\hbar\omega}{2K}\right)$$

$$= \frac{\hbar\omega}{4} + \frac{\hbar\omega}{4} = \frac{\hbar\omega}{2}.$$

Therefore, as we should expect,

$$\overline{E_0} = \frac{h\nu}{2}.$$

3. Verify the correspondence principle by showing that the motion of a quantum particle localized in a very narrow Gaussian wave packet can be described by Newton's equation, $F_x = m\ddot{x}$; but prove that such a packet will inevitably broaden rapidly with time.

Solution

We know from the text discussion that the expectation value of the x-component of momentum for a wave packet of any shape will be given by

$$\bar{p}_x = m \frac{d\bar{x}}{dt} .$$

Differentiating this once more with respect to time, we obtain

$$\frac{d}{dt} \bar{p}_x = m \frac{d^2\bar{x}}{dt^2} .$$

The expectation value of x follows from the formula

$$x = \int \Psi^* x \Psi \, dx,$$

assuming $\Psi(x, t)$ to be normalized. Therefore, it is plain that if the wave packet is so narrow that the particle must be very close to some point $x = x_1$, then approximately

$$\bar{x} = x_1 \int \Psi^* \Psi \, dx = x_1;$$

and the right-hand side of the above expectation value equation of motion becomes $m\ddot{x}_1$. Since x_1 is itself arbitrary, we see that the equation will be identical to the Newtonian equation if, under the same conditions, the left-hand side reduces to F_{x_1}.

Applying the expectation formula, the left-hand side becomes:

$$\frac{d}{dt} \bar{p}_x = \frac{d}{dt} \int \Psi^* \frac{\hbar}{i} \frac{\partial}{\partial x} \Psi \, dx$$

$$= \left[\Psi^* \frac{\hbar}{i} \frac{\partial}{\partial x} \left(\frac{\partial \Psi}{\partial t} \right) + \frac{\hbar}{i} \frac{\partial \Psi}{\partial x} \left(\frac{\partial \Psi^*}{\partial t} \right) \right] dx$$

But again Schrödinger's equation may be used to eliminate the time derivatives

$$\frac{\partial \Psi}{\partial t} = \frac{i\hbar}{2m} \frac{d^2\Psi}{dx^2} - \frac{i}{\hbar} V(x)\Psi$$

and

$$\frac{\partial \Psi^*}{\partial t} = - \frac{i\hbar}{2m} \frac{d^2\Psi^*}{dx^2} + \frac{i}{\hbar} V(x)\Psi^*.$$

The result is:

$$\frac{d}{dt} \bar{p}_x = - \frac{\hbar^2}{2m} \int \left[\frac{d^2}{dx^2} \left(\Psi^* \frac{d\Psi}{dx} \right) - \Psi^* \frac{d^2\Psi}{dx^2} \left(\frac{d\Psi}{dx} \right) \right] dx$$

$$- \int \Psi^* \left(\frac{dV}{dx} \right) \Psi \, dx$$

However, Green's identity can be applied to prove that the first integral must vanish; thus

$$\frac{d}{dt}\bar{p}_x = -\int \Psi^* \left[\frac{dV(x)}{dx}\right]\Psi\, dx.$$

But if x is almost certainly x_1, this can be written as

$$\frac{d}{dt}\bar{p}_x = -\frac{dV(x_1)}{dx_1}\int \Psi^*\Psi\, dx$$

$$= -\frac{dV(x_1)}{dx_1} = F_{x_1}.$$

Thus the correspondence principle is verified.

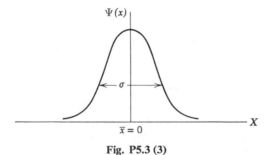

$$\bar{x} = 0$$

Fig. P5.3 (3)

It can be demonstrated that the Gaussian wave packet

$$\Psi = \sqrt{\frac{\sigma}{\tau\pi^{\frac{1}{2}}}}\, e^{-\frac{\left(x - \frac{\bar{p}_x}{m}t\right)^2}{2\tau}}\, e^{\frac{i}{\hbar}\bar{p}_x\left(x - \frac{\bar{p}_x}{2m}t\right)}$$

where σ is the standard deviation (measuring the width of the distribution) and

$$\tau = \sigma^2 + \frac{i\hbar}{m}t,$$

is the shape that causes the product $\Delta x\, \Delta p_x$ to take its minimum value of $\hbar/2$ under the uncertainty principle. At zero time this becomes simply

$$\Psi = \sqrt{\frac{1}{\sigma\pi^{\frac{1}{2}}}}\, e^{-\frac{x^2}{\sigma^2}}\, e^{\frac{i}{\hbar}\bar{p}_x x},$$

which has the appearance shown in Fig. P5.3 (3).

But the width of the packet must also be measured by Δx, and it follows from the relation

$$(\Delta x)^2 = \overline{x^2} - (\bar{x})^2,$$

together with $\bar{x} = 0$ as above, that

$$\Delta x = [\overline{x^2}]^{\frac{1}{2}} = \left[\int \Psi^*(x)\, x^2\, \Psi(x)\, dx\right]^{\frac{1}{2}}$$

$$= \left[\frac{1}{\sigma\pi^{\frac{1}{2}}} \int x^2 e^{-\frac{x^2}{\sigma^2}}\, dx\right]^{\frac{1}{2}} = \left[\frac{1}{\sigma\pi^{\frac{1}{2}}}\, \frac{\sigma^3\pi^{\frac{1}{2}}}{2}\right]^{\frac{1}{2}}$$

$$= \frac{\sigma}{\sqrt{2}} \, .$$

Returning to the time-dependent form, it follows that the probability density will be given by:

$$|\Psi(x, t)|^2 = \frac{\sigma}{|\tau|\,\pi^{\frac{1}{2}}}\, e^{\frac{-\sigma^2\left(x - \frac{p_x}{m}t\right)^2}{2|\tau|^2}}$$

Since, however,

$$|\tau|^2 = \sigma^4 + \frac{\hbar^2}{m^2} t^2 = \sigma^4\left(1 + \frac{\hbar^2}{\sigma^4 m^2} t^2\right),$$

we see that at $t = 0$

$$|\Psi(x, 0)|^2 = \frac{1}{\sigma\pi^{\frac{1}{2}}}\, e^{-\frac{x^2}{\sigma^2}} \, .$$

This must be the basic form of $|\Psi(x, t)|^2$, and it is the same form that entered into the calculation of Δx above. Thus, to see how Δx varies with time we may apply the relation

$$\Delta x = \frac{\sigma}{\sqrt{2}}$$

with σ replaced by

$$\frac{\sqrt{|\tau|^2}}{\sigma} = \sigma\sqrt{1 + \frac{\hbar^2}{\sigma^4 m^2} t^2} \, .$$

The result is

$$\Delta x = \sigma\sqrt{\frac{1}{2} + \frac{\hbar^2}{2\sigma^4 m^2} t^2} \, ,$$

which establishes that the wave packet will broaden parabolically with time.

Exercises 5.3

1. Show that the following hold true:

   a. $L_x L_y - L_y L_x = i\hbar L_z$.

   b. $L^2 L_x = L_x L^2$.

   c. $\dfrac{i}{\hbar}\, [HP_x - P_x H] = F_x$.

2. Find $\bar{x}$ for a particle in the state represented by:

$$\psi = N \left[\sin x + \frac{i}{2} \sin 3x \right] \quad \text{for} \quad 0 < x < 2$$

$$\psi = 0 \quad \text{for} \quad x < 0, x > 2\pi$$

Answer. $\bar{x} = N^2 \frac{5}{4}\pi^2$.

3. Consider the eigenequation

$$F\psi = \lambda\psi,$$

where F is the operator for any quantity f and λ is the eigenvalue. If λ is a constant, show that

$$(\bar{f})^2 = \overline{f^2},$$

where $(\bar{f})^2$ indicates the square of the expectation value of f and $\overline{f^2}$ represents the expectation value of f^2.

4. Prove that the correspondence principle holds for the classical relation $M_x = \dot{l}_x$ as long as the motion of the quantum particle can be described by a very narrow wave packet.

6

Motions of a Particle

6.1 Interactions with Rectangular Potential Barriers

Free particles manifest themselves to our senses only in regions of varying potential energy, as when a measurement is attempted and a particle is caused to interact with others in some measuring device. However, because of our earlier generalization of the constant V to the potential function $V(x, y, z)$ by application of the conservative force relation $\mathbf{F} = -\nabla V(x, y, z)$, we possess the capability of determining the motion of a particle in such a region. We need merely to solve the appropriate Schrödinger equation there,

$$\left[-\frac{\hbar^2}{2m} \nabla^2 + V(x, y, z) \right] \Psi = i\hbar \frac{\partial \Psi}{\partial t},$$

in which the form of $V(x, y, z)$ specific to the region must be inserted. When the boundary conditions are satisfied, the resulting Ψ-function will contain the desired information, which may then be extracted by applying the proper operator if the particle is in an eigenstate, or by using the expectation formula if it is not.

From the mathematical point of view, the simplest kind of potential variation is the step function (Fig. 6.1):

$$V(x) = \begin{cases} O & \text{for} \quad x < 0 \\ V & \text{for} \quad x \geq 0 \end{cases}$$

Imagining a particle to be approaching from the left with the energy E, the change in potential at $x = 0$ will present a barrier to its motion. It is

438

this situation that we shall consider first. Because of the force represented by the change in potential, how will the motion of the particle be affected?

In most real cases, of course, the potential will build up gradually, rather than increase abruptly; but this presents certain difficulties that can best be treated a little later. Also, actual potential barriers often cannot be considered infinitely wide, so that a finite width will eventually have to be assigned.

Clearly, if the energy E of the particle is greater than the potential energy V, the effect of the barrier may be quite different than if E is less than V. Accordingly, we shall study the two cases separately, beginning

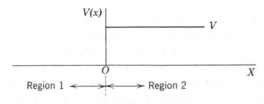

Fig. 6.1

with the one in which $E > V$. Furthermore, it is desirable to introduce a certain amount of stability into the problem by assuming that a steady stream of identical particles of mass m, rather than a single particle, is incident on the barrier. Time dependence may then be suppressed in the usual way and Schrödinger's equation simplified to

$$\left[-\frac{\hbar^2}{2m}\frac{d^2}{dx^2} + V(x) \right]\psi = E\psi \tag{1.1}$$

or

$$\frac{d^2}{dx^2}\psi_1 + \frac{2m}{\hbar^2}E\psi_1 = 0 \tag{1.2}$$

in region 1 where $V(x) = 0$, and

$$\frac{d^2}{dx^2}\psi_2 + \frac{2m}{\hbar^2}(E - V)\psi_2 = 0 \tag{1.3}$$

in region 2 where $V(x) = V$.

Using A and B to indicate arbitrary constants, the general solution of (1.2) may evidently be written in the form

$$\psi_1 = A e^{\frac{i}{\hbar}\sqrt{2mE}\,x} + B e^{-\frac{i}{\hbar}\sqrt{2mE}\,x} \tag{1.4}$$

or, since in region 1 the linear momentum

$$p_1 = \sqrt{2mE},$$ (1.5)

as

$$\psi_1 = Ae^{\frac{i}{\hbar}p_1 x} + Be^{-\frac{i}{\hbar}p_1 x}.$$ (1.6)

Moreover, recalling that to introduce time dependence we must multiply by the factor $e^{-\frac{i}{\hbar}Et}$,

$$\Psi_1 = \psi_1 e^{-\frac{i}{\hbar}Et} = Ae^{\frac{i}{\hbar}(p_1 x - Et)} + Be^{-\frac{i}{\hbar}(p_1 x + Et)},$$ (1.7)

we see that the term associated with the constant A represents a plane wave propagating in the positive x-direction [(1.6) to (1.11) of Chapter 5], whereas the term associated with the constant B represents a similar wave propagating in the negative x-direction. The former may be identified with particles incident on the barrier and the latter with particles reflected by it.

In the same way, the linear momentum in region 2 will be

$$p_2 = \sqrt{2m(E - V)}.$$ (1.8)

Because $E > V$, this must be a real quantity; the general solution of (1.3) can be written as

$$\psi_2 = Ce^{\frac{i}{\hbar}p_2 x} + De^{-\frac{i}{\hbar}p_2 x},$$ (1.9)

where the term with the constant C leads to a plane wave propagating in the positive x-direction, which can be identified with particles transmitted by the barrier. The last term can only produce a plane wave propagating in the negative x-direction; but, because the barrier is infinitely wide, we have no reason to think that any reflected particles will exist in region 2. Therefore, the constant D must be set equal to zero, leaving

$$\psi_2 = Ce^{\frac{i}{\hbar}p_2 x}.$$ (1.10)

To determine the constants A, B, and C in (1.6) and (1.10), we must apply three initial or boundary conditions. Only two are readily available; if we use them, however, two of the constants can at least be expressed in terms of the other one. We have the boundary conditions:

$$\left.\begin{array}{c}[\psi]_{x=0}\\[2mm]\left[\dfrac{d\psi}{dx}\right]_{x=0}\end{array}\right\} \text{ must be continuous.}$$ (1.11)

These follow immediately from considering that, because ψ, E, and V are all finite, $d^2\psi/dx^2$ must be finite everywhere—through (1.2) and (1.3); this can only be true if $d\psi/dx$ exists and is continuous, while $d\psi/dx$ can exist only if ψ is continuous.

From the first boundary condition, the fact that ψ must be continuous across the barrier, it follows that

$$[\psi_1]_{x=0} = [\psi_2]_{x=0}, \tag{1.12}$$

$$A + B = C; \tag{1.13}$$

whereas the second yields

$$\left[\frac{d\psi_1}{dx}\right]_{x=0} = \left[\frac{d\psi_2}{dx}\right]_{x=0}, \tag{1.14}$$

$$\frac{i}{\hbar} p_1 \left[Ae^{\frac{i}{\hbar}p_1 x} - Be^{-\frac{i}{\hbar}p_1 x} \right]_{x=0} = \frac{i}{\hbar} p_2 \left[Ce^{\frac{i}{\hbar}p_2 x} \right]_{x=0},$$

$$A - B = \frac{p_2}{p_1} C. \tag{1.15}$$

Solving (1.13) and (1.15) for B and C in terms of A, we obtain:

$$B = \frac{(p_1 - p_2)}{(p_1 + p_2)} A \tag{1.16}$$

$$C = \frac{2p_1}{(p_1 + p_2)} A \tag{1.17}$$

These relations define the amplitudes of the reflected and transmitted waves in terms of the amplitude of the incident wave and the momentum of the particles that the waves represent in the two regions.

Because we are considering the behavior of a stream of particles, each of which is described by the wave functions ψ_1 and ψ_2, the probability density $\psi^*\psi$ must be generalized to a probability density current before the foregoing results can be utilized. If we define the latter as the time rate of change of the probability of finding a particle in a particular volume,

$$\mathbf{S} = \frac{d}{dt} \int \Psi^*\Psi \, d\mathbf{r}, \tag{1.18}$$

proceeding as in (3.35) to (3.38) of Chapter 5 and converting to a surface integral by means of Green's theorem, it follows that

$$\mathbf{S} = -\frac{i\hbar}{2m} (\Psi^*\nabla\Psi - \nabla\Psi^*\Psi). \tag{1.19}$$

With this relation it is easy to show that for any Ψ-function of the form

$$\Psi = \text{constant } e^{\pm \frac{i}{\hbar}(p_x x - Et)},$$ (1.20)

as above, the associated probability density current is

$$S_x = |\text{constant}|^2 \frac{p_x}{m}.$$ (1.21)

The transmissivity T of a potential barrier is defined as the ratio of the transmitted to the incident probability density current; therefore, applying (1.21) and (1.17), we see that in the present circumstances

$$T = \frac{|C|^2 \dfrac{p_2}{m}}{|A|^2 \dfrac{p_1}{m}} = \frac{4p_1 p_2}{(p_1 + p_2)^2}.$$ (1.22)

Similarly, the reflectivity R of the barrier is defined as the ratio of the reflected to the incident probability density current; accordingly, if we use (1.16) with (1.21),

$$R = \frac{|B|^2 \dfrac{p_1}{m}}{|A|^2 \dfrac{p_1}{m}} = \frac{(p_1 - p_2)^2}{(p_1 + p_2)^2}.$$ (1.23)

As a quick check,

$$T + R = \frac{4p_1 p_2 + p_1{}^2 - 2p_1 p_2 + p_2{}^2}{(p_1 + p_2)^2} = \frac{(p_1 + p_2)^2}{(p_1 + p_2)^2} = 1,$$ (1.24)

which clearly should be true.

Recalling that $p_1 = \sqrt{2mE}$ and $p_2 = \sqrt{2m(E - V)}$, we see (1.23) to show that when

$$V \to 0, \qquad p_2 \to p_1 \quad \text{and} \quad R \to 0,$$ (1.25)

while if

$$V \to E, \qquad p_2 \to 0 \quad \text{and} \quad R \to 1.$$ (1.26)

Thus, as we might anticipate from classical considerations, the reflectivity will become appreciable only when the energy of the barrier is of the same order as the energy of the particle. However, a classical model would not lead us to expect the reflection that will occur when V is very small relative to E. This is a purely quantum-mechanical effect which arises from the wave nature of the particles involved and has no counterpart in point object mechanics.

An even more striking quantum-mechanical effect occurs when $E < V$. It will be clear that in this case, although (1.2) continues to hold in region 1, (1.3) must be modified to

$$\frac{d^2}{dx^2}\psi_2 - \frac{2m}{\hbar^2}(V - E)\psi_2 = 0 \tag{1.27}$$

for region 2. This has the general solution

$$\psi_2 = C'e^{\frac{p_2 x}{\hbar}} + Ce^{-\frac{p_2 x}{\hbar}}, \tag{1.28}$$

where

$$p_2 = \sqrt{2m(V - E)} \tag{1.29}$$

and, of course, the exponentials are now real. Hence, for $\psi^*\psi$ to remain finite at large x, we must place C' equal to zero, resulting in

$$\psi_2 = Ce^{-\frac{p_2 x}{\hbar}}. \tag{1.30}$$

In region 1, as before [(1.6) and (1.5)],

$$\psi_1 = Ae^{\frac{i}{\hbar}p_1 x} + Be^{-\frac{i}{\hbar}p_1 x}$$

with

$$p_1 = \sqrt{2mE}.$$

Applying the first of the boundary conditions (1.11), we see that once again

$$A + B = C \tag{1.31}$$

is required; whereas the second of the conditions yields

$$\frac{i}{\hbar}p_1\left[Ae^{\frac{i}{\hbar}p_1 x} - Be^{-\frac{i}{\hbar}p_1 x}\right]_{x=0} = -\frac{p_2}{\hbar}\left[Ce^{-\frac{p_2 x}{\hbar}}\right]_{x=0}$$

or

$$A - B = i\frac{p_2}{p_1}C. \tag{1.32}$$

To calculate the reflectivity, as in (1.23), it is desirable to solve these two relations for A and B in terms of C. The result is

$$A = \frac{C}{2}\left(1 + i\frac{p_2}{p_1}\right), \tag{1.33}$$

$$B = \frac{C}{2}\left(1 - i\frac{p_2}{p_1}\right); \tag{1.34}$$

it is then evident that R must equal unity for all permissible values of p_1 and p_2:

$$R = \frac{|B|^2}{|A|^2} = \frac{1 + \left(\dfrac{p_2}{p_1}\right)^2}{1 + \left(\dfrac{p_2}{p_1}\right)^2} = 1 \qquad (1.35)$$

Together with this finding that all particles will be reflected, however, we must consider the fact that the wave function in region 2 will be given by (1.30),

$$\psi_2 = Ce^{-\frac{p_2 x}{\hbar}}.$$

At $x = 0$,

$$\psi_2 = C; \qquad (1.36)$$

and because C cannot in general be zero, we must conclude that unless $V \to \infty$, so that $p_2 = \sqrt{2m(V - E)} \to \infty$, the wave function will decay

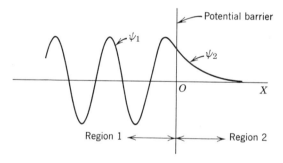

Fig. 6.2

exponentially into the barrier, as shown in Fig. 6.2. Thus $\psi_2^*\psi_2$ will be nonzero in region 2, which can only mean that some particles may penetrate a limited distance into the barrier.

This unique quantum effect is one of considerable practical importance, because virtually all potential barriers acting to contain quantum particles in a certain region are actually of finite width, and often narrow enough to allow a few particles to penetrate them entirely. It is the fundamental mechanism of both electron tunneling, featured in various solid state diodes, and the radioactive decay of many atomic nuclei.

The preceding approach can easily be extended to obtain an approximate expression for the transmissivity of a barrier with the known width b and height $V > E$ (Fig. 6.3). Equation (1.2) continues to apply in region 1; so in that region

with

$$\psi_1 = Ae^{\frac{i}{\hbar}p_1 x} + Be^{-\frac{i}{\hbar}p_1 x}$$

$$p_1 = \sqrt{2mE},$$

(1.37)

as in (1.6) and (1.5). In region 2 the governing equation will be (1.27); and if we agree to approximate by neglecting reflection from the potential step

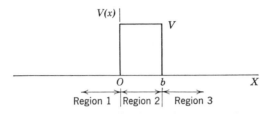

Fig. 6.3

at b (thereby limiting ourselves to a relatively thick barrier), the appropriate solution will be given by (1.30) and (1.29):

$$\psi_2 = Ce^{-\frac{p_2 x}{\hbar}}$$

$$p_2 = \sqrt{2m(V - E)}$$

(1.38)

An equation of the form (1.2) will also hold in region 3; therefore, the solution will follow (1.6) and (1.5), except that the coefficient of the reflected wave must be set equal to zero:

$$\psi_3 = De^{\frac{i}{\hbar}p_3 x}$$

(1.39)

$$p_3 = \sqrt{2mE} = p_1$$

(1.40)

Since, following (1.22), the transmissivity of the barrier will evidently be given by

$$T = \frac{|D|^2 \frac{p_3}{m}}{|A|^2 \frac{p_1}{m}} = \frac{|D|^2}{|A|^2},$$

(1.41)

it is required to express D in terms of A; but now, of course, we have four boundary conditions: both ψ and $d\psi/dx$ must be continuous at $x = b$ as well as at $x = 0$. Combining the results of the first two,[1] we obtain

$$C = \frac{D}{2}\left(1 + \frac{p_1}{ip_2}\right)e^{\frac{b}{\hbar}(ip_1 + p_2)}, \tag{1.42}$$

while B may be eliminated between the results of the last two [(1.31) and (1.32)] to yield

$$A = \frac{C}{2}\left(1 + i\frac{p_2}{p_1}\right). \tag{1.43}$$

Consequently, substitution for C from (1.42) gives

$$A = \frac{D}{4}\left(1 - i\frac{p_1}{p_2}\right)\left(1 + i\frac{p_2}{p_1}\right)e^{i\frac{b}{\hbar}p_1}e^{\frac{b}{\hbar}p_2}; \tag{1.44}$$

and when (1.41) is applied, the result is:

$$T \simeq \frac{D^2}{\frac{D^2}{16}\left(1 + \frac{p_1^2}{p_2^2}\right)\left(1 + \frac{p_2^2}{p_1^2}\right)\left(\cos^2\frac{b}{\hbar}p_1 + \sin^2\frac{b}{\hbar}p_1\right)e^{\frac{2b}{\hbar}p_2}}$$

$$\simeq \frac{16e^{-\frac{2b}{\hbar}p_2}}{\left(1 + \frac{p_1^2}{p_2^2}\right)\left(1 + \frac{p_2^2}{p_1^2}\right)} \tag{1.45}$$

It is not difficult to establish that, since $V > E$, this expression will be dominated by the term $e^{\frac{-2b}{\hbar}p_2}$; thus, although approximate, the relation clearly shows that the transmissivity of the barrier depends sensitively on both its width b and its height V, appearing in $p_2 = \sqrt{2m(V - E)}$. When either becomes large enough, T will approach zero, and the wave function ψ_2 will die out within the barrier. Of course, if V becomes infinite relative to E, the wave function ψ_1 will not even penetrate the barrier at $x = 0$, because ψ_2 must then vanish in accordance with (1.30).

Consider the case of radioactive decay. An atomic nucleus may be visualized as an assembly of particles whose motions are confined to the same small region of space by a high thin potential barrier created by their mutual attractive forces. If we somehow establish that each particle will strike the barrier 10^x times per second and, from (1.45), compute that the probability of its being transmitted through the barrier each time it

[1] Bohm, D., *Quantum Theory*, pp. 238–240, Prentice-Hall, Englewood Cliffs, N.J. 1951.

strikes is $e^{-\beta}$, the probability of a particle escaping in 1 sec must be

$$\lambda = \frac{10^{\alpha}}{e^{\beta}}. \tag{1.46}$$

Because λ is also the probability that any atom in a given group of N atoms will decay in one second, the total number of atoms in the group which should decay in 1 sec will be λN. This must be equal to the depletion rate, if no new atoms are added,

$$-\frac{dN}{dt} = \lambda N = \frac{10^{\alpha}}{e^{\beta}} N. \tag{1.47}$$

Separating variables and integrating from N_0 atoms at time zero to N atoms at time t, we obtain:

$$\int_{N_0}^{N} \frac{dN}{N} = -\lambda \int dt \tag{1.48}$$

$$\ln \left(\frac{N}{N_0} \right) = -\lambda t \tag{1.49}$$

$$N = N_0 e^{-\lambda t} = N_0 e^{-\frac{10^{\alpha}}{e^{\beta}} t} \tag{1.50}$$

Equation (1.50), giving the number of atoms N that will still be present at any time t in a group which consisted of N_0 at time zero, is the well-verified law of radioactive decay. As will be clear from above, λ is not easy to calculate accurately from first principles, since α must depend on the details of the particle motion within the nucleus and β on the detailed nonlinear shape of the potential barrier; but it may be determined experimentally without much difficulty.[2]

To understand the operation of a tunnel diode, we must begin by recognizing that the surface of any metal specimen presents a potential barrier of definite height and thickness to the free electrons in the specimen. Because of this, the average kinetic energy E of the free electrons, proportional to the so-called Fermi-level energy E_f, may differ from one type of isolated specimen to another[3] (Fig. 6.4).

If, however, the surfaces of two such metallic pieces are joined together by means of a thin sheet of some semiconducting material, the effective surface potential of metal 1 will be reduced and electrons will flow from it

[2] Evans, R. E., *The Atomic Nucleus*, pp. 470–510, McGraw-Hill, New York, 1955.
[3] Kittel, C., *Introduction to Solid State Physics*, 2nd edition, pp. 383–401, Wiley, New York, 1957.

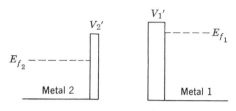

Fig. 6.4

to metal 2 until the Fermi level is the same for both. When this equilibrium condition is attained, there will be an excess of negative charge carriers (electrons) in metal 1 and an excess of positive charge carriers (missing electrons, called holes) in metal 2, thereby further altering the effective surface potential of both specimens (Fig. 6.5).

Now if an oscillating voltage is applied, the effect will be to increase the average energy of the electrons in metal 1 a certain amount above that determined by E_f during the positive half-cycle, and to decrease it by an equal amount for the negative half-cycle. This may be represented by raising or lowering the Fermi level an amount ΔE (Fig. 6.6).

From (1.45) we know that, if the width of the potential barrier of metal 1 does not change, its transmissivity will vary inversely with the factor

$$e^{\sqrt{2m[V_1-(E_f\pm\Delta E)]}},$$

so it follows that an exponentially increasing current will flow when the applied voltage is positive, while very little if any flow will occur when it is reversed (Fig. 6.7). This type of behavior is exactly that required for rectification or switching purposes and is utilized directly in the tunnel diode. Furthermore, it underlies the operation of *p–n* junctions and, thus, of transistors.[4]

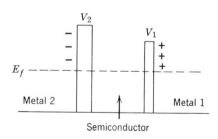

Fig. 6.5

[4] Hartman, T. E., "Electron Tunneling," *International Science and Technology,* pp. 74–88, June 1964.

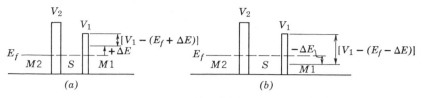

Fig. 6.6

Closely related to the problem of the rectangular potential barrier is that of the motion of a quantum particle in a rectangular potential well, for example (Fig. 6.8):

$$V(x) = \begin{cases} 0 & \text{for} \quad 0 \leqq x \leqq a \\ V & \text{for} \quad x < 0 \quad \text{and} \quad x > a \end{cases}$$

Generally speaking, of course, the wave function of the particle may be expected to penetrate a certain distance into the potential barriers on either side. But if, to begin with, we restrict ourselves to the case where the height V of the barriers is infinite relative to the energy E of the particle, we know from the discussion of equation (1.45) that the wave function will vanish

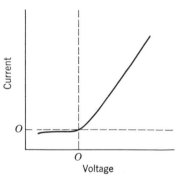

Fig. 6.7

at the faces of the barriers, regardless of their width. Under such circumstances it is again reasonable to suppress time dependence and write (1.2) as the Schrödinger equation to be satisfied in the well,

$$\frac{d^2\psi}{dx^2} + \frac{2m}{\hbar^2} E\psi = 0, \tag{1.51}$$

together with the boundary conditions

$$[\psi]_{x=0} = 0 \tag{1.52}$$

and

$$[\psi]_{x=a} = 0. \tag{1.53}$$

It is more satisfactory to write the solution of (1.51) in the form

$$\psi = A \sin \frac{\sqrt{2mE}}{\hbar} x + B \cos \frac{\sqrt{2mE}}{\hbar} x \tag{1.54}$$

than in the form (1.4) to facilitate application of the boundary conditions.

We see that

$$\psi(0) = B = 0 \tag{1.55}$$

and

$$\psi(a) = A \sin \frac{\sqrt{2mE}}{\hbar} a = 0. \tag{1.56}$$

Since A cannot be zero in general, the last condition can only be satisfied if

$$\frac{\sqrt{2mE}}{\hbar} a = n\pi \qquad \{n = 0, 1, 2, 3, \ldots \tag{1.57}$$

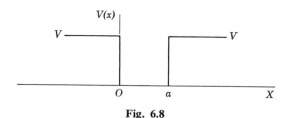

Fig. 6.8

or

$$E = E_n = \frac{(n\pi\hbar)^2}{2ma^2} \qquad \{n = 0, 1, 2, 3, \ldots \tag{1.58}$$

Hence, the solution becomes

$$\psi = \psi_n = A_n \sin \sqrt{\frac{2m}{\hbar^2} \frac{(n\pi\hbar)^2}{2ma^2}} = A_n \sin \frac{n\pi}{a} x. \tag{1.59}$$

The coefficients A_n remain to be determined, but this can be accomplished by normalization. Applying (2.26) of Chapter 5,

$$\int \psi_n^* \psi_n \, dx = 1,$$

we see that

$$\int_0^a A_n^2 \sin^2 \frac{n\pi}{a} x \, dx = 1, \tag{1.60}$$

$$A_n^2 \left[\frac{x}{2} - \frac{\sin \frac{2n\pi}{a} x}{\frac{4n\pi}{a}} \right]_0^a = 1, \tag{1.61}$$

$$A_n^2 \left(\frac{a}{2} \right) = 1$$

or

$$A_n = \sqrt{\frac{2}{a}} .$$ (1.62)

Thus the final wave functions, each of which is an acceptable solution, must be:

$$\psi_n = \sqrt{\frac{2}{a}} \sin \frac{n\pi}{a} x \quad \{n = 0, 1, 2, 3, \ldots$$ (1.63)

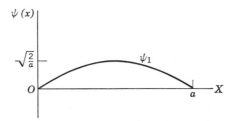

Fig. 6.9

Omitting the trivial case when $n = 0$, the next three of these,

$$\psi_1 = \sqrt{\frac{2}{a}} \sin \frac{\pi}{a} x$$ (1.64)

$$E_1 = \frac{(\pi\hbar)^2}{2ma^2},$$ (1.65)

$$\psi_2 = \sqrt{\frac{2}{a}} \sin \frac{2\pi}{a} x$$ (1.66)

$$E_2 = \frac{(2\pi\hbar)^2}{2ma^2},$$ (1.67)

$$\psi_3 = \sqrt{\frac{2}{a}} \sin \frac{3\pi}{a} x$$ (1.68)

$$E_3 = \frac{(3\pi\hbar)^2}{2ma^2},$$ (1.69)

are illustrated in Figs. 6.9, 6.10 and 6.11.

Here again we have encountered a special quantum mechanical phenomenon. In the classical case, a "particle" oscillating in a potential well may have any energy [(1.64) of Chapter 2], but not in this case. It can only have one of the discrete energies given by (1.58); and if it is to change from one

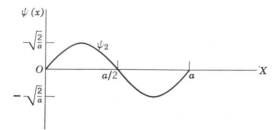

Fig. 6.10

to another, it must do so discontinuously. The reason for this should be clear: the behavior of the particle is controlled by its wave properties. Since only those wave functions which always vanish at $x = 0$ and $x = a$ are acceptable in the present circumstances, we should expect them to resemble the standing waves associated with the eigenfrequencies of a vibrating string stretched between fixed points at 0 and a, as in fact they do [(2.59) of Chapter 4 and Fig. 4.5]. Stated in another way, the boundary conditions of a quantum particle trapped in a potential well are necessarily such as to restrict the wave function of the particle to certain well-defined eigenfunctions, each with its own energy eigenvalue. Even when boundary conditions become more complex, as they must for the real potentials of most bound particles, we may be sure that the same features will reappear.

As illustrated in equations (1.64) to (1.69) and the accompanying figures, both the number of nodes of the wave functions and their related energies increase with n, usually called the principal quantum number. It must be emphasized that specifying n or, alternatively, the wave number k_n, since (1.57) can also be written as

$$\frac{n\pi}{a} = \frac{\sqrt{2mE_n}}{\hbar} = \frac{p_n}{\hbar} = k_n, \qquad (1.70)$$

is equivalent to specifying the configuration of the wave function and its energy E_n.

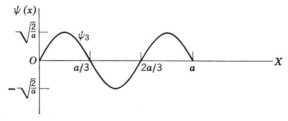

Fig. 6.11

Furthermore, if n is given and we want to include time dependence, we need merely multiply by the known exponential factor to obtain the proper wave function; for example with $n = 2$,

$$\Psi_2 = \sqrt{\frac{2}{a}}\left(\sin\frac{2\pi}{a}x\right)e^{-\frac{i}{\hbar}E_2 t} \tag{1.71}$$

On the other hand, if n is not known the general solution can be expressed as

$$\Psi = \sqrt{\frac{2}{a}}\sum_{n=1}^{\infty}\left(\sin\frac{n\pi}{a}x\right)e^{-\frac{i}{\hbar}E_n t} \tag{1.72}$$

and the required values of observables calculated from the expectation formula (3.28) of Chapter 5.

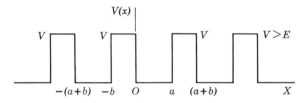

Fig. 6.12

The ultimate problem involving rectangular potential barriers and wells is one in which wells alternate with barriers of finite width and height $V > E$ (Fig. 6.12). Special interest attaches to this type of potential, for it is a simplification of the periodic potential an electron would experience in moving through a regular array of positive ions, as in many metallic or semiconductor crystals. Clearly, we could proceed with the solution by combining the two preceding cases; however, a way of reducing the resultant algebraic complications has been devised by Kronig and Penney.[5] They begin by noting that the solutions of the time-independent Schrödinger equation for a case of this kind [(1.2) and (1.27)],

$$\frac{d^2\psi}{dx^2} - \frac{2m}{\hbar^2}[V(x) - E]\psi = 0 \tag{1.73}$$

with $V(x)$ as described in Fig. 6.12, can be shown to be of the form

$$\psi_k = e^{ikx}u_k(x), \tag{1.74}$$

[5] Kittel, C., *Introduction to Solid State Physics*, 2nd edition, pp. 279–283, Wiley, New York, 1957.

where the $u_k(x)$ are functions known to be periodic in the interval $(a + b)$, and to depend on the wave number k, but are otherwise unknown. This is called Bloch's theorem.

The next step must be to establish the form of the unknown functions $u_k(x)$ by substituting ψ as given by (1.74) back into (1.73) and solving the resulting equation. Since

$$\frac{d\psi_k}{dx} = e^{ikx}\frac{du_k}{dx} + u_k ike^{ikx}, \tag{1.75}$$

$$\frac{d^2\psi_k}{dx^2} = e^{ikx}\frac{d^2u_k}{dx^2} + \frac{du_k}{dx}ike^{ikx} - u_k k^2 e^{ikx} + ike^{ikx}\frac{du_k}{dx}; \tag{1.76}$$

and the governing equation in $u_k(x)$ becomes

$$e^{ikx}\frac{d^2u_k}{dx^2} + 2ike^{ikx}\frac{du_k}{dx} - k^2 e^{ikx}u_k - \frac{2m}{\hbar^2}[V(x) - E]e^{ikx}u_k = 0 \tag{1.77}$$

or, letting

$$\frac{k^2\hbar^2}{2m} = E_k, \tag{1.78}$$

$$\frac{d^2u_k}{dx^2} + 2ik\frac{du_k}{dx} - \frac{2m}{\hbar^2}[V(x) - E + E_k]u_k = 0. \tag{1.79}$$

It may be verified by substitution that in a typical well region, where $V(x) = 0$, solutions of the form

$$u_w = A_1 e^{i(\gamma-k)x} + A_2 e^{-i(\gamma+k)x} \tag{1.80}$$

with

$$\gamma = \frac{\sqrt{2mE}}{\hbar} \tag{1.81}$$

will satisfy this equation, as will solutions of the form

$$u_b = A_3 e^{(\delta-ik)x} + A_4 e^{-(\delta+ik)x} \tag{1.82}$$

with

$$\delta = \frac{\sqrt{2m(V - E)}}{\hbar} \tag{1.83}$$

in a typical barrier region, where $V(x) = V$. These, of course, simply represent generalizations of the solutions for the isolated well and barrier cases studied above [(1.4) and (1.28)], as may readily be seen by substituting them in (1.74) to form ψ-functions independent of k.

To exploit the dependence of $u(x)$ on k in (1.80) and (1.82), we must first determine the arbitrary constants A_1 through A_4 by applying the usual continuity boundary conditions and the fact that the functions must be periodic in x:

$$[u_w]_{x=0} = [u_b]_{x=0}, \tag{1.84}$$

$$A_1 + A_2 = A_3 + A_4; \tag{1.85}$$

$$\left[\frac{du_w}{dx}\right]_{x=0} = \left[\frac{du_b}{dx}\right]_{x=0}, \tag{1.86}$$

$$i(\gamma - k)A_1 - i(\gamma + k)A_2 = (\delta - ik)A_3 - (\delta + ik)A_4; \tag{1.87}$$

$$[u_w]_{x=a} = [u_b]_{x=a} = [u_b]_{x=-b}, \tag{1.88}$$

$$A_1 e^{i(\gamma-k)a} + A_2 e^{-i(\gamma+k)a} = A_3 e^{-(\delta-ik)b} + A_4 e^{(\delta+ik)b}; \tag{1.89}$$

$$\left[\frac{du_w}{dx}\right]_{x=a} = \left[\frac{du_b}{dx}\right]_{x=a} = \left[\frac{du_b}{dx}\right]_{x=-b}, \tag{1.90}$$

$$i(\gamma - k)A_1 e^{i(\gamma-k)a} - i(\gamma + k)A_2 e^{-(\gamma+k)a}$$
$$= (\delta - ik)A_3 e^{-(\delta-ik)b} - (\delta + ik)A_4 e^{(\delta+ik)b}. \tag{1.91}$$

Equations (1.85), (1.87), (1.89) and (1.91) constitute a set of linear homogeneous algebraic equations which can only have a nonzero solution for the A's if the determinant of the coefficients vanishes, that is, if:

$$\begin{vmatrix} 1 & 1 & 1 & 1 \\ i(\gamma - k) & -i(\gamma + k) & -(\delta - ik) & (\delta + ik) \\ e^{i(\gamma-k)a} & e^{-i(\gamma+k)a} & -e^{-(\delta-ik)b} & -e^{(\delta+ik)b} \\ i(\gamma - k)e^{i(\gamma-k)a} & -i(\gamma + k)e^{-(\gamma+k)a} & -(\delta - ik)e^{-(\delta-ik)b} & (\delta + ik)e^{(\delta+ik)b} \end{vmatrix}$$
$$= 0 \tag{1.92}$$

This equation can be reduced to

$$\frac{(\delta^2 - \gamma^2)}{2\gamma\delta} \sinh \delta b \sin \gamma a + \cosh \delta b \cos \gamma a = \cos k(a + b), \tag{1.93}$$

which remains troublesome to work with; but if we agree to limit our analysis to the case of high, thin barriers, where $b \to 0$ and $V \to \infty$ so that $\delta \gg \gamma$, then we can approximate the hyperbolic functions by the first two terms of their series representations and rewrite the equation in the form:

$$\frac{\delta^2 ab}{2}\left(1 + \frac{\delta^2 b^2}{6}\right)\frac{\sin \gamma a}{\gamma a} - \frac{\gamma^2 b}{2}\left(1 + \frac{\delta^2 b^2}{6}\right)\frac{\sin \gamma a}{\gamma}$$
$$+ \left(1 + \frac{\delta^2 b^2}{2}\right)\cos \gamma a = \cos k(a + b) \tag{1.94}$$

Now, provided that

$$\lim_{\substack{b \to 0 \\ \delta \to \infty}} \frac{\delta^2 ab}{2} = \Delta \tag{1.95}$$

where Δ indicates some finite value, (1.93) further reduces through (1.94) to

$$\Delta \frac{\sin \gamma a}{\gamma a} + \cos \gamma a = \cos ka, \tag{1.96}$$

which defines the variation of k for this special case.

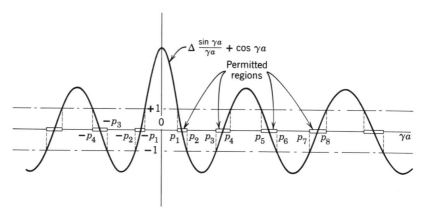

Fig. 6.13

The transcendental equation (1.96) in γa represents the final condition for nonzero values of A_1, A_2, A_3, and A_4 to exist. In other words, nonvanishing wave functions of the form (1.74) can only exist in regions where γa has real values according to (1.96). These must be those regions of the curve represented by the left-hand side of the equation which fall between the limits of $+1$ and -1, since $\cos ka$ on the right-hand side can take no values outside this range (Fig. 6.13). Because

$$\gamma a = \frac{\sqrt{2mE}}{\hbar} a, \tag{1.97}$$

using (1.81), we conclude that the particle can only have the energies given by

$$E = \frac{\hbar^2}{2ma^2} (\gamma a)^2, \tag{1.98}$$

where γa must fall within one of the permitted regions indicated in the figure (p_1 to p_2, $-p_1$ to $-p_2$, p_3 to p_4, $-p_3$ to $-p_4$, etc.). It is evident from (1.70) and (1.97) that

$$\gamma a = ka; \tag{1.99}$$

therefore, this equation may also be written as

$$E = \frac{\hbar^2}{2ma^2}(ka)^2 = \frac{\hbar^2 k^2}{2m}. \tag{1.100}$$

We note that the width of the permitted regions increases with γa, as might be expected from the fact that γa measures particle energy for a given width of well. We may also infer that the width of any one permitted region will decrease as the value of Δ increases. For it follows from (1.96) and (1.99) that, if we allow Δ to approach infinity, $\sin \gamma a$ must approach zero, or

$$\gamma a \to n\pi \quad \{n = 0, 1, 2, 3, \ldots. \tag{1.101}$$

This means that (1.98) will reduce to the discrete set of energy eigenvalues (1.58),

$$E \to E_n = \frac{(n\pi\hbar)^2}{2ma^2}. \tag{1.102}$$

In other words, the probability of the particle tunneling through the barriers will vanish. But if Δ is made to approach zero, the width of the permitted regions will increase until all energy values become possible. The inference is that Δ measures the energy with which the particle is bound to the lattice.

Assuming a loosely bound state, particle energy may be plotted as a function of the wave number k by means of (1.100). If all regions were permitted for γa in Fig. 6.13, all values of k would be possible and E would vary parabolically with k, as in the dashed curve shown in Fig. 6.14. However, because γa can only take on values lying between p_1 and p_2, $-p_1$ and $-p_2$, etc., this must also be true for ka. Discontinuities in the energy must occur at

$$k = \pm \frac{p_2}{a}, \quad \pm \frac{p_4}{a}, \ldots \tag{1.103}$$

where

$$\pm p_2 = \pm\pi, \quad \pm p_4 = \pm 2\pi, \ldots, \tag{1.104}$$

because we know from (1.96) that the breaks must come at

$$\cos ka = \pm 1, \tag{1.105}$$

or when

$$k = \pm \frac{n\pi}{a} \quad \{n = 0, 1, 2, 3, \ldots. \tag{1.106}$$

These regions in k-space, within which the energy of the particle can vary

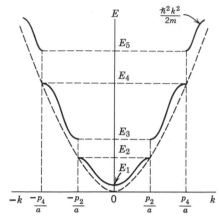

Fig. 6.14

continuously, but on the boundaries of which such discontinuities occur, are called Brillouin zones. For the one-dimensional case studied here, they are simply line segments; but in the three-dimensional generalization they become volumes, while the bounding discontinuities change from points to surfaces.

The energies that fall within Brillouin zones are said to constitute allowed energy bands, and those that fall in the gaps between zones are called forbidden bands. For example, in Fig. 6.14 the first allowed band would consist of the energies between E_1 and E_2, the first forbidden band of those between E_2 and E_3, the second allowed band of those between E_3 and E_4, and so on (see Fig. 6.15). It should be clear that these restrictions on possible particle energies represent the ultimate effect of the boundary conditions imposed by the periodic potential.

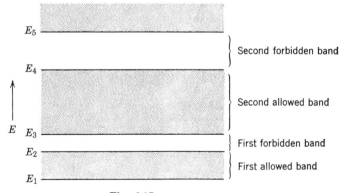

Fig. 6.15

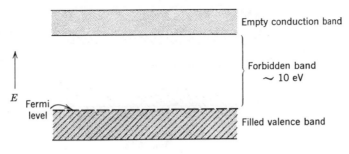

Fig. 6.16

The energy band structure of a crystal is of central importance in analyzing its physical properties. Later we shall consider several applications in detail, but on the basis of the preceding discussion alone it is easy to understand how the band structure determines whether a crystal is an insulator, a conductor, or a semiconductor.[6]

When such crystals are analyzed, it is found that the energy states in the first allowed band must belong to electrons whose function is to bond the positive ions together; accordingly, it is called the valence band. This is separated from the group of higher states which can belong to electrons that are free to move, called the conduction band, by a forbidden band whose width varies for each of the three types. In insulators the forbidden band is too wide for electrons to be agitated thermally from the filled valence band into the empty conduction band (Fig. 6.16). In conductors, on the other hand, though the valence band remains filled, the conduction band is also partly filled and remains so even at very low temperatures; usually the width of the forbidden band is small (Fig. 6.17).

Semiconductors are distinguished by the fact that the forbidden band is of intermediate width. Basically, there are two types. In intrinsic semiconductors the width is such that electrons can be thermally excited from

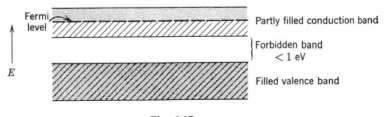

Fig. 6.17

[6] Nussbaum, A., *Electromagnetic and Quantum Properties of Materials*, pp. 147–226, Prentice-Hall, Englewood Cliffs, N.J., 1966.

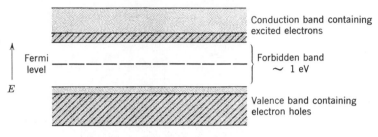

Fig. 6.18

the filled valence band to the empty conduction band at ordinary temperatures, leaving positively charged holes behind them. As the temperature increases, more electrons will be raised to higher levels and the conductivity will continue to increase (6.18). The width of the forbidden band may be somewhat larger in extrinsic semiconductors; but crystals of this kind necessarily contain impurity atoms which provide energy states capable of accepting thermally agitated electrons from the valence band, as well as states that can donate electrons to the conduction band at room temperature (Fig. 6.19).

It will be noted that the Fermi-level energy, E_f, which we saw to play an important role in the operation of tunnel diodes, also enters prominently here. In fact, the effective number of electrons in a band, that is, the number free to move under the influence of an applied electric field, can be shown to be proportional to

$$\left[\frac{dE}{dk}\right]_{k=k_1} \tag{1.107}$$

where k_1 marks the level to which the band is filled. Therefore, more than any other single quantity, E_f characterizes the conductivity of crystals.[7]

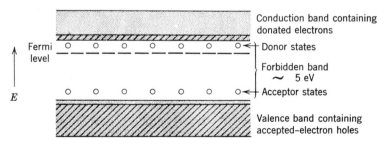

Fig. 6.19

[7] Wert, C. A., and R. M. Thomson, *Physics of Solids*, pp. 230–254, McGraw-Hill, New York, 1964.

Problems 6.1

1. Electrons of energy E are directed toward a region in space where the effective potential is described by:

$$V(x) = \begin{cases} -V & \text{for} \quad -c \leqq x \leqq c \\ 0 & \text{for} \quad x < -c \text{ and } x > c \end{cases}$$

Calculate the transmissivity T of the region.

Solution

It must be recognized that, even though the energy of the particles exceeds that of the "barrier," some of the particles may be reflected because of their wave properties. Diagrammatically, we can subdivide the region of interest in the same way as before [Fig. P6.1 (1)].

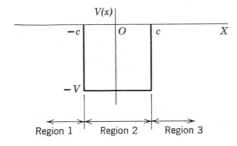

Fig. P6.1 (1)

In region 1 the Schrödinger equation to be satisfied is

$$\frac{d^2}{dx^2}\psi_1 + \frac{2m}{\hbar^2}E\psi_1 = 0,$$

which has the solutions

$$\psi_1 = Ae^{\frac{i}{\hbar}p_1 x} + Be^{-\frac{i}{\hbar}p_1 x}$$

with

$$p_1 = \sqrt{2mE}.$$

In region 2, on the other hand, we must satisfy

$$\frac{d^2}{dx^2}\psi_2 + \frac{2m}{\hbar^2}(E+V)\psi_2 = 0,$$

whose solutions are

$$\psi_2 = Ce^{\frac{i}{\hbar}p_2 x} + De^{-\frac{i}{\hbar}p_2 x}$$

where

$$p_2 = \sqrt{2m(E+V)}.$$

In region 3 an equation of the same form as that for region 1 will govern,

$$\frac{d^2}{dx^2}\,\psi_3 + \frac{2m}{\hbar^2}\,E\psi_3 = 0;$$

however, the possibility of particles moving in the negative x-direction can be neglected and the solutions written as

$$\psi_3 = Fe^{\frac{i}{\hbar}p_3 x},$$

with

$$p_3 = \sqrt{2mE} = p_1.$$

To evaluate four of the constants A, B, C, D, and F in terms of the other one, we may apply the boundary conditions:

$$\left.\begin{array}{c} [\psi]_{x=\pm c} \\[4pt] \left[\dfrac{d\psi}{dx}\right]_{x=\pm c} \end{array}\right\} \text{ must be continuous;}$$

and because we are interested in

$$T = \frac{|F|^2 \dfrac{p_3}{m}}{|A|^2 \dfrac{p_1}{m}} = \frac{|F|^2}{|A|^2},$$

our principal objective must be to obtain F in terms of A.

It is left for Exercise 6.1(1) to prove that

$$F = \frac{A}{\left[\cos\dfrac{2p_1 c}{\hbar} + i\sin\dfrac{2p_1 c}{\hbar}\right]\left[\cos\dfrac{2p_2 c}{\hbar} - \dfrac{i}{2}\left(\dfrac{p_1}{p_2} + \dfrac{p_2}{p_1}\right)\sin\dfrac{2p_2 c}{\hbar}\right]};$$

but if this relation is used, the expression for the transmissivity becomes

$$T = \frac{1}{\cos^2\dfrac{2p_2 c}{\hbar} + \dfrac{1}{4}\left(\dfrac{p_1}{p_2} + \dfrac{p_2}{p_1}\right)^2 \sin^2\dfrac{2p_2 c}{\hbar}}$$

$$= \frac{1}{1 + \dfrac{1}{4}\left(\dfrac{p_1}{p_2} - \dfrac{p_2}{p_1}\right)^2 \sin^2\dfrac{2p_2 c}{\hbar}}.$$

Generally speaking, T will be less than unity; therefore, as anticipated, some reflection must occur. The two exceptions are the trivial one when there is no barrier ($p_2 = p_1$), and the one when constructive interference occurs for certain wavelengths at $x = c(p_2 - \alpha\pi\hbar/2c$ with $\alpha = 0, 1, 2, \ldots)$.

2. If a metal M has a very thin layer of metal oxide MO on it, and this layer is impervious to oxygen, explain how further growth of the layer can take place and estimate the rate at which its thickness will increase [Fig. P6.1 (2a)].

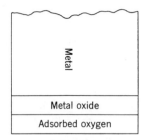

Fig. P6.1 (2a)

Solution

Consider the potential barrier as it would appear to electrons in the metal [Fig. P6.1 (2b)]; if the barrier is sufficiently thin, they will equalize the energy levels on both sides by tunneling, with the result that metal ions will be left on one side and oxide ions will appear on the other [Fig. P6.1 (2c)]. The resulting electric field across the barrier will now cause the M^+ ions to diffuse to the outside where they can form new MO molecules.

MO

M

O

Fig. P6.1 (2b)

In the exercises it is required to prove the following approximate relationship for the transmissivity of the oxide layer:

$$T \approx \frac{1}{1 + \beta c^2},$$

where β is a constant $\left(\dfrac{V^2}{E} \dfrac{2m}{\hbar^2} \right)$ and $2c$ is the thickness of the barrier. If N is the number of electrons which tunnel through the barrier in each second, let

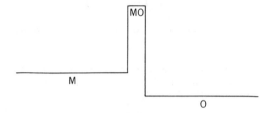

Fig. P6.1 (2c)

us assume that

$$N \propto T$$

and that the growth rate will be proportional to the tunneling rate:

$$\frac{dc}{dt} \propto N \propto T$$

or

$$\frac{dc}{dt} = \frac{D}{1 + \beta c^2}$$

where D is the proportionality constant.

Then

$$(1 + \beta c^2)\, dc = D\, dt;$$

therefore,

$$c + \frac{\beta}{3} c^3 = Dt + F$$

with F representing an integration constant. But for $c = 0$ at $t = 0$, $F = 0$; and we conclude that

$$c + \frac{\beta}{3} c^3 = Dt.$$

In general β is greater than unity, so that to a good approximation

$$c \propto t^{1/3}.$$

In spite of the fact that actual oxidation processes are much more complicated than the simplified picture given here, this type of growth law has been observed for a wide variety of metals.

3. Calculate the expectation values of the common observables and prove that the uncertainty principle is satisfied for a particle in an infinitely deep, rectangular potential well of width a with the wave functions

$$\psi_n = \sqrt{\frac{2}{a}} \sin \frac{n\pi}{a} x \qquad \{n = 0, 1, 2, 3, \ldots.$$

Solution

The expectation value of the position coordinate will be given by:

$$\bar{x} = \int_0^a \psi_n x \psi_n \, dx;$$

therefore:

$$\bar{x} = \frac{2}{a} \int_0^a x \sin^2 \frac{n\pi}{a} x \, dx$$

$$= \frac{2}{a} \left[\frac{x^2}{4} - \frac{x \sin \frac{2n\pi}{a} x}{\frac{4n\pi}{a}} - \frac{\cos \frac{2n\pi}{a} x}{8\left(\frac{n\pi}{a}\right)^2} \right]_0^a$$

$$= \frac{2}{a} \left(\frac{a^2}{4} - \frac{a^2}{8(n\pi)^2} + \frac{a^2}{8(n\pi)^2} \right) = \frac{a}{2}$$

As we might expect, the most probable location of the particle is at the center of the well; also as we should expect:

$$\bar{p}_x = \int_0^a \sqrt{\frac{2}{a}} \sin\left(\frac{n\pi}{a} x\right) \left[\frac{\hbar}{i} \frac{\partial}{\partial x} \sqrt{\frac{2}{a}} \sin\left(\frac{n\pi}{a} x\right)\right] dx$$

$$= \frac{\hbar}{i} \frac{2n\pi}{a^2} \int_0^a \sin\frac{n\pi}{a} x \cos\frac{n\pi}{a} x \, dx = 0$$

The expectation value of the energy will be given by:

$$E = \int_0^a \psi_n H \psi_n \, dx;$$

but since

$$H\psi_n = E_n \psi_n,$$

$$\bar{E} = \int_0^a \psi_n E_n \psi_n \, dx = E_n \int_0^a \psi_n^2 \, dx = E_n.$$

The particle is in the definite energy state

$$E_n = \frac{(n\pi\hbar)^2}{2ma^2}.$$

Let us consider the implications of the uncertainty principle. First, it is required that

$$\Delta E \, \Delta t \geq \hbar,$$

but $\Delta E = 0$, so that $\Delta t = \infty$. That is, we can say nothing about the time at which the particle will be in a particular energy state. Next, it is required that

$$\Delta p_x \, \Delta x \geq \hbar.$$

But

$$p_x = \sqrt{2mE_n} = \sqrt{\frac{(n\pi\hbar)^2}{a^2}},$$

or

$$|p_x| = \frac{n\pi\hbar}{a};$$

the only uncertainty in p_x arises from its sign,

$$\Delta p_x = 2|p_x| = \frac{2n\pi\hbar}{a}.$$

Because the particle may be anywhere in the well, the uncertainty in its position must be $\Delta x = a$. Thus,

$$\Delta p_x \, \Delta x = \frac{2n\pi\hbar}{a} a = 2n\pi\hbar.$$

In the lowest state for which the energy is not zero, $n = 1$; therefore,

$$\Delta p_x \, \Delta x = 2\pi\hbar > \hbar,$$

which establishes that the uncertainty principle is satisfied.

4. Investigate the motion of a particle in the potential well of the preceding problem if it is not in an eigenstate, but is initially described by the wave function

$$\Psi(x, 0) = \sqrt{\frac{1}{a}} \sin \frac{\sqrt{2mE_1}}{\hbar} x + \sqrt{\frac{1}{a}} \sin \frac{\sqrt{2mE_2}}{\hbar} x.$$

Solution

In this case we must use the time-dependent solutions of the Schrödinger equation,

$$\Psi_n(x, t) = A_n \sin \frac{\sqrt{2mE_n}}{\hbar} x e^{-\frac{i}{\hbar} E_n t},$$

and try to satisfy the initial condition by superimposing them:

$$\Psi(x, t) = \sum_{n=1}^{\infty} \Psi_n(x, t) = \sum_{n=1}^{\infty} A_n \sin \frac{\sqrt{2mE_n}}{\hbar} x e^{-\frac{i}{\hbar} E_n t}.$$

However, since we know that at time zero

$$\Psi(x, 0) = \sum_{n=1}^{\infty} A_n \sin \frac{\sqrt{2mE_n}}{\hbar} x = \sqrt{\frac{1}{a}} \sin \frac{\sqrt{2mE_1}}{\hbar} x + \sqrt{\frac{1}{a}} \sin \frac{\sqrt{2mE_2}}{\hbar} x,$$

if follows immediately that

$$A_1 = \sqrt{\frac{1}{a}}, \qquad A_2 = \sqrt{\frac{1}{a}}$$

and all other $A_n = 0$. Hence the general solution must be

$$\Psi(x, t) = \sqrt{\frac{1}{a}} \sin \frac{\sqrt{2mE_1}}{\hbar} x e^{-\frac{i}{\hbar} E_1 t} + \sqrt{\frac{1}{a}} \sin \frac{\sqrt{2mE_2}}{\hbar} x e^{-\frac{i}{\hbar} E_2 t}$$

where, from the formula developed in the text,

$$E_1 = \frac{(\pi \hbar)^2}{2ma^2}$$

and

$$E_2 = \frac{(2\pi \hbar)^2}{2ma^2}.$$

Let us consider the significance of the given initial condition. Substituting the values of E_1 and E_2, we can write this as

$$\Psi(x, 0) = \Psi_1(x, 0) + \Psi_2(x, 0) = \sqrt{\frac{1}{a}} \sin \frac{\pi}{a} x + \sqrt{\frac{1}{a}} \sin \frac{2\pi}{a} x;$$

and plotting $\Psi(x, 0)$ as a function of x, we obtain a curve of the type shown in Fig. P6.1 (4). This shows that to begin with the particle tends to be localized in the left-hand side of the well.

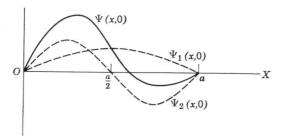

Fig. P6.1 (4)

The expectation value of x is calculated below:

$$\bar{x} = \int_0^a \Psi^* x \Psi \, dx = \int_0^a \left(\sqrt{\frac{1}{a}} \sin \frac{\sqrt{2mE_1}}{\hbar} x e^{\frac{i}{\hbar}E_1 t} + \sqrt{\frac{1}{a}} \sin \frac{\sqrt{2mE_2}}{\hbar} x e^{\frac{i}{\hbar}E_2 t} \right) x$$

$$\cdot \left(\sqrt{\frac{1}{a}} \sin \frac{\sqrt{2mE_1}}{\hbar} x e^{-\frac{i}{\hbar}E_1 t} + \sqrt{\frac{1}{a}} \sin \frac{\sqrt{2mE_2}}{\hbar} x e^{-\frac{i}{\hbar}E_2 t} \right) dx$$

$$= \frac{1}{a} \int_0^a x \sin^2 \frac{\sqrt{2mE_1}}{\hbar} x \, dx + \frac{1}{a} \int_0^a x \sin^2 \frac{\sqrt{2mE_2}}{\hbar} x \, dx$$

$$+ \frac{1}{a} \left(e^{\frac{i}{\hbar}(E_1 - E_2)t} + e^{-\frac{i}{\hbar}(E_1 - E_2)t} \right) \int_0^a x \sin \frac{\sqrt{2mE_1}}{\hbar} x \sin \frac{\sqrt{2mE_2}}{\hbar} x \, dx$$

$$= \frac{1}{a} \left[\frac{a^2}{4} \right] + \frac{1}{a} \left[\frac{a^2}{4} \right] + \frac{1}{a} \left[2 \cos \frac{(E_1 - E_2)}{\hbar} t \right] \int_0^a x \sin \frac{\sqrt{2mE_1}}{\hbar} x \sin \frac{\sqrt{2mE_2}}{\hbar} x \, dx$$

$$= \frac{a}{2} + \frac{2}{a} \cos \frac{(E_1 - E_2)}{\hbar} t \left[\frac{\dfrac{2mE_1}{\hbar}}{\left(\dfrac{2mE_1}{\hbar} \right)^2 - \left(\dfrac{2mE_2}{\hbar} \right)^2} \right].$$

The expectation value of x is not constant in time; rather, it oscillates about the center of the well, starting at an initial position to the left of the center and moving back and forth between this and a corresponding point to the right of the center.

5. Separate the three-dimensional Schrödinger equation in Cartesian coordinates,

$$\nabla^2 \psi + \frac{2m}{\hbar^2} [E - \nabla(x, y, z)]\psi = 0,$$

assuming that

$$\psi(x, y, z) = X(x) \, Y(y) Z(z)$$

and

$$V(x, y, z) = V_x(x) + V_y(y) + V_z(z).$$

Solution

With $V(x, y, z)$ as given, it follows that we may write the total energy E as the sum of separate x, y, and z-direction energies,

$$E = E_x + E_y + E_z;$$

thus, substituting in the given equation, we obtain:

$$YZ\frac{d^2X}{dx^2} + XZ\frac{d^2Y}{dy^2} + XY\frac{d^2Z}{dz^2} + \frac{2m}{\hbar}\left([E_x - V_x]\right.$$

$$\left. + [E_y - V_y] + [E_z - V_z]\right)XYZ = 0$$

Dividing through by XYZ and collecting terms in the same variable, we obtain

$$\frac{1}{X}\frac{d^2X}{dx^2} + \frac{2m}{\hbar^2}[E_x - V_x] + \frac{1}{Y}\frac{d^2Y}{dy^2} + \frac{2m}{\hbar^2}[E_y - V_y]$$

$$+ \frac{1}{Z}\frac{d^2Z}{dz^2} + \frac{2m}{\hbar^2}[E_z - V_z] = 0.$$

But now, because the first two terms depend only on x, the second two only on y, the last two only on z, and x, y, z are all independent variables, we may conclude that each pair must vanish separately. Thus the original equation may be replaced by:

$$\frac{d^2X}{dx^2} + \frac{2m}{\hbar^2}[E_x - V_x]X = 0$$

$$\frac{d^2Y}{dy^2} + \frac{2m}{\hbar^2}[E_y - V_y]Y = 0$$

$$\frac{d^2Z}{dz^2} + \frac{2m}{\hbar^2}[E_z - V_z]Z = 0$$

Each of these one-dimensional equations can be solved in the same manner as in the text. Also, it is interesting to note that

$$|\psi(x, y, z)|^2 = |X(x)|^2\,|Y(y)|^2\,|Z(z)|^2;$$

in other words, the total probability density in this case is the product, not the sum, of the separate probability densities.

6. Using the results of the preceding problem, determine the eigenfunctions and energies for a particle confined in an impenetrable rectangular "box" with sides of length l_1, l_2, and l_3.

Solution

The potential inside the box may be described by:

$$V_x(x) = 0 \quad \text{for} \quad 0 \leq x \leq l_1$$
$$V_y(y) = 0 \quad \text{for} \quad 0 \leq y \leq l_2$$
$$V_z(z) = 0 \quad \text{for} \quad 0 \leq z \leq l_3$$

Therefore, the wave functions

$$\psi(x, y, z) = X(x)\,Y(y)\,Z(z)$$

may be obtained by solving the equations:

$$\frac{d^2 X}{dx^2} + \frac{2m}{\hbar^2} E_x X = 0$$

$$\frac{d^2 Y}{dy^2} + \frac{2m}{\hbar^2} E_y Y = 0$$

$$\frac{d^2 Z}{dz^2} + \frac{2m}{\hbar^2} E_z Z = 0$$

Each of these has the same form as (1.51) and, since the wave functions must always vanish at the walls, the same type of boundary conditions as those expressed in (1.52) and (1.53). Hence, each of the solutions must have the form given in (1.63). We conclude that

$$\psi_n = \sqrt{\frac{2}{l_1}} \sin \frac{n_1 \pi}{l_1} x \sqrt{\frac{2}{l_2}} \sin \frac{n_2 \pi}{l_2} y \sqrt{\frac{2}{l_3}} \sin \frac{n_3 \pi}{l_3} z$$

where, following (1.58),

$$E = E_x + E_y + E_z = \frac{\pi^2 \hbar^2}{2m} \left[\left(\frac{n_1}{l_1}\right)^2 + \left(\frac{n_2}{l_2}\right)^2 + \left(\frac{n_3}{l_3}\right)^2 \right] = E_n$$

and

$$n_1 = 0, 1, 2, 3, \ldots$$
$$n_2 = 0, 1, 2, 3, \ldots$$
$$n_3 = 0, 1, 2, 3, \ldots$$

The expression in the outer brackets must be equivalent to n^2. If, for example, all three sides of the box are equal, $l_1 = l_2 = l_3 = l$, the expression for the energy becomes

$$E_n = \frac{\pi^2 \hbar^2}{2ml^2} (n_1^2 + n_2^2 + n_3^2),$$

and the square of the total quantum number n is equal to the sum of the squares of the component quantum numbers n_1, n_2, and n_3:

$$n^2 = n_1^2 + n_2^2 + n_3^2$$

7. When the equilibrium concentration of electrons in the conduction band of an extrinsic semiconductor (n_e) is low, its ratio to the free electron concentration in the pure material (N) can be described by the Maxwell-Boltzmann distribution:

$$\frac{n_e}{N} = e^{(E_f - E_i)/kT}$$

where E_f represents the Fermi-level energy, E_i the energy at the center of the forbidden band, k Boltzmann's constant, and T the absolute temperature. Similarly, the equilibrium concentration of electron holes in the valence band (n_h) is given by

$$\frac{n_h}{N} = e^{(E_i - E_f)/kT}.$$

Find how variations in the Fermi level will affect the ratio of n_e to n_h.

Solution

When $E_f = E_i$,

$$n_e = n_h = N.$$

This is the situation for the pure material (provided the effective mass of a hole is equal to the effective mass of an electron[8]), where the ratio of n_e to n_h should be unity. But when $E_f > E_i$, the exponent in the relation

$$n_e = Ne^{(E_f - E_i)/kT}$$

will be positive; the exponential will exceed unity and n_e will be greater than N. On the other hand, the exponential in the expression

$$n_h = Ne^{(E_i - E_f)/kT}$$

will be negative and n_h will be less than N. Obviously these conditions will reverse when $E_f < E_i$.

More generally, we may divide the first equation by the second and see that

$$\frac{n_e}{n_h} = e^{2(E_f - E_i)kT} = \frac{n_e^2}{N^2}$$

or

$$n_e n_h = N^2 = \text{constant.}$$

If, under equilibrium conditions, the electron concentration in the conduction band increases, the hole concentration in the valence band must necessarily decrease in proportion, and vice versa.

Exercises 6.1

1. By applying the boundary conditions in Problem 6.1 (1), verify the relation:

$$F = \frac{A}{\left[\cos\dfrac{2p_1 c}{\hbar} + i \sin\dfrac{2p_1 c}{\hbar}\right]\left[\cos\dfrac{2p_2 c}{\hbar} - \dfrac{i}{2}\left(\dfrac{p_1}{p_2} + \dfrac{p_2}{p_1}\right)\sin\dfrac{2p_2 c}{\hbar}\right]}$$

2. Prove that for the potential barrier shown in Fig. E6.1 (2) and a particle energy $E < V$, the transmissivity may be approximated by the expression.

$$T \approx \frac{1}{1 + \dfrac{V^2}{E}\dfrac{2mc^2}{\hbar^2}}.$$

[8] Kittel, C., *Introduction to Solid State Physics*, 2nd edition, pp. 288–296, Wiley, New York, 1957.

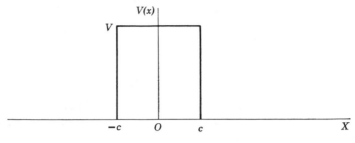

Fig. E6.1 (2)

3. Show that the equation defining the probability density current,

$$S_x = |\text{constant}|^2 \frac{p_x}{m},$$

follows from the relation

$$\mathbf{S} = -\frac{i\hbar}{2m}(\Psi^* \, \nabla\Psi - \nabla\Psi^*\Psi)$$

when the wave function has the form

$$\Psi = \text{constant } e^{\pm\frac{i}{\hbar}(p_x x - E t)}.$$

4. Assuming that α-particles strike the potential barrier of each nucleus of a substance, initially containing N_0 atoms, ν times per second, derive an expression for the half-life τ of the substance as a function of the transmissivity T, where τ is defined as the time required to attain the condition where the number of undecayed atoms

$$N = \tfrac{1}{2}N_0.$$

Answer. $\tau = \dfrac{\ln 2}{\nu T}$.

5. Using the expression for the transmissivity T developed in Problem 6.1 (2) and the result of the preceding problem, find how the half-life τ will vary as a function of the velocity v of the emitted α-particles. Also, how satisfactorily does this model explain the well-known empirical relation for radioactive decay,

$$\tau = k_1 v^{k_2}$$

where k_1 and k_2 are constants?

6. If an electron trapped in a one-dimensional potential well drops from level E_m to level E_n, where $m > n$, what is the magnitude of the quantum of energy that must be released? Calculate the characteristic wavelength of this quantum if $m = 2$, $n = 1$, and the potential well has a width of 2×10^{-8} cm.

Answer. $\lambda = 441$ Å.

7. If at time zero the wave function for a particle confined in a rectangular
potential well of width a is given by

$$\Psi(x, 0) = \begin{cases} C \sin \dfrac{2\pi x}{a} & \text{for} \quad 0 \leqq x \leqq a \\ \\ 0 & \text{for} \quad x > a \quad \text{and} \quad x < 0, \end{cases}$$

prove that the constant C must have the value $\sqrt{2/a}$.

8. If the normalized wave function for a particle constrained to move along a
straight line of length l is

$$\Psi(x, t) = \sqrt{\frac{2}{3l}} \sin \frac{\pi x}{l} e^{-\frac{i}{\hbar} E_1 t} + \sqrt{\frac{1}{3l}} \sin \frac{2\pi x}{l} e^{-\frac{i}{\hbar} E_2 t},$$

calculate the expectation value of its linear momentum.

Answer. $\bar{p}_x = \dfrac{8\sqrt{2}}{9l} \hbar \sin \dfrac{(E_2 - E_1)}{\hbar} t.$

6.2   The Quantum Oscillator and Hydrogenlike Atoms

In addition to having some finite height and width, most real trapping
potentials are nonrectangular in shape, thereby complicating the boundary
conditions that the wave function must satisfy in still another way. The

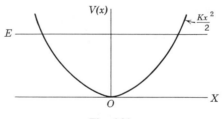

Fig. 6.20

result is that different mathematical methods must be used. It is convenient to introduce these by analyzing the motion of a particle of mass m
and energy E trapped in a parabolic potential well described by

$$V(x) = \frac{Kx^2}{2}, \tag{2.1}$$

where K indicates a constant (Fig. 6.20). Clearly, this corresponds to the
simple harmonic oscillator potential of classical mechanics [(2.26) of
Chapter 3 with Fig. 3.5)], and K must be the equivalent of a spring constant.

It is reasonable to guess that the case will be one of fundamental importance, since the other turned out to be; but independently of this, it should prove interesting to compare the conclusions which follow from the two methods of solution.

The proper Schrödinger equation is easy to write. We know that stationary states will exist, so it should suffice to solve the eigen equation (2.20) of Chapter 5,

$$H\psi = E\psi;$$

and replacing the variables in the expression for the total energy,

$$E = \frac{p_x^2}{2m} + \frac{Kx^2}{2}, \tag{2.2}$$

by their operator equivalents, we obtain

$$H = -\frac{\hbar^2}{2m}\frac{d^2}{dx^2} + \frac{Kx^2}{2}. \tag{2.3}$$

It follows that the governing equation of motion will be:

$$\frac{d^2\psi}{dx^2} - \frac{mK}{\hbar^2}x^2\psi + \frac{2mE}{\hbar^2}\psi = 0 \tag{2.4}$$

Because of the term involving x^2, this equation cannot be solved in the same way as before [(2.30) to (2.53) of Chapter 3]. Actually, it is representative of a class of second order ordinary differential equations with coefficients which are functions of the independent variable only. Such equations remain linear and may be solved in terms of certain well-known special functions. In the present case, as will be shown below, these prove to be the Hermite polynomials; elsewhere they may be Bessel functions, Legendre functions, or one of a variety of others.[9]

The form of (2.4) suggests the following substitutions in the interests of simplicity:

$$\frac{2mE}{\hbar^2} = \gamma \tag{2.5}$$

$$\frac{mK}{\hbar^2} = \alpha^2 \tag{2.6}$$

The equation then becomes

$$\frac{d^2\psi}{dx^2} + (\gamma - \alpha^2 x^2)\psi = 0; \tag{2.7}$$

[9] Hochstadt, H., *Special Functions of Mathematical Physics*, pp. 1–58, Holt, Rinehart, and Winston, New York, 1961.

and it is immediately apparent that x can always be chosen large enough to make γ negligible with respect to $\alpha^2 x^2$.

This means that in the regions where x is large we may simply solve the equation

$$\frac{d^2\psi}{dx^2} - \alpha^2 x^2 \psi = 0, \qquad (2.8)$$

which is satisfied by the functions

$$\psi = e^{\pm\frac{\alpha x^2}{2}}, \qquad (2.9)$$

because

$$\frac{d^2\psi}{dx^2} = \alpha^2 x^2 e^{\pm\frac{\alpha x^2}{2}} \pm \alpha e^{\pm\frac{\alpha x^2}{2}} \qquad (2.10)$$

and the last term will be negligible for large x. Also, since every acceptable wave function must remain finite for all x, we can drop the positive exponential, leaving only

$$\psi = e^{-\frac{\alpha}{2} x^2}. \qquad (2.11)$$

To extend this solution through the regions where x is small, we will introduce a factor in the form of a power series in x, $f_v(x)$, and determine its coefficients by substituting the resulting form,

$$\psi = e^{-\frac{\alpha}{2} x^2} f_v(x), \qquad (2.12)$$

back into the complete equation of motion (2.7). This is most easily accomplished by introducing a new variable u, such that

$$u = \alpha^{\frac{1}{2}} x; \qquad (2.13)$$

then the required power series becomes

$$F_v(u) = a_0 + a_1 u + a_2 u^2 + a_3 u^3 + \cdots = \sum_{v=0}^{\infty} a_v u^v \qquad (2.14)$$

and (2.12) takes the form

$$\psi = e^{-\frac{u^2}{2}} F_v(u). \qquad (2.15)$$

Recasting (2.7) in terms of the new variable u, we obtain

$$\alpha e^{-\frac{u^2}{2}} \frac{d^2 F_v}{du^2} - \alpha u e^{-\frac{u^2}{2}} \frac{dF_v}{du} + \alpha u^2 e^{-\frac{u^2}{2}} F_v - \alpha e^{-\frac{u^2}{2}} \left(F_v + u \frac{dF_v}{du} \right)$$

$$+ \gamma e^{-\frac{u^2}{2}} F_v - \alpha u^2 e^{-\frac{u^2}{2}} F_v = 0$$

or

$$\frac{d^2F_\nu}{du^2} - 2u\,\frac{dF_\nu}{du} + \left(\frac{\gamma}{\alpha} - 1\right)F_\nu = 0. \tag{2.16}$$

But since, when the power series (2.14) is used for $F_\nu(u)$,

$$\frac{dF_\nu}{du} = \sum_\nu \nu a_\nu u^{\nu-1} = a_1 + 2a_2 u + 3a_3 u^2 + \cdots \tag{2.17}$$

and

$$\frac{d^2F_\nu}{du^2} = \sum_\nu \nu(\nu-1)a_\nu u^{\nu-2} = 2\cdot 1a_2 + 3\cdot 2a_3 u + 4\cdot 3a_4 u^2 + \cdots, \tag{2.18}$$

it follows that (2.16) can also be written as:

$$2\cdot 1a_2 \qquad + 3\cdot 2a_3 u \qquad + 4\cdot 3a_4 u^2 + \cdots$$
$$-2a_1 u \qquad - 4a_2 u^2 - \cdots$$
$$+ \left(\frac{\gamma}{\alpha} - 1\right)a_0 + \left(\frac{\gamma}{\alpha} - 1\right)a_1 u + \left(\frac{\gamma}{\alpha} - 1\right)a_2 u^2 + \cdots = 0 \tag{2.19}$$

In part, at least, the required coefficients a_ν are determined by (2.19); for if the equation is to be satisfied, all of the coefficients of the separate powers of u must vanish; that is,

$$2\cdot 1a_2 + \left(\frac{\gamma}{\alpha} - 1\right)a_0 = 0$$

$$3\cdot 2a_3 + \left(\frac{\gamma}{\alpha} - 1 - 2\right)a_1 = 0$$

$$4\cdot 3a_4 + \left(\frac{\gamma}{\alpha} - 1 - 4\right)a_2 = 0$$

$$\cdots \cdots \cdots \cdots \cdots \cdots \cdots \cdots$$

$$(\nu+2)(\nu+1)a_{\nu+2} + \left(\frac{\gamma}{\alpha} - 1 - 2\nu\right)a_\nu = 0$$

or

$$a_{\nu+2} = \frac{\left[\dfrac{\gamma}{\alpha} - (2\nu+1)\right]}{(\nu+2)(\nu+1)}\,a_\nu. \tag{2.20}$$

This is a recursion formula defining $a_2, a_4, a_6, \ldots$ in terms of arbitrary a_0, and $a_3, a_5, a_7, \ldots$ in terms of arbitrary a_1. Clearly, only terms involving odd powers of u will appear in the series (2.14) for $F_\nu(u)$ when a_0 is zero, whereas only terms involving even powers will appear if a_1 is zero.

Equation (2.7) is a second order ordinary differential equation, so a_0 and a_1 could serve as the two arbitrary constants required in its solution and be used to satisfy specific boundary conditions. However, one important difficulty remains. Both of the series for $F_\nu(u)$ which result from incorporating the recursion relation (2.20) with a_0 or a_1 zero, behave like e^{u^2} for large x.[10] This means that the wave function (2.15) would become infinite at large x, which is not permissible. It happens though, that the terms which dominate the series when x is large are those for which ν is large; thus we may circumvent the difficulty by agreeing to terminate both series before ν becomes large, say with the nth term.

This can easily be accomplished by requiring that, in addition to (2.20), the following relationship be satisfied:

$$\gamma = (2n + 1)\alpha \tag{2.21}$$

The numerator of (2.20) will then vanish when ν becomes n; therefore, the nth coefficient will become zero, and all subsequent even coefficients as well if n is even, or all subsequent odd coefficients if it is odd. Thus, if we further require that

$$a_1 = 0 \quad \text{if} \quad n \text{ is even} \tag{2.22}$$

or

$$a_0 = 0 \quad \text{if} \quad n \text{ is odd,} \tag{2.23}$$

the series will certainly terminate with the nth term.

Actually, when the recursion relation (2.20) and the special requirements (2.21) to (2.23) are applied to the series (2.14) for $F_\nu(u)$, the result is a well-known set of polynomials. They are called the Hermite polynomials[11] and indicated by the symbol $H_n(u)$; one formula for calculating them is given below, and the first few are listed:

$$H_n(u) = (-1)^n e^{u^2} \frac{d^n}{du^n} e^{-u^2} \tag{2.24}$$

$$H_0 = 1 \tag{2.25}$$

$$H_1 = 2u \tag{2.26}$$

$$H_2 = 4u^2 - 2 \tag{2.27}$$

$$H_3 = 8u^3 - 12u \tag{2.28}$$

$$\cdots \cdots \cdots$$

[10] Pauling, L., and E. B. Wilson, *Introduction to Quantum Mechanics*, pp. 71, 72, McGraw-Hill, New York, 1935.

[11] Abramowitz, M., and I. A. Stegun, *Handbook of Mathematical Functions*, pp. 773–802, Dover, New York, 1965.

It follows that when we write (2.15) in the form

$$\psi_n = N_n e^{-\frac{u^2}{2}} H_n(u), \tag{2.29}$$

where N_n represents a normalization constant, the resulting wave functions will satisfy the equation of motion (2.16) and, thus, (2.7) for both large and small values of x. Since it can be shown[12] that the relation

$$\int_{-\infty}^{\infty} |\psi_n(u)\psi_m(u)|\, du = 0, \qquad m \neq n \tag{2.30}$$

will be satisfied by the functions, they are orthogonal; and the constant N_n can be evaluated by applying the usual requirement that

$$\int_{-\infty}^{\infty} |\psi_n(u)|^2\, du = 1. \tag{2.31}$$

The result is:

$$N_n = \sqrt{\frac{1}{2^n n!}\left(\frac{\alpha}{\pi}\right)^{\frac{1}{2}}} \tag{2.32}$$

The final wave functions can now be constructed; using (2.29), (2.24) to (2.28), (2.32), and (2.13) to make the transition back to the variable x, we obtain

$$\psi_0 = \left(\frac{\alpha}{\pi}\right)^{\frac{1}{4}} e^{-\frac{u^2}{2}}(1) = \left(\frac{\alpha}{\pi}\right)^{\frac{1}{4}} e^{-\frac{\alpha}{2}x^2}, \tag{2.33}$$

as stated in (3.31) of Chapter 5,

$$\psi_1 = \frac{1}{\sqrt{2}}\left(\frac{\alpha}{\pi}\right)^{\frac{1}{4}} e^{-\frac{u^2}{2}}(2u) = \sqrt{2}\left(\frac{\alpha^3}{\pi}\right)^{\frac{1}{4}} x e^{-\frac{\alpha}{2}x^2} \tag{2.34}$$

. . . .

Several of these are illustrated in Fig. 6.21. It will be noted that in each case the number of zeros is equal to n, not counting those which occur at the ends, and that even n's lead to even functions whereas odd n's lead to odd functions.

By the preceding expedients we have in effect satisfied the boundary conditions, for we are assured that each of the eigenfunctions (2.29) will remain continuous and smooth as it passes out of the well and dies exponentially in the potential barrier. Only n, the principal quantum number, continues to be arbitrary; and, of course, specifying this is equivalent to specifying one eigenfunction to decribe the particle's motion.

[12] Courant, R., and D. Hilbert, *Methods of Mathematical Physics*, Vol. 1, 1st English edition, pp. 91–93, Interscience, New York, 1963.

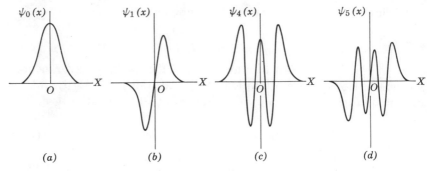

Fig. 6.21

In particular, when n is given the energy of the particle is determined. From (2.5), (2.6), and (2.21) we see that

$$E = \frac{\hbar^2}{2m}\gamma = \frac{\hbar^2}{2m}(2n+1)\alpha = \frac{\hbar^2}{2m}(2n+1)\frac{\sqrt{mK}}{\hbar} = (n+\tfrac{1}{2})\frac{h}{2\pi}\sqrt{\frac{K}{m}} = E_n$$

(2.35)

or, setting

$$\frac{1}{2\pi}\sqrt{\frac{K}{m}} = \frac{\omega}{2\pi} = \nu$$

(2.36)

in line with the classical definition of oscillation frequency (Fig. 3.7),

$$E_n = (n+\tfrac{1}{2})h\nu \qquad \{n = 0, 1, 2, 3, \dots .$$

(2.37)

Thus, the energy levels that may be occupied by a quantum harmonic oscillator are as shown in Fig. 6.22, where E_0 is the energy eigenvalue of ψ_0, E_1 that of ψ_1, and so on. Contrary to a classical oscillator of the same kind, it can have none of the energies in between and must change discretely from one step to another if it gains or loses energy, although it can never have less than the amount $h\nu/2$.

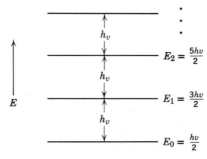

Fig. 6.22

It is also instructive to compare a typical position probability distribution which follows from this solution with the corresponding classical distribution. For example, using (2.34), $|\psi_1(x)|^2$ is easily seen to be

$$|\psi_1|^2 = 2\left(\frac{\alpha^3}{\pi}\right)^{1/2} x^2 e^{-\alpha x^2}, \tag{2.38}$$

whereas classically we know from (2.29) of Chapter 3 that the motion must be bounded by

$$x = \pm\sqrt{\frac{2E}{K}},$$

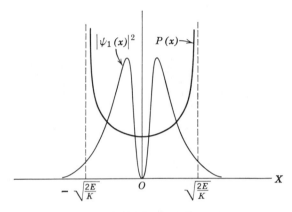

Fig. 6.23

and intuition tells us that the probability $P(x)$ of finding the mass at some particular x will be small at $x = 0$ and large near these limits. It is not difficult to prove that

$$P(x) = \frac{1}{\pi\left(\dfrac{2E}{K} - x^2\right)^{1/2}}. \tag{2.39}$$

Superimposed plots of (2.38) and (2.39) are illustrated in Fig. 6.23.

We see that, in accordance with our earlier results, a finite probability exists that the particle may be found in the classically forbidden region where V is greater than E. Also, Fig. 6.23 makes it appear that the quantum oscillator is most likely to be found in regions where the classical oscillator is least likely to be found. However, as n increases it soon becomes apparent that the classical probability curve represents an increasingly accurate average of the quantum curve (Fig. 6.24).

This constitutes another application of the correspondence principle and, in fact, suggests a way in which approximate wave functions can be obtained. When the energy of the particle is high, as must be the case if n is large, its wavelength must be small; this follows from the fact that $E = h\nu$ and $\nu = c/\lambda$, making λ inversely proportional to E. It can be shown by analogy with geometrical optics[13] that, in a region where the potential $V(x)$ changes smoothly and slowly relative to the wave function, the latter can be approximated quite well by the expression

$$\psi(x) = \phi(x)e^{\pm\frac{i}{\hbar}\int p_x\, dx} \tag{2.40}$$

where ϕ is some slowly varying function of x.

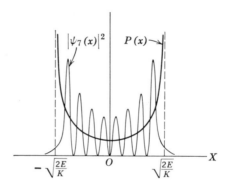

Fig. 6.24

Since the original equation of motion (2.4) is of the form

$$\frac{d^2\psi}{dx^2} + \frac{2m}{\hbar^2}[E - V(x)]\psi = 0, \tag{2.41}$$

with

$$p_x = \sqrt{2m[E - V(x)]} \tag{2.42}$$

it may be written as

$$\frac{d^2\psi}{dx^2} + \left(\frac{p_x}{\hbar}\right)^2\psi = 0. \tag{2.43}$$

Substitution of (2.40) leads to a required form for $\phi(x)$:

$$-\left(\frac{\hbar}{p_x}\right)\frac{d^2\phi}{dx^2} \pm 2i\frac{d\phi}{dx} \pm i\frac{\phi}{p_x}\frac{dp_x}{dx} = 0 \tag{2.44}$$

[13] Powell, J. L., and B. Crasemann, *Quantum Mechanics*, pp. 89–95, Addison-Wesley, Reading, Mass., 1961.

or, with $\lambda = h/p_x$ very small as assumed,

$$\frac{2}{\phi}\frac{d\phi}{dx} + \frac{1}{p_x}\frac{dp_x}{dx} = 0, \tag{2.45}$$

the solution of which is

$$\phi = Cp_x^{-\frac{1}{2}}, \tag{2.46}$$

C being an arbitrary constant.

We conclude that

$$\psi = Cp_x^{-\frac{1}{2}}e^{\pm\frac{i}{\hbar}\int p_x dx} \tag{2.47}$$

should be an approximate wave function under the conditions stated; it is called the Wentzel-Kramers-Brillouin (or just WKB) approximation. Though it obviously cannot hold in classical regions where the momentum p_x goes to zero, as near the limits of motion for an oscillator, it is nevertheless very useful for dealing with cases where the shape of the potential is not simple.[14] For example, when $V > E$, (2.47) becomes

$$\psi = \{2m[E - V(x)]\}^{-\frac{1}{4}}\left\{Ae^{\frac{1}{\hbar}\int\sqrt{2m[V(x)-E]}\,dx} + Be^{-\frac{1}{\hbar}\int\sqrt{2m[V(x)-E]}\,dx}\right\} \tag{2.48}$$

where A and B now represent arbitrary constants. It is evident that if $V \gg E$, so that $[V(x) - E] \simeq V(x)$, this expression must depend critically on the negative exponential only,

$$e^{-\frac{1}{\hbar}\int\sqrt{2mV(x)}\,dx}. \tag{2.49}$$

Hence, if $V(x) = Kx^2/2$ as in (2.1), we obtain the asymptotic form (2.11) for $\psi(x)$ directly.

The method of solution developed for the quantum oscillator is the key to understanding a solution of even more importance in quantum mechanics: that for the motion of an electron in a hydrogenlike atom. In this case the electron is bound by an inverse square Coulomb force and, consequently moves in a potential well described by the function

$$V(r) = -\frac{Ze^2}{r} \tag{2.50}$$

where Z is the atomic number, e the electronic charge, and r the distance separating the nucleus and the electron at any time. For hydrogen itself, $Z = 1$ and the system consists of a single proton at the origin of coordinates with one electron moving around it (Fig. 6.25), spherical

---

[14] Bohm, D., *Quantum Theory*, pp. 264–298, Prentice-Hall, Englewood Cliffs, N.J. 1958.

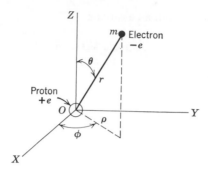

Fig. 6.25

coordinates being suggested by the form of the potential. For more complicated atoms, a positive ion with Z protons in the nucleus and $Z - 1$
electrons surrounding it may be imagined to replace the proton at O;
by this means the solution may be extended across the entire periodic table
of the elements.

The mass of even one proton is so much greater that the mass of an
electron that it is reasonable to assume the former will not move. In
other words, the problem to be solved is the quantum analog of the two-
body central-force problem studied in detail earlier [(3.1) to (3.29) in
Chapter 3]. We saw then that the potential could be represented one-
dimensionally as shown in Fig. 6.26, where the constant B could have a
value similar to that required in (2.50).

The reference line for the particle energy E is shown on this figure to
emphasize the fact that we will concentrate on the case in which the
particle remains bound to the nucleus. It would be possible, of course, to
analyze the motion of a particle which eventually escapes merely by

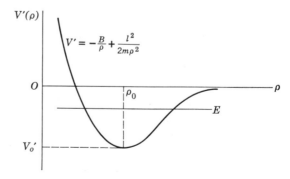

Fig. 6.26

assigning it a higher energy. It is also possible to start with a general two-body problem [(3.98) to (3.111) of Chapter 3] and end up with two equations of motion—one describing the movement of the center of mass of the complete atom with respect to a fixed origin, and one describing the movement of a fictitious mass

$$\mu = \frac{m_{\text{electron}} m_{\text{nucleus}}}{(m_{\text{electron}} + m_{\text{nucleus}})} \tag{2.51}$$

with respect to the nucleus.[15] But since for our assumption, $m_{\text{nucleus}} \gg m_{\text{electron}}$,

$$\mu \rightarrow m_{\text{electron}} = m, \tag{2.52}$$

we shall not trouble to do so.

Instead, suppressing time dependence and noting that, because

$$E = \frac{p^2}{2m} - \frac{Ze^2}{r}, \tag{2.53}$$

$$H = -\frac{\hbar^2}{2m} \nabla^2 - \frac{Ze^2}{r}, \tag{2.54}$$

we shall immediately write the governing Schrödinger equation as

$$\nabla^2 \psi + \frac{2m}{\hbar^2} \left(E + \frac{Ze^2}{r} \right) \psi = 0 \tag{2.55}$$

or, using the expression given in (2.146) of Chapter 4 for ∇^2, as:

$$\frac{1}{r^2} \frac{\partial}{\partial r} \left(r^2 \frac{\partial}{\partial r} \psi \right) + \frac{1}{r^2 \sin \theta} \frac{\partial}{\partial \theta} \left(\sin \theta \frac{\partial \psi}{\partial \theta} \right)$$

$$+ \frac{1}{r^2 \sin^2 \theta} \frac{\partial^2 \psi}{\partial \phi^2} + \frac{2m}{\hbar^2} \left(E - \frac{Ze^2}{r} \right) \psi = 0 \tag{2.56}$$

Now, if we assume $\psi(r, \theta, \phi)$ to have the particular form

$$\psi = R(r)\Theta(\theta)\Phi(\phi) \tag{2.57}$$

in the way developed before (Section 4.2), substitution in (2.56) and division by $R\Theta\Phi$ will yield:

$$\frac{1}{Rr^2} \frac{d}{dr} \left(r^2 \frac{dR}{dr} \right) + \frac{1}{\Theta r^2 \sin \theta} \frac{d}{d\theta} \left(\sin \theta \frac{d\Theta}{d\theta} \right) + \frac{1}{\Phi r^2 \sin^2 \theta} \frac{d^2\Phi}{d\phi^2}$$

$$+ \frac{2m}{\hbar^2} \left(E - \frac{Ze^2}{r} \right) = 0 \tag{2.58}$$

[15] Pauling, L., and E. B. Wilson, *Introduction to Quantum Mechanics*, pp. 112–115, McGraw-Hill, New York, 1935.

But multiplication by $r^2 \sin^2 \theta$ will reduce the third term to a function of ϕ only. Since this must then be equal to a sum of terms that are independent of ϕ, both it and they must be equal to the same constant, say $-\alpha^2$:

$$\frac{1}{\Phi} \frac{d^2\Phi}{d\phi^2} = -\alpha^2 \tag{2.59}$$

$$-\frac{\sin^2 \theta}{R} \frac{d}{dr}\left(r^2 \frac{dR}{dr}\right) - \frac{\sin \theta}{\Theta} \frac{d}{d\theta}\left(\sin \theta \frac{d\Theta}{d\theta}\right)$$

$$-(r^2 \sin^2 \theta) \frac{2m}{\hbar^2}\left(E - \frac{Ze^2}{r}\right) = -\alpha^2 \tag{2.60}$$

Furthermore, division of the last equation by $-\sin^2 \theta$ produces

$$\frac{1}{R} \frac{d}{dr}\left(r^2 \frac{dR}{dr}\right) + r^2 \frac{2m}{\hbar^2}\left(E - \frac{Ze^2}{r}\right) + \frac{1}{\Theta \sin \theta} \frac{d}{d\theta}\left(\sin \theta \frac{d\Theta}{d\theta}\right) - \frac{\alpha^2}{\sin^2 \theta} = 0, \tag{2.61}$$

the first two terms of which are independent of θ, whereas the second two terms are independent of r. Thus, equating the parts to each other and the constant $-\beta^2$, we obtain:

$$\frac{1}{\Theta \sin \theta} \frac{d}{d\theta}\left(\sin \theta \frac{d\Theta}{d\theta}\right) - \frac{\alpha^2}{\sin^2 \theta} = -\beta^2 \tag{2.62}$$

$$\frac{1}{R} \frac{d}{dr}\left(r^2 \frac{dR}{dr}\right) + r^2 \frac{2m}{\hbar^2}\left(E - \frac{Ze^2}{r}\right) = \beta^2 \tag{2.63}$$

The three second order ordinary differential equations (2.59), (2.62), and (2.63) are fully equivalent to the second order partial differential equation (2.56) under the assumption (2.57). Therefore, we may solve them separately and be certain that the product of their solutions will be the required ψ-function.

The solutions of (2.59),

$$\frac{d^2\Phi}{d\phi^2} + \alpha^2\Phi = 0,$$

can be written down directly; they are

$$\Phi = e^{\pm i\alpha\phi}. \tag{2.64}$$

But these will be single-valued, such that

$$\Phi(0) = \Phi(2\pi), \tag{2.65}$$

and thus capable of entering into an acceptable wave function, only if

$$\pm\alpha = 0, 1, 2, \ldots. \tag{2.66}$$

Moreover, the normalization requirement

$$\int_0^{2\pi} \Phi^*\Phi \, d\phi = 1 \tag{2.67}$$

leads immediately to the conclusion that the constants to be associated with these solutions are

$$C = \frac{1}{\sqrt{2\pi}} . \tag{2.68}$$

The final solutions must be:

$$\Phi = \frac{1}{\sqrt{2\pi}} e^{i\alpha\phi} \qquad \{\alpha = 0, \pm 1, \pm 2, \ldots \tag{2.69}$$

Equation (2.62),

$$\frac{1}{\Theta \sin\theta} \frac{d}{d\theta}\left(\sin\theta \frac{d\Theta}{d\theta}\right) - \frac{\alpha^2}{\sin^2\theta} + \beta^2 = 0,$$

can be solved by the same general method as the equation for the quantum oscillator [(2.4) to (2.37)]; this is demonstrated in Problem 6.2(3). However, to simplify, the trial solution comparable to (2.15) can be written as

$$\Theta = \sin^{|\alpha|}\theta \, (a_0 + a_1 \cos\theta + a_2 \cos^2\theta + \cdots), \tag{2.70}$$

and the recursion relation which is ultimately obtained then has the form

$$a_\nu = \frac{(\nu + |\alpha| - 1)(\nu + |\alpha| - 2) - \beta^2}{\nu(\nu - 1)} a_{\nu-2}. \tag{2.71}$$

The resulting series will diverge as $\cos\theta \to 1$. However, if we place

$$\nu = \gamma - |\alpha| + 2, \tag{2.72}$$

where γ represents any integer, (2.71) yields

$$a_{\gamma-|\alpha|+2} = \frac{(\gamma - |\alpha| + 2 + |\alpha| - 1)(\gamma - |\alpha| + 2 + |\alpha| - 2) - \beta^2}{(\gamma - |\alpha| + 2)(\gamma - |\alpha| + 2 - 1)} a_{\gamma-|\alpha|}$$

$$= \frac{(\gamma + 1)\gamma - \beta^2}{(\gamma - |\alpha| + 2)(\gamma - |\alpha| + 1)} a_{\gamma-|\alpha|}; \tag{2.73}$$

and it becomes apparent that, if

$$\beta^2 = \gamma(\gamma + 1), \tag{2.74}$$

the last nonvanishing coefficient will be that for which

$$\nu = \gamma - |\alpha|. \tag{2.75}$$

As before in (2.22) and (2.23), we must place $a_1 = 0$ if $\gamma - |\alpha|$ is even and $a_0 = 0$ if it is odd to be certain that the series will terminate.

Analogously to the use of the Hermite polynomials (2.24) earlier, all of these requirements may be met by using the associated Legendre functions of order $|\alpha|$ and degree γ. They are indicated by the symbol $P_\gamma^{|\alpha|} (\cos \theta)$ and may be calculated from the formula[16]

$$P_\gamma^{|\alpha|}(\cos \theta) = \frac{1}{2^\gamma \gamma!} \sin^{|\alpha|} \theta \, \frac{d^{|\alpha|+\gamma}}{d \cos \theta^{|\alpha|+\gamma}} (\cos^2 \theta - 1)^\gamma. \qquad (2.76)$$

It follows that the solutions of (2.62), with β^2 given by (2.74), may be expressed in the following way:

$$\Theta = BP_\gamma^{|\alpha|}(\cos \theta) \qquad \{\gamma = |\alpha|, |\alpha| + 1, |\alpha| + 2, \ldots \qquad (2.77)$$

where the restriction on γ follows from (2.75) and the fact that it must be an integer. By normalizing in the usual way the constant B can be shown to have the value

$$B = \sqrt{\frac{(2\gamma + 1)(\gamma - |\alpha|)!}{2(\gamma + |\alpha|)!}} . \qquad (2.78)$$

Equation (2.63) can also be solved by a series approximation. If we make the replacement suggested by (2.74) and multiply through by R/r^2, the equation takes the form:

$$\frac{1}{r^2} \frac{d}{dr}\left(r^2 \frac{dR}{dr}\right) + \left[-\frac{\gamma(\gamma + 1)}{r^2} + \frac{2m}{\hbar^2}\left(E - \frac{Ze^2}{r}\right)\right] R = 0. \qquad (2.79)$$

This being the equation that determines the radial part of the wave function, it is convenient to transform to the positive variable

$$\rho = 2\eta r \qquad (2.80)$$

with η representing a constant defined below. Using

$$S(\rho) = R(r), \qquad (2.81)$$

(2.79) becomes:

$$\frac{1}{\rho^2} \frac{d}{d\rho}\left(\rho^2 \frac{dS}{d\rho}\right) + \left[-\frac{\gamma(\gamma + 1)}{\rho^2} + \frac{2m}{\hbar^2} \frac{E}{4\eta^2} + \frac{m}{\hbar^2} \frac{Ze^2}{\eta\rho}\right] S = 0. \qquad (2.82)$$

Hence, if we set

$$\eta = \frac{\sqrt{2m(-E)}}{\hbar} \quad \text{or} \quad E = -\frac{\eta^2\hbar^2}{2m}, \qquad (2.83)$$

[16] Abramowitz, M., and I. A. Stegun, *Handbook of Mathematical Functions*, pp. 331–357, Dover, New York, 1965.

where the minus sign is inserted to assure that the electron will remain bound to the nucleus, together with

$$\frac{mZe^2}{h^2\eta} = \delta, \tag{2.84}$$

the equation of motion to be solved reduces to:

$$\frac{1}{\rho^2}\frac{d}{d\rho}\left(\rho^2\frac{dS}{d\rho}\right) + \left[-\frac{\gamma(\gamma+1)}{\rho^2} - \frac{1}{4} + \frac{\delta}{\rho}\right]S = 0 \tag{2.85}$$

Expanding the first term, we may rewrite this as

$$\frac{d^2S}{d\rho^2} + \frac{2}{\rho}\frac{dS}{d\rho} - \frac{\gamma(\gamma+1)}{\rho^2}S + \frac{\delta}{\rho}S - \frac{S}{4} = 0; \tag{2.86}$$

so it is apparent that, for ρ very large, the asymptotic form will be

$$\frac{d^2S}{d\rho^2} - \frac{S}{4} = 0. \tag{2.87}$$

Equation (2.87) obviously has the solutions

$$S = e^{\pm\rho/2}, \tag{2.88}$$

but only the negative exponential can enter into a satisfactory wave function. Thus if, as for the quantum oscillator (2.15), we assume a solution of the form

$$S = Ae^{-\rho/2}F_\mu(\rho), \tag{2.89}$$

where

$$F_\mu(\rho) = \rho^\gamma(b_0 + b_1\rho + b_2\rho^2 + \cdots), \tag{2.90}$$

and substitute this back into the differential equation (2.86), a recursion relation defining the coefficients of the series will be obtained; it is:[17]

$$b_\mu = \frac{(\gamma+\mu) - \delta}{(\gamma+\mu)(\gamma+\mu+1) - \gamma(\gamma+1)}b_{\mu-1} \tag{2.91}$$

Again the series must be terminated to avoid divergence, and this can evidently be accomplished by requiring that

$$\delta = \gamma + \mu. \tag{2.92}$$

The power series in ρ which satisfies the recursion relation (2.91) and the added condition (2.92) reduces to the $(2\gamma + 1)$th derivative of

---

[17] Slater, J. C., *Quantum Theory of Atomic Structure*, Vol. 1, pp. 170–177, McGraw-Hill, New York, 1960.

another well-known set of orthogonal polynomials—the Laguerre poly-nomials[18] of degree $\delta + \gamma$, $L_{\delta+\gamma}(\rho)$. The resulting functions can be calcul-ated from the formula

$$L_{\delta+\gamma}^{2\gamma+1}(\rho) = \frac{d^{2\gamma+1}}{d\rho^{2\gamma+1}}\left[e^\rho \frac{d^{\delta+\gamma}}{d\rho^{\delta+\gamma}} (\rho^{\delta+\gamma}e^{-\rho})\right]. \qquad (2.93)$$

Applying these results, we see that the solution of (2.79) can be expressed in the following way:

$$R = Ae^{-\rho/2}\rho^\gamma L_{\delta+\gamma}^{2\gamma+1}(\rho) \qquad \{\delta = \gamma + 1, \gamma + 2, \ldots \qquad (2.94)$$

where

$$\rho = 2\eta r = \frac{\sqrt{8m(-E)}}{\hbar} r. \qquad (2.95)$$

The normalization constant can be shown to have the value

$$A = -\sqrt{\left(\frac{2me^2Z}{\hbar^2\delta}\right)^3 \frac{(\delta - \gamma - 1)!}{2\delta(\delta + \gamma)!^3}}. \qquad (2.96)$$

We now have the solutions of (2.56) which have the form

$$\psi = R(r)\Theta(\theta)\Phi(\phi);$$

they are represented by (2.94) and (2.95),

$$R = Ae^{-\rho/2}\rho^\gamma L_{\delta+\gamma}^{2\gamma+1}(\rho)$$

where

$$\delta = \gamma + 1, \gamma + 2, \ldots$$

and

$$\rho = \frac{\sqrt{8m(-E)}}{\hbar} r,$$

by (2.77),

$$\Theta = BP_\gamma^{|\alpha|}(\cos \theta)$$

where

$$\gamma = |\alpha|, |\alpha| + 1, |\alpha| + 2, \ldots,$$

and by (2.69),

$$\Phi = Ce^{i\alpha\phi}$$

where

$$\alpha = 0, \pm1, \pm2, \ldots.$$

Of course, the normalization constants A, B, and C are defined by (2.96), (2.78), and (2.68), while the standard functions $L_{\delta+\gamma}^{2\gamma+1}(\rho)$ and $P_\gamma^{|\alpha|}$ $(\cos \theta)$

[18] Abramowitz, M., and I. A. Stegun, *Handbook of Mathematical Functions*, pp. 509, 778, Dover, New York, 1965.

are given by (2.93) and (2.76). It only remains to interpret the integers α, γ, and δ from the physical point of view.

The one whose meaning is the easiest to understand is δ, for it is evident from the equations by which it was originally defined that it is closely related to the energy of the particle. Squaring (2.84) and substituting for η from (2.83), we see that $-E$ is, in fact, inversely proportional to δ_2:

$$\delta^2 = -\frac{m^2 Z^2 e^4}{\hbar^4 \dfrac{2mE}{\hbar^2}} = -\frac{m Z^2 e^4}{2\hbar^2 E},$$

$$-E = \left(\frac{m Z^2 e^4}{2\hbar^2}\right)\frac{1}{\delta^2}. \tag{2.97}$$

This suggests that we should interpret δ as the principal quantum number n to be consistent with our earlier usage of the term,

$$\delta = n \qquad \{n = 1, 2, 3, \ldots \tag{2.98}$$

To understand the physical meaning of α and γ it is necessary to examine the eigenequations involving the z-component of angular momentum and total angular momentum operators, L_z and L^2. We know from Section 5.3 that these two operators commute; therefore, it is possible for the same eigenfunction $\psi(r, \theta, \phi)$ to satisfy both equations:

$$L_z\psi = l_{0_z}\psi \tag{2.99}$$

$$L^2\psi = l_0^2\psi \tag{2.100}$$

where the angular momentum itself is indicated by l_0.

The operator L_z is defined in rectangular coordinates by (2.53) of Chapter 5; and transformed to spherical coordinates, it becomes

$$L_z = \frac{\hbar}{i}\frac{\partial}{\partial\phi}. \tag{2.101}$$

Consequently, (2.99) expands to

$$\frac{\partial\psi}{\partial\phi} + \frac{l_{0_z}}{i\hbar}\psi = 0, \tag{2.102}$$

which evidently has solutions of the form

$$\psi = \Gamma(r, \theta)\Phi(\phi), \tag{2.103}$$

providing Φ satisfies the ordinary differential equation

$$\frac{d\Phi}{d\phi} + \frac{l_{0_z}}{i\hbar}\Phi = 0. \tag{2.104}$$

The solution of (2.104) is

$$\Phi = \text{constant } e^{i\frac{l_{0_z}}{\hbar}\phi};\tag{2.105}$$

and comparison of this result with (2.69),

$$\Phi = \frac{1}{\sqrt{2\pi}}e^{i\alpha\phi}\qquad \{\alpha = 0, \pm1, \pm2, \ldots,$$

forces us to the conclusion that

$$\alpha = \frac{l_{0_z}}{\hbar}.\tag{2.106}$$

In other words, the eigenvalues of the z-component of the particle's angular momentum must be $0, \pm\hbar, \pm2\hbar, \ldots$; the integer α represents the physical requirement that l_{0_z} be quantized. Because the z-component of the angular momentum of an electron moving about an atomic nucleus is closely related to the magnetic properties of the atom,[19] it is customary to call α the magnetic quantum number and designate it by m_l,

$$\alpha = m_l\qquad \{m_l = 0, \pm1, \pm2, \ldots.\tag{2.107}$$

Similarly, when the operator L^2 is transformed into spherical coordinates it becomes

$$L^2 = -\hbar^2\left[\frac{1}{\sin\theta}\frac{\partial}{\partial\theta}\left(\sin\theta\frac{\partial}{\partial\theta}\right) + \frac{1}{\sin^2\theta}\frac{\partial^2}{\partial\phi^2}\right].\tag{2.108}$$

Thus, by writing out (2.100) we obtain:

$$\left[\frac{1}{\sin\Theta}\frac{\partial}{\partial\theta}\left(\sin\theta\frac{\partial}{\partial\theta}\right) + \frac{1}{\sin^2\theta}\frac{\partial^2}{\partial\phi^2}\right]\psi + \frac{l_0^2}{\hbar^2}\psi = 0\tag{2.109}$$

This, clearly has solutions of the form

$$\psi = R(r)\Theta(\theta)\Phi(\phi)\tag{2.110}$$

where, from above, Φ is given by the functions

$$\Phi = e^{im_l\phi}\qquad \{m_l = 0, \pm1, \pm2, \ldots,\tag{2.111}$$

provided Θ satisfies the following ordinary differential equation:

$$\frac{1}{\Theta\sin\theta}\frac{d}{d\theta}\left(\sin\theta\frac{d\Theta}{d\theta}\right) - \frac{m_l^2}{\sin^2\theta} + \frac{l_0^2}{\hbar^2} = 0\tag{2.112}$$

[19] Eisberg, R. M., *Fundamentals of Modern Physics*, pp. 327–338, Wiley, New York, 1961.

With m_l replacing α as in (2.107), and with

$$\beta^2 = \frac{l_0^{\,2}}{\hbar^2},\tag{2.113}$$

this is exactly the same as (2.62). But we also know from (2.74) that

$$\beta^2 = \gamma(\gamma + 1);$$

therefore,

$$\gamma(\gamma + 1) = \frac{l_0^{\,2}}{\hbar^2}.\tag{2.114}$$

Evidently the fact that γ must be an integer represents a quantizing condition imposed on the total angular momentum of the particle. Thus γ is called the angular momentum quantum number and assigned the special symbol l,

$$\gamma = l \qquad \{l = 0, 1, 2, \ldots.\tag{2.115}$$

By making use of these results, our solutions may now be summarized in the following way:

$$\psi_{n l m_l} = R_{nl}(r)\Theta_{l m_l}(\theta)\Phi_{m_l}(\phi)\tag{2.116}$$

where

$$R_{nl} = A e^{-\frac{\rho}{2}}\rho^l L_{n+l}^{2l+1}(\rho), \qquad \rho = \frac{\sqrt{8m(-E)}}{\hbar}\,r\tag{2.117}$$

$$\Theta_{l m_l} = B P_l^{|m_l|}(\cos\theta)\tag{2.118}$$

$$\Phi_{m_l} = C e^{i m_l \phi}\tag{2.119}$$

and

$$n = 1, 2, 3, \ldots\tag{2.120}$$

$$l = 0, 1, 2, \ldots, n - 1\tag{2.121}$$

$$m_l = 0, \pm 1, \pm 2, \ldots, l\tag{2.122}$$

The latter restrictions on the quantum numbers follow directly from the requirements $\gamma = |\alpha|, |\alpha| + 1, |\alpha| + 2, \ldots$ and $\delta = \gamma + 1, \gamma + 2, \ldots$, first expressed in (2.77) and (2.94), when it is recognized that $\alpha = m_l$, $\gamma = l$, and $\delta = n$. The derivatives of the Laguerre polynomials, $L_{n+l}^{2l+1}(\rho)$, and the associated Legendre functions, $P_l^{|m_l|}(\cos\theta)$, can be calculated from (2.93) and (2.76) by making these same identifications, while (2.96), (2.78), and (2.68) will give the proper values of the normalization constants A, B, and C.

The eigenvalues of the problem follow from (2.97), (2.114), and (2.106):

$$E = -\left(\frac{mZ^2 e^4}{2\hbar^2}\right)\frac{1}{n^2},$$

or in terms of the radius of the smallest Bohr orbit [Problem 3.3(2)]

$$a_0 = \frac{\hbar^2}{me^2},$$

$$E = -\frac{1}{n^2}\left(\frac{Z^2 e^2}{2a_0}\right) \tag{2.123}$$

with

$$l_0 = \sqrt{l(l+1)}\,\hbar \tag{2.124}$$

and

$$l_{0_z} = m_l \hbar. \tag{2.125}$$

Of course the values that n, l, and m_l can have are restricted in the manner indicated by (2.120) to (2.122).

From the expressions (2.116) to (2.122) the eigenfunctions can be calculated; those for $n = 1$ and $n = 2$ only are listed below, though they have been tabulated through relatively large values of n:[20]

$$n = 1, \quad \text{therefore} \quad l = 0 \quad \text{and} \quad m_l = 0$$

$$\psi_{100} = \frac{1}{\sqrt{\pi}}\left(\frac{Z}{a_0}\right)^{3/2} e^{-\frac{Z}{a_0} r} \tag{2.126}$$

$$n = 2, \quad \text{therefore,} \quad l = 0, 1 \quad \text{and} \quad m_l = 0, +1, -1$$

$$\psi_{200} = \frac{1}{4\sqrt{2\pi}}\left(\frac{Z}{a_0}\right)^{3/2}\left(2 - \frac{Z}{a_0} r\right) e^{-\frac{Z}{2a_0} r} \tag{2.127}$$

$$\psi_{210} = \frac{1}{4\sqrt{2\pi}}\left(\frac{Z}{a_0}\right)^{5/2} r e^{-\frac{Z}{2a_0} r} \cos\theta \tag{2.128}$$

$$\psi_{211} = \frac{1}{4\sqrt{2\pi}}\left(\frac{Z}{a_0}\right)^{5/2} r e^{-\frac{Z}{2a_0} r} \sin\theta \cos\phi \tag{2.129}$$

$$\psi_{21-1} = \frac{1}{4\sqrt{2\pi}}\left(\frac{Z}{a_0}\right)^{5/2} r e^{-\frac{Z}{2a_0} r} \sin\theta \sin\phi \tag{2.130}$$

If n were equal to 3, then l could be 0, 1, and 2, while m_l could have the values 0, +1, −1, +2, and −2; nine wave functions would then be possible: ψ_{300}, ψ_{310}, ψ_{311}, ψ_{31-1}, ψ_{320}, ψ_{321}, ψ_{32-1}, ψ_{322}, and ψ_{32-2}. It will be noted that the number of wave functions increases as n^2. In every case when $l = 0$,

[20] Pauling, L., and E. B. Wilson, *Introduction to Quantum Mechanics*, pp. 132–146, McGraw-Hill, New York, 1935.

so that $m_l = 0$, all angular dependence vanishes and the resulting wave function is spherically symmetrical.

The wave functions (2.127) to (2.130) can easily be plotted, but instead it is customary to plot the radial position probability density associated with each:

$$|\psi_{nlm_l}|^2 \, 4\pi r^2 \qquad (2.131)$$

Since, if terms involving products of differentials are neglected, the volume between two spherical shells of radius r and $r + dr$ is approximately $4\pi r^2 \, dr$, the total probability that the electron will be found in such a region is just

$$|\psi_{nlm_l}|^2 \, 4\pi r^2 \, dr. \qquad (2.132)$$

Therefore, the resulting curves provide a picture of the relative frequency with which the electron will occupy each r-position about the atomic core. They replace the definite orbits of classical mechanics and, for this reason, are called atomic orbitals. Those corresponding to the functions

$$|\psi_{100}|^2 = \frac{1}{\pi a_0{}^3} e^{-\frac{2}{a_0} r}, \qquad (2.133)$$

$$|\psi_{200}|^2 = \frac{1}{32\pi a_0{}^3} \left(2 - \frac{r}{a_0}\right)^2 e^{-\frac{r}{a_0}}, \qquad (2.134)$$

and

$$\left|\psi_{210}\right|^2_{\theta=0} = \frac{1}{32\pi a_0{}^5} r^2 e^{-\frac{r}{a_0}} \qquad (2.135)$$

for the case of $Z = 1$ are illustrated in Figs. 6.27, 6.28, and 6.29.

Figure 6.27 emphasizes the fact that the lowest Bohr orbit ($n = 1$) is merely the most probable position for a real electron; there is a finite probability that it may be found a considerable distance on either side of this orbit. When $n = 2$, instead of occupying a circular orbit with the radius $4a_0$, or an elliptical orbit of the type proposed by Sommerfeld [Problem 3.3(3)], the behavior of the electron is much more complex. If the angular momentum quantum number l is zero, it will most probably be found in a circular orbit with the radius $5a_0$; however, there is a smaller peak probability that it may be found in the lowest Bohr orbit, and a positive probability that it may be found anywhere in this vicinity except at $r = 2a_0$.

On the other hand, when $l \neq 0$ but $m_l = 0$, the probability density will vanish at the XY-plane (where $\cos \theta = 0$) and increase to a maximum along the Z-axis (where $\cos \theta = 1$) at $r = 4a_0$. If $m_l \neq 0$, it will vanish at the Z-axis (where $\sin \theta = 0$) and peak at $r = 4a_0$ in the XY-plane (where

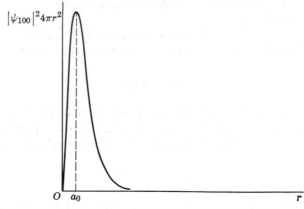

Fig. 6.27

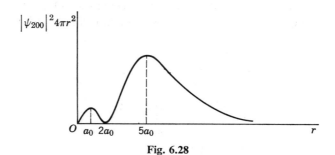

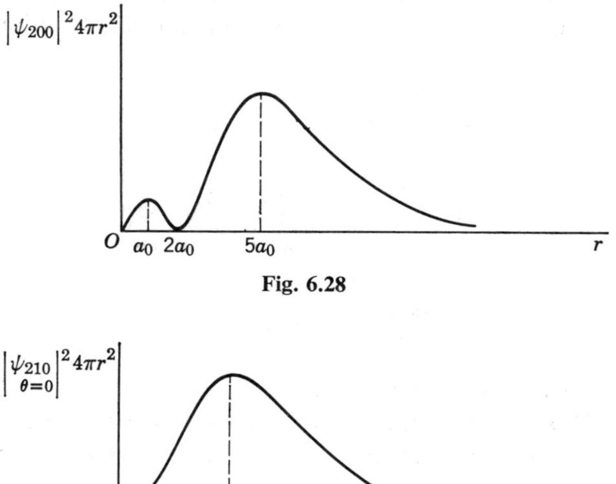

Fig. 6.28

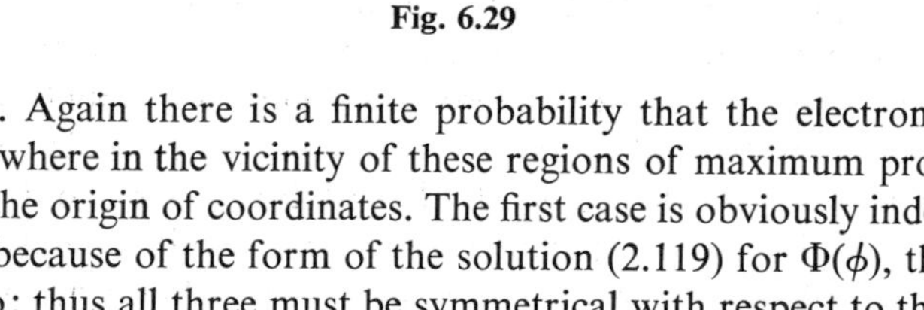

$$\left|\psi_{210}\right|^2_{\theta=0} 4\pi r^2$$

Fig. 6.29

$\sin \theta = 1$). Again there is a finite probability that the electron may be found anywhere in the vicinity of these regions of maximum probability, except at the origin of coordinates. The first case is obviously independent of ϕ, but because of the form of the solution (2.119) for $\Phi(\phi)$, the others will be too; thus all three must be symmetrical with respect to the Z-axis.

These same facts may be represented more pictorially by constructing three-dimensional probability "clouds," whose density is everywhere proportional to the probability of finding the electron there. Figures 6.27 to

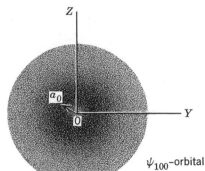

Fig. 6.30

6.29, in effect, constitute profiles of the density variation along selected radial directions in such clouds. In a cross section cut by the YZ-plane, the spherical cloud represented by (2.133) and Fig. 6.27 would appear as shown in Fig. 6.30. A similar cross section through the spherical cloud described by (2.134) and Fig. 6.28 would appear as shown in Fig. 6.31.

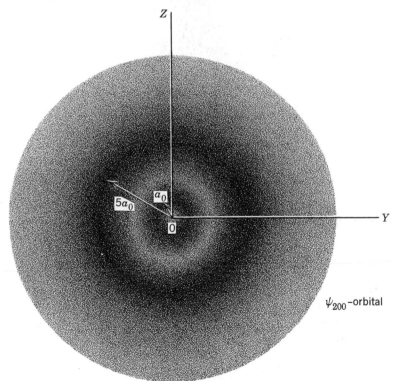

Fig. 6.31

However, the nonspherical cloud indicated by the general form of (2.135),

$$|\psi_{210}|^2 = \frac{1}{32\pi a_0{}^5} r^2 e^{-\frac{r}{a_0}} \cos^2 \theta,\tag{2.136}$$

and Fig. 6.29 consists of two egg-shaped lobes symmetrical with respect to the Z-axis; a corresponding cross section is shown in Fig. 6.32.

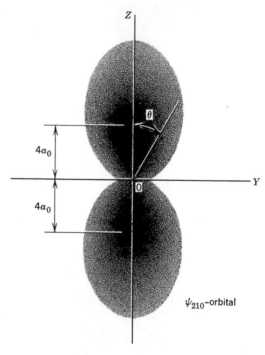

Fig. 6.32

The orbital that follows from (2.129),

$$|\psi_{211}|^2 = \frac{1}{32\pi a_0{}^5} r^2 e^{-\frac{r}{a_0}} \sin^2 \theta,\tag{2.137}$$

represents a cloud which resembles that of Fig. 6.32 in cross section but is, in fact, doughnut-shaped and symmetrical with respect to the XY-plane as well as to the Z-axis (Fig. 6.33). The ψ_{21-1}-orbital cloud looks exactly the same, because

$$|\psi_{21-1}|^2 = \frac{1}{32\pi a_0{}^5} r^2 e^{-\frac{r}{a_0}} \sin^2 \theta \tag{2.138}$$

just as in (2.137), but it must be associated with a particle rotating in an opposite sense about the Z-axis.

This fact may be demonstrated by constructing a vector diagram of the angular momentum for the case under consideration:

$$l = 1, \quad m_l = 0, +1, -1 \tag{2.139}$$

We know from (2.125) that the z-component of the angular momentum

$$l_{0_z} = m_l \hbar;$$

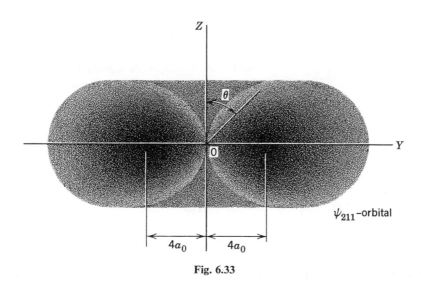

ψ_{211}-orbital

Fig. 6.33

and let us suppose for a moment that the angular momentum itself, instead of being given by (2.124),

$$l_0 = \sqrt{l(l+1)}\hbar,$$

is given by

$$l_0 = l\hbar. \tag{2.140}$$

Then it is easy to see that there are only three possible orientations of the angular momentum vector (Fig. 6.34). Clearly, the horizontal vector, which may point any direction in the XY-plane, is to be associated with the ψ_{210}-cloud of Fig. 6.32; whereas the vertical vectors relate to Fig. 6.33.

Following the right-hand screw rule, the ψ_{211}-orbital must represent clockwise circulation about the Z-axis and the ψ_{21-1}-orbital, counterclockwise circulation.

Actually, of course, l_0 is not exactly equal to $\hbar$ when $l = 1$; instead, from (2.124), it is equal to $\sqrt{2}\hbar$. Thus it cannot point in precisely the Z-direction, but must be inclined to this just enough so that l_{0_z} will still equal unity. If the angular momentum vector $\mathbf{l_0}$ is inclined to the Z-axis, the plane of particle motion, to which the vector must remain perpendicular, must also be tilted relative to the XY-plane; but because $\mathbf{l_0}$ may point anywhere along the surface of the cone whose side is $\sqrt{2}\hbar$, this angle of tilt cannot be precisely defined. Here again we see the uncertainty principle at work; the angular momentum of the particle is specified, so the plane of its motion cannot be exactly localized.

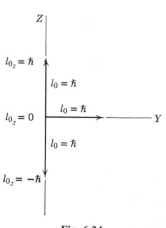

Fig. 6.34

Observing the difference between the ψ_{100} and ψ_{200}-orbitals in Figs. 6.30 and 6.31, or Figs. 6.27 and 6.28, it is apparent that the energy quantum number n controls the size of the probability cloud and the number of maxima that it contains, since only this quantum number has a different value for the two orbitals. As n increases, the negative values of E will decrease (2.123); and the electron will become less tightly bound to the nucleus.

In the same way, a comparison of the ψ_{200} and ψ_{210}-orbitals of Figs 6.31 and 6.32, for which only the value of the angular momentum quantum number l is different, will make it clear that l controls the shape of the cloud. All orbitals for which $l = 0$, regardless of the value of n, will be spherically symmetrical; as l increases, the number of opposed lobes, like those shown in Figs. 6.32 and 6.33, will also increase.

Finally, considering the ψ_{210} and ψ_{211}, ψ_{21-1}-orbitals shown in Figs. 6.32 and 6.33—which differ only in the value of the z-component of angular momentum quantum number m_l—in relation to the vector diagram of Fig. 6.34, we see that m_l controls the orientation of the cloud in space and the sense of the particle's rotation about the origin.

Because the angular momentum states indicated by the l-values were originally associated with well-known lines in absorption and emission spectra, while the orientations defined by the m_l-values were first related to the fine structure of these lines, it is common to label orbitals with letters identifying such spectral lines, rather than with the quantum numbers themselves.[21] For example, all orbitals for which $l = 0$ may be assigned the subscript s, all for which $l = 1$, the subscript p, and so on; on the other hand, those orientations for which $m_l = 0$ can be indicated by attaching the additional subscript z to the appropriate letter subscript above, those for which $m_l = 1$, the additional subscript x, and so on. The first few of these symbols, being the ones most used, are listed in the following table:

n-value	1		2				3							
l-value	0	0	1			0	1			2				
Orbital shape	s	s	p			s	p			d				
m_l-value	0	0	0	1	-1	0	0	1	-1	0	1	2	-1	-2
Orbital orientation	—	—	p_z	p_x	p_y	—	p_z	p_x	p_y	d_{zx}	$d_{z^2-x^2}$	d_{xy}	$d_{y^2-z^2}$	d_{yz}

Hence, the orbitals featured in the preceding discussion may also be written as:

$$\psi_{100} = \psi_{1s} \tag{2.141}$$

$$\psi_{200} = \psi_{2s} \tag{2.142}$$

$$\psi_{210} = \psi_{2p_z} \tag{2.143}$$

$$\psi_{211} = \psi_{2p_x} \tag{2.144}$$

$$\psi_{21-1} = \psi_{2p_y} \tag{2.145}$$

and, of course, one can continue in the manner suggested by the table.[22]

It will be noted that all orbitals having the same n and l-values, such as the ψ_{2p_x}, ψ_{2p_y}, and ψ_{2p_z}-orbitals, can be distinguished only by their m_l-values; they are called degenerate states, because for each the energy and angular momentum must be the same. Actually, it is an experimental fact that two additional degenerate states must be associated with every orbital characterized by some unique combination of n, l, and m_l-values. Thus a fourth quantum number, which has the constant numerical value $\frac{1}{2}$ but may be either positive or negative, is required to identify all of the states that an electron is capable of occupying in a hydrogenlike atom. For reasons to be explained below, this is called the spin quantum number and designated by

$$m_s = \pm\tfrac{1}{2}. \tag{2.146}$$

[21] Herzberg, G., *Atomic Spectra and Structure*, Dover, New York, 1944.
[22] Hume-Rothery, W., *Atomic Theory for Students of Metallurgy*, pp. 79–96, Institute of Metals, London, 1962.

The value of $\pm\frac{1}{2}$ for m_s may be measured directly by observing the splitting of spectral lines which occurs when a strong magnetic field is applied to a hydrogenlike atom.[23] But P. Dirac was the first to show that if the Schrödinger equation we have solved is corrected for relativistic effects and supplemented by the vector potential of an applied electromagnetic field, its solution requires a fourth quantum number with the values $\pm\frac{1}{2}$ which must be associated with the electron spinning about its own axis.[24]

Observing the relativistic requirements (1.81) and (1.96) of Chapter 2,

$$\mathbf{p} = \frac{m\mathbf{v}}{\sqrt{1 - \dfrac{v^2}{c^2}}}$$

and

$$E^2 = p^2 c^2 + m^2 c^4,$$

where m is used for the rest mass instead of m_0, he identifies the linear momentum operator as in (2.37) of Chapter 5,

$$\mathbf{P} = \frac{\hbar}{i}\nabla,$$

but introduces the new vector operator $\boldsymbol{\sigma}$ with the components

$$\sigma_x = -i\alpha_y\alpha_z, \qquad \sigma_y = -i\alpha_z\alpha_x, \qquad \sigma_z = -i\alpha_x\alpha_y, \qquad (2.147)$$

where

$$\alpha_x = \frac{v_x}{c}, \qquad \alpha_y = \frac{v_y}{c}, \qquad \alpha_z = \frac{v_z}{c} \qquad (2.148)$$

are defined to be the components of a vector $\boldsymbol{\alpha}$, as well as the additional new scalar operator

$$\alpha_4 = \sqrt{1 - \frac{v^2}{c^2}}. \qquad (2.149)$$

With the vector potential of the electromagnetic field indicated by $\mathbf{A}$ and the magnetic and electric field intensities by $\mathbf{H}$ and $\mathbf{E}$ in the usual way [(3.28) to (3.36) of Chapter 2], he then shows that the Schrödinger equation

[23] Born, M., *Atomic Physics*, 5th edition, pp. 149–197, Hafner, New York, 1950.
[24] Lindsay, R. B., and H. Margenau, *Foundations of Physics*, pp. 501–514, Dover, New York, 1957.

corresponding to (2.55) is

$$-\left[\frac{\hbar^2}{2m}\nabla^2 + \left(E + \frac{Ze^2}{r}\right)\left(1 + \frac{1}{2mc^2}\right)\right]\psi$$

$$+\left[\frac{\hbar e}{icm}\mathbf{A}\cdot\nabla + \frac{e^2}{2mc^2}A^2\right]\psi$$

$$+\left[\frac{\hbar e}{2mc}\boldsymbol{\sigma}\cdot\mathbf{H} + \frac{\hbar e}{2imc}\boldsymbol{\alpha}\cdot\mathbf{E}\psi\right] = 0 \qquad (2.150)$$

and that the following relations must hold for the components of $\boldsymbol{\sigma}$:

$$\sigma_x{}^2 = \sigma_y{}^2 = \sigma_z{}^2 = 1 \qquad (2.151)$$

If the speed of light c is considered large relative to the speed of the particle v, then all of the terms involving $1/c$ may be neglected and (2.150) reduces to (2.55),

$$\nabla^2\psi + \frac{2m}{\hbar^2}\left(E + \frac{Ze^2}{r}\right)\psi = 0;$$

thus it is easy to see that the preceding results apply in the nonrelativistic limit.

The terms in the second set of brackets represent expected effects of a vector potential $\mathbf{A}$ on a relativistic electron, but the two terms in the last set of brackets are unique to this formulation. The energy of a particle with a magnetic moment $\boldsymbol{\mu}$, due to a magnetic field $\mathbf{H}$, is $\boldsymbol{\mu}\cdot\mathbf{H}$; so we see the first of these terms to imply that the electron has a magnetic moment of

$$\boldsymbol{\mu} = \frac{1}{2}\frac{\hbar e}{mc}\boldsymbol{\sigma}. \qquad (2.152)$$

The quantity $\hbar e/mc$, originally called a Bohr magnetron, is the standard unit of magnetic moment for an electron due to its own spin. Hence (2.150) establishes that a magnetic moment with a magnitude of $\frac{1}{2}$, in conventional units, should be associated with the electron because of its intrinsic spin. Furthermore, because of the requirement expressed in (2.151), the eigenvalues of the "spin matrices" (2.147) must be $+1$ and -1. This means that the vector describing the orientation of the magnetic moment can only point parallel or antiparallel to the direction of the magnetic field. It can be demonstrated that the spin quantum number m_s is equal to the electron's intrinsic magnetic moment in much the same way that the magnetic quantum number m_l was shown to be equal to the z-component of the electron's angular momentum about the nucleus. Thus (2.146),

$$m_s = \pm\tfrac{1}{2},$$

turns out to be a natural consequence of the complete theory. It should be mentioned, however, that the second term in the brackets cannot be explained merely by attributing spin to the electron in the classical sense.

For our purposes, the principal conclusion to be drawn from this discussion is that we should write

$$\psi_{nlm_lm_s} \tag{2.153}$$

to identify a hydrogenlike orbital completely. Each of the orbitals described above actually represents two orbitals, differing only in the sign of the spin quantum number; a complete list should read:

$$\psi_{100\frac{1}{2}} \qquad \psi_{100-\frac{1}{2}} \qquad \psi_{200\frac{1}{2}} \qquad \psi_{200-\frac{1}{2}} \qquad \psi_{210\frac{1}{2}} \qquad \psi_{210-\frac{1}{2}} \cdots \tag{2.154}$$

The same distinction can be made in writing the mathematical descriptions of the wave functions simply by including a factor α to indicate the $+$ spin state or a factor β to indicate the $-$ spin state:

$$\psi_{100\frac{1}{2}} = \frac{1}{\sqrt{\pi}}\left(\frac{Z}{a_0}\right)^{3/2} e^{-\frac{Z}{a_0}r} \alpha \tag{2.155}$$

$$\psi_{100-\frac{1}{2}} = \frac{1}{\sqrt{\pi}}\left(\frac{Z}{a_0}\right)^{3/2} e^{-\frac{Z}{a_0}r} \beta \tag{2.156}$$

From now on we shall apply the four quantum numbers n, l, m_l, and m_s in accordance with the principles laid down above; but it must be emphasized that these principles have been developed for only one type of fundamental particle—electrons. For bosons (like photons) and baryons (like protons and neutrons) other quantum numbers may enter,[25] and the magnitude of the spin quantum number may no longer be $\frac{1}{2}$.

Before proceeding with illustrations and additional applications of the ideas developed for the quantum oscillator and hydrogenlike atoms, it is important to note that these problems—indeed, most quantum mechanical eigenproblems—can be solved directly by matrix methods.[26] In all such cases the basic mathematical requirement is to find the eigenvalues associated with a linear Hermitian matrix operator representing an observable quantity; this can usually be done with the help of the physical

[25] Yang, C. N., *Elementary Particles*, Princeton University Press, Princeton, N.J., 1962.

[26] Green, H. S., *Matrix Mechanics*, Noordhoff, Groningen, 1965.

principle expressed in the general commutation relation first postulated by Heisenberg:

$$\mathscr{A}\mathscr{H} - \mathscr{H}\mathscr{A} = i\hbar\dot{\mathscr{A}}, \tag{2.157}$$

where $\mathscr{H}$ indicates the matrix of the Hamiltonian operator and $\mathscr{A}$ the matrix operator of any other observable.

It is not difficult to establish that this relation is the quantum mechanical expression of the Newtonian equation of motion, and that it reduces to the commutation relations given earlier [(3.8) to (3.10) of Chapter 5] when $\mathscr{H}$ has its usual form.[27] In particular, with

$$\mathscr{H} = \frac{p^2}{2m} + V(q) \tag{2.158}$$

where $p = m\dot{q}$, it follows that

$$qp - pq = i\hbar. \tag{2.159}$$

If $\mathscr{H}$ can be written in the form

$$\mathscr{H} = \frac{1}{2m}(\mathscr{A}^*\mathscr{A}) + \alpha_1, \tag{2.160}$$

where $\mathscr{A}$ and $\mathscr{A}^*$ are matrices with the complex elements

$$A = [p + if(q)] \tag{2.161}$$
$$A^* = [p - if(q)] \tag{2.162}$$

and α_1 is simply a number, then the largest of the values of α_1 which are possible for any particular problem will be the smallest eigenvalue for that problem. This may be understood by comparing $\mathscr{H}$ as given by (2.158) with the expression resulting from (2.160) to (2.162),

$$\mathscr{H} = \frac{1}{2m}(p^2 + ipf(q) - if(q)p + [f(q)]^2) + \alpha_1$$

$$= \frac{1}{2m}(p^2 - i[f(q)p - pf(q)] + [f(q)]^2) + \alpha_1. \tag{2.163}$$

It follows that

$$V(q) = \frac{1}{2m}([f(q)]^2 - i[f(q)p - pf(q)]) + \alpha_1. \tag{2.164}$$

Taking the general form of (2.159) to be

$$[f(q)p - pf(q)] = i\hbar\frac{d}{dq}f(q), \tag{2.165}$$

[27] Messiah, A., *Quantum Mechanics*, Vol. 1., pp. 317–319, Wiley, New York, 1961.

(2.164) becomes

$$V(q) = \frac{1}{2m} [f(q)]^2 + \hbar \frac{d}{dq} f(q) + \alpha_1. \tag{2.166}$$

Consequently, if we place

$$f(q) = \frac{\hbar}{\zeta_1} \frac{d}{dq} \zeta_1 \tag{2.167}$$

where $\zeta_1 = \zeta_1(q)$ represents the eigenvector corresponding to the eigenvalue α_1, then

$$\frac{d}{dq} f(q) = \frac{\hbar}{\zeta_1} \frac{d^2}{dq^2} \zeta_1 - \hbar \left(\frac{1}{\zeta_1} \frac{d}{dq} \zeta_1 \right)^2 ; \tag{2.168}$$

and (2.166) yields

$$V(q) = \frac{1}{2m} \left(\frac{\hbar^2}{\zeta_1} \frac{d^2}{dq^2} \zeta_1 \right) + \alpha_1$$

or

$$\left[-\frac{\hbar^2}{2m} \frac{d^2}{dq^2} + V(q) \right] \zeta_1 = \alpha_1 \zeta_1. \tag{2.169}$$

Identifying ζ with the ψ-function used previously, and α with the energy E, this is Schrödinger's time-independent equation (1.1) in the variable q instead of x. Furthermore, the transformation of the commutation relation through (2.165) and (2.167) may be shown to be equivalent to the process that led to the identification of the differential operator for the linear momentum before [(2.32) to (2.38) of Chapter 5]. Thus the two methods are fully equivalent; but the present one has the advantage of avoiding the mystical connotations of the ψ-function and focusing attention on the central problem of finding eigenvalues, defined to be the only possible results of measurements.

Once the matrices $\mathscr{A}$ and $\mathscr{A}^*$ are known, they can be used to obtain all of the remaining eigenvalues from α_1, as well as all of the other eigenvectors recursively from ζ_1. This may be seen by placing

$$2m\alpha_1 = a_1, \tag{2.170}$$

$$2m\mathscr{H} = \mathscr{B} \tag{2.171}$$

in (2.160) and defining

$$\mathscr{B}_j = \mathscr{A}^*_{(j)} \mathscr{A}_{(j)} + a_j, \tag{2.172}$$

$$\mathscr{B}_{j+1} = \mathscr{A}_{(j)} \mathscr{A}^*_{(j)} + a_j \tag{2.173}$$

where the subscripts of a and $\mathscr{B}$ refer to the particular eigenvalue involved and the subscripts of $\mathscr{A}$ and $\mathscr{A}^*$ indicate the number of times these operators are to be applied. Moreover, if ζ represents any normalized eigenvector of $\mathscr{B}$, vectors

$$\eta_n = \mathscr{A}_n \mathscr{A}_{n-1} \cdots \mathscr{A}_1 \zeta \tag{2.174}$$

can also be defined with the property that

$$\eta_{(n)}^* \eta_{(n)} \geq 0. \tag{2.175}$$

Thus, if $n = 1$,

$$\eta_1 = \mathscr{A}_1 \zeta; \tag{2.176}$$

and, because j must also be one in this case, (2.172) becomes

$$\mathscr{B}_1 = \mathscr{A}_1^* \mathscr{A}_1 + a_1, \tag{2.177}$$

while we know that when $\mathscr{B} = \mathscr{B}_1$,

$$\mathscr{B}_1 \zeta = a \zeta. \tag{2.178}$$

Therefore, using (2.177) and the fact that $\zeta^* \zeta = 1$,

$$\begin{aligned}
\eta_1^* \eta_1 &= \mathscr{A}_1^* \zeta^* \mathscr{A}_1 \zeta = \zeta^* \mathscr{A}_1^* \mathscr{A}_1 \zeta \\
&= \zeta^* (\mathscr{B}_1 - a_1) \zeta = \zeta^* \mathscr{B}_1 \zeta - \zeta^* a_1 \zeta \\
&= \zeta^* a \zeta - \zeta^* a_1 \zeta = a \zeta^* \zeta - a_1 \zeta^* \zeta \\
&= (a - a_1) \geq 0, \tag{2.179}
\end{aligned}$$

establishing that no eigenvalue less than a_1 can exist:

$$a \geq a_1 \tag{2.180}$$

Similarly, when $n = 2$,

$$\eta_2 = \mathscr{A}_2 \mathscr{A}_1 \zeta, \tag{2.181}$$

equations (2.177) to (2.179) apply for $j = 1$. But for $j = 2$,

$$\mathscr{B}_2 = \mathscr{A}_2^* \mathscr{A}_2 + a_2 \tag{2.182}$$

from (2.172), while from (2.173),

$$\mathscr{B}_2 = \mathscr{A}_1 \mathscr{A}_1^* + a_1; \tag{2.183}$$

and, of course,

$$\mathscr{B}_2 \zeta = a \zeta. \tag{2.184}$$

Hence,

$$\begin{aligned}
\eta_2^* \eta_2 &= \mathscr{A}_2^* \mathscr{A}_1^* \zeta^* \mathscr{A}_2 \mathscr{A}_1 \zeta = \zeta^* \mathscr{A}_1^* \mathscr{A}_2^* \mathscr{A}_2 \mathscr{A}_1 \zeta^* \\
&= \zeta^* \mathscr{A}_1^* (\mathscr{B}_2 - a_2) \mathscr{A}_1 \zeta \\
&= \zeta^* \mathscr{A}_1^* \mathscr{B}_2 \mathscr{A}_1 \zeta - \zeta^* \mathscr{A}_1^* a_2 \mathscr{A}_1 \zeta; \tag{2.185}
\end{aligned}$$

however, it follows from (2.183) and (2.177) that

$$\mathcal{B}_2\mathcal{A}_1 = \mathcal{A}_1\mathcal{A}_1^*\mathcal{A}_1 + a_1\mathcal{A}_1 = \mathcal{A}_1(\mathcal{A}_1^*\mathcal{A}_1 + a_1)$$

$$= \mathcal{A}_1\mathcal{B}_1; \tag{2.186}$$

so

$$\eta_2^*\eta_2 = \zeta^*\mathcal{A}_1^*\mathcal{A}_1\mathcal{B}_1\zeta - \zeta^*\mathcal{A}_1^*a_2\mathcal{A}_1\zeta$$

$$= a\zeta^*\mathcal{A}_1^*\mathcal{A}_1\zeta - a_2\zeta^*\mathcal{A}_1^*\mathcal{A}_1\zeta$$

$$= (a - a_2)\eta_1^*\eta_1$$

$$= (a - a_1)(a - a_2) \geqq 0. \tag{2.187}$$

The same process may be continued to establish that, in general,

$$\eta_{(n)}^*\eta_{(n)} = (a - a_1)(a - a_2)\cdots(a - a_n) \geqq 0. \tag{2.188}$$

This inequality may be used to find $a_2, a_3, \ldots, a_n$ once the value of a_1 is fixed and the specific form of $\mathcal{A}$ and $\mathcal{A}^*$ is determined.

We can also see that the eigenvector ζ_j corresponding to the eigenvalue determined by a_j can be calculated from the formula

$$\zeta_j = \mathcal{A}_1^*\mathcal{A}_2^*\cdots\mathcal{A}_{j-1}^*\eta_{j-1}, \tag{2.189}$$

provided the vector η_{j-1} satisfying the condition

$$\mathcal{A}_j\eta_{j-1} = 0 \tag{2.190}$$

is known. For by applying the operator $\mathcal{B}$ to (2.189) we obtain

$$\mathcal{B}\zeta_j = \mathcal{B}\mathcal{A}_1^*\mathcal{A}_2^*\cdots\mathcal{A}_{j-1}^*\eta_{j-1}$$

$$= \mathcal{A}_1^*\mathcal{A}_2^*\cdots\mathcal{A}_{j-1}^*\mathcal{B}_j\eta_{j-1}, \tag{2.191}$$

since it follows from (2.173) that

$$\mathcal{B}_{j-1}\mathcal{A}_{j-1}^* = \mathcal{A}_{j-1}^*\mathcal{B}_j. \tag{2.192}$$

Therefore, if the condition (2.190) holds,

$$\mathcal{A}_j^*\mathcal{A}_j\eta_{j-1} = (\mathcal{B}_j - a_j)\eta_{j-1} = 0, \tag{2.193}$$

so that

$$\mathcal{B}_j\eta_{j-1} = a_j\eta_{j-1}, \tag{2.194}$$

and (2.191) becomes

$$\mathcal{B}\zeta_j = \mathcal{A}_1^*\mathcal{A}_2^*\cdots\mathcal{A}_{j-1}^*a_j\eta_{j-1}$$

$$= a_j\mathcal{A}_1^*\mathcal{A}_2^*\cdots\mathcal{A}_{j-1}^*\eta_{j-1} = a_j\zeta_j, \tag{2.195}$$

as required.

Equation (2.189) shows that operating on an eigenvector with the proper $\mathscr{A}^*$ generates another eigenvector whose eigenvalue is one greater than that of the original eigenvector. Thus, if we know ζ_1 to be a normalized eigenvector,

$$\zeta_2 = N_2 \mathscr{A}_1^* \zeta_1 \tag{2.196}$$

where N_2 represents the appropriate normalization constant; in general,

$$\zeta_{n+1} = N_{n+1} \mathscr{A}_n^* \zeta_1. \tag{2.197}$$

To illustrate how these principles may be applied, let us reconsider the case of the one-dimensional harmonic oscillator, for which

$$V(q) = \frac{Kq^2}{2} \tag{2.198}$$

and (2.158) becomes

$$\mathscr{H} = \frac{1}{2}\left(\frac{p^2}{m} + Kq^2\right). \tag{2.199}$$

Expressing this in the form (2.160) or (2.172) is facilitated by grouping the constants outside the brackets. If we place

$$\frac{p^2}{m} = \beta P^2, \qquad p = \sqrt{m\beta}\, P \tag{2.200}$$

and

$$Kq^2 = \beta Q^2, \qquad q = \sqrt{\frac{\beta}{K}}\, Q, \tag{2.201}$$

so that

$$\mathscr{H} = \frac{\beta}{2}(P^2 + Q^2), \tag{2.202}$$

then the value that β must have may be determined through (2.159):

$$qp - pq = \sqrt{\frac{\beta}{K}}\, m\beta\, (QP - PQ)$$

$$= \frac{\beta}{\omega}(QP - PQ) = i\hbar, \tag{2.203}$$

with $\sqrt{K/m} = \omega$ in the usual way. Evidently, we may place

$$\beta = \hbar\omega \tag{2.204}$$

as long as the commutation principle is applied in the form

$$QP - PQ = i. \tag{2.205}$$

Equation (2.205) and the resulting expression for the Hamiltonian operator,

$$\mathscr{H} = \frac{\hbar\omega}{2}(P^2 + Q^2), \tag{2.206}$$

together with the requirement that the largest possible value of $\alpha_1 = a_1/2m$ should be selected, suggest that in this case the specific form of (2.161) and (2.162) should be:

$$\mathscr{A} = \sqrt{m\hbar\omega}(P - iQ) \tag{2.207}$$

$$\mathscr{A}^* = \sqrt{m\hbar\omega}(P + iQ) \tag{2.208}$$

For then, applying (2.171) to (2.206) to obtain

$$\mathscr{B} = m\hbar\omega(P^2 + Q^2) \tag{2.209}$$

and equating this to the expression that follows from (2.172) and (2.205),

$$
\begin{aligned}
\mathscr{B} = \mathscr{B}_1 = \mathscr{A}_1{}^*\mathscr{A}_1 + a_1 \\
= m\hbar\omega(P^2 - iPQ + iQP + Q^2) + a_1 \\
= m\hbar\omega(P^2 + Q^2) + im\hbar\omega(QP - PQ) + a_1 \\
= m\hbar\omega(P^2 + Q^2) - m\hbar\omega + a_1,
\end{aligned}
\tag{2.210}
$$

immediately defines $a_1 = m\hbar\omega$ and, thus, the smallest eigenvalue of $\mathscr{H}$:

$$\alpha_1 = \frac{a_1}{2m} = \frac{\hbar\omega}{2} \tag{2.211}$$

The selection of $\mathscr{A} = \sqrt{m\hbar\omega}(P + iQ)$ and $\mathscr{A}^* = \sqrt{m\hbar\omega}(P - iQ)$ is ruled out by the fact that it yields $\alpha_1 = a_1/2m = -\hbar\omega/2$, a smaller value.

With $\mathscr{A}$ and $\mathscr{A}^*$ given by (2.207) and (2.208), not only does

$$\mathscr{A}^*\mathscr{A} = m\hbar\omega(P^2 + Q^2) - m\hbar\omega, \tag{2.212}$$

but also

$$\mathscr{A}\mathscr{A}^* = m\hbar\omega(P^2 + Q^2) + m\hbar\omega; \tag{2.213}$$

hence, subtracting these, we obtain the relation

$$\mathscr{A}\mathscr{A}^* - \mathscr{A}^*\mathscr{A} = 2m\hbar\omega. \tag{2.214}$$

Using this it is easy to see that, for example,

$$
\begin{aligned}
\mathscr{A}_2{}^*\mathscr{A}_2 = \mathscr{A}_1{}^*\mathscr{A}_1{}^*\mathscr{A}_1\mathscr{A}_1 = \mathscr{A}^*\mathscr{A}^*\mathscr{A}\mathscr{A} \\
= \mathscr{A}^*(\mathscr{A}\mathscr{A}^* - 2m\hbar\omega)\mathscr{A} = \mathscr{A}^*\mathscr{A}\mathscr{A}^*\mathscr{A} - \mathscr{A}^*2m\hbar\omega\mathscr{A} \\
= \mathscr{A}^*\mathscr{A}(\mathscr{A}^*\mathscr{A} - 2m\hbar\omega),
\end{aligned}
\tag{2.215}
$$

and in general

$$\mathscr{A}^*_{(n)}\mathscr{A}_{(n)} \doteq \mathscr{A}^*\mathscr{A}(\mathscr{A}^*\mathscr{A} - 2m\hbar\omega)\cdots(\mathscr{A}^*\mathscr{A} - 2m\omega(n - 1)) \tag{2.216}$$

where $n = 1, 2, 3, \ldots$. Consequently, it follows from the way in which the inequality (2.188) was developed that in this case

$$\eta^*_{(n)}\eta_{(n)} = (a - a_1)(a - a_1 - 2m\hbar\omega)\cdots(a - a_1 - 2m\hbar\omega(n - 1)) \geqq 0, \tag{2.217}$$

assuming ζ to be normalized.

Therefore, if $n = 1$,

$$a \geqq a_1; \tag{2.218}$$

if $n = 2$,

$$a \geqq a_1 \tag{2.219}$$

or

$$a \geqq 3a_1, \tag{2.220}$$

since $a_1 = m\hbar\omega$; and so on. In other words, using (2.170) and the fact that there can be no eigenvalue of $\mathscr{H}$ smaller than $\alpha_1 = a_1/2m = \hbar\omega/2$, (2.211), the energy eigenvalues must be:

$$\alpha_1 = \frac{\hbar\omega}{2} \tag{2.221}$$

$$\alpha_2 = \frac{3\hbar\omega}{2} \tag{2.222}$$

$$\alpha_3 = \frac{5\hbar\omega}{2} \tag{2.223}$$

$$\cdot$$
$$\cdot$$
$$\cdot$$

This is just the result obtained before in (2.37) and verified by actual matrix calculations in Problem 6.2(b). It is left for Exercise 6.2(10) to verify (2.123), giving the energy levels of a hydrogenlike atom, by the same method.

To find the eigenvector ζ_1 whose eigenvalue is α_1,

$$\mathscr{H}\zeta_1 = \alpha_1\zeta_1, \tag{2.224}$$

notice first that this implies

$$\mathscr{A}^*\mathscr{A}\zeta_1 = 0; \tag{2.225}$$

because, applying (2.170) to (2.172), we know

$$\mathscr{B}\zeta_1 = a_1\zeta_1 \tag{2.226}$$

means that

$$(\mathscr{A}^*\mathscr{A} + a_1)\zeta_1 = a_1\zeta_1. \tag{2.227}$$

Thus, if $\mathscr{A}$ and $\mathscr{A}^*$ have the general form given in (2.161) and (2.162), with b and c representing positive constants,

$$\mathscr{A}^*\mathscr{A}\,\zeta_1 = ([bp - icf(q)][bp + icf(q)])\zeta_1$$

$$= (b^2p^2 + ibcpf(q) - icbf(q)p + c^2[f(q)]^2)\zeta_1$$

$$= (b^2p^2 - ibc[f(q)p - pf(q)] + c^2[f(q)]^2)\zeta_1 = 0 \tag{2.228}$$

or, using (2.165),

$$\left(b^2p^2 + \hbar bc\,\frac{d}{dq}f(q) + c^2[f(q)]^2\right)\zeta_1 = 0. \tag{2.229}$$

If we separately require that

$$b^2p^2\zeta_1 = 0, \tag{2.230}$$

it follows that

$$\frac{d}{dq}f(q)\zeta_1 = -\frac{c}{\hbar b}[f(q)]^2\zeta_1 \tag{2.231}$$

or

$$f(q)\frac{d}{dq}\zeta_1 + \zeta_1\frac{d}{dq}f(q) = -\frac{c}{\hbar b}[f(q)]^2\zeta_1. \tag{2.232}$$

When $f(q)$ is simply q, (2.232) becomes

$$\frac{d}{dq}\zeta_1 = -\left(\frac{c}{\hbar b}q + \frac{1}{q}\right)\zeta_1, \tag{2.233}$$

which may be approximated by

$$\frac{d}{dq}\zeta_1 = -\frac{c}{\hbar b}q\zeta_1 \tag{2.234}$$

for large q; and this will be satisfied if ζ_1 has the form

$$\zeta_1 = e^{-\frac{c}{2\hbar b}q^2}. \tag{2.235}$$

For the harmonic oscillator functions (2.207) and (2.208), $b = 1$ and $c = -\sqrt{mK}$ with $f(q) = q$; hence, selecting the negative square root for physical reasons,

$$\frac{c}{b} = |\sqrt{mK}|. \tag{2.236}$$

We conclude that under these circumstances

$$\zeta_1 = e^{\frac{-|\sqrt{mK}|}{2\hbar}q^2} \tag{2.237}$$

With $\zeta(q)$ replacing $\psi(x)$, (2.237) is identical to (2.11); and it will be plain that the same restrictions used in obtaining that equation have also been applied in the course of the present development [(2.320), (2.234), and (2.236)]. Equation (2.197) may now be used to generate the remaining eigenvectors. This too is left for an exercise [6.2(9)]; but it should be clear that repeated applications of the operator $\mathscr{A}^*$ will have the general effect of producing successive multiplications by the variable q, accompanied by a cyclic exchange between even and odd functions [(2.33), (2.34), and Fig. 6.21].

Time dependence may be introduced by multiplying the right-hand side of (2.237) by the factor e^{-iwt} in the usual way [(2.51) of Chapter 5]. This can easily be seen by noting that $\mathscr{A}$, as it appears in (2.228), must actually be multiplied by such a factor in order to satisfy the general commutation relation (2.157),

$$\mathscr{A}\mathscr{H} - \mathscr{H}\mathscr{A} = i\hbar\dot{\mathscr{A}}.$$

Since from (2.171)

$$\mathscr{H} = \frac{\mathscr{B}}{2m}, \tag{2.238}$$

$$\mathscr{A}\mathscr{B} - \mathscr{B}\mathscr{A} = 2im\hbar\dot{\mathscr{A}}; \tag{2.239}$$

but, using (2.172) and the fact that $a_1 = m\hbar\omega$,

$$\mathscr{B} = \mathscr{A}^*\mathscr{A} + m\hbar\omega. \tag{2.240}$$

Therefore,

$$\mathscr{A}\mathscr{A}^*\mathscr{A} + \mathscr{A}m\hbar\omega - \mathscr{A}^*\mathscr{A}\mathscr{A} - m\hbar\omega\mathscr{A} = 2im\hbar\dot{\mathscr{A}}, \tag{2.241}$$

$$(\mathscr{A}\mathscr{A}^* - \mathscr{A}^*\mathscr{A})\mathscr{A} = 2im\hbar\dot{\mathscr{A}}; \tag{2.242}$$

and substituting from (2.214), we obtain

$$2m\hbar\omega\mathscr{A} = 2im\hbar\dot{\mathscr{A}}$$

or

$$\frac{d}{dt}\mathscr{A} = -i\omega\mathscr{A}. \tag{2.243}$$

This will be satisfied if $\mathscr{A}$ is the product of a factor depending only on q, as developed above, and the factor $e^{-i\omega t}$. Writing $m\omega$ instead of $\sqrt{mK}$, we conclude that in general

$$\zeta_1(q, t) = N_1 e^{-\left(\frac{m\omega}{2\hbar}q^2 + i\omega t\right)} \tag{2.244}$$

where N_1 represents the proper normalization constant.

Problems 6.2

1. If in Schrödinger's equation

$$V(x) = \begin{cases} \dfrac{m\omega_0^2}{2}x^2 & \text{for} \quad x > 0 \\ +\infty & \text{for} \quad x \leq 0 \end{cases}$$

as shown in Fig. P6.2 (1a), obtain expressions for E_n and $\psi_n(x)$; also plot $\psi_n(x)$ schematically.

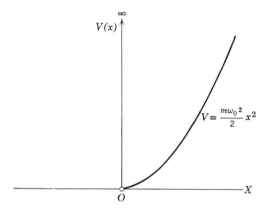

$V(x)$

$$V = \frac{m\omega_0^2}{2}x^2$$

O

X

Fig. P6.2 (1a)

Solution

For $x \leq 0, \psi(x) = 0$, because $V(x)$ is infinite relative to E; for $x > 0$ we may use the one-dimensional harmonic oscillator result (2.29),

$$\psi_n = N_n e^{-\frac{u^2}{2}} H_n(u)$$

where

$$u = \alpha^{1/2}x,$$

$$\alpha = \frac{\sqrt{mK}}{\hbar},$$

$$N_n = \left(\frac{1}{2^n n!}\sqrt{\frac{\alpha}{\pi}}\right)^{1/2}$$

and the $H_n(u)$ are the Hermite polynomials,

$$H_0 = 1$$

$$H_1 = 2u$$

$$H_2 = 4u^2 - 2$$

$$H_3 = 8u^3 - 12u$$

$$H_4 = 16u^4 - 48u^2 + 12$$

$$\begin{matrix} \cdot & & \cdot \\ \cdot & & \cdot \\ \cdot & & \cdot \end{matrix}$$

Considering the fact that ψ must be continuous at $x = 0$,

$$[N_n e^{-u^2/2} H_n(u)]_{u=0} = 0.$$

We have no way of making N_n or $e^{-u^2/2}$ zero when $u = 0$; therefore, we must examine the $H_n(u)$. Clearly, $H_0(u)$, $H_2(u)$, $H_4(u)$, ... will not become zero when $u = 0$, but $H_1(u)$, $H_3(u)$, $H_5(u)$, ... will; thus, we may satisfy this boundary condition by requiring that n be odd. The solutions will be

$$\psi_n(u) = N_n H_n(u) e^{-u^2/2}$$

with

$$E_n = (n + \tfrac{1}{2})h\nu,$$

as in (2.37), where

$$n = 1, 3, 5 \ldots.$$

The energy levels and wave functions are illustrated in Figs. P6.2 (1b–1e).

$n = 1, 3, 5\ldots$

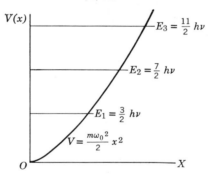

Fig. P6.2 (1b)

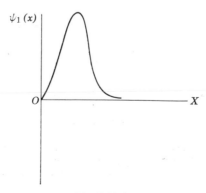

Fig. P6.2 (1c)

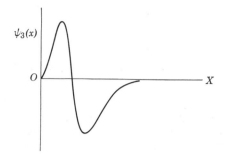

Fig. P6.2 (1d)

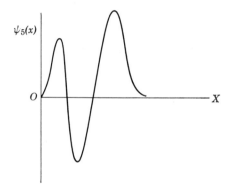

Fig. P6.2 (1e)

2. Find the eigenfunctions and associated energies for a three-dimensional quantum harmonic oscillator; also, assuming the oscillator to be isotropic, specify all degrees of degeneracy for $n = 0$, $n = 1$, and $n = 2$.

Solution

Since in this case the potential energy can be written in the form

$$V = \frac{K_1}{2} x^2 + \frac{K_2}{2} y^2 + \frac{K_3}{2} z^2,$$

it is evident that the total energy can be expressed as

$$E = E_x + E_y + E_z.$$

Therefore, just as in Problem 6.1 (5), the governing Schrödinger equation can be separated into three ordinary differential equations, each of which has the form of the one-dimensional oscillator equation (2.4), by the assumption that

$$\psi(x, y, z) = \psi_1(x)\psi_2(y)\psi_3(z).$$

The equations are:

$$\frac{d^2\psi_1}{dx^2} - \frac{mK_1}{\hbar^2}x^2\psi_1 + \frac{2mE_x}{\hbar^2}\psi_1 = 0$$

$$\frac{d^2\psi_2}{dy^2} - \frac{mK_2}{\hbar^2}y^2\psi_2 + \frac{2mE_y}{\hbar^2}\psi_2 = 0$$

$$\frac{d^2\psi_3}{dz^2} - \frac{mK_3}{\hbar^2}z^2\psi_3 + \frac{2mE_z}{\hbar^2}\psi_3 = 0$$

Hence, applying the known solution (2.29) of (2.4), we conclude that:

$$\psi = N_{n_{1,2,3}}H_{n_{1,2,3}}(u_{1,2,3})e^{-\frac{1}{2}(u_1{}^2+u_2{}^2+u_3{}^2)}$$

with

$$N_{n_{1,2,3}} = N_{n_1}N_{n_2}N_{n_3},$$

$$H_{n_{1,2,3}}(u_{1,2,3}) = H_{n_1}(u_1)H_{n_2}(u_2)H_{n_3}(u_3)$$

and

$$u_1 = \alpha_1^{1/2}x_1, \qquad \alpha_1 = \frac{\sqrt{mK_1}}{\hbar}$$

$$u_2 = \alpha_2^{1/2}x_2, \qquad \alpha_2 = \frac{\sqrt{mK_2}}{\hbar}$$

$$u_3 = \alpha_3^{1/2}x_3, \qquad \alpha_3 = \frac{\sqrt{mK_3}}{\hbar}.$$

Also, from (2.37),

$$E = (n_1 + \tfrac{1}{2})h\nu_1 + (n_2 + \tfrac{1}{2})h\nu_2 + (n_3 + \tfrac{1}{2})h\nu_3$$

where

$$n_1 = 0, 1, 2, \ldots$$
$$n_2 = 0, 1, 2, \ldots$$
$$n_3 = 0, 1, 2, \ldots$$

and, of course,

$$\nu_1 = \frac{1}{2\pi}\sqrt{\frac{K_1}{m}}, \qquad \nu_2 = \frac{1}{2\pi}\sqrt{\frac{K_2}{m}}, \qquad \nu_3 = \frac{1}{2\pi}\sqrt{\frac{K_3}{m}}.$$

However, if the oscillator is isotropic,

$$\nu_1 = \nu_2 = \nu_3 = \nu;$$

and the expression for the energy becomes

$$E = (n_1 + n_2 + n_3 + \tfrac{3}{2})h\nu$$

or, with

$$n_1 + n_2 + n_3 = n,$$

$$E = (n + \tfrac{3}{2})h\nu \qquad \{n = 0, 1, 2, \ldots.$$

But now more than one eigenfunction may exist for a given energy eigenvalue; therefore, the system is degenerate, as illustrated in the following table:

n	n_1	n_2	n_3	Degree of degeneracy
0	0	0	0	0
1	0	0	1	
	0	1	0	3
	1	0	0	
2	0	0	2	
	0	2	0	
	2	0	0	
	1	1	0	
	1	0	1	6
	0	1	1	
$\vdots$				$\vdots$
j				$\dfrac{(j + 1)(j + 2)}{2}$

3. Solve the Θ-equation (2.62) for a hydrogenlike atom,

$$\frac{1}{\Theta \sin \theta} \frac{d}{d\theta} \left(\sin \theta \frac{d\Theta}{d\theta} \right) - \frac{\alpha^2}{\sin^2 \theta} = -\beta^2.$$

Solution

Rearranging, we obtain

$$\frac{1}{\sin \theta} \frac{d}{d\theta} \left(\sin \theta \frac{d\Theta}{d\theta} \right) + \left(\beta^2 - \frac{\alpha^2}{\sin^2 \theta} \right) \Theta = 0;$$

however, placing

$$\cos \theta = \xi,$$

we may write

$$\Theta = \Theta(\xi)$$

with

$$d\xi = -\sin \theta \, d\theta,$$

and this becomes

$$\frac{d}{d\xi} (1 - \xi^2) \frac{d\Theta}{d\xi} + \left(\beta^2 - \frac{\alpha^2}{1 - \xi^2} \right) \Theta = 0.$$

First, let us consider the asymptotic form of this equation which results when

$$\xi \to \pm 1.$$

Introducing another variable

$$\zeta = 1 - \xi^2$$

such that

$$\zeta \to 0 \quad \text{as} \quad \xi \to \pm 1$$

and

$$d\zeta = -2\xi \, d\xi,$$

the term involving β^2 will become negligible as $\zeta \to 0$ and we may write the equation as:

$$4 \frac{d}{d\zeta} \zeta \frac{d\Theta}{d\zeta} - \frac{\alpha^2}{\zeta} \Theta = 0.$$

Assuming a solution of the form

$$\Theta = \zeta^b$$

where b is a constant,

$$\frac{d\Theta}{d\zeta} = b\zeta^{b-1}$$

and

$$\frac{d}{d\zeta} \zeta \frac{d\Theta}{d\zeta} = \frac{d(b\zeta^b)}{d\zeta} = b^2 \zeta^{b-1};$$

so substitution gives

$$4b^2 \zeta^{b-1} - \alpha^2 \zeta^{b-1} = 0$$

or

$$4b^2 = \alpha^2,$$

$$b = \pm \frac{\alpha}{2}.$$

Therefore, for $\xi \to \pm 1$,

$$\Theta = (1 - \xi^2)^{\pm \frac{\alpha}{2}};$$

but the solution $(1 - \xi^2)^{-\frac{\alpha}{2}}$ cannot enter into an acceptable wave function because it is divergent. We conclude that

$$\Theta = (1 - \xi^2)^{\frac{\alpha}{2}}$$

will be a satisfactory solution in this region.

To adapt the solution to the region of small ξ, we shall introduce a function $F(\xi)$ and assume in the usual way that

$$\Theta(\xi) = (1 - \xi^2)^{\frac{\alpha}{2}} F(\xi).$$

Now

$$\frac{d\Theta}{d\xi} = (1 - \xi^2)^{\frac{\alpha}{2}} \frac{dF}{d\xi} - \alpha\xi(1 - \xi^2)^{\frac{\alpha}{2}-1} F$$

and

$$(1 - \xi^2) \frac{d\Theta}{d\xi} = (1 - \xi^2)^{\frac{\alpha}{2}+1} \frac{dF}{d\xi} - \alpha\xi(1 - \xi^2)^{\frac{\alpha}{2}} F,$$

so that

$$\frac{d}{d\xi}(1 - \xi^2)\frac{d\Theta}{d\xi} = (1 - \xi^2)^{\frac{\alpha}{2}+1}\frac{d^2F}{d\xi^2} - (2\alpha + 2)\xi(1 - \xi^2)^{\frac{\alpha}{2}}\frac{dF}{d\xi}$$

$$- \alpha(1 - \xi^2)^{\frac{\alpha}{2}}F + \alpha^2\xi^2(1 - \xi^2)^{\frac{\alpha}{2}-1}F.$$

Substituting these values in the original differential equation for $\Theta(\xi)$ and dividing through by $(1 - \xi^2)^{\frac{\alpha}{2}}$, we obtain

$$(1 - \xi^2)\frac{d^2F}{d\xi^2} - 2(\alpha + 1)\xi\frac{dF}{d\xi} - \alpha F + \frac{\alpha^2\xi^2}{1 - \xi^2}F + \beta^2 F - \frac{\alpha^2}{1 - \xi^2}F = 0$$

or

$$(1 - \xi^2)\frac{d^2F}{d\xi^2} - 2(\alpha + 1)\xi\frac{dF}{d\xi} + (\beta^2 - \alpha - \alpha^2)F = 0.$$

If we assume that $F(\xi)$ has the form of a power series,

$$F(\xi) = \sum_{\nu=0}^{\infty} a_\nu \xi^\nu$$

and substitute in this equation, the result is

$$\sum_{\nu=0}^{\infty} \{(1 - \xi^2)\nu(\nu - 1)a_\nu\xi^{\nu-2} - 2(\alpha + 1)\nu a_\nu\xi^\nu + (\beta^2 - \alpha - \alpha^2)a_\nu\xi^\nu\} = 0$$

or

$$\sum_{\nu=0}^{\infty} \{\nu(\nu - 1)a_\nu\xi^{\nu-2} - [\nu(\nu - 1) + 2(\alpha + 1)\nu - (\beta^2 - \alpha - \alpha^2)]a_\nu\xi^\nu\} = 0.$$

Replacing ν by $\nu + 2$ in the first term alone gives

$$\sum_{\nu=0}^{\infty} \{(\nu + 2)(\nu + 1)a_{\nu+2} - [\nu(\nu - 1) + 2(\alpha + 1)\nu - (\beta^2 - \alpha - \alpha^2)]a_\nu\}\xi^\nu = 0,$$

which implies the recursion relation

$$(\nu + 2)(\nu + 1)a_{\nu+2} = [\nu(\nu - 1) + 2(\alpha + 1)\nu - \beta^2 + \alpha + \alpha^2]a_\nu$$

or

$$a_{\nu+2} = \frac{[(\alpha + \nu)(\alpha + \nu + 1) - \beta^2]}{(\nu + 2)(\nu + 1)}a_\nu$$

where a_0 and a_1 are arbitrary. With ν replaced by $\nu - 2$ and the absolute value of α indicated, this is the same recursion relation given as (2.71) in the text.

Let us investigate the behavior of this series as $\xi \to +1$. Applying the recursion relation we see that for large values of ν

$$\frac{a_{\nu+2}}{a_\nu} \to \frac{(\alpha + \nu)(\alpha + \nu + 1)}{(\nu + 2)(\nu + 1)}.$$

But consider the series

$$(1 - \xi)^{-\alpha} = 1 + \alpha\xi + \frac{\alpha(\alpha + 1)}{2!}\xi^2 + \cdots$$

$$+ \underbrace{\frac{\alpha(\alpha + 1) \cdots (\alpha + \nu - 1)}{\nu!}}_{a_\nu'} \xi^\nu \cdots$$

$$+ \underbrace{\frac{\alpha(\alpha + 1) \cdots (\alpha + \nu - 1)(\alpha + \nu)(\alpha + \nu + 1)}{(\nu + 2)!}}_{a_{\nu+2}'} \xi^{\nu+2} + \cdots$$

It is evident that

$$\frac{a_{\nu+2}'}{a_\nu'} = \frac{(\alpha + \nu)(\alpha + \nu + 1)}{(\nu + 2)(\nu + 1)}$$

and thus that

$$F(\xi) \underset{\xi \to +1}{\to} (1 - \xi)^{-\alpha}.$$

Consequently,

$$\Theta \underset{\xi \to +1}{\to} (1 - \xi^2)^{\alpha/2}(1 - \xi)^{-\alpha} = (1 - \xi)^{\alpha/2}(1 + \xi)^{\alpha/2}(1 - \xi)^{-\alpha} = (1 - \xi)^{-\alpha/2}(1 + \xi)^{\alpha/2},$$

which diverges as $\xi \to +1$ because of the term $(1 - \xi)^{-\alpha/2}$. In the same way it can be shown that

$$\Theta \underset{\xi \to -1}{\to} (1 + \xi)^{-\alpha/2},$$

which also diverges.

Therefore, we must terminate the series to make this an acceptable solution. If we let

$$\beta^2 = \gamma(\gamma + 1),$$

where γ is an integer such that

$$\gamma = \alpha + \nu_{max},$$

this will make $a_{\nu_{max}+2} = 0$; and $F(\xi)$ will become a polynomial of degree ν_{max}, provided we also set

$$a_1 = 0 \quad \text{if} \quad \nu_{max} \text{ is an even integer,}$$

$$a_0 = 0 \quad \text{if} \quad \nu_{max} \text{ is an odd integer.}$$

From the solution of the Φ-equation we know that $\alpha = 0, \pm1, \pm2, \ldots$; therefore, the only possible values of γ are $0, 1, 2, \ldots$ and the only necessary condition is that

$$\gamma \geq |\alpha|.$$

We conclude that

$$F_{\gamma|\alpha|}(\xi) = \sum_{\nu=0}^{\gamma-|\alpha|} a_\nu \xi^\nu,$$

where

$$a_{\nu+2} = \frac{[(\nu + |\alpha|)(\nu + |\alpha| + 1) - \gamma(\gamma + 1)]}{(\nu + 1)(\nu + 2)} a_\nu$$

with

$$a_0 = 0 \quad \text{for} \quad (\gamma - |\alpha|) \text{ odd}$$
$$a_1 = 0 \quad \text{for} \quad (\gamma - |\alpha|) \text{ even,}$$

will constitute a satisfactory series. Thus the final solutions will be

$$\Theta(\xi) = (1 - \xi^2)^{\frac{|\alpha|}{2}} F_{\gamma|\alpha|}(\xi);$$

but, of course, it can be shown that these are exactly the associated Legendre functions,

$$\Theta = P_\gamma^{|\alpha|} (\cos \theta).$$

4. Show that when $l = (n - 1) = |m_l|$, the electron is confined mainly to the XY-plane and that the electron density plot indicates a diffuse circular orbit.

Solution

Legendre's associated functions can be calculated from the formula

$$P_l^{|m_l|}(\xi) = (1 - \xi^2)^{\frac{|m_l|}{2}} \frac{d^{|m_l|}}{d\xi^{|m_l|}} P_l(\xi),$$

where

$$P_l(\xi) = \frac{1}{2^l l!} \frac{d^l}{d\xi^l} (\xi^2 - 1)^l.$$

Thus,

$$P_l^{|m_l|}(\xi) = \frac{(1 - \xi^2)^{\frac{|m_l|}{2}}}{2^l l!} \frac{d^{|m_l|+l}}{d\xi^{|m_l|+l}} (\xi^2 - 1)^l,$$

which is the same as (2.76) when ξ^2 is replaced by $\cos^2 \theta$ and $(1 - \xi^2)$ by $\sin^2 \theta$. But because in this case $l = |m_l|$, we have:

$$P_l^l(\xi) = \frac{(1 - \xi^2)^{\frac{l}{2}}}{2^l l!} \frac{d^{2l}}{d\xi^{2l}} (\xi^2 - 1)^l$$

$$= \frac{(2l)!}{2^l l!} (\sin^2 \theta)^{\frac{l}{2}}$$

$$= \frac{(2l)!}{2^l l!} (\sin \theta)^l.$$

This shows that

$$|\Theta_{lm_l}|^2 \propto (\sin \theta)^{2l}.$$

The appropriate Laguerre polynomials are also given by the formula

$$L_{n+l}^{2l+1}(\rho) = \sum_{\kappa=0}^{n-l-1} (-1)^{\kappa+1} \frac{[(n + l)!]^2 \rho^\kappa}{(n - l - 1 - \kappa)! \, (2l + 1 + \kappa)! \kappa!}.$$

However, with

$$n = l + 1$$

this reduces to

$$L_{2l+1}^{2l+1}(\rho) = - \frac{[(2l + 1)!]^2}{(2l + 1)!} = -(2l + 1)!,$$

since $\kappa = 0$. We conclude that

$$R_{nl} \propto e^{-\frac{\rho}{2}} \rho^l$$

or, with

$$\rho = \frac{2Z}{na_0} r$$

from (2.117) and (2.123),

$$R_{nl} \propto e^{-\frac{Zr}{na_0}} r^l;$$

hence,

$$|R_{nl}|^2 \propto e^{-\frac{2Zr}{na_0}} r^{2l}.$$

It is evident from (2.119) that $|\Phi_{ml}|^2$ will be a constant; thus:

$$|\Psi_{nlm_l}|^2 = |R_{nl}|^2 |\Theta_{lm_l}|^2 |\Phi_{m_l}|^2 \propto r^{2l} e^{-\frac{2Zr}{na_0}} (\sin \theta)^{2l}$$

But $(\sin \theta)^{2l}$ has a maximum at $\theta = \pi/2$; and $r^{2l}e^{-2Zr/na_0}$, when multiplied by the r^2 of the volume element, has a maximum at $r = n^2a_0/Z$, as proved in the next problem. Therefore, the electron will most likely be found in a diffuse circular orbit in the XY-plane, the cross-section of which is illustrated in Fig. P6.2 (4).

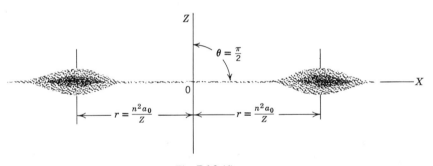

Fig. P6.2 (4)

5. Calculate the expectation value $\bar{r}$ from $R_{nl}(r)$ for the $n = l + 1$ state of a hydrogenlike atom; also, show that the most probable r will equal n^2a_0/Z.

Solution

We know that

$$R_{nl}(\rho) = Ae^{-\frac{\rho}{2}} \rho^l L_{n+l}^{2l+1}(\rho)$$

where, from the previous problem,

$$\rho = \frac{2Z}{na_0} r = 2\eta r$$

and

$$L_{2l+1}^{2l+1}(\rho) = -(2l + 1)!.$$

To evaluate A we may, therefore, write

$$\int_0^\infty A^2 e^{-2\eta r}(2\eta r)^{2l}[-(2l + 1)!]^2\, r^2\, dr = 1,$$

$$A^2(2\eta)^{2l}[(2l + 1)!]^2 \int_0^\infty e^{-2\eta r} r^{2l+2}\, dr = 1;$$

and integration yields

$$A^2(2\eta)^{2l}[(2l + 1)!]^2\, \frac{2(l + 1)!}{(2\eta)^{2l+3}} = 1,$$

$$A^2\, \frac{[(2l + 1)!]^2[2l + 2]!}{(2\eta)^3} = 1.$$

Thus,

$$A^2 = \frac{(2\eta)^3}{[(2l + 1)!]^2(2l + 2)(2l + 1)}$$

$$= \frac{(2\eta)^3}{[(2l + 1)!]^3(2l + 2)};$$

with $l = n - 1$ this becomes

$$A^2 = \frac{(2\eta)^3}{2n[(2n - 1)!]^3},$$

and with $\eta = Z/na_0$,

$$A = \pm\sqrt{\left(\frac{2Z}{na_0}\right)^3 \frac{1}{2n[(2n - 1)!]^3}}.$$

It follows that

$$R_{nl} = -Ae^{-\eta r}(2\eta r)^l[(2l + 1)!],$$

where positive values can be obtained by taking the negative square root of A; this accounts for the value of A given in (2.96).

Now if $P(r) = |R_{nl}|^2$ defines the probability density, we know that the expectation value of r is given by

$$\bar{r} = \int_0^\infty rP(r)\, dr$$

$$= [(2l + 1)!]^2 A^2(2\eta)^{2l} \int_0^\infty (re^{-2\eta r}r^{2l})r^2\, dr$$

$$= [(2l + 1)!]^2 A^2(2\eta)^{2l} \int_0^\infty r^{2l+2}e^{-2\eta r}\, dr$$

$$= [(2l + 1)!]^2 A^2(2\eta)^{2l}\, \frac{(2l + 3)!}{(2\eta)^{2l+4}}$$

$$= A^2\, \frac{[(2l + 1)!]^2(2l + 1)(2l + 2)(2l + 3)}{(2\eta)^4}$$

or, substituting for A^2,

$$\bar{r} = \frac{(2\eta)^3}{2n[(2n-1)!]^3} \frac{[(2l+1)!]^3(2l+2)(2l+3)}{(2\eta)^4}$$

$$= \frac{1}{2\eta} \frac{[(2n-1)!]^3}{[(2n-1)!]^3} \frac{2n}{2n}(2n+1)$$

$$= \frac{2n+1}{2\eta} .$$

Thus, replacing η with its value of Z/na_0, we obtain

$$\bar{r} = (n + \tfrac{1}{2})\frac{na_0}{Z} ;$$

evidently, when $n = 1$ and $Z = 1$,

$$\bar{r} = \tfrac{3}{2}a_0.$$

On the other hand for the most probable r, $P(r)$ must be a maximum; so that

$$\frac{dP(r)}{dr} = 0$$

and

$$\frac{d^2P(r)}{dr} < 0.$$

Since in effect

$$P(r) = A^2[(2l+1)!]^2(2\eta)^{2l}[e^{-2\eta r}r^{2l}]r^2,$$

it follows that

$$\frac{dP(r)}{dr} = A^2[(2l+1)!]^2(2\eta)^{2l} \frac{d}{dr}[e^{-2\eta r}r^{2l+2}]$$

$$= A^2[(2l+1)!]^2(2\eta)^{2l}[-2\eta e^{-2\eta r}r^{2l+2} + (2l+2)r^{2l+2-1}e^{-2\eta r}] = 0;$$

therefore, it must be true that

$$2l + 2 = 2\eta r,$$

or

$$r = \frac{l+1}{\eta} = \frac{(l+1)na_0}{Z} .$$

Substituting $l = n - 1$, we arrive at

$$r = \frac{n^2a_0}{Z} ,$$

which is the result used in the preceding problem. When $n = 1$ and $Z = 1$, this gives a most probable radius of

$$r = a_0,$$

as opposed to $\bar{r} = \tfrac{3}{2}a_0.$

6. If the matrices $\mathscr{A}$ and $\mathscr{A}^*$ for an harmonic oscillator are given as

$$\mathscr{A} = \sqrt{2m\hbar\omega} \begin{bmatrix} 0 & \sqrt{1} & 0 & 0 & 0 \\ 0 & 0 & \sqrt{2} & 0 & 0 \\ 0 & 0 & 0 & \sqrt{3} & 0 \\ 0 & 0 & 0 & 0 & \sqrt{4} \end{bmatrix}$$

and

$$\mathscr{A}^* = \sqrt{2m\hbar\omega} \begin{bmatrix} 0 & 0 & 0 & 0 \\ \sqrt{1} & 0 & 0 & 0 \\ 0 & \sqrt{2} & 0 & 0 \\ 0 & 0 & \sqrt{3} & 0 \\ 0 & 0 & 0 & \sqrt{4} \end{bmatrix},$$

show that the commutation relation is satisfied, find the elements of $[q_{jk}]$ and $[p_{jk}]$, and verify that the eigenvalues are $E_n = (n + \tfrac{1}{2})\hbar\omega$ where $n = 0, 1, 2, 3$.

Solution

We may immediately calculate that:

$$\mathscr{A}^*\mathscr{A} = 2m\hbar\omega \begin{bmatrix} 0 & 0 & 0 & 0 \\ 0 & 1 & 0 & 0 \\ 0 & 0 & 2 & 0 \\ 0 & 0 & 0 & 3 \end{bmatrix} \qquad \mathscr{A}\mathscr{A}^* = 2m\hbar\omega \begin{bmatrix} 1 & 0 & 0 & 0 \\ 0 & 2 & 0 & 0 \\ 0 & 0 & 3 & 0 \\ 0 & 0 & 0 & 0 \end{bmatrix}$$

Thus,

$$\mathscr{A}\mathscr{A}^* - \mathscr{A}^*\mathscr{A} = 2m\hbar\omega I;$$

but we also know from (2.207) and (2.208) that

$$\mathscr{A} = \sqrt{m\hbar\omega}\,(P - iQ) \quad \text{and} \quad \mathscr{A}^* = \sqrt{m\hbar\omega}\,(P + iQ),$$

so

$$\mathscr{A}^*\mathscr{A} = m\hbar\omega(P^2 + Q^2) + im\hbar\omega(QP - PQ)$$

$$\mathscr{A}\mathscr{A}^* = m\hbar\omega(P^2 + Q^2) - im\hbar\omega(QP - PQ).$$

It follows that

$$\mathscr{A}\mathscr{A}^* - \mathscr{A}^*\mathscr{A} = -2im\hbar\omega(QP - PQ) = 2m\hbar\omega I,$$

which shows the commutation relation to be satisfied in the form (2.205),

$$QP - PQ = i.$$

The matrix elements of Q and P evidently will be given by

$$[Q_{jk}] = \frac{i}{2\sqrt{m\hbar\omega}}\,(\mathscr{A} - \mathscr{A}^*), \quad [P_{jk}] = \frac{1}{2\sqrt{m\hbar\omega}}\,(\mathscr{A} + \mathscr{A}^*);$$

but since

$$Q = \sqrt{\frac{K}{\hbar\omega}}\, q, \quad P = \sqrt{\frac{1}{m\hbar\omega}}\, p,$$

these become

$$[q_{jk}] = \frac{i}{2m\omega}(\mathscr{A} - \mathscr{A}^*) \quad \text{and} \quad [p_{jk}] = \tfrac{1}{2}(\mathscr{A} + \mathscr{A}^*).$$

Therefore,

$$[q_{jk}] = i\sqrt{\frac{\hbar}{2m\omega}}
\begin{bmatrix}
0 & \sqrt{1} & 0 & 0 & 0 \\
-\sqrt{1} & 0 & \sqrt{2} & 0 & 0 \\
0 & -\sqrt{2} & 0 & \sqrt{3} & 0 \\
0 & 0 & -\sqrt{3} & 0 & \sqrt{4}
\end{bmatrix}$$

and

$$[p_{jk}] = \sqrt{\frac{m\hbar\omega}{2}}
\begin{bmatrix}
0 & \sqrt{1} & 0 & 0 & 0 \\
\sqrt{1} & 0 & \sqrt{2} & 0 & 0 \\
0 & \sqrt{2} & 0 & \sqrt{3} & 0 \\
0 & 0 & \sqrt{3} & 0 & \sqrt{4}
\end{bmatrix}.$$

To calculate the eigenvalues, we note that

$$\mathscr{A}\mathscr{A}^* + \mathscr{A}^*\mathscr{A} = 2m\hbar\omega(P^2 + Q^2) = 4\, m\mathscr{H},$$

using (2.206). Thus

$$\mathscr{H} = \frac{\hbar\omega}{2}
\begin{bmatrix}
1 & 0 & 0 & 0 \\
0 & 3 & 0 & 0 \\
0 & 0 & 5 & 0 \\
0 & 0 & 0 & 7
\end{bmatrix}$$

as required.

Exercises 6.2

1. Find $\psi_n(x)$ and E_n for a quantum particle of mass m trapped in the potential well

$$V(x) = \begin{cases} \beta x & \text{for } x > 0, \ \beta = \text{constant} \\ +\infty & \text{for } x \leq 0 \end{cases}$$

by solving the appropriate Schrödinger equation.

2. Estimate the form of $\psi(x)$ in the preceding problem by means of the WKB approximation and compare results.

3. Prove that the classical position probability density for the simple harmonic oscillator is given by:

$$P(x) = \frac{1}{\pi \left(\dfrac{2E}{K} - x^2 \right)^{1/2}}$$

4. Write the time-independent Schrödinger equation for a hydrogenlike atom in rectangular coordinates referred to an arbitrary fixed origin, and separate this into two equations—one describing the motion of the center of mass $m_c = m_{\text{electron}} + m_{\text{nucleus}}$, and the other describing the motion of the fictitious mass given in (2.51), $\mu = m_{\text{electron}} m_{\text{nucleus}} / (m_{\text{electron}} + m_{\text{nucleus}})$.

5. Show that for the solution (2.77),

$$\Theta = R P_\gamma^{|\alpha|}(\cos \theta) \qquad \{\gamma = |\alpha|, |\alpha| + 1, |\alpha| + 2, \ldots ,$$

normalization leads to the value

$$B = \sqrt{\frac{(2\gamma + 1)(\gamma - |\alpha|)!}{2(\gamma + |\alpha|)!}} .$$

6. Establish that $\dfrac{d^2 P(r)}{dr^2} < 0$ at $r = a_0$ in Problem 6.2 (5).

7. Compute the wavelength of the quantum of radiation emitted by an electron making a transition from the ψ_{2s} to the ψ_{1s}-state in a helium atom, using the Bohr condition:

$$E_1 - E_2 = h\nu_{12}.$$

8. Calculate the hydrogenic wave functions ψ_{300} and ψ_{310}; also sketch their radial probability density curves.

9. Given the eigenfunction

$$\zeta_1 = e^{-\frac{m\omega}{2\hbar} q^2}$$

for the harmonic oscillator, apply the formula

$$\zeta_{n+1} = N_{n+1} \mathscr{A}_n^* \zeta_1$$

to obtain $\zeta_2(q)$ and $\zeta_3(q)$.

10. For a hydrogenlike atom at rest it can be shown that in the equation

$$\mathscr{H}\psi = E\psi,$$

$$\mathscr{H} = \frac{1}{2m}\left(p_r^2 + \frac{l(l + 1)\hbar^2}{r^2} - \frac{2mZe^2}{r} \right).$$

Writing the operators $\mathscr{A}$ and $\mathscr{A}^*$ in the form

$$\mathscr{A} = p + i\left(b + \frac{c}{r} \right)$$

$$\mathscr{A}^* = p - i\left(b + \frac{c}{r} \right)$$

with *b* and *c* representing numbers to be determined, use the matrix mechanics method to verify that the possible energy levels are given by

$$E = -\left(\frac{mZ^2e^4}{2\hbar^2}\right)\frac{1}{(l+j)^2}$$

where $j = 1, 2, 3, \ldots$

6.3   Atomic, Molecular, and Crystalline Structures

While the state of motion, or orbital, of an electron in a hydrogenlike atom is entirely determined by the quantum numbers n, l, m_l, and m_s, it is also a physical fact that no two electrons in the same atom can occupy an orbital characterized by identical values of these four numbers. This may be verified by considering the well-established electronic structure of the first few atoms in the periodic table of the elements.

From the preceding section it follows that, in order of ascending energy, the orbitals available in any hydrogenlike atom should be:

$$\psi_{300\frac{1}{2}},\ \psi_{300-\frac{1}{2}},\ \psi_{310\frac{1}{2}},\ \cdots$$

$$\psi_{200\frac{1}{2}},\ \psi_{200-\frac{1}{2}},\ \psi_{210\frac{1}{2}},\ \psi_{210-\frac{1}{2}},\ \psi_{211\frac{1}{2}},\ \psi_{211-\frac{1}{2}},\ \psi_{21-1\frac{1}{2}},\ \psi_{21-1-\frac{1}{2}}$$

$$\psi_{100\frac{1}{2}},\ \psi_{100-\frac{1}{2}}$$

E

In practice, however, states with larger *l*-values at a given value of *n* will move to slightly higher energies if the ideal system is perturbed,[28] as when more than one electron is present. Thus in the present case the ordering required is:

$$\psi_{310\frac{1}{2}},\ \cdots$$

$$\psi_{300\frac{1}{2}},\ \psi_{300-\frac{1}{2}}$$

$$\psi_{210\frac{1}{2}},\ \psi_{210-\frac{1}{2}},\ \psi_{211\frac{1}{2}},\ \psi_{211-\frac{1}{2}},\ \psi_{21-1\frac{1}{2}},\ \psi_{21-1-\frac{1}{2}}$$

$$\psi_{200\frac{1}{2}},\ \psi_{200-\frac{1}{2}}$$

$$\psi_{100\frac{1}{2}},\ \psi_{100-\frac{1}{2}}$$

E

Assuming that each electron will occupy a state of the lowest possible energy, there is no difficulty in understanding why the single electron of hydrogen ($Z = 1$) will be found in either the $\psi_{100\frac{1}{2}}$ or $\psi_{100-\frac{1}{2}}$-orbital. But, by the same reasoning, it would appear possible that both of the two electrons of

---

[28] Powell, J. I., and B. Crasemann, *Quantum Mechanics*, pp. 216–229, Addison-Wesley, Reading, Mass., 1962.

helium ($Z = 2$) might be found in one of these orbitals, and this is not the case. One of the electrons will always occupy the $\psi_{100\frac{1}{2}}$-orbital, and the other the $\psi_{100-\frac{1}{2}}$-orbital. Furthermore, although two of the three electrons of lithium ($Z = 3$) will be in these same orbitals, the third will occupy one of the ψ_{200}-orbitals. In other words, rather than go into an orbital that already contains an electron, it will remain in one of next highest energy. The states of the electrons in the first ten elemental atoms will suffice to show that this behavior is repeated throughout the periodic table:

Element	H	He	Li	Be	B	C	N	O	F	Ne
Z	1	2	3	4	5	6	7	8	9	10
$\psi_{100\frac{1}{2}}$	X	X	X	X	X	X	X	X	X	X
$\psi_{100-\frac{1}{2}}$		X	X	X	X	X	X	X	X	X
$\psi_{200\frac{1}{2}}$			X	X	X	X	X	X	X	X
$\psi_{200-\frac{1}{2}}$				X	X	X	X	X	X	X
$\psi_{21-1\frac{1}{2}}$					X	X	X	X	X	X
$\psi_{21-1-\frac{1}{2}}$						X	X	X	X	X
$\psi_{211\frac{1}{2}}$							X	X	X	X
$\psi_{211-\frac{1}{2}}$								X	X	X
$\psi_{210\frac{1}{2}}$									X	X
$\psi_{210-\frac{1}{2}}$										X

The particular order in which the ψ_{21}-orbitals are occupied depends on configurational details which we cannot take time to consider; but independently of this, it is quite clear that each orbital is effectively filled by a single electron.

It can be established much more generally that the same restriction applies to any closed quantum system; that is, every particle in such a system must have a unique wave function. This is one way of stating the Pauli exclusion principle which, even though the physical reasons why it is true are not fully understood, is of central importance in all studies of fundamental particle motions.[29]

The table also suggests why the noble gas atoms possess extraordinary stability and are generally nonreactive; each represents a condition in which all of the orbitals at a certain energy level are filled by the electrons required to neutralize the nuclear charge. At helium ($_2$He), for example, the two electrons needed to neutralize the charge of the two protons in the nucleus just fill the ψ_1-states. Eight more electrons are required to fill the ψ_2-states, so this occurs at neon ($_{10}$Ne), which has ten protons in the nucleus. In the same way, argon ($_{18}$A), krypton ($_{36}$Kr), xenon ($_{54}$Xe), and

[29] Messiah, A. *Quantum Mechanics*, Vol. 2, pp. 582–619, Wiley, New York, 1962.

radon ($_{86}$Ra) all represent successively filled energy levels. Atoms with one electron in excess of the number required to fill a level exhibit a tendency to lose this electron and, thus, become positively ionized; whereas those that are only one electron short of filling a level tend to add an electron and become negatively ionized.

The groups of orbitals at such energy levels are often called "shells" and labeled according to the following convention:

$$\psi_{100\frac{1}{2}}, \psi_{100-\frac{1}{2}}\} \qquad K\text{-shell}$$

$$\psi_{200\frac{1}{2}}, \psi_{200-\frac{1}{2}}, \psi_{21-1\frac{1}{2}}, \psi_{21-1-\frac{1}{2}}, \psi_{211\frac{1}{2}}, \psi_{211-\frac{1}{2}}, \psi_{210\frac{1}{2}}, \psi_{210-\frac{1}{2}}\} \qquad L\text{-shell}$$

$$\psi_{300\frac{1}{2}}, \psi_{300-\frac{1}{2}}, \psi_{31-1\frac{1}{2}}, \psi_{31-1-\frac{1}{2}}, \psi_{311\frac{1}{2}}, \psi_{311-\frac{1}{2}}, \psi_{310\frac{1}{2}}, \psi_{310-\frac{1}{2}}\} \qquad M\text{-shell}$$

· ·

Of course, using the notation explained in the last section, these orbitals can also be written in the following way:

$$\psi_{1s}\alpha, \psi_{1s}\beta\} \qquad K\text{-shell}$$

$$\psi_{2s}\alpha, \psi_{2s}\beta, \psi_{2p_y}\alpha, \psi_{2p_y}\beta, \psi_{2p_x}\alpha, \psi_{2p_x}\beta, \psi_{2p_z}\alpha, \psi_{2p_z}\beta\} \qquad L\text{-shell}$$

$$\psi_{3s}\alpha, \psi_{3s}\beta, \psi_{3p_y}\alpha, \psi_{3p_y}\beta, \psi_{3p_x}\alpha, \psi_{3p_x}\beta, \psi_{3p_z}\alpha, \psi_{3p_z}\beta\} \qquad M\text{-shell}$$

· ·

It is common to condense this still further, writing simply:

$$(1s)^2\} \qquad K\text{-shell}$$

$$(2s)^2(2p)^6\} \qquad L\text{-shell}$$

$$(3s)^2(3p)^6\} \qquad M\text{-shell}$$

· · · · · · · · · · · · · · · ·

with each superscript indicating the number of electrons in the bracketed state when all of the orbitals are filled. The latter form has the advantage that it can readily be adapted to the case when some of the orbitals are not filled, making it possible to describe the electronic structure of any atom consisely. To illustrate, the appropriate expressions for some of those listed in the preceding table are:

$$_2\text{He}, \quad (1s)^2$$

$$_3\text{Li}, \quad (1s)^2(2s)^1$$

$$_9\text{F}, \quad (1s)^2(2s)^2(2p)^5$$

$$_{10}\text{Ne}, \quad (1s)^2(2s)^2(2p)^6$$

Excited and ionized atomic states can easily be expressed in the same way. For example, a simple excited state of $_3$Li might be $(1s)^2(2s)^0(2p)^1$, whereas for the $_3$Li$^+$ and $_9$F$^-$ ions we would have $(1s)^2(2s)^0$ and $(1s)^2(2s)^2(2p)^6$. The shell structure of such ions becomes especially prominent in radial density plots of the type presented in Figs. 6.27 to 6.29; positively ionized lithium, sodium, and potassium are illustrated in Fig. 6.35 with the *K*, *L*, and *M*-shells labeled.

The motions possible for electrons in molecules are naturally more complicated than those in a hydrogenlike atom. However, they may be determined with reasonable accuracy by forming linear combinations of occupied atomic orbitals in such a way as to minimize the potential energy

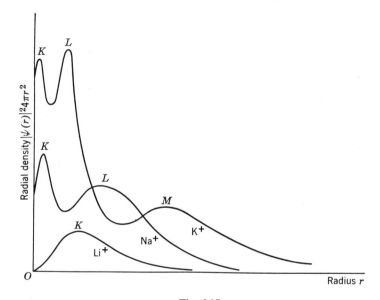

Fig. 6.35

of the system, while nevertheless satisfying the exclusion principle.[30] This can perhaps best be explained by considering the behavior of two hydrogen atoms (I and II) in their ground state, or state of lowest energy, which happen to move into close proximity.

Since each atom possesses two 1s-orbitals of the form given in (2.155) and (2.156),

$$\psi_{100\frac{1}{2}} = \frac{1}{\sqrt{\pi}}\left(\frac{Z}{a_0}\right)^{3/2} e^{-\frac{Z}{a_0}r}\,\alpha$$

$$\psi_{100-\frac{1}{2}} = \frac{1}{\sqrt{\pi}}\left(\frac{Z}{a_0}\right)^{3/2} e^{-\frac{Z}{a_0}r}\,\beta,$$

[30] Slater, J. C., *Quantum Theory of Molecules and Crystals*, McGraw-Hill, New York, 1965.

and the single electron may occupy either of these, four linear combinations are possible:

$$\psi_{130\frac{1}{2}}(I) + \psi_{100\frac{1}{2}}(II) \tag{3.1}$$

$$\psi_{100-\frac{1}{2}}(I) + \psi_{100-\frac{1}{2}}(II) \tag{3.2}$$

$$\psi_{100\frac{1}{2}}(I) + \psi_{100-\frac{1}{2}}(II) \tag{3.3}$$

$$\psi_{100-\frac{1}{2}}(I) + \psi_{100\frac{1}{2}}(II) \tag{3.4}$$

But it is apparent that, because of the exclusion principle, the first two represent repulsive states, while the last two represent attractive states. In other words, if the electrons are in the same type of orbital, the atoms will certainly repel one another, their nuclei also being mutually repulsive; however, if the electrons are in different types of orbitals, the atoms may become bonded together, each sharing the other's electron.

The component and total potential energies in the two cases are illustrated in Fig. 6.36 as a function of the internuclear separation distance R:

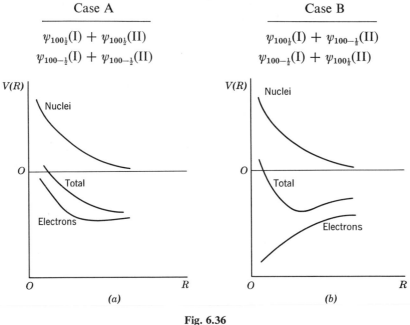

Fig. 6.36

Only in Case B does the total potential energy of the system possess a minimum, making a condition of stable equilibrium possible.

Because the density of the composite probability clouds will be proportional to the absolute squares of the sums (3.1) to (3.4), it is possible to provide a somewhat more pictorial representation of these two states by

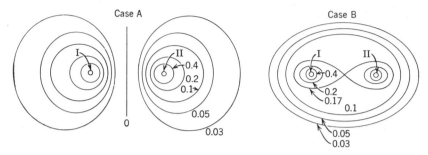

Fig. 6.37

constructing figures of the same type as Figs. 6.30 to 6.33 or, more simply, by plotting contours of constant density out to some arbritary small value, as shown in Fig. 6.37. The overall distortion of the two atoms which is characteristic of closed-shell repulsion, and the concentration of negative charge in the region between the two positive nuclei which is the central feature of the so-called covalent bond, show up particularly clearly in plots of this type. Case B obviously represents an elementary molecule.

More complicated molecules can also be described by superimposing the basic atomic orbitals in much the same way; the water molecule H_2O provides a convenient example. In this case, as symmetry considerations will establish, only the $2p_y$ and $2p_z$-orbitals of the oxygen atom, $(1s)^2(2s)^2(2p)^4$, are available for bonding with the $1s$-orbitals of the hydrogen atoms. Thus, limiting the representation to one outer contour line, the hydrogens tend to take the positions shown in Fig. 6.38, and the final result is as illustrated in Fig. 6.39. Judging from a comparison of computed and measured values of the angle α, quite an accurate description of the H_2O molecule can be obtained in this way.

It will be evident that the formation of a covalent bond involves the partial transfer of an electron from one atom to another, and the question arises as to just how much of the electron is transferred in any given case. The fact is that this depends on the entire composition of the two

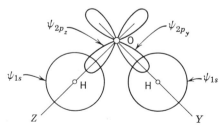

Fig. 6.38

atoms involved, varying from about one half for those elements farthest removed from the noble gases in the periodic table (C, Si, Ge, etc.) to nearly one for those elements nearest to them (Na, Cl, Li. etc.). As a result the former enter into the strongest covalent bonds, whereas the latter join together in what is called an ionic bond.

In a pure ionic bond the electron is effectively removed from one of the atoms and added to the other. The result is that the atom which loses the electron becomes positively ionized, while the atom which acquires it becomes negatively ionized; they then attract one another electrostatically, with nuclear and closed-shell repulsion opposing. As noted earlier, for

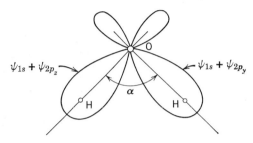

Fig. 6.39

atoms adjacent to the noble gases the end result of this exchange process is to allow both atoms to form closed shells. Various molecular combinations become possible under these circumstances.

Since the forces involved are electrostatic in both cases, ionic and covalent bonds differ only in the time-averaged location of the shared electron or electrons relative to the two nuclei. In a covalent bond an electron spends most of its time in the region between the two nuclei; in an ionic bond it remains closely associated with one nucleus at all times. This means, however, that the former is highly directional, whereas the latter is omnidirectional.

Actually, all types of interatomic bonds differ only in the way that the position probability density of the outer, or valence, electrons is distributed in the region surrounding the nuclei as a function of time. The strongest ones are the two discussed above, but three other kinds can be distinguished.

The van der Waals bond has its origin in dipole moments created by spatial separations of positive and negative charge concentrations associated with transient electron configurations. Such an instantaneous charge separation in an atom or molecule will induce a corresponding charge separation, with its related dipole moment, in a neighboring atom or molecule; this in turn will interact with the original dipole moment; and so on. Noble gas atoms can only be joined together by magnetic forces arising in this way; and the same kind of forces are present to some extent in all molecules and crystals, since even configurations of atomic electrons which are symmetrical on the average may not be so instantaneously. Permanent charge separations are also possible in molecules, of course, and these can lead to bonding through static magnetic forces. This is the weakest type of bond.

The hydrogen bond, only slightly stronger, arises in highly unsymmetrical molecules when the electronic configuration is such as to "expose" at least one hydrogen nucleus through a reduction in the amount of screening afforded by the electron cloud.[31] Extra negative ions may then

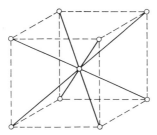 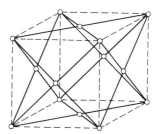

Fig. 6.40. Body-centered cubic (bcc).   **Fig. 6.41.** Face-centered cubic (fcc).

be attracted to the molecule electrostatically. A good example is provided by the H_2O molecule shown in Fig. 6.39; both of the hydrogen nuclei are capable of forming such a bond. It is this molecular characteristic which is largely responsible for the fact that water can crystallize in several different ways with decreasing temperature.

The metallic bond exists in metal crystals and comes about through one or more of the outer electrons of each atom being transferred, not to any other specific atom, but to all of the others. Consequently, a large number of electrons become free to move through the crystal; and the result is that concentrations of negative charge are maintained in the interstices between the positive metal ions, to which the latter are then attracted electrostatically. The presence of these free electrons is the reason for the high electrical conductivity of metals like copper. It should also be noted, however, that the outer shells of the ions may be incomplete in some cases, so that additional covalent bonds may be formed; notably, the *d*-orbitals of most of the transition metals (Fe, Co, Ni, etc.) are only partly filled.

[31] Pauling, L., *The Nature of the Chemical Bond*, 3rd edition, Cornell University Press, Ithaca, N.Y., 1960.

Author Index

539

Subject Index